DENDROLOGY

McGraw-Hill Series in Forest Resources

Avery and Burkhart: Forest Measurements
Dana and Fairfax: Forest and Range Policy
Daniel, Helms, and Baker: Principles of Silviculture
Davis and Johnson: Forest Management
Duerr: Introduction to Forest Resource Economics
Ellefson: Forest Resources Policy: Process, Participants, and Programs
Harlow, Harrar, Hardin, and White: Textbook of Dendrology
Klemperer: Forest Resource Economics and Finance
Laarman and Sedjo: Global Forests: Issues for Six Billion People
Nyland: Silviculture: Concepts and Applications
Sharpe, Hendee, Sharpe, and Hendee: Introduction to Forest and Renewable
    Resources
Sinclair: Forest Products Marketing
Stoddart, Smith, and Box: Range Mangement

Walter Mulford was Consulting Editor of this series from its inception in 1931 until
    January 1, 1952.

Henry J. Vaux was Consulting Editor of this series from January 1, 1952 until July 1,
    1976.

Paul V. Ellefson, University of Minnesota is currently our Consulting Editor.

TEXTBOOK OF DENDROLOGY

EIGHTH EDITION

William M. Harlow
SUNY College of Environmental Science
and Forestry; deceased

Ellwood S. Harrar
School of Forestry
Duke University; deceased

James W. Hardin
Department of Botany
North Carolina State University

Fred M. White
Division of Forest Resources
North Carolina Department of Environment,
Health, and Natural Resources

McGRAW-HILL, INC.

New York   St. Louis   San Francisco   Auckland   Bogotá   Caracas
Lisbon   London   Madrid   Mexico City   Milan   Montreal   New Delhi
San Juan   Singapore   Sydney   Tokyo   Toronto

This book was set in Times Roman by The Clarinda Company
The editors were Anne C. Duffy and John M. Morriss;
the production supervisor was Richard A. Ausburn.
The cover was designed by Rafael Hernandez.
Project supervision was done by Tage Publishing Service, Inc.

On the cover: Pond cypress (*Taxodium distichum* var. *imbricarium*) in October
at Jones Lake, North Carolina.
Photo by Dr. Alice B. Russell; Nikon N-90 and AF Nikon 20 mm 1:2.8
with circular polarizer filter, using Fujichrome Velvia ISO 50.

TEXTBOOK OF DENDROLOGY

This book is printed on acid-free paper.

4 5 6 7 8 9 10 FGRFGR 9 9 8 7

ISBN 0-07-026572-0

Library of Congress Cataloging-in-Publication Data

Textbook of dendrology / William M. Harlow . . . [et al.].—8th ed.
        p.   cm.—(McGraw-Hill series in forest resources)
      Includes bibliographical references (p.   ) and index.
      ISBN 0-07-026572-0
    1. Trees—United States.   2. Trees—Canada.   3. Forest plants—
United States.   4. Forest plants—Canada.   I. Harlow, William
Moorehouse, (date).   II. Series.
QK110.T48   1996
582.16097—dc20   95-22377

ABOUT
THE AUTHORS

JAMES W. HARDIN is professor of Botany and Curator of the Herbarium at North Carolina State University (NCSU). He received his Ph.D. degree from the University of Michigan. Although he has been at NCSU for his entire professional career, he has been Visiting Professor at the Mountain Lake Biological Station (Virginia) and the University of Oklahoma Biological Station during several summers. Professor Hardin is a systematic botanist and taught dendrology for several years, then systematics for nearly 35 years. He has twice received an Outstanding Teacher Award at NCSU, and in 1991, received the Meritorious Teaching Award presented by the Association of South-eastern Biologists. He is the author of several books, laboratory manuals, agriculture bulletins, and many journal articles mainly dealing with woody plants. Professor Hardin is a past President of the Southern Appalachian Botanical Club, Highlands Biological Station, Inc., the Association of Southeastern Biologists, and the American Society of Plant Taxonomists. He was, for 6 years, Editor of the *ASB Bulletin,* and for 6 years, Editor-in-Chief of the journal *Systematic Botany.*

FRED M. WHITE is Assistant State Forester for Management in the Division of Forest Resources of the North Carolina Department of Environment, Health, and Natural Resources. He did his undergraduate work at the University of the South and received his M.F. degree from Duke University. Between 1960 and 1980 he was professor of Silviculture and Director of the Duke Forest. He is also the coauthor of two volumes of Hough's *Encyclopedia of American Woods.*

CONTENTS

PREFACE

In preparing this new eighth edition of The Textbook of Dendrology, the seventh edition provided a true litmus test for many of the changes we added to this edition. We appreciate the many constructive comments and suggestions made by past users of this textbook.

In this edition, the seven introductory chapters have a new arrangement which we think provides a more logical sequence for the student. Each successive chapter builds on the information which precedes it. An exception to this is the use of the key in Chapter 4, which requires a knowledge of the terminology explained in Chapter 7. However, Chapter 7 should be closest to Chapters 8 and 9 where the terms are used most extensively.

Several changes in format in Chapters 8 and 9 have been made to provide consistency of presentation and an easier and more efficient way of finding information on geographical and altitudinal range and habitat. The larger type is used for the more important characteristics of the most important trees, in contrast to the smaller type for general descriptions and treatment of the trees of secondary importance. A few new illustrations have been added to show the general form of the trees.

A section on the pronunciation of scientific names has been added to the chapter on nomenclature. We feel that oral communication is very necessary, and at least an understandable pronunciation and correct spelling of tree names are important corollaries to their identification. Accent marks indicating long and short vowel sounds have been added to the names of trees in Chapters 8 and 9. These may seem to be an unnecessary burden, but we consider them a useful addition for the sake of some consistency and intelligible communication. They are certainly harmless enough if overlooked. These marks are omitted when writing the names.

A section on "keys" has been added to the chapter on identification. This includes a description of the basic construction and use of keys for identification and artificial keys to the genera described in the text. These summer and winter keys should provide practice in the use of keys of different forms, show artificial groupings of genera based on rather obvious features which makes them easier to remember, provide an exercise in the use and understanding of morphological terminology, and present a quick and useful means of identification for the important tree genera included in this textbook.

The expected and assumed expertise of the dendrologist has broadened in recent years and continues to expand to meet the needs of employers and of the public in general. For instance, the field of "urban forestry" makes it important to know the commonly cultivated, ornamental, native or exotic trees in lawns, parks, or along streets. The field of "wildlife biology" places emphasis on the trees which provide cover, nesting sites, and food for various wildlife species. Renewed interest in "natural history" demands some knowledge of edible or poisonous plants and plant parts, as well as their various practical uses by people. Interest in "global forestry" requires knowledge of important international trees in terms of their economic uses, conservation, and management. The present interest and concern for wetland delineation and management make it important to identify the tree species which are good indicators of wetlands or at least usually inhabit such sites. The concern for preservation of threatened and endangered species and biodiversity makes it imperative that the dendrologist be aware of conservation issues. We have attempted to address this expanded scope of dendrology by adding more information on all these topics.

We greatly appreciate and are pleased to acknowledge the contributions to this eighth edition from Elizabeth A. Hardin, Technical Communication, North Carolina State University, for the line drawings in Chapter 7 and her expertise in technical writing and use of computers; Stephen B. Bambara and Nancy Leidy, Entomology, North Carolina State University, for use of their SEM photos of pollen grains; the U.S. Forest Service Photo Collections, National Agricultural Library, for use of many photographs; Dr. Larry Mellichamp, Biology, University of North Carolina, Charlotte, for use of his photograph of *Carpinus* fruit; and especially Dr. Alice B. Russell, North Carolina Cooperative Extension Service and Urban Tree Specialist, North Carolina State University, for providing the photo for the cover, for her careful reading and very appropriate suggestions and additions throughout the book, and for trying many plants in the generic keys, which led to substantial and much-needed improvements. We also thank the following reviewers of this edition for their careful reading of the manuscript and useful suggestions: Michael Bridgen, SUNY College of Environmental Science and Forestry; Robert Eckert, University of New Hampshire; Paul Ellefson, University of Minnesota; Duane L. Green, University of Delaware; Scott Merkle, University of Georgia; Carl Mohn, University of Minnesota; Paula Piehl, Potomac State College; and John Stuart, Humboldt State University. We also appreciate the many constructive comments and suggestions of several instructors and students, for whom this book is written. Chapter 6 has been written by Fred White and all other changes and additions have been made by James Hardin.

James W. Hardin
Fred M. White

1

INTRODUCTION

A knowledge and understanding of the names of trees, their habits, ranges, habitats, and distinguishing characteristics are basic to all studies in forestry, environmental sciences, and advanced studies of the botany, genetics, and chemistry of tree species. Although *dendrology* literally means "the study of trees," the term has been variously defined and debated over the years, reflecting to a great extent what various instructors think should be included in a dendrology course. Steiner (1980) presented an interesting and revealing summary of the diverse opinions. The circumscription established in 1937, the first edition of this textbook, was the identification and classification of woody plants including geographical distributions and silvical characteristics. We basically agree but expand the scope somewhat and essentially follow Dayton (1945) in saying that *dendrology covers those subdisciplines of botany and forestry that deal with the taxonomy, nomenclature, morphology, phenology, ecology, and geographic range of trees.*

Trees are the largest and some of the most impressive plants in the world. But it is not only their size but also their age, shape, dominance in their community, beauty of flowers, fruits, or leaves, and potential uses by man that inspire a feeling of wonder and excitement in all of us. The importance of trees to the world (man and the rest of the biota) as sources of food, shelter, shade, fuel, wood products, oxygen from photosynthesis, erosion control, and so on, expand our appreciation of the key roles of woody vegetation. To learn their identity, relationships, life history, habitats, and distribution adds to the appreciation of these giants of the plant kingdom. We hope your interest in nature will be enhanced by the study of dendrology. We also hope that your powers of observation, discrimination, conceptualization, and your general curiosity will be greatly expanded by this experience.

The world's population will reach six billion at the turn of the century. People will divide or share over five billion hectares of forests, open woodlands, and shrublands; (i.e., about 40% of the earth's land surface). The enormous demands on this area in terms of economic yield, conservation, environmental impacts, sustainability, and management make it imperative that the dendrologist think in terms of "international forestry" (Laarman and Sedjo, 1992). The general principles and techniques of identification learned first as a dendrology student with your local trees can someday be applied internationally. Additional information and color pictures regarding important trees of the world may be found elsewhere, such as in Hora (1981).

To most of us, a tree is quite distinctive; yet the line of demarcation between trees and shrubs is by no means clear. A given species may be shrubby near the extremities of its range, at, or near timberline and still attain large proportions elsewhere. For example, the Alaska-cedar is ordinarily a moderately large tree, but in exposed situations at timberline it is often reduced to a dwarfed or even heathlike shrub; and white spruce, an important pulpwood tree of eastern Canada, is shrubby in habit in the far north. Poison sumac is generally a shrub in the bogs of the Great Lakes area, yet it can be a 25-ft tree in the low woods of Georgia. Similarly, the distinction between shrubs and vines is often poorly defined for several native species of woody plants are at first vinelike and then become shrubby as they approach maturity; or, in other cases, some shrubs may become vinelike at the ends of long branches.

For the sake of convenience, a tree may be defined as a woody plant which at maturity is 13 ft (4 m) or more in height, with a single trunk at least 3 inches (7½ cm) in diameter, unbranched for at least several feet above the ground, and having a more or less definite crown (Little, 1979). Shrubs, in contrast, are smaller and usually exhibit several erect, spreading, or prostrate stems with a general bushy appearance. Lianas are climbing vines; plants of this sort are extremely numerous in the rain-drenched forests of the tropics, although a few species such as the wild grape, moonseed, trumpet creeper, crossvine, greenbrier, and Virginia creeper are indigenous to temperate regions.

The area included in this text is North America, excluding Mexico and extreme southern California, southern Texas, and southern peninsular Florida. These southern areas of the United States have about 120 species of subtropical trees which would greatly expand the scope of this book, and although fascinating, few of these trees are important to forestry in the United States.

This book is not an identification manual and does not cover all the woody species for any particular portion of the country. Detailed keys to species are omitted. Comparative tables covering family, generic, and specific features are provided in addition to the keys to genera. These generic keys should give you experience with the use of keys as well as the characteristics of genera. More time should be spent with keys to local species.

Although a number of nomenclatural changes reflect recent research and literature, the nomenclature generally follows the U.S. Forest Service checklist (Little, 1979), as do vernacular or common names. Additional commonly used names have been added for some species. Names of cultivated or other economically important species follow Bailey et al. (1976), Mabberley (1987), or Terrell et al. (1986).

USE OF THIS TEXTBOOK

A knowledge, understanding, and appreciation of plant classification, nomenclature, identification, tree variation, habitat and range, and morphology are requisite to all work in dendrology. Accordingly, each of these topics will be discussed in several chapters at the beginning. The chapter on morphology, in particular, is of primary importance. This can be used as an illustrated glossary in addition to the more complete glossary at the end of the book.

The chapters describing gymnosperms and angiosperms are arranged into families following a classification system based on evolutionary relationships. The families are briefly described. Then the "distinguishing characteristics" of genera and species are given within the families and often with tables for comparison of the most important characters. The most important species have the most detailed descriptions, discussions, illustrations, and range map. Less important species are described more briefly. Geographical area, general habitats, and elevations are given under the heading of "Range." More detailed discussions of tree sizes, habitats, associates, tolerance, economic importance, uses, diseases, and natural history are given under the heading of "General Description."

2

CLASSIFICATION

Classification is the ordering of items into groups having common characteristics and into a hierarchy of successively more inclusive groups. It therefore involves two processes, grouping and ranking. We classify almost instinctively nearly everything in our daily lives, and this process of organization or compartmentalization aids us in bringing order out of chaos and increases our efficiency of recalling and using information. Think of cars, clothes, furniture, jewelry, tools, or almost anything else. In your own mind you can think of different kinds of these items and of a hierarchical grouping for them. For cars there are different makes such as GM/Ford/Toyota, then sedans/vans/trucks, 4/6/8 cylinder, stick-shift/automatic, 4-wheel drive, and so on. This is a classification. Go into any store and you will find that items for sale are grouped by various features in common. You soon learn where to look for certain items, which makes your shopping much easier and efficient. You use a classification.

Plant classifications follow the same logic. The system is a hierarchy of categories, each level having the characteristics of those above. The classification of western red-cedar and white oak are given here as examples (Table 2-1).

In the above classification the *Pinophyta* are the gymnosperms; the *Magnoliophyta* are the angiosperms, which are subdivided into two classes, the *Magnoliopsida* (dicots) and *Liliopsida* (monocots). In some earlier classifications the gymnosperms and angiosperms were considered as classes in one division, the *Tracheophyta* (including all vascular plants), or *Spermatophyta* (including the seed plants). Monocots and dicots would then have been considered as subclasses.

Fagaceae are those flowering dicots including oaks, beech, and chestnuts; and you would know that white oak, *Quercus alba*, would have certain characteristics which place it in each of the more inclusive categories above it. You could also safely predict that another genus of the family, such as *Lithocarpus*, would have characteristics of

4

TABLE 2-1   SYSTEM OF CLASSIFICATION

Division	Pinophyta	Magnoliophyta
Class	Pinopsida	Magnoliopsida
Subclass		Magnoliidae
Order	Pinales	Fagales
Family	Cupressaceae	Fagaceae
Genus	*Thuja*	*Quercus*
Species	*Thuja plicata*	*Quercus alba*

the family and all categories above. Such a classification expresses relationships based on similarities and serves as a powerful data storage and information retrieval system.

Systematic botany began with classifications based on uses and obvious differences and on predetermined, or a priori, decisions about the characteristics to be used. These were *artificial* classifications. For instance, Linnaeus (1753) based his system of classification simply on numbers of stamens and pistils in flowers, so all flowers, for instance, with 10 stamens and 1 pistil were classified together. This combined redbud and chinaberry—unrelated and in different orders according to modern beliefs. But it was a simple system to use and served to popularize botany in those times. From the late 1700s to the beginning of the 1900s, classifications were based on character similarities shown by the plants themselves; that is, an a posteriori grouping based on many characters held in common. These were the *natural* systems or *phenetic* systems, based on observation rather than pure logic. These gave rise to most of our presently recognized families, genera, and species and led to a simple linear sequence of families still used in many floristic manuals and herbaria.

Post-Darwinian thinking led to the realization that these similarities could mean descent from a common ancestor or evolutionary lineage and that groups were "natural" because they were derived from a common ancestor. The evolutionary lineage of a group is its *phylogeny,* and classifications of the early and middle 1900s attempted to be *phylogenetic.* Thus a taxon at any level should represent one evolutionary line evolved from a common ancestor. Taxonomic methods today utilize many techniques (morphology, anatomy, cytology, palynology, analytical chemistry of secondary products, enzymes, ribosomal RNA, and nuclear, mitochondrial, or chloroplast DNA) in an attempt to develop a realistic phylogeny based on as many characteristics as possible.

Although evolutionary thought and phylogenetic classifications gave new meaning to "natural groups," they had very little effect on the recognition of the families, genera, and species described earlier. Phylogenetic classification is a three-dimensional system of branches—an evolutionary tree—so the arrangement of families was changed drastically. Any linear sequence is, of course, artificial.

One of the difficulties of reconstructing plant phylogeny is in recognizing *convergent evolution;* that is, the independent origin of similar features in different evolutionary lineages. The question always arises as to whether similarities among groups or individuals reflect common ancestry (*patristic similarities*) or convergence (*homoplastic similarities*). Homoplastic similarities may be due to similar selective pressures from environmental adaptations or reproductive strategies. Examples are the similar spiny fruits of Ohio buckeye and horse-chestnut of Europe or the serotinous cones of unrelated pines. Misinterpretation of homoplastic for patristic similarities can lead to differences of opinion and therefore different classifications. As techniques of comparative study continue to improve, classifications should change to reflect new information brought to bear on evolutionary relationships. One of the keys to a successful classification is the realization that some plant attributes are more useful than others in determining relationships and establishing a classification. Indeed some variation may be misleading or simply constitute environmental or evolutionary noise. One of the tasks in plant systematics is to determine the most dependable characteristics, and from these the most realistic, phylogenetic classification.

In the early 1960s an attempt was made to describe the actual character changes and branching patterns of evolutionary lines—known as *cladistics*. Precise analyses of large data sets using computer-generated comparisons were possible, and *cladograms* of many plant groups began to appear in the literature. About this same time there was a revival of phenetic classifications, and phenograms were also computer-generated with the use of several techniques of cluster analysis. There have been, and continue to be, vigorous debates over the value of each. For additional reading on classifications, see Cronquist (1988), Jones and Luchsinger (1986), Radford (1986), Stuessy, (1990), and Zomlefer (1994).

Taxonomic Categories

Species   [Same word for singular or plural; abbreviations: sp. (sing.), spp. (pl.). The word *specie* means "money in coin" and cannot be used as the singular of biological species.] In classifications, the species is the focal point—the basic unit of taxonomy and classification. It is the basic group of potentially interbreeding populations of individuals which share many characteristics and which are more or less distinct from related species in phenotypic characters, often ecological requirements, and reproduction. We also think of species as the smallest group whose members share mutual phylogenetic relatedness. To the conservation biologist, it is the basis of biodiversity. In Chapter 5 we consider various kinds of within-species variation; however, in defining species we demand a recognizable, consistent, and persistent discontinuity in characters between closely related species. Such discontinuities in characters generally reflect a breeding discontinuity (i.e., lack of interbreeding between species), but this in itself cannot be used as a primary criterion for recognizing plant species. Hybridization between species is fairly common in plants, yet the species maintain their relative distinctness due to a fairly effective barrier to wholesale genetic exchange. A species is a concept that is variously defined, so there can be disagreements among taxonomists about the level of recognition of a taxon. A species by one taxonomist may be a variety or subspecies by another and vice versa. These are taxonomic decisions and some taxonomists maintain a much broader view of the species than others. Decisions regarding the level of recognition may also change because of a recent and better understanding of the patterns of variation. A flexible species concept is obviously necessary to accommodate the complexity of nature as well as our level of understanding.

Infraspecific Taxa   Some patterns of within-species variation are appropriately recognized by the categories of *subspecies, varietas* (variety), and *forma* (form) in that descending order. The classical category below the species is variety, and it is still the most commonly used although subspecies has become more popular since the 1950s. There are no agreed-upon distinctions between these two categories, and either may be used as the sole infraspecific category, representing a genetic and morphological subdivision of a species. They are sufficiently distinct to warrant formal recognition, but not enough to be called a species, mainly because of the lack of consistent discontinuities. These infraspecific categories usually reflect a geographical part of the species range, such as the three varieties of American basswood; the Coast Douglas-fir and Rocky Mountain Douglas-fir varieties; or the Rocky Mountain bristlecone pine and Great Basin bristlecone pine varieties. Some varieties may represent an ecotype with some reproductive discontinuity, as *Juniperus virginiana* var. *silicicola.* Or they may reflect an early stage in speciation (see Chapter 5). Although this practice is seldom followed, both subspecies and variety may be used if the pattern of variation warrants this much hierarchical classification. The category of subspecies is not used in this text.

The "variety" used in horticulture is now better known as *cultivar.* This is a distinctive and uniform morphological or physiological type artificially maintained and propagated. Some have originated in the wild, but the majority have arisen in cultivation either spontaneously or as induced mutants or artificial hybrids. The important point is that they are maintained by cultivation. Examples are the copper beech, *Fagus sylvatica* 'Cuprea', the yellow-berried American holly, *Ilex opaca* 'Canary', and the frequently seen lombardy poplar, *Populus nigra* 'Italica'.

The category of "form," seldom used now, is of lesser rank than variety, and where used, defines distinct phenotypes of individuals rather than populations. These may be based on some unusual pubescence, flower color, or atypical leaf shape.

Superspecific Categories   The categories above the level of species serve to show natural (i.e., evolutionary) groupings of the taxa below them. *Genus* (genus, singular; genera, plural; there is no such word as "genuses") functions to group together similar species and indicate the relative differences/similarities with other such genera. A genus is *monotypic* if it includes only one species. In like manner, a *family* is composed of genera; *order* composed of families, and so on. The top level in plant classification is the *division* (or *phylum*). Depending on the number and complexity of the groupings recognized, there are additional categories available such as subclass (see the oak classification above), subfamily, subgenus, and so on. The hierarchical system is designed to accommodate the range of information available on particular groups.

These various categories are recognizable by the endings of the words. Note the accents for pronunciation (see Chapter 3).

Division	-ó-phy-ta	Order	-à-les
Class	-óp-si-da	Family	-à-ce-ae
Subclass	`-i-dae		

Family names are treated as plural nouns; therefore, it is correct to say "The Pinaceae *are* of great economic importance." The ending -aceae is pronounced as -a-see-ee, the ae being a diphthong and pronounced as a long e. There are several exceptions to this -aceae ending, sanctioned by long use and permitted as correct alternatives. Two of these, which include trees, are Palmae (the palms) and Leguminosae (the legumes).

As indicated, plant classification is partly a matter of opinion, and various classifications differ at all levels of the system. Some families recognized here differ from those in earlier editions of this textbook. For example, legumes are treated as three separate families rather than the single Fabaceae. On the other hand, the Taxodiaceae is here combined with the Cupressaceae based on some recent studies. Again, plant classifications are dynamic rather than static and should reflect the best information available at the time and therefore should change as information dictates.

3

NOMENCLATURE

The assignment of names to organisms is called *nomenclature;* we are concerned here with botanical nomenclature. Historically, there have been two nomenclatural systems, *common names* and *scientific names.* The forester and environmental scientist are well advised to learn both in order to communicate effectively with all people.

Common or Vernacular Names   Common names have a place in everyday speech and writing, but they are not precise enough to be used in very exact or scientific communication. Actually the term *vernacular,* meaning "native to a region" is more correct than the term *common.* The reason is that vernacular names are often locally used, are usable in only a single language, often differ among regions, and therefore are not at all "common" in the sense of widespread or in general use. *Common name* is used here to mean "familiar" in contrast to the scientific name.

How trees acquire common names is an interesting story not only in dendrology but also in the social development of a people in relation to their use and enjoyment of the forest.

The chief characteristics of trees usually influence the selection of their common names, although the names of many botanists have also been commemorated in this way. A few examples are:

1 *Habitat.* Swamp white oak, sandbar willow, alpine fir, river birch, mountain hemlock

2 *Some distinctive feature.* Weeping willow, bigleaf maple, whitebark pine, bitternut hickory, cutleaf birch, quaking aspen, overcup oak

3 *Locality or region.* Pacific yew, Idaho white pine, southern red oak, Ohio buckeye, Virginia pine, Carolina basswood

4 *Use.* Canoe birch, sugar maple, tanoak, paper-mulberry

5 *In commemoration.* Nuttall oak, Engelmann spruce, Sargent cypress, Douglas-fir

6 *Adaptation of names from other languages* (e.g., Indian, Latin, Spanish). Chinkapin, hickory, arborvitae, tacamahac poplar

The common names in this text follow those given by Little (1979), except in a few cases, and some additional ones are given as secondary alternatives. Commercial names for lumber are also given by Little (1979) and are not repeated here.

Scientific Names   Because of the great profusion of common names, it is necessary to have a standardized, universal system which can be used throughout the world. Such a system has been developed through the use of Latin or Latinized names because the laws governing Latin syntax remain constant relative to modern languages. Scientific names have followed standard usage since the middle 1700s when Linnaeus (1753) published his monumental *Species Plantarum.* He gave the generic name; the species designation, consisting then of a short descriptive phrase; and finally in the otherwise blank margin, a single word set in italics. He called this the "trivial" name and used it as an indexing device. His students and followers soon found it convenient to write the generic name followed by the trivial name. This practice led to the *generic name* followed by a *specific epithet* for each plant, the combination constituting *binomial nomenclature.*

The complete designation of a tree or other plant consists of three parts: (1) a generic name, (2) a specific epithet, and (3) the full or abbreviated name of the person, or persons, that originally published the name and description or made a later change. Thus in the scientific name *Tilia americana* L., *Tilia* is the generic name, *americana* is the epithet, and L. (for Linnaeus) is the describing author. The name of the species is the binomial, *Tilia americana;* the epithet never stands alone. The author's name is omitted except in scientific writing, where it is used at least once to establish the plant's exact identity. It is customary to underline the binomial in handwritten or typewritten work, and to set it in italics in print; the author's name, when it appears, is not underlined or italicized. Generic names begin with a capital letter; epithets begin with a small letter.

Tilia americana is the scientific name of the American basswood, and no other species anywhere in the world may have this name. Other basswoods will, of course, be in the genus *Tilia* but with other epithets. A varietal name, if any, follows the binomial. For example, south Florida slash pine is known as *Pinus elliottii* var. *densa* Little & Dorman.

One frequently encounters a scientific name followed by names of authors first in parentheses and then others following the parentheses. This indicates a transfer between genera or a change in taxonomic level. *Taxodium distichum* (L.) Rich., was originally *Cupressus disticha* L. Linnaeus originally placed baldcypress in the genus with true cypresses. Later, L. C. Richard recognized the differences and made a new genus, *Taxodium,* and transferred this species to the new combination *Taxodium distichum.* Sand post oak was originally described as *Quercus margaretta* Ashe but later Sargent changed it to *Quercus stellata* var. *margaretta* (Ashe) Sarg. In both these cases, the author's name in parentheses is the original describer, and the second author made the transfer. The original designation is the "name-bringing synonym" or *basionym* of the new combination.

When the scientific name is followed by the names of two or more authors (e.g., *Pinus jeffreyi* Grev. & Balf.), it means that both authors were responsible for the new name. Some binomials are followed by two authors connected by "ex." For example, *Pinus torreyana* Parry ex Carr. In this case, Charles C. Parry, the discoverer, used this name on specimens but not in print, so it was not validly published. A specimen was sent to Carriere, who validly published the name with a description and credited the name to Parry. In other cases, two author names may be connected with "in," which is mainly of bibliographic interest. *Pinus edulis* Engelm. in Wisliz. indicates that Engelmann gave the name and description for the species of pinyon pine, but it was published in the book by Wislizenus. In both these examples, the describing author's name may be given alone.

Interspecific hybrids are designated by either a formula, such as *Pinus palustris* × *taeda,* or a binomial with a "times" sign between the generic name and epithet, as *P.* × *sondereggeri.* Intergeneric hybrids are designated by the "×" before the generic name; for example, × *Cupressocyparis* for *Chamaecyparis* × *Cupressus.*

Cultivar names are sometimes designated after an epithet either by "cv." before the name or usually by use of single quotes; for example, *Gleditsia triacanthos* cv. Moraine or *G. triacanthos* 'Moraine'. The flowering dogwood with rich ruby red bracts is *Cornus florida* 'Cherokee Chief'. These cultivar names are governed by the *International Code of Nomenclature for Cultivated Plants* (Brickell, 1980).

Whenever a species is first divided into subspecies or varieties, the part of the species which includes the "type specimen" of the species is automatically treated as an equivalent taxon to the one or more named. Its epithet is a repeat of the specific epithet and without an authority. For example, when Fernald named *Fraxinus americana* var. *biltmoreana* in 1947 as the pubescent form of white ash, it automatically established *F. americana* var. *americana* for the typical, glabrous individuals of the species. In usual practice, the subspecies or varietal names are omitted unless there is some reason to specify a particular infraspecific taxon.

Sometimes when taxonomic concepts differ among authors or taxa have been combined, it is important to indicate which concept is being considered. For instance, in splitting the legumes into three families, Fabaceae can refer to the original, all-inclusive one, or just that part minus the Mimosaceae and Caesalpiniaceae. Two Latin terms are useful here; *s. lat.* (sensu lato) means in the broad sense; *s. str.* (sensu stricto) means in the narrow sense. Thus Fabaceae s. lat. would indicate the family including all legumes.

The use of scientific names and the coinage of new ones are governed by the *International Code of Botanical Nomenclature* (Greuter, 1994). (See also Jeffrey, 1973, and Walters and Keil, 1988.) Although taxonomy is unregulated and a matter of opinion, as indicated earlier, the application of names for any group (taxon) below the order level is stringently controlled by 62 articles (the rules) which provide for a method of naming taxonomic groups, each with only one correct name, and a means of putting names of the past in order and providing for names of the future. This may involve avoiding and rejecting names that do not conform to the rules.

Scientific names are generally stable, so when an old familiar name is changed, some people are upset. One must realize, however, that there are two valid reasons for changing a scientific name: nomenclatural and taxonomic. A *nomenclatural reason* is the necessity to bring the name in compliance with the rules of nomenclature in the Code. One rule is that of "priority" (i.e., the earliest valid name must be used). For example, in 1950 it was found that the name for Douglas-fir [*Pseudotsuga taxifolia* (Poir.) Britton] was based on an earlier name which lacked priority, so a change had to be made to *P. menziesii* (Mirb.) Franco. A more recent change of this type, for yellow buckeye, was from *Aesculus octandra* Marshall (published in 1785), used in most literature through the 1980s, to *A. flava* Solander (published in 1778) (Meyer and Hardin, 1987). A *taxonomic reason* occurs when the available evidence indicates the need for a change in classification. For example, studies by Grant and Thompson (1975) and O'Connell et al. (1988) indicated that the mountain paper birch is distinct from paper birch so should be called *Betula cordifolia* Regel rather than *Betula papyrifera* var. *cordifolia* (Regel) Fern. Likewise, the study by Gillis (1971) showed a generic difference between the sumacs and their poisonous relatives, so poison sumac, *Rhus vernix* L. was changed to *Toxicodendron vernix* (L.) Kuntze. When a change is made for a valid reason, it takes less energy and adrenaline to learn the new one than it does to complain about the change. Taxonomy and nomenclature must keep abreast of new knowledge.

DERIVATIONS OF SCIENTIFIC NAMES

Scientific names come from a variety of sources just as with common names. There are four main sources for generic names as indicated below, with some examples.

1 In commemoration. *Carnegiea, Kalmia, Maclura, Washingtonia.*
2 Descriptive. *Gymnocladus, Liriodendron, Lithocarpus, Oxydendrum.*
3 Fanciful, mythological, or poetic. *Diospyros.*
4 Original common names in their native lands. *Asimina, Catalpa, Ginkgo, Tsuga, Yucca.*

Specific epithets have also been derived from many sources as indicated by the examples below.

1 Descriptive of structure. *alba, flava, gigantea, latifolia, rubra, pubescens, spinosa.*
2 Descriptive of habitat. *aquatica, palustris, sylvatica.*
3 Uses. *edulis, tinctoria.*
4 Locality where first found. *alleghaniensis, californica, caroliniana, virginica.*
5 Resembling another plant. *bignonioides, strobiformis, taxifolia.*
6 Commemorative. *ashei, fraseri, menziesii, thomasii.*
7 A noun, rather than adjective, and often an old Latin or Greek common name and sometimes old generic names. *negundo, strobus.*

The endings of epithets follow Latin grammar, so they often differ, e.g., *virginiana, virginiensis, virginica,* or *virginianum.*

The list below includes most of the trees in this text. For more extensive lists and more information, see Borror (1960), Coombes (1985), Fernald (1950), Gledhill (1989), Jones and Luchsinger (1986), Little (1979), or Radford (1986).

Abies. Tall tree
Acer. Sharp
acuminata. acuminate, long-pointed
Aesculus. Ancient Latin name for an oak with edible acorns
Agave. Noble or admired one
agrifolia. Field leaf
Ailanthus. Reaching to heaven
alata. Winged
alba. White
albicaulis. White-barked
Albizia. For F. del Albizzi
alleghaniensis. From the Alleghany mountains
Alnus. Ancient Latin name for alder
alternifolia. Alternate-leaved
altissima. Tall
amabilis. Pleasing or lovely
Amelanchier. French name for serviceberry
americana. From America
angustifolia. Narrow leaf
anomala. Unlike others
aquatica. Growing in water
Aralia. From French-Canadian name "aralie"
arboreum. Treelike
Arbutus. Ancient Latin name for European madrone
aristata. Awned, sharp-pointed
arizonica. From Arizona
aromatica. Aromatic
ashei. For W. W. Ashe, USFS
Asimina. From American Indian name
attenuata. Tapering
australis. Southern
azederach. Persian for noble tree

balfouriana. For J. H. Balfour, botanist
balsamea. Balsamlike
balsamifera. Yielding a fragrant resin (balsam)
banksiana. For Joseph Banks, botanist
barbatum. Bearded
Betula. Shining (bark)
bicolor. Two-colored
bifolia. Two-leaved
bignonioides. Like Bignonia

biloba. Two-lobed
biflora. Two-flowered
borbonia. For Gaston Bourbon, French patron of botany
borealis. Northern
bracteata. With bracts
brevifolia. Short-leaved
Bumelia. Ancient Greek name for European ash

californica. From California
Calocedrus. Beautiful cedar
canadensis. From Canada
Carnegiea. For Andrew Carnegie, philanthropist
carolinae-septentrionalis. From North Carolina
caroliniana. From the Carolinas
Carpinus. Latin name for hornbeam, or Celtic for a yoke made of this wood
Carya. Ancient Greek name
Castanea. Ancient Latin name from Castania, Greece, known for its trees
Castanopsis. Chestnutlike
Casuarina. Malay word describing twigs
Catalpa. Cherokee Indian name
cathartica. Purgative
Celtis. Ancient Greek name
cembroides. Like *Pinus cembra*
Cercis. Ancient Greek name from "kerkis," as weaver's shuttle appearing like the fruit
Cereus. Wax candle
cerifera. Wax-bearing
Chamaecyparis. Low-growing cypress
chinensis. From China
chrysolepis. Golden-scaled
chrysophylla. Golden-leaved
cinerea. Ash gray
Cladrastis. Brittle shoots
clausa. Closed, serotinous
clava-hercules. Hercules' club
coccinea. Scarlet
communis. Common
concolor. One color
contorta. Twisted
copallina. Yielding copal gum
cordifolia. Heart-shaped leaves
cordiformis. Heart-shaped
Cornus. Ancient Latin name for cornelian cherry
cornuta. Horn-shaped
Corylus. Ancient Latin name for hazelnut
coulteri. For Thomas Coulter, botanist

crassifolia. Thick-leaved
Crataegus. Greek "kratos" meaning strength, referring to the hard wood
Cupressus. Conical-shaped
Cycas. Ancient Greek name for a palm resembling habit of cycad

decidua. Deciduous
decurrens. Decurrent leaf bases
deltoides. Delta-like, triangular-shaped
densiflorus. Crowded flowers
dentata. Dentate, toothed
deppeana. For Ferdinand Deppe, a German botanist
dioicus. Dioecious
Diospyros. Divine fruit
distichum. Two-ranked
diversilobum. Variable lobing
douglasii. For David Douglas, botanist
drummondii. For Thomas Drummond, botanist
dunnii. For G. W. Dunn, collector

echinata. Prickly
edulis. Edible
Elaeagnus. Ancient Greek name applied to a willow
elliottii. For Stephen Elliott, botanist
ellipsoidalis. Ellipsoidal in shape
emoryi. For W. H. Emory, southwest collector
engelmannii. For George Engelmann, physician and botanist in St. Louis and authority
   on conifers
equisetifolia. Horsetail-like "leaves"
excelsior. Lofty, higher

Fagus. Ancient Latin name for beech
falcata. Sickle-shaped
Ficus. Ancient Latin name for fig
filifera. Bearing threads
flava. Yellowish
flexilis. Flexible
florida. Flowering
floridana. From Florida
fragilis. Fragile
fraseri. For John Fraser, collector
Fraxinus. Ancient Latin name for ash
fremontii. For J. C. Fremont, explorer

gambelii. For William Gambel, naturalist
garryana. For Nicholias Garry, explorer

geminata. Twinned
giganteus. Gigantic
Ginkgo. From a Japanese name (gin-kyo)
glabra. Glabrous
glandulosa. Glandular
glauca. Glaucous
Gleditsia. For J. G. Gleditsch, botanist
Gordonia. For James Gordon, nurseryman
grandiflora. Showy-flowered
grandidentata. Large-toothed
grandifolia. Large-leaved
grandis. Large
Gymnocladus. Bare-branched

Halesia. For Stephen Hales, botanical writer
Hamamelis. Ancient Greek name for another tree with pear-shaped fruit
hemisphaerica. Hemispherical
heterophylla. Diversely-leaved

Ilex. Ancient Latin name for an oak (*Quercus ilex*)
illinoinensis. From Illinois
imbricaria. Overlapping
incana. Gray

japonica. From Japan
jeffreyi. For John Jeffrey, plant explorer
Juglans. Jupiter's nut
julibrissin. Native Iranian name
Juniperus. Ancient Latin name for juniper

Kalmia. For Peter Kalm, a student of Linnaeus who found this plant in America
kelloggii. For Albert Kellogg, botanist
kentukea. From Kentucky

laciniosa. Shaggy
laevigata, laevis. Polished, smooth
lambertiana. For A. B. Lambert, botanist
lanuginosa. Softly hairy
laricina. Like European larch
Larix. Ancient Latin name for larch
lasianthus. Hairy-flowered
lasiocarpa. Hairy-fruited
latifolia. Broad-leaved
laurifolia. Laurel-leaved
lawsoniana. For Peter Lawson, nurseryman

leiophylla. Smooth-leaved
Leitneria. For E. T. Leitner, naturalist
lenta. Pliable
Libocedrus. Resinous cedar
Liquidambar. Liquid amber (resin)
Liriodendron. Lily tree
Lithocarpus. Stony seed
lobata. Lobed
lutea. Yellow
lyallii. For David Lyall, naturalist
lyrata. Lyre-shaped

Maclura. For William Maclure, geologist
macrocarpa. Large-fruited
macrophyllum. Large-leaved
magnifica. Magnificent
Magnolia. For Pierre Magnol, botanist
Malus. Ancient Latin name for apple
margarettiae. For Margaret H. Wilcox, Mrs. W. W. Ashe
mariana, marilandica. From Maryland
maximum. Largest
Melia. From Greek name for ash
menziesii. For Archibald Menzies, naturalist
mertensiana. For F. C. Mertens, botanist
Metasequoia. Close (i.e., similar) to Sequoia
michauxii. For F. A. Michaux, botanist
microphylla. Small-leaved
monophylla. One-leaved
monosperma. One-seeded
montana. Mountain
monticola. Mountain dwelling
Morus. Ancient Latin name for mulberry
muehlenbergii. For G. H. E. Muhlenberg, botanist
muricata. Rough with hard, sharp points
Myrica. Fragrant
myristiciformis. Shape of *Myristica* (nutmeg)

neomexicana. From New Mexico
negundo. Ancient Malayan name for tree with similar leaves
nigra. Black
nootkatensis. From Nootka Sound, B.C., Canada
nuttallii. For Thomas Nuttall, botanist
Nyssa. Water nymph

oblongifolia. Oblong-leaved
occidentalis. Western

octandra. Eight-stamened
odorata. Fragrant
opaca. Opaque, not glossy
Osmanthus. Fragrant flower
osteosperma. Bonelike seed or fruit wall
Ostrya. Greek meaning "shell," for the inflated covering of the fruit
ovalis, ovata. Ovate-shaped
Oxydendrum. Sour tree

pagoda. Pagoda-shaped
pallida. Pale
palmetto. From Spanish common name, palmito
palustris. Swampy land
papyrifera. Paper-bearing
parryi. For C. C. Parry, botanist and explorer
parviflora. Small-flowered
Paulownia. For Anna Paulowna
pensylvanica, pennsylvanica. From Pennsylvania
Persea. Ancient Greek name for another tree
persica. Persian
phanerolepis. Conspicuous-scaled
phellos. Corky
Picea. Pitch (resin)
Pinus. Ancient Latin name for pine
Platanus. Ancient Greek name for the plane tree
plicata. Folded
pomifera. Apple-bearing
ponderosa. Heavy, large
populifolia. Poplar-leaved
Populus. Ancient Latin name for poplar
prinus. Ancient Greek name for oak
procera. Very tall
profunda. Deep (swamp)
Prunus. Latin for plum
pseudoacacia. False *Acacia*
Pseudotsuga. False hemlock
Ptelea. Ancient Greek name for an elm with similar winged fruit
pumila. Dwarf
pungens. Pungent, prickly
purshiana. For F. Pursh, botanist
pyramidata. Pyramidlike
Pyrus. Ancient Latin name for pear

quadrangulata. Four-angled
quadrifolia. Four-leaved
Quercus. Ancient Latin name for oak

racemosa. In a raceme
radiata. Radiating outward
radicans. With rooting stems
regia. Royal
resinosa. Resinous
Rhamnus. Ancient Greek name for prickly shrubs
Rhododendron. Rose tree
rhombifolia. Diamond-shaped leaves
Rhus. Ancient Greek name for sumac
rigida. Rigid, stiff
Robinia. For Jean Robin, herbalist
rubens. Blushed with red
rubra. Red

Sabal. American Indian name
sabiniana. For Joseph Sabine, naturalist
saccharinum, saccharum. Sugary
Salix. Ancient Latin name for willow
Sapindus. Indian soap
Sassafras. American Indian name
scopulorum. Of cliffs or rocks
sempervirens. Always living
Sequoia. For Cherokee Indian, Sequoiah
Sequoiadendron. Sequoia tree
serotina. Of late season
serrulata. Serrulate, small teeth
shumardii. For B. F. Shumard, geologist
silicicola. Growing in sand
sitchensis. From Sitka Island, Alaska
Sorbus. Ancient Latin name for this tree
speciosa. Showy
spicatum. Spikelike
spinosa. Spiny, prickly
stellata. Starlike (hairs)
strobiformis. Like *Pinus strobus*
strobus. Ancient Latin name for gum-yielding tree
styraciflua. Resin (styrax)-flowing
sylvatica, sylvestris. Of the forest
Symplocos. Connected (stamens)

taeda. Torch of resinous pine wood
Tamarix. Ancient Latin name, Tamaris River
taxifolia. *Taxus* (yew)-like leaves
Taxodium. Yew-like
Taxus. Ancient Latin name for yew

tetraptera. Four-winged
texana, texensis. From Texas
thomasii. For David Thomas, horticulturist
Thuja. Ancient Greek name; resinous
thyoides. Thuja-like
Tilia. Ancient Latin name for basswood; wing
tinctoria. Used for dyeing
tomentosa. Tomentose, densely hairy
torreyana. For John Torrey, botanist
Toxicodendron. Poison tree
tremuloides. Aspenlike, trembling
triacanthos. Three-thorned
trichocarpa. Hairy-fruited
trifoliata. Three-leaflet
triloba. Three-lobed
tripetala. Three-petaled
Tsuga. Japanese name for hemlock
tulipifera. Tulip-bearing
typhina. Cattail-like

Ulmus. Ancient Latin name for elm
Umbellularia. Little-umbelled

velutina. Velvety
vernix. Varnish
virginiana. From Virginia

Washingtonia. For George Washington
wislizeni. For F. A. Wislizenus, collector
wrightii. For Charles Wright, collector

Yucca. Carib Indian name

Zanthoxylum. Yellow wood

PRONUNCIATION OF SCIENTIFIC NAMES

Botanical Latin, distinct from Classical or Reformed Academic Latin, has no standardized, worldwide pronunciation. The sound of a word can vary because of three variables: first the sounds of the individual letters; second the short or long vowel sounds; and third, the syllable being accented. There are a number of rules governing the "correct" sound but also many exceptions to the rules. Many American botanists/dendrologists follow the "traditional English system" and pronounce scientific names as though they were English words; others prefer the more classical sound. Therefore, you will hear slightly different pronunciations even among professionals. Because oral communication is so necessary, at least an understandable pronunciation of tree names should be considered important along with their correct spelling and identification. Some of the general guidelines are given here.

- Vowel sounds are either "long" and sound more or less like we say the letter, or "short" and modified. For example, the long *A* in *Àcer,* the short *i* in *flóridus,* the long *i* in *bìcolor,* the short *e* in *Oxydéndrum.* In various books (Little, 1979) and in this text-book, long and short vowel sounds are indicated by two different accent marks. The grave accent (`) designates the *long* English sound of the vowel; the acute accent (´) indicates the *short* or modified sound. These accent marks are not to be used when the names are written elsewhere.
- All single vowels are pronounced.
- Double vowels that form a diphthong are pronounced as a single syllable. (Ex.: *ae* as in see; *au* as in cause; *eu* as in yew). In most other double vowels, both are pronounced (Ex., *-ii* as ee-eye; *-ea* and *-ia* as ee-ah).
- An *a* at the end of a word is always pronounced as a separate syllable and has an ah sound (Ex., *vérna* as vér-nah). An *e* at the end of a word is also always pronounced and has a long ee sound (Ex., *arvénse* as are-vén-see; *occidentàle* as oc-see-den-tày-lee; *vulgàre* as vul-gày-ree).
- A final *es* sounds like ees (Ex., *clava-hércules* as cla-vah-hér-cue-lees).
- *ch* within a word is generally pronounced as a *k* (Ex., *echinàta* as ek-i-này-ta); if at the beginning of a word, it sounds like the ch in choice (Ex., *chi-nén-sis*). *ph* has the sound of *f* (Ex., *phéllos* as fél-los).
- When *Ts, Ps,* or *Pt* is at the beginning of a word, the first letter is silent (Ex., *Tsùga* as sù-ga; *Pseudolárix* as su-do-lá-rix; *Ptèlea* as teè-lee-ah).
- The *-oi-* in many specific epithets, meaning "like," or "having the form of" is pronounced in two different ways. Some consider it as two separate vowels (following Latin rules) and say *platanoides* as plat-a-no-ì-dees. Others consider it a diphthong and pronounce it as in oil (Ex., plat-a-noí-dees; *deltoides* is either del-to-ì-dees or del-toí-dees).
- *y* is always a vowel with the sound of a short *i* (Ex., *diphyllus* as di-fíl-us).

As for the syllable accented, there are some rules, but there are also many exceptions some of which preserve the sound of the related English word or commemorative name. Again, some guidelines.

- The accent is *never* on the last syllable.
- Words of two syllables are *always* accented on the first syllable (Ex., *Quércus, Àcer*).
- Words of more than two syllables are accented on the next-to-the-last syllable (*penult*) if that syllable is *long.* It is long if the penult ends in a long vowel, a diphthong, or a consonant (which makes the vowel short but the syllable long) (Ex., *banksiàna* as bank-si-à-nah; *formòsus* as for-mò-sus; *amoènus* as a-moè-nus; *decúmbens* as de-cúm-bens; *cruéntus* as cru-én-tus).
- Words of more than two syllables are accented on the third syllable from the end (*antepenult*) if the *penult* is *short.* It is therefore the penult that governs the position of

the accent. (Ex., *serótina* as se-ró-ti-nah; *flóridus* as fló-ri-dus; *sylvática* as syl-vá-ti-ca). Some exceptions preserve the sound of commemorative names (Ex., *thómasii* as tómas-ee-eye ; jàmes-ee-eye ; but yet we say *Halesia* as Ha-lè-see-ah rather than Hàle-zee-ah although it is for Steven Hales).

• The accent is never further from the end than the antepenult, and usually only one syllable is accented.

• Words derived from a single classical root are pronounced like the related English word (Ex., *rígida* = rigid; *ovàta* = ovate).

• Words from two roots should be accented to preserve the sounds of both related English words [Ex., Rhodo-dén-dron; macro-phyl´lum rather than ma-cró-phyl-lum; sem-per-vì-rens rather than sem-pér-vi-rens (although the latter is correct according to a different rule)]. Yet there are many exceptions such as Zan-thóx-y-lum rather than Zantho-xỳlum (the *x* in the latter is pronounced as a *z*), and Gymnóc-cla-dus rather than Gymno-clà-dus).

For more discussion of this, and more rules for pronunciation, see Radford (1986) and Stearn (1992).

4

IDENTIFICATION

Identification of trees is one of the primary objectives of a course in dendrology and certainly a necessity for those in various disciplines dealing with vegetation. The process of identifying an unknown tree or any plant is one of mental multivariate analysis, for there are numerous characters and character states that are potentially analyzed by our minds to reach a decision. (A *character* is a kind of trait; e.g., bark or leaf shape; *character state* is the particular form of that trait; e.g., shaggy bark or ovate leaf.) Obviously, the more characters available and known, the more dependable the answer. Yet in many cases, tree species can be identified easily and correctly by analysis of less than a half dozen characters. Tree identification takes into account geographic area, habitat, form, bark, twig, leaves, taste or aroma, flowers, and fruits (i.e., the whole plant in its natural setting). One consciously, or subconsciously and almost automatically after some experience, considers many characters and character states before an identification is made.

There are some shortcuts to identification. The easiest method is to ask someone who knows. Another popular method is to use illustrations in state or regional tree guides. This method can be slow, undependable, and discouraging but still appropriate for the novice. A much better approach is to use identification keys available, to genera in this text, and to species in some field guides and more technical manuals of the plants of a state or region. One must understand considerable morphological terminology to use these manuals effectively. (For a guide to floristic manuals, see Frodin, 1984, or Little and Honkala, 1976.)

When attempting to identify an unknown tree, one should analyze the character states available, possibly overall form, bark, habitat, and locality first, then leaf and/or twig, odor or taste, fruit or cone, then flower and any other details. The order of analysis is not important and is generally governed by the conspicuousness and availability of the various parts.

To check a tentative identification, one could ask someone more knowledgeable, carefully compare the unknown with available illustrations and descriptions of the suspected species, or check labeled trees in a botanical garden, *arboretum* (a garden of trees), or labeled specimens in a *herbarium*. A herbarium is a library of dried, pressed, and mounted specimens carefully arranged in one of several sequences. Most colleges and universities throughout the world maintain a herbarium, often with several hundred thousand specimens and generally in a biology or botany department. The largest herbaria in the United States and Canada are at museums, botanical gardens, and universities. Some examples are the New York Botanical Garden (with over 5 million specimens), Harvard University Herbaria (nearly 5 million), U.S. National Herbarium at the Smithsonian Institution (ca. 4.5 million), Missouri Botanical Garden (ca. 4 million), the Field Museum in Chicago (ca. 2.5 million), and the Canadian Agricultural Herbaria in Ottawa (over 1 million). Most college or university herbaria have between 25,000 and 500,000 specimens (Holmgren et al., 1990).

Identification in the field, laboratory, or herbarium is sometimes routine and simple, but at other times it is a real challenge—a job of detective work demanding ingenuity in pulling together all the available evidence to solve the riddle. This keeps tree identification exciting.

KEYS TO GENERA

The *genus* is the common level of recognition, even in "folk botany" or "ethnobiological classifications" throughout the world (Berlin, 1992). It is the usual group of plants or animals most easily recognized as distinct based on general appearance. Most people, therefore, have a name for pines, oaks, hickories, cherries, maples, and so on. These are genera. Distinguishing the family and species often requires detailed examination of more technical characters. Therefore, the genus is the most useful and practical unit for recognition and the reason to begin your study of tree identification with an artificial key to genera.

Using keys is one of the fastest and most popular methods of identifying unknowns. A key is an analytical device which usually has a series of two brief contradictory descriptions. To use a key, you compare the characteristics of the unknown plant to both descriptions. The one matching the plant either leads to a name for the plant or to another set of contrasting statements. You continue this pattern until, if all the correct choices have been made, you arrive at the correct name for the unknown. Making "correct" choices hinges on your ability to understand the descriptive terminology used in the key as well as your ability to accurately interpret those features of the plant in question. (See Chapter 7 and the Glossary for this terminology.) Another possible stumbling block to using keys correctly is the nature of the key itself. You will find that some keys are ambiguous and more difficult to use than others. When you key something out, always check a description, illustration, or herbarium specimen to be sure you are correct. If you have made a wrong choice, you may reach a place in the key where neither of the choices fit the characteristics of your unknown.

In that case, go back to a place in the key where you were uncertain and try the other direction. Or, you may need to start over.

There are two basic types of keys. The "synoptic key" presents a condensed description of the more important technical characters which form the basis of their phylogenetic arrangement. This type is seldom used for ordinary identification. The "diagnostic key" contains only the conspicuous characters which are most usable for identification. These keys are usually "artificial" in that the sequence of the plants is based on obvious similarities or "key characters" which do not necessarily indicate evolutionary relationships. This will be obvious in the keys here, for some combine both conifers and flowering plants.

The most acceptable key is *dichotomous,* which presents only two contrasting statements. Each pair of choices is called a *couplet,* and each choice is called a *lead.* Keys may be written in either of two formats based on how the leads and couplets are arranged. In the *indented key,* one or more couplets are indented (and included) under the lead having the characters which are correct for those couplets. The contrasting lead is presented only after the indented couplet or couplets. (See the summer keys A–F for this type of format.) The advantage of the indented key is that it is readily apparent which plants share certain characteristics, for they are all indented under those characteristics. Also the couplets do not have to be numbered (see the first summer key to keys) because you follow the key by the degree of indentation (i.e., if a lead is correct, it will either give you the name of the plant, or you go to the next couplet indented under it). Numbers are sometimes used to make it easier to recognize the two leads of a couplet. (See the summer keys A–F.) It is also easier to work backward in an indented key to determine the characteristics of a particular plant. The disadvantages of the indented key are that it wastes space when the key is very long and that the two leads of a given couplet may be rather far apart. You recognize the second lead of a couplet by the same number, if used, the same degree of indentation, and the same "lead word."

The second type of format is the *bracketed key.* In this form the two leads of a couplet are kept together, and each lead will either end in a plant name or the number of the couplet to which you would go next. Alternate couplets are indented for easier recognition. (See the summer key G or winter key E for this format.) This format is advantageous for very long keys because the left margin is maintained and there is little wasted space. However, the disadvantages are that it is nearly impossible to see similarities among the plants, it is harder to work backward to obtain the characteristics of a plant, backtracking is more difficult when a mistake has been made, the couplets must be numbered, and there has to be a number at the end of the lead which sends you to another couplet.

The keys that follow are artificial, diagnostic keys to the genera described in this textbook. Each genus is defined only in terms of the species described here. Some genera include species that are so different that they occur in different parts of the key. Such cases are indicated by "in part" (in pt.) placed after the generic name.

The keys are written to give you an opportunity to practice using keys in both formats, to help you learn the genera of trees and their morphological characteristics, and to group them by their obvious features which makes them easier for you to remember. The more you use keys, the more proficient you will become.

The abbreviations used in the keys are: *lf.,* leaf; *lvs.,* leaves; *lfts.,* leaflets; *fls.,* flowers; *frt.,* fruit. For the winter key, it is advisable to use a 10× handlens to observe some of the features. It is also a good practice to examine several twigs or several buds, leaf scars, stipular scars, and so on, to make certain you are interpreting all the structures correctly. When the character is variable or interpretation is difficult, the genus often appears in more than one place in the key.

SUMMER KEYS TO GENERA (AND WINTER KEYS TO EVERGREENS)

Key to Keys

Plant evergreen
    Lvs. acicular, linear, subulate, or scalelike; width less than 5 mm
        Lvs. acicular or narrowly linear . . . . A
        Lvs. subulate or scalelike . . . . B
    Lvs. of various shapes; width over 5 mm C
Plant deciduous; or succulent and lvs. lacking
    Lvs. lacking on succulent plants; or, when present on a nonsucculent plant,
    acicular, linear, scalelike, or subulate; width less than 5 mm . . . . D
    Lvs. of various shapes; width over 5 mm
        Lvs. opposite or whorled . . . . E
        Lvs. alternate
            Lvs. compound . . . . F
            Lvs. simple . . . . G

Key A (evergreen; lvs. acicular or narrowly linear)

1 Lvs. acicular and in fascicles of 1–5 in the axils of primary scale lvs. . . . . . .*Pinus*
1 Lvs. narrowly linear and not in fascicles
    2 Lvs. oriented in 2 ranks; seeds single, axillary, and enclosed by a
        fleshy aril
        3 Lvs. ½–1 in. long, flexible, the apex soft-pointed; seed partially
            enclosed by a scarlet aril . . . .*Taxus*
        3 Lvs. 1–3½ in. long, stiff, the apex prickly-pointed; seed
            completely enclosed by a green to purplish aril . . . .*Torreya*
    2 Lvs. in more than 2 ranks; seeds enclosed in a strobilus (cone)
        4 Lf. attached to a peg which persists on the twig after lf.
        dehiscence
            5 Lf. sessile on a peg; twigs very rough due to conspicuous,
                persistent pegs; lf. 4-angled or flat in cross section . . . .*Picea*
            5 Lf. petiolate on a peg; twigs only slightly rough due to short,
                inconspicuous pegs; lf. flat or rounded in cross section. . . . . *Tsuga*
        4 Lf. attached directly on the twig; i.e., without a peg
            6 Lf. sessile and leaving a round, smooth scar on the twig; seed
                cones erect . . . .*Abies*

6 Lf. petiolate or with a decurrent base; seed cones pendent
    7 Lvs. petiolate, diverging in a spiral all around twig; seed
    cones oblong with exserted 3-lobed bracts between
    flattened scales . . . .*Pseudotsuga*
    7 Lvs. slightly narrowed into a long, decurrent base,
    spirally arranged but diverging in 2 ranks; seed cones
    ovoid and smooth with peltate scales . . . .*Sequoia*

Key B (evergreen; lvs. subulate or scalelike)

1 Lvs. not imbricated, the twig visible in the internodes; fls. present; seeds
in individual capsules, or samaras in woody conelike aments
    2 Lvs. alternate; fls. bisexual, white or pinkish; capsules splitting
    lengthwise and exposing small seeds with a tuft of hairs at one end . . . .*Tamarix*
    2 Lvs. whorled; fls. unisexual and inconspicuous; frt. winged and
    held by woody bracts forming a conelike ament . . . .*Casuarina*
1 Lvs. imbricated, the twig usually hidden by the lvs.; fls. absent; seeds in a cone
    3 Branchlets not flattened into sprays (i.e., the twigs arising in
    radial, three-dimensional orientations)
        4 Seed cone fleshy and berrylike; seeds wingless; plant
        dioecious . . . .*Juniperus*
        4 Seed cone leathery or woody; seeds winged; plant monoecious
            5 Lvs. alternate; seed cone oblong-ovoid, 2–3½ in.
            long . . . .*Sequoiadendron*
            5 Lvs. opposite or whorled; seed cone subglobose, less than
            2 in. in diameter . . . .*Cupressus*
    3 Branchlets flattened (i.e., the twigs forming two-dimensional
    sprays)
        6 Twigs round in cross section, the facial and lateral lvs.
        similar; seed cones globose with peltate scale/bracts,
        leathery but becoming woody when seeds dispersed . . . . *Chamaecyparis*
        6 Twigs flattened in cross section, the facial and lateral lvs.
        different; seed cones oblong with thin, flattened scale/bracts,
        woody
            7 Seed cones ¾–1½ in. long, 6-scaled, duck-bill like; lvs.
            opposite appearing as whorls of 4 . . . .*Calocedrus*
            7 Seed cones ⅓–½ in. long, 6–12 scaled; lvs. opposite
            in 4 ranks . . . .*Thuja*

Key C (evergreen; lvs. broad)

1 Lvs. opposite . . . .*Osmanthus*
1 Lvs. alternate
    2 Lvs. compound or appearing so by mechanical splitting
        3 Lvs. pinnately compound; seeds borne on the margins
        of sporophylls . . . .*Cycas*

    3 Lvs. appearing palmately compound; seeds in a drupe
       4 Petioles prickly; southwestern . . . .*Washingtonia*
       4 Petioles smooth; southeastern . . . .*Sabal*
2 Lvs. simple
    5 Lvs. with parallel venation
       6 Stem unbranched below inflorescence; lvs. in a basal
          rosette; ovary inferior . . . .*Agave*
       6 Stem branched; lvs. in terminal clusters; ovary superior . . . .*Yucca*
    5 Lvs. with pinnate venation
       7 Lvs. aromatic when crushed
          8 Lvs. covered or dotted with minute, yellow glands
             (use handlens) . . . .*Myrica*
          8 Lvs. without yellow glands (use handlens)
             9 Stipular scars encircling the twig; frt. a follicle in a
                conelike aggregate . . . .*Magnolia*
             9 Stipular scars lacking; frt. a drupe
                10 Terminal bud 3–4 scaled; frt. ½–¾ in. in diameter,
                    dark blue-black or black; lvs. spicy when crushed;
                    southeastern . . . .*Persea*
                10 Terminal bud naked; frt. ¾–1 in. in diameter,
                    yellow-green; lvs. pungent-spicy when crushed;
                    western . . . .*Umbellularia*
       7 Lvs. not aromatic when crushed
          11 Frt. an acorn in a cup, or nuts enclosed in a spiny bur
             12 Lvs. without yellow scales below; frt. an acorn
                in a cup
                13 Acorn in a thin, scaly cup . . . .*Quercus* (in pt.)
                13 Acorn in a prickly cup . . . .*Lithocarpus*
             12 Lvs. covered with yellow scales below; frt. in a
                spiny bur . . . .*Castanopsis*
          11 Frt. not an acorn or nut enclosed in a bur
             14 Lvs. aculeate margined, or at least
                the apex spiny-tipped . . . .*Ilex*
             14 Lvs. entire (rarely toothed on vigorous shoots)
                or shallowly serrulate
                15 Sap milky (check broken petiole)
                   16 Stipular scars encircling twig . . . .*Ficus*
                   16 Stipular scars lacking . . . .*Bumelia*
                15 Sap clear
                 17 Frt. a capsule
                   18 Lf. margin entire . . . .*Rhododendron*
                   18 Lf. margin serrulate . . . .*Gordonia*
                 17 Frt. a drupe or berry
                   19 Pith chambered; fls. yellow . . . .*Symplocos*

19 Pith solid and homogeneous; fls. white
  20 Frt. black; bark gray; twig with
    pungent odor when broken;
    southeastern .... *Prunus* (in pt.)
  20 Frt. orange; bark red-brown; twig
    lacking pungent odor when broken;
    northwestern .... *Arbutus*

Key D (succulents without lvs.; or lvs. deciduous and less than 5 mm wide)

1 Lvs. lacking; stem succulent .... *Carnegiea*
1 Lvs. present; stem woody
  2 Lvs. acicular, borne spirally on long and indeterminate short-
    shoots; seeds in cones with flat scales .... *Larix*
  2 Lvs. narrowly linear, subulate, or scalelike; seeds in cones
    or capsules
    3 Lvs. narrowly linear or subulate, borne on long and
      determinate short-shoots; seeds in cones with peltate scales .... *Taxodium*
    3 Lvs. scalelike on long shoots; seeds in capsules; flowers
      white to pink .... *Tamarix*

Key E (deciduous; lvs. broad, opposite, or whorled)

1 Lvs. compound
  2 Lvs. palmately compound; frt. a capsule with large seeds .... *Aesculus*
  2 Lvs. pinnately compound or trifoliolate; frt. a samara
    3 Lfts. coarsely serrate or lobed; frt. a double samara .... *Acer* (in pt.)
    3 Lfts. entire, serrulate, or serrate; frt. a single samara .... *Fraxinus* (in pt.)
1 Lvs. simple
  4 Lvs. palmately or pinnipalmately veined
    5 Back of lvs. with erect, branched hairs; pith hollow
      in second year; fruit a persistent, ovoid capsule .... *Paulownia*
    5 Back of lvs. without branched hairs; pith solid; frt. an
      elongated, linear capsule or double samara
      6 Lf. blades usually all palmately lobed; frt. a double
        samara .... *Acer* (in pt.)
      6 Lf. blades only rarely lobed; frt. an elongated,
        linear capsule .... *Catalpa*
  4 Lvs. pinnately veined
    7 Lf. venation arcuate; lf. scars connected by a narrow
      ridge .... *Cornus* (in pt.)
    7 Lf. venation not arcuate; lf. scars not connected by a ridge
      8 Petiole short, stout, purplish; vascular bundle scars
        1; frt. a drupe; eastern .... *Chionanthus*
      8 Petiole long and slender; vascular bundle scars many;
        frt. a samara; western .... *Fraxinus* (in pt.)

Key F (deciduous; lvs. broad, alternate, compound)

1 Lf. trifoliolate
 2 Frt. a thin, round samara; lfts. entire or serrulate; shrub or
  small tree . . . .*Ptelea*
 2 Frt. a drupe; lfts. coarsely toothed or lobed; shrub or vine
  (POISONOUS TO THE TOUCH) . . . .*Toxicodendron* (in pt.)
1 Lf. with 5 or more lfts
 3 Lvs. 2- or 3-pinnately compound
  4 Lfts. ½ in. or less long, the main vein of lft. near one margin;
   fls. in globose heads, the stamens long exserted . . . .*Albizia*
  4 Lfts. ½ in. or more long, the main vein of lft. near center; fls.
   in racemes or panicles
   5 Lvs. 1½ to 4 ft long
    6 Lfts. entire; without prickles on stem or lf . . . .*Gymnocladus*
    6 Lfts. serrulate; with prickles on midrib below, on
     petiole, and scattered or in a circle around stem at the node . . . . . .*Aralia*
   5 Lvs. 1½ ft or less long
    7 Lfts. 1–2 in. long; margin serrate or lobed; apex acuminate . . . . . .*Melia*
    7 Lfts. less than 1 in. long; margin entire or slightly
     crenulate; apex rounded, obtuse, or emarginate . . . .*Gleditsia*
 3 Lvs. 1-pinnately compound
  8 Lvs. and twigs with milky cell sap when broken; frts. reddish,
   hairy, and in an erect, dense panicle . . . .*Rhus*
  8 Lvs. and twigs with clear cell sap (NOTE: if petiole reddish,
   do not break petiole; see no. 13); frts. not as above
   9 Stipular spines or thorns present
    10 Stipular spines present on vigorous shoots; thorns absent . . . . .*Robinia*
    10 Stipular spines absent; thorns long and often branched . . . . . .*Gleditsia*
   9 Stipular spines and thorns absent
    11 Margin glandular-toothed only near base; crushed
     lfts. with an unpleasant odor . . . .*Ailanthus*
    11 Margin entire or toothed throughout; crushed lfts. odorless
     or fragrant (NOTE: if petiole reddish, *do not* crush the
     lfts.; see no. 13)
     12 Lft. margins entire
      13 Petiole and rachis reddish; frt. a white drupe
       (POISONOUS TO THE TOUCH) . . . . . .*Toxicodendron* (in pt.)
      13 Petiole and rachis green; frt. a legume or
       berrylike and yellowish
       14 Lfts. 5–11, each more than 1 in. wide, neither
        lanceolate nor falcate; frt. a legume; base of
        petiole nearly enclosing lateral bud; eastern . . . . .*Cladrastis*
       14 Lfts. 11–19, each 1 in. or less wide, lanceolate
        and falcate; frt. berrylike and yellowish; petiole
        below lateral bud; western . . . .*Sapindus*

12 Lft. margins serrate

    15 Pith chambered; frt. a nut enclosed in an indehiscent husk
    . . . .*Juglans*

    15 Pith solid; frt. a pome or a nut in a dehiscent husk

        16 Stipules or stipular scars present; buds resinous; frt.
        a cluster of small, red pomes . . . .*Sorbus*

        16 Stipules and stipular scars absent; buds not
        resinous; frt. a nut in a more or less dehiscent
        husk . . . .*Carya*

Key G (deciduous; lvs. broad, alternate, simple)

1 Lvs. and twigs lepidote (covered with silvery or brownish, scalelike,
stellate hairs) . . . .*Elaeagnus*

1 Lvs. and twigs not lepidote 2

    2 Lvs. typically entire margined; lobed or not 3

    2 Lvs. typically serrate, serrulate, or crenate margined; lobed or not 17

3 Stipules or stipular scars encircling twig 4

3 Stipules or stipular scars lacking, or if present, not encircling twig 5

    4 Lvs. typically 4-lobed with a broadly truncate or notched apex; frt.
    an aggregate of samaras . . . .*Liriodendron*

    4 Lvs. not lobed; apex obtuse to acuminate; frt. an aggregate
    of follicles . . . .*Magnolia*

5 Lf. flabellate (fan-shaped) with dichotomous veins . . . .*Ginkgo*

5 Lf. variously shaped but not flabellate; venation pinnate or palmate 6

    6 Lvs. palmately veined (with 3 or more prominent veins arising at
    or near the base of the blade) 7

    6 Lvs. pinnately veined (with 1 major midrib) 8

7 Lvs. cordate at base, not lobed, not aromatic; frt. a legume . . . .*Cercis*

7 Lvs. cuneate at base, unlobed or 2 or 3 lobed at apex, aromatic; frt.
a drupe . . . .*Sassafras*

    8 Thorns present; sap milky (observable in broken petiole and young frt.) 9

    8 Thorns lacking; sap clear 10

9 Stipules or stipular scars present; frt. a large, globose, multiple of dry,
greenish drupes . . . .*Maclura*

9 Stipules or stipular scars absent; frt. a single black drupe . . . .*Bumelia*

    10 Lvs. usually oblanceolate, 7–12 in. long, malodorous when
    crushed; frt. a berry 3–5 in. long . . . .*Asimina*

    10 Lvs. and frt. not as above 11

11 Terminal bud lacking, pseudoterminal bud present; frt. a globose berry . .*Diospyros*

11 Terminal bud present; frt. a drupe, elliptical berry, or acorn 12

    12 Lvs. and twigs spicy-aromatic when crushed . . . .*Sassafras*

    12 Lvs. and twigs not spicy-aromatic when crushed 13

13 Pith chambered . . . .*Symplocos*

13 Pith solid and homogeneous or diaphragmed 14

    14 Pith diaphragmed . . . .*Nyssa*

14 Pith homogeneous 15

15 Buds with 2 nearly valvate scales; lf. venation arcuate . . . .*Cornus* (in pt.)

15 Buds with imbricate scales; lf. venation typically pinnate 16

   16 Stipules or stipular scars absent; vascular bundle scars 3;
     frt. a dry drupe; plant dioecious . . . .*Leitneria*

   16 Stipules or stipular scars present; vascular bundle scars more
     than 3; frt. an acorn; plant monoecious . . . .*Quercus* (in pt.)

17 Lvs. palmately veined (with 3 or more prominent veins arising at or
   near the base) 18

17 Lvs. pinnately veined (with a single midrib and equal secondary veins)
   or pinnipalmate (with lowest secondary veins larger than the others 21

   18 Lf. lobes 3–7; frt. dry, in a globose multiple 19

   18 Lf. lobes 2 or 3 or not lobed; frt. fleshy, in a multiple or single 20

19 Lvs. finely serrate; frt. a multiple of capsules; stipular scars slitlike
   and eventually inconspicuous . . . .*Liquidambar*

19 Lvs. coarsely serrate; frt. a multiple of achenes; stipular scars
   encircling twig . . . .*Platanus*

   20 Stems often bearing thorns; sap clear; frt. a pome . . . .*Crataegus*

   20 Stem lacking thorns; sap of broken petiole milky; frt.
     a multiple of drupelets . . . .*Morus*

21 Lvs. distinctly pinnately lobed 22

21 Lvs. not lobed 23

   22 Twigs lacking thorns; frt. an acorn . . . .*Quercus* (in pt.)

   22 Twigs often bearing thorns; frt. a pome . . . .*Crataegus*

23 Lvs. distichous (2-ranked) 24

23 Lvs. in 3 or more ranks 34

   24 Lvs. with broad, cordate to truncate base; frt. nutlike and
     attached to a long, leafy bract . . . .*Tilia*

   24 Lvs. with rounded, cuneate, or nearly cordate base; frt. not as above 25

25 Lf. margin irregularly crenate, crenate-dentate, or sinuate; frt. a woody
   capsule; buds naked . . . .*Hamamelis*

25 Lf. margin serrate or serrulate; frt. a pome, nutlet, nut, drupe, or
   samara; buds scaly 26

   26 Lf. margin widely serrate with 1 tooth per secondary vein 27

   26 Lf. margin closely serrate, serrulate, or doubly serrate, with many
     teeth per secondary vein 28

27 Stipular scars long and nearly encircling twig; lf. 2× or less longer than
   wide, base broadly cuneate; nuts in a weak-spined husk . . . .*Fagus*

27 Stipular scars short; lf. 3× or more longer than wide, base narrowly
   cuneate or acute; nuts in a stiff-spined bur . . . .*Castanea*

   28 Twigs with conspicuous white lenticels lengthening horizontally
     with age . . . .*Betula*

   28 Twigs with more- or- less circular lenticels, often indistinct 29

29 Terminal bud present; fls. showy, white, in crowded racemes; frt.
   a pome . . . .*Amelanchier*

29 Terminal bud absent, pseudoterminal bud present; fls. small and in
aments or small clusters, individually inconspicuous; frt. a nut,
samara, or drupe 30
  30 Lf. base symmetrical; fls. in aments 31
  30 Lf. base asymmetrical; fls. in small fascicles or cymes 33
31 Lf. with 5–8 pairs of lateral veins; shrubs (eastern) or small trees
(western) . . . .*Corylus*
31 Lf. with 9 or more pairs of lateral veins; trees (eastern) 32
  32 Bark flaking into narrow, vertical shreds; nutlets enclosed in
papery sacs . . . .*Ostrya*
  32 Bark smooth but trunk fluted ("muscular"); nutlets subtended by
3-lobed, leafy bracts . . . .*Carpinus*
33 Lf. margin doubly serrate; frt. a flattened samara . . . .*Ulmus*
33 Lf. margin singly serrate; frt. a drupe . . . .*Celtis*
  34 Lf. margins deeply crenate, sinuate, or coarsely serrate, 1 tooth
per secondary vein; frt. an acorn or nut in a spiny bur 35
  34 Lf. margin serrate, doubly serrate, or serrulate, more than one
tooth per secondary vein; frt. not as above 36
35 Buds clustered at tip of twig; frt. an acorn . . . .*Quercus* (in pt.)
35 Buds more equally spaced along twig; frt. a nut enclosed by a
spiny bur . . . .*Castanea*
  36 Branches often armed with thorns 37
  36 Branches usually not armed with thorns 39
37 Pomes with stony core (endocarp); fls. solitary or in compound
corymbs . . . .*Crataegus*
37 Pomes with papery cores (endocarp); fls. in simple corymbs 38
  38 Buds glabrous; frt. pyriform, with stone cells (grit cells) . . . .*Pyrus*
  38 Buds white pubescent; frt. globose, lacking stone cells . . . .*Malus*
39 Lf. blades long and slender, over 4× longer than wide; buds with
1 caplike scale . . . .*Salix*
39 Lf. blades only 1–4× longer than wide; buds with more than
1 scale or naked 40
  40 Pith chambered 41
  40 Pith solid and homogeneous 42
41 Lf. thick and leathery; terminal bud present; frt. an elliptical berry . . . .*Symplocos*
41 Lf. thin and membranous; terminal bud absent; frt. dry, 4-winged . . . .*Halesia*
  42 Lateral buds stalked; nutlets in a persistent, woody, conelike ament . . . . .*Alnus*
  42 Lateral buds sessile; frt. not as above 43
43 Petiole 1½ in. or more long; blade deltate, broadly ovate, or ovate-lanceolate . .44
43 Petiole 1 in. or less long; blade lanceolate, elliptic, or oval 45
  44 Cell sap clear; terminal bud present; frt. a capsule with comose
seeds . . . .*Populus*
  44 Cell sap milky (in broken petiole of young lf.); terminal bud
absent; frt. a multiple of drupelets . . . .*Morus*
45 Petiole with 2 glands just below blade or at base of blade . . . .*Prunus* (in pt.)

45 Petiole lacking glands 46

    46 Lf. with stiff, straight hairs along midrib below; vascular bundle
       scars 1; frt. a capsule . . . .*Oxydendrum*

    46 Lf. lacking stiff, straight hairs along midrib below; vascular
       bundle scars usually 3; frt. a pome or drupe 47

47 Buds long and slender, scaly; fls. white; frt. a small pome . . . .*Amelanchier*

47 Buds small, naked, and tomentose; fls. greenish-yellow; frt. a drupe . . .*Rhamnus*

WINTER KEYS TO DECIDUOUS GENERA

Key to Keys or Unique Genera

Lf. scars lacking (the evident round scars are twig scars which lack bundle scars);
   twigs dehiscing with the leaves
     Twig yellow, red-brown, or purplish; lvs. scalelike if persisting on terminal
       branchlets; pith white or greenish . . . .*Tamarix*
     Twig greenish or brown; lvs. linear or subulate if persisting on terminal
       branches; pith brown . . . .*Taxodium*
Lf. scars present; twigs persisting after leaf dehiscence
   Lf. scars opposite or whorled . . . . .A
   Lf. scars alternate
     Twigs armed with thorns, spines, or prickles . . . . .B
     Twigs not armed
       Twigs covered with numerous silvery or brownish
         lepidote scales . . . .*Elaeagnus*
       Twigs lacking lepidote scales
         Pith diaphragmed, chambered, or chambered only at the nodes . . .C
         Pith solid and homogeneous
           Buds apparently lacking, or present and naked, indistinctly
             scaly and appearing naked, or with 1 caplike scale . . . . .D
           Buds evident and with 2 to many distinct scales . . . . .E

Key A   (lf. scars opposite or whorled)

1 Pith chambered or hollow in the internodes . . . .*Paulownia*

1 Pith solid and homogeneous in the internodes

    2 Lf. scars large and broad; twigs often stout (over $\frac{3}{16}$ in. diameter).

       3 Bundle scars forming a closed circle or ellipse; terminal bud
         absent . . . .*Catalpa*

       3 Bundle scars forming an open *U* or *V*; terminal bud present
         4 Bundle scars many, forming a *U*; buds with 2 or 3 pairs
           of scales . . . .*Fraxinus*

         4 Bundle scars 3 or in 3 groups in a *V*; buds with about
           6 pairs of scales . . . .*Aesculus*

2 Lf. scars small or narrow; twigs slender or moderate (usually less
than ³⁄₁₆ in. in diameter).

   5 Bundle scars 1; opposite lf. scars separated . . . .*Chionanthus*
   5 Bundle scars 3; opposite lf. scars meeting or connected by a ridge

   6 Buds with more than 2 valvate or imbricate scales . . . . .*Acer* (in pt.)
   6 Buds with 2 valvate scales

   7 Pith brown . . . .*Acer* (in pt.)
   7 Pith white or greenish . . . .*Cornus* (in pt.)

Key B (lf. scars alternate; twigs with thorns, spines, or prickles)

1 Twig stout, with many prickles; lf. scar nearly encircling twig . . . .*Aralia*
1 Twig slender, lacking prickles

   2 Twigs with stipular spines present, at least on vigorous branches;
   thorns lacking . . . .*Robinia*
   2 Twigs with thorns present; stipular spines lacking

   3 Thorns 2–3+ branched . . . .*Gleditsia*
   3 Thorns not branched

   4 Thorns terminating spur branches

   5 Sap clear and not sticky

   6 Terminal bud lacking . . . .*Prunus* (in pt.)
   6 Terminal bud present

   7 Buds white pubescent . . . .*Malus*
   7 Buds glabrous . . . .*Pyrus*

   5 Sap milky and sticky . . . .*Bumelia*

   4 Thorns at nodes in leaf axils

   8 Twigs with milky sap; bundle scars many in a circle . . . .*Maclura*
   8 Twigs with clear sap; bundle scars 3 . . . .*Crataegus*

Key C (lf. scars alternate; twigs not armed; pith diaphragmed or chambered)

1 Pith chambered, at least at the nodes by the second year

   2 Lf. scars 3-lobed, each with a *U*-shaped cluster of bundle scars . . . .*Juglans*
   2 Lf. scars half-round, narrow, or *U*-shaped; bundle scars 1–3

   3 Terminal bud absent

   4 Lateral buds superposed, with the lower one smaller . . . .*Halesia*
   4 Lateral buds solitary

   5 Bundle scars 1; buds black with 2 scales . . . .*Diospyros*
   5 Bundle scars 3; buds brownish with 4 or more scales . . . .*Celtis*

   3 Terminal bud present

   6 Terminal bud long pointed, naked, and densely rusty
   pubescent . . . .*Asimina*
   6 Terminal bud conical or oval, with scales ciliate on
   the margin . . . .*Symplocos*

1 Pith diaphragmed

   7 Stipular scar encircling twig

  8 Terminal bud with a single caplike scale . . . .*Magnolia*
  8 Terminal bud with 2 valvate scales . . . .*Liriodendron*
 7 Stipular scars absent
  9 Terminal bud naked, rusty pubescent . . . .*Asimina*
  9 Terminal bud scaly and glabrous . . . .*Nyssa*

Key D (lf. scars alternate; twigs not armed; pith solid and homogeneous; buds apparently lacking, or naked, or with 1 scale)

1 Terminal bud present
 2 Bud with 1 caplike scale; stipular scar encircling twig . . . .*Magnolia*
 2 Bud indistinctly scaly, naked, or appearing naked; stipular
  scars lacking or not encircling twig
  3 Bundle scars many scattered or in 3 C-shaped groups;
   buds sessile and scaly . . . .*Carya* (in pt.)
  3 Bundle scars 3 or more but not in 3 groups; buds stalked,
   naked except for 2 small scales . . . .*Hamamelis*
1 Terminal bud lacking
 4 Twigs with spur branches . . . .*Maclura*
 4 Twigs lacking spur branches
  5 Buds with 1 caplike scale
   6 Bundle scars 3 in a narrow *U*-shaped lf. scar; stipular
    scars not encircling twig . . . .*Salix*
   6 Bundle scars 5–9 in a lf. scar which encircles the bud;
    stipular scar encircling twig . . . .*Platanus*
  5 Buds naked or appearing so, or apparently lacking
   7 Buds apparently lacking, only barely visible
    8 Buds covered by leaf scar, but scar often split and
     showing the downy, naked bud . . . .*Robinia*
    8 Buds barely visible, scaly, and glabrous . . . .*Gleditsia*
   7 Buds naked or appearing so because of dense covering of hairs
    9 Stipules or stipular scars conspicuous; lf. scars
     half-round . . . .*Rhamnus*
    9 Stipules lacking or scars inconspicuous; lf. scars horseshoe-
     shaped, *U*-shaped, heart-shaped, or 3-lobed
     10 Bundle scars several in 3 groups
      11 Lf. scar 3-lobed, each lobe with a *C*-shaped
       group of bundle scars; sap clear; pith white . . .*Melia*
      11 Lf. scar horseshoe-shaped or *U*-shaped with
       3 irregular groups of bundle scars; sap milky;
       pith brownish . . . .*Rhus*
     10 Bundle scars 1–6(9), not in 3 groups
      12 Lf. scar heart-shaped; pith salmon-
       colored . . . .*Gymnocladus*
      12 Lf. scar horseshoe-shaped around bud;
       pith white

13 Buds silvery or yellowish silky,
partially buried; bundle scars 3;
lenticels large and brown . . . .*Ptelea*
13 Buds bronze silky, protruding from
twig; bundle scars 3–6(9); lenticels
small and white . . . .*Cladrastis*

Key E (lf. scars alternate; twig not armed; pith solid and homogeneous; buds with 2 or more scales)

1 Spur shoots conspicuous and at every node after first year 2
1 Spur shoots lacking or less frequent if present 4
   2 Buds elongate-conical; bundle scars 3 . . . .*Betula*
   2 Buds rounded; bundle scars 1 or 2 3
3 Bundle scars 2; lf. scars without decurrent base . . . .*Ginkgo*
3 Bundle scar 1; lf. scar raised on a decurrent base . . . .*Larix*
   4 Buds distinctly stalked; twigs somewhat 3-angled with one angle
      extending down from lf. scar . . . .*Alnus*
   4 Buds essentially sessile (fl. buds of *Cercis* superposed and stalked);
      twigs essentially terete 5
5 Terminal bud present or apparently so 6
5 Terminal bud replaced by pseudoterminal bud 20
   6 Twigs green with spicy aroma; bundle scar 1 . . . .*Sassafras*
   6 Twigs brown, gray, or reddish, not spicy; bundle scars 3 to many 7
7 Lateral buds mostly ½ in. or more long 8
7 Lateral buds usually less than ½ in. long 10
   8 Lowest bud scale of lateral bud directly over lf. scar; lf. scar
      triangular or 3-lobed . . . .*Populus* (in pt.)
   8 Lowest bud scale of lateral bud not over lf. scar; lf. scar half-round
      or slender and crescent-shaped 9
9 Stipular scars lacking; lf. scars slender and crescent-shaped; bundle
scars 3 . . . .*Amelanchier*
9 Stipular scars present and nearly encircling twig; lf. scars half-round;
bundle scars usually many . . . .*Fagus*
   10 Lf. scars somewhat 3-lobed or shield-shaped; bundle scars many,
      mostly in 3 *C*-shaped groups, 1 group per lobe . . . .*Carya* (in pt.)
   10 Lf. scars round, half-round, shield-shaped, or narrow, not lobed
      or only barely so; bundle scars not in 3 *C*-shaped groups 11
11 Bundle scars 8 or more 12
11 Bundle scars 3–5(7), sometimes divided 13
   12 Buds (terminal and several lateral) clustered at tip of twig; terminal
      bud with several brown scales; bundle scars scattered . . . .*Quercus*
   12 Buds more equally spaced along twig; terminal bud with 2 purple
      scales; bundle scars forming a *U* . . . .*Toxicodendron*
13 Stipular scars present 14
13 Stipular scars lacking or inconspicuous even with a handlens 16

14 Twig with almond aroma . . . .*Prunus*
14 Twig lacking almond aroma 15
15 Buds with 1–3 visible scales . . . . *Malus*
15 Buds with 4 or more visible scales . . . .*Populus* (in pt.)
   16 Lf. scars crowded near end of twig, often appearing whorled . .*Cornus* (in pt.)
   16 Lf. scars more equally spaced along twig 17
17 Terminal bud ⅛ in. long; pith terete . . . .*Leitneria*
17 Terminal bud over ¼ in. long; pith 5-sided 18
   18 Buds resinous with long hairs mainly on inner scales . . . .*Sorbus*
   18 Buds not resinous, the scales glabrous or ciliate margined 19
19 Terminal buds ovoid and glossy; lateral buds small and diverging;
   twigs with or without corky wings . . . .*Liquidambar*
19 Terminal buds elongated and not glossy; lateral buds elongated and
   recurved toward twig; twigs without corky wings . . . .*Amelanchier*
   20 Bundle scar 1 21
   20 Bundle scars 2 to many 22
21 Lf. scars raised; buds with 2 imbricate scales, nearly black, entirely
   exposed; lenticels orange; twig grayish brown . . . .*Diospyros*
21 Lf. scars sessile; buds with 3–6 imbricate scales, reddish, partly
   embedded; lenticels dark; twig yellow-green to red . . . .*Oxydendrum*
   22 Stipular scars lacking 23
   22 Stipular scars present 26
23 Twigs stout (¼ in. in diameter or more) with brown pith;
   bundle scars many . . . .*Ailanthus*
23 Twigs slender with white pith; bundle scars 2 or 3 24
   24 Buds with 4 or more scales, broadly conical; lf. scar narrowly elliptical . .*Celtis*
   24 Buds with 2 visible scales, often superposed; lf. scar broadly cordate or
      shield-shaped 25
25 Lf. scars raised, 2-ranked, with a fringe at the top . . . .*Cercis*
25 Lf. scars sessile, more than 2-ranked or sometimes opposite, lacking
   fringe at top . . . .*Sapindus*
   26 Buds long and slender (length 5–7 times width), obliquely divergent
      over lf. scar . . . .*Fagus*
   26 Buds shorter and more ovoid (length 2–4 times width), more nearly
      above lf. scar 27
27 Lf. scars in more than 2 ranks 28
27 Lf. scars in 2 ranks (distichous lf. arrangement) 30
   28 Pith 5-angled; visible bud scales 2 or 3 . . . .*Castanea*
   28 Pith round; visible bud scales 3 to many 29
29 Twigs with milky sap; bundle scars many in nearly circular lf. scar . . . .*Morus*
29 Twigs with clear sap; bundle scars 3 in a 3-lobed lf. scar . . . .*Albizia*
   30 Visible bud scales 2 or 3(4) 31
   30 Visible bud scales 4–12 33
31 Pith 5-angled . . . .*Castanea*
31 Pith terete 32

32 Buds broadly ovoid (dome-shaped), obliquely asymmetrical; bud
scales red or greenish; lenticels inconspicuous and not becoming
horizontal . . . .*Tilia*

32 Buds narrowly ovoid, symmetrical; bud scales brownish; lenticels
many and raised and becoming horizontal on branch . . . .*Betula*

33 Bundle scars somewhat sunken; buds oriented to one side of lf. scar . . . .*Ulmus*

33 Bundle scars not sunken; buds more directly over lf. scar 34

34 Bud scales vertically striated . . . .*Ostrya*

34 Bud scales not vertically striated 35

35 Bud scales 4–6; buds terete in cross section; pith triangular . . . .*Corylus*

35 Bud scales 6–12; bud somewhat angled in cross section; pith terete or
5-angled . . . .*Carpinus*

5

VARIATION

Natural variation is universal and characteristic of all biological systems. "No two trees are *exactly* alike with respect to all characteristics" would be just as true as saying "no two people are exactly alike." The objective in scientific classification of organisms is to determine just how much two or more things must be alike to be classified together (i.e., belong to the same taxonomic category) and how different they must be to be classified in separate categories. In most instances, differences among taxa (taxonomic groups such as species) are at a much greater magnitude than differences among members within a group (such as a species). In this chapter we are concerned with only the variation within a species.

Within-species variation is responsible at first for the feeling of frustration and uncertainty in species identification. Unfortunately, such variation may lead to guessing at the identification rather than careful consideration of all variable characters. By observing many individuals of a species, one begins to acquire an appreciation for the *range in variation* to be expected in a particular species. As a result, the concept of a species changes from a narrow, typological one to a broader, populational one. A single tree, therefore, is but one sample of a species population. With a broad concept of a species, differences (discontinuities) among species, or the chance between-species hybrid, can be better understood and recognized.

Although variation may create problems for beginning students, it is the chief reason why one's interest in forest trees is never dulled, even after spending years in the same region. It also adds excitement and may broaden one's species concept and enrich one's appreciation for natural variation to see a well-known species in different habitats and localities and the differences which may exist in various characteristics. In addition, the lack of distinct discontinuities among species, that is, the overlap in the ranges of variation, leads to the fascinating questions of "Why?" and whether or not our classification and nomenclature are realistic.

Normal variation between sexually reproducing individuals comes about by mutations, genetic segregation, and recombination. Beyond this, there are distinct patterns of variation that can and should be recognized by the dendrologist when considering the differences observed between individuals and populations of a given species over its entire geographical and ecological range. According to the following outline, variation can be classified initially as either *intrinsic* (originating within the individual or species) or *extrinsic* (originating from outside, i.e., coming from another species). These terms will become clearer after considering the examples.

TYPES OF VARIATION

I Intrinsic
   Phenotypic plasticity
   Developmental plasticity
   Abnormal (mutational)
   Chromosomal
   Nonadaptive
   Ecotypic
   Clinal
   Reproductive
   Speciational
II Extrinsic
   Hybrid
   Introgressive

Phenotypic Plasticity Also thought of as *ecophenic variation,* this type of variation is the direct response of plant form to environmental factors (i.e., environmentally induced variation). The term "phenotypic plasticity" means the capacity of organisms with the same genetic makeup (genotype) to vary in its visible characteristics (phenotype) due to varying environmental conditions. Examples of this are seen in both within-tree and between-tree variation. Deeply lobed, smaller, and thicker leaves in the sun contrast sharply with shallowly lobed, larger, and thinner leaves in the shade as seen frequently in many oaks and maples; very hairy leaves in the sun versus glabrous leaves in the shade are found in basswood. The occurrence of two or more leaf types on the same plant, as in these examples, is called *heterophylly.* Also smaller, stunted trees with smaller leaves and nuts growing under poor, dry conditions versus larger trees with large leaves and nuts growing under mesic conditions can be found in the hickories and buckeyes. Such environmental variation affects not only morphological but also anatomical and physiological character states.

Another type of phenotypic plasticity within a tree is often associated with the stress morphology created by extreme midseason drought or defoliation due to a late spring freeze, severe insect damage, or chemical spraying. Leaves of "second flushes" from regular branches or sucker shoots are often atypical and bizarre in shape and size.

Phenotypic plasticity is nongenetic in that the acquired, environmentally induced differences are not inherited. Transplanting trees to other environmental conditions will cause a reversal of form, or different variants from different habitats when brought into a common garden will ultimately result in similar forms. Although these changes are reversible and nongenetic, the *extent* of the plasticity is under genetic control, for different species show different degrees of plasticity and the variation may involve different characters.

Developmental Plasticity   In dendrology we normally focus our attention on the mature tree and mature leaves and are often unaware of immature stages or the fact that certain well-known leaf types are actually the juvenile form. The developmental or phase change from juvenile to mature form is called a *heteroblastic change.* Two common examples of this are the lobed leaves of sassafras and mulberry, most common on saplings or vigorous sprouts. The older trees of these two species may not have any lobed leaves. Some other species, such as water oak, characteristically have a remarkable variety of different lobed leaf shapes on seedlings, saplings, or vigorous sprouts in marked contrast with the unlobed leaf of the mature crown. Also seedlings of trees with pinnately divided leaves may have one or two simple leaves just above the cotyledons as in buckeye, ash, or hickory. In southern red oak, the leaves of the lower part of the crown have a very different shape and lobing from those of the upper part. These patterns of developmental changes are characteristic of certain species and are generally not reversible by environmental conditions. They are thus under stronger genetic control than the phenotypic plasticity previously described.

In junipers, false cypress, and arborvitae, the subulate (awl) leaves are juvenile forms, and the scale leaves are mature forms. Pruning or browsing of mature branches causes new growth of juvenile leaf form. This juvenile foliage can be maintained through repeated vegetative propagation and at one time led to the generic name *Retinispora* (or *Retinospora*) for juvenilelike cultivars of *Chamaecyparis* and *Thuja* commonly used in the nursery trade. This type of heteroblastic change is usually not affected by environmental differences; yet when some junipers with scale leaves are placed in the shade, the juvenile awl leaves are formed. This indicates a complex environment–genotype interaction, and the genetics of this phenomenon is not completely understood.

Finally, *seasonal heteromorphism* occurs when the first-formed leaves on a twig of adult individuals normally differ from the later-developed leaves on the same twig. This may be seen among the leaves of some deciduous trees such as several species of poplar (Eckenwalder, 1980), sweetgum (Zimmerman and Brown, 1971), and oak (Baranski, 1975). It is not entirely clear whether this is strictly developmental or partly environmentally induced.

Abnormal (Mutational)   Although mutations are the ultimate source of all genetic variation, most effects are rather minor and not obvious. Some examples of obvious mutational effects in trees are genetic dwarfs in conifers (Franklin, 1970). The hairless peach (nectarine) also arose as a spontaneous mutant in east Asia, although a similar mutant occurred in France in the seventeenth century. Pink-flowered dogwoods were derived as a mutant form of the common "white-flowered" (really white-bracted) type. The navel orange (with a tiny rudimentary second fruit embedded at the apex of the normal one) arose as a mutant; likewise, the original grapefruit was probably a natural mutation of the Asian shaddock (with large fruits up to 20 cm in diameter and weighing up to 11 lb). A number of other mutants have become important in the horticultural trade, such as the thornless forms of honey locust, called the *Moraine* locust.

Chromosomal The *n* number of chromosomes is the *haploid* number found, following meiosis, in the subsequent gametophyte phase of the life cycle. The *2n,* or *diploid,* number is formed at fertilization and is the number in the cells of the sporophyte phase—the tree. The actual chromosome number in trees covers a range from $n = 8$ in hophornbeam to $n = 16$ in sweetgum, with higher numbers ($n = 16$ in hickory, 19 in willow, 20 in buckeye, 23 in ash, 41 in basswood, 42 in white birch) probably representing ancient polyploid derivatives. Cells in a hickory leaf, therefore, have $2n = 32$ chromosomes. Changes in chromosome number in trees are of two kinds: *aneuploid,* in which a given haploid set is increased or decreased by the addition or deletion of one or more chromosomes; and *polyploid,* in which additional full haploid sets become associated in the cells. Examples of aneuploidy are sweetgum—some trees have $n = 15$ and others $n = 16$; willow $n = 19$ and 22; beefwood tree $n = 11$, 12, and 13; and hackberry $n = 10$, 11, and 14. In some cases, aneuploid differences are correlated with morphological differences; in others, it is not detectable except by counting the chromosomes.

Polyploidy is rare in gymnosperms (ca. 1.5 percent of the species) and much more common in angiosperms (ca. 50 percent). Among gymnosperms, redwood is a good example with $2n = 6x = 66$ (x designates the base number, so redwood would be a hexaploid, i.e., 6 times 11). Examples of angiosperm polyploids are southern magnolia ($3x = 114$), white birch with three ploidy levels ($4x = 56$, $5x = 70$, $6x = 84$), and white ash also with three ploidy levels ($2x = 46$, $4x = 92$, $6x = 138$). *Betula × murrayana* (Barnes and Dancik, 1985), of hybrid derivation, is octoploid ($8x = 112$).

In some cases the differences in chromosome number might be correlated with significant phenotypic differences. In other cases, however, the variation related to aneuploidy or polyploidy might be undetectable by morphological characteristics although they may reflect chemical differences (Black-Shaefer and Beckmann, 1989) or physiological ecotypes. In other cases, particularly if polyploidy has arisen in an interspecific hybrid, there are detectable morphological differences, and often the polyploid shows an adaptive superiority over the ancestral diploids, thus often occupying disturbed or more extreme habitats. Polyploidy may be a mechanism of overcoming hybrid sterility, for by chromosome doubling, the hybrid can reproduce and the hybrid character combinations are maintained. An example of this is the *Betula alleghaniensis × pumila* derivative, *B. × murrayana,* mentioned in the preceding paragraph.

Nonadaptive When a particular variant is not associated with any environmental condition, it may be a nonadaptive trait that occurs scattered throughout the species population. Such is the case in southern magnolia in which some trees have leaves that are green and only slightly hairy below while other trees have leaves that are densely rusty-pubescent below. Such trees are often side by side in the same habitat. In some cases, such traits are controlled by single genes. Baranski (1975) found that much of the variation in leaf form (Fig. 5-1), bark, and so on among trees of white oak is explained by nonadaptive, more or less random, genetic variation. In Carolina basswood, different trees in a local population may be very different in leaf pubescence, some glabrous from the beginning, some tomentose at first then becoming glabrate, others remaining tomentose. This led earlier to a multiplication of species and varietal names for what, in reality, is nonadaptive, genetic variation in one species and variety (Hardin, 1990).

FIGURE 5-1   Representative leaf forms of white oak, all drawn to scale. (*From Baranski 1975, N.C. Agric. Exp. Sta. Bul. no. 236, Raleigh.*)

Ecotypic   An *ecotype,* or ecological race, is a distinct morphological or physiological form, or population, resulting from selection by a distinct ecological condition. It is adapted genetically to factors of its local habitat. Ecotypes within a species are able to interbreed freely, but the offspring are naturally selected in each habitat. Ecotypic variation, therefore, is habitat-correlated genetic variation unlike nonadapted variation, and inherited unlike ecophenic variation. Transplant or common garden experiments will distinguish an ecotype (which would maintain its morphological form) from an ecophene (which would change in relation to its new environment).

Many trees with broad ecological ranges have evolved ecotypes adapted to different climatic or edaphic (soil) conditions. Eastern redcedar (*Juniperus virginiana*) has an ecotype (earlier called *J. silicicola*) which is adapted to coastal foredunes and coastal river sandbanks (Adams, 1986). Black cottonwood shows photoperiodic (day length) effects on growth, development, and phenology which are ecotypic (Howe et al., 1993). Numerous provenance studies of trees reveal such ecotypes, and, therefore, it is most important to select the proper source of seeds for any planting to be successful.

On the other hand, some broad-ranging species lack ecotypic or clinal differentiation and instead apparently have a highly plastic "general-purpose genotype" such as found in white oak (Baranski, 1975). With such built-in plasticity and broad ecological amplitude, there is no selective pressure to establish specific ecotypes for different ecological conditions.

Clinal   A *cline* is a character gradient correlated with a geographical or ecological gradient. Most environmental factors, such as temperature, rainfall, and photoperiod, vary in a gradual, continuous fashion, and thus one would expect a gradual, continuous variation in a wide-ranging species rather than discontinuous, ecotypic variation. Each population along the gradient is more or less homogeneous and adapted to the environment at that point along the gradient. Mergen (1963) found in white pine a decrease in needle length and number of stomata and an increase in number of resin ducts with increasing latitude in North America. Steiner (1979) described bud-burst timing among populations in several pines. Hardin (1957) found that red buckeye shows an east–west cline in two characters, the calyx length and pubescence of the lower leaf surface. The calyx becomes shorter and more bell-shaped from the Atlantic coast to Texas and there is a gradual increase westward in the percent of plants in a population with tomentose or woolly leaves. Barnes (1975) described a north–south cline in leaf shape, size, and tooth number in trembling aspen in western North America. Yellow birch and sweet birch show latitudinal and elevational clines in phenology of growth initiation and cessation (Sharik and Barnes, 1976). Eastern redcedar varies in biochemical constituents as well as vegetative morphology along a northeast-southwest transect (Flake et al., 1969). In a study of the California closed-cone pines, Millar et al. (1988) found that divergence in populations within a species was generally clinal. Clinal variation in morphology, physiology, and chemistry is common in forest trees.

Reproductive   Various reproductive strategies are important determinants of variation at both the population and species level. There are three basic types of breeding systems: outcrossing, inbreeding, and apomixis. Each type has advantages and disadvantages in terms of the long-term survival and evolution of the species. Most species actually maintain a "winning" combination of several strategies.

Outcrossing (*xenogamy,* crossing between individual plants) theoretically leads to greater genetic variation within populations, and, assuming some gene flow among populations, there are fewer differences among populations. Outcrossing is promoted by various floral mechanisms, self-incompatibility, and the monoecious and dioecious conditions. Dioecious plants, such as ginkgo, holly, and ash, are obligate outcrossers. In contrast, *inbreeding* (*autogamy,* selfing within a single, bisexual flower, and *geitonogamy,* crossing between flowers of one plant) leads to less genetic variation within a population and greater differences among populations of a species. Several floral mechanisms promote such a breeding system.

Apomixis is a specialized mechanism that is a substitution of an asexual process for the normal sexual reproduction. It may give rise to an unusual pattern of within-population and between-population variation. This may occur in two basic ways, the first being *vegetative apomixis,* in which the plants reproduce by root sprouts or other means of vegetative propagation in place of sexual seed formation. A good example among trees is bigtooth aspen and trembling aspen, in which, over extensive areas in the Great Lakes region or central Rockies, reproduction is principally by root suckering, despite the potential for regeneration by seeds (Barnes and Wagner, 1981). The local *clones* (asexually reproduced populations in which all individuals are essentially alike) are extensive.

The other type of apomixis, often called true apomixis, is *agamospermy*—the asexual formation of a seed found in certain tree species such as citrus, alder, mountain-ash, serviceberry, and hawthorn (Campbell and Dickinson, 1990). Many apomicts maintain some degree of sexual reproduction and therefore some genetic variation in their offspring. Other apomictic populations, if only agamospermous, are quite uniform in their characteristics because of the lack of genetic segregation and recombination. If such occurs in interspecific hybrids, it is a way of stabilizing and maintaining particular hybrid forms, with each apomictic population possibly being slightly different. Such a combination of interspecific hybridization and agamospermy leads to the formation of a bewildering array of populations carrying different combinations of the parental characters, but each different and fairly uniform. This forms what is called the *agamic complex,* which, fortunately for the dendrologist, is very infrequent among forest trees.

Speciational   If ecotypes, portions of a cline, or populations of autogamous plants become *genetically isolated* through spatial or reproductive barriers of some type, the distinct population can continue to diverge genetically. This is the primary mode of species formation (speciation). The degree of differentiation, in terms of morphology, ecology, and reproductive isolation, may be gradual and at first lack distinct discontinuities. Such an early stage of incipient speciation gives rise to patterns of primary intergradation where the divergent population is only slightly distinct from the parental one.

Sometimes these diverging populations are recognized by taxonomists as varieties or subspecies. The Pacific slope and Rocky Mountain forms of Douglas-fir may represent incipient and incomplete speciation, for in certain areas the two types intergrade. The large fruited form of devilwood, found in the dry pine scrub of south peninsular Florida, is probably another good example of incipient speciation, and it is considered a variety of the widespread *Osmanthus americanus* of more mesic environments (Hardin, 1974). California sycamore of stream banks in California, with 3- to 5-lobed leaves, and Arizona sycamore of canyons in Arizona and New Mexico, with 5- to 7-lobed leaves, are called species, but they are not very distinct and are considered by some as varieties of *Platanus racemosa* (see Little, 1979).

Hybrid Chance hybrids between species may occur in nature when the parental types are closely related and not isolated spatially or genetically. This leads to an occasional F_1 hybrid, generally recognized as intermediate in character states between those of the suspected parents. Such hybrids may survive in a disturbed habitat or in one that is somewhat intermediate between those of the parents. An example is the rather rare hybrid chestnut which is a cross between the American chestnut and the chinkapin (Johnson, 1988). Other occasional hybrids occur between yellow birch and bog birch, mentioned in connection with polyploidy, and between mountain paper birch and gray birch (DeHond and Campbell, 1989). The hybrid between Coulter pine and Jeffrey pine in California (B. J. Zobel, 1951) and the hybrid between white and chestnut oaks in the southern Appalachians (Hardin, 1975) are other good examples; several others could be given, for hybridization is fairly common among forest trees. See Little (1979) for hybrids listed under the species.

Introgressive In many cases, hybridization in forest trees goes beyond the F_1 hybrid to the formation of hybrid swarms or introgressive populations when the hybrids backcross repeatedly to one or both of the parental species. Introgression is therefore the transfer of genes (and character states) from one species into another across a strong but incomplete barrier to interbreeding (i.e., secondary intergradation).

Introgression forms not only an intermediate population but also a bridge across the morphological and ecological gaps between the species, and it also generally broadens the range of variation in the parental species. When related species overlap in distribution, introgression may occur in local areas of disturbance or intermediate habitats where the introgressants can survive. Much of this is only *localized introgression* where the hybrid population is rather obvious and there is no widespread influence on the morphology of the parental species (Hardin, 1975). There are some examples of *dispersed introgression* where the genetic influence of one species is detected far from the site of original hybridization (Hardin, 1957b). In all cases, the parental species maintain their general distinctness in the face of this "genetic contamination," and they are still considered to be "good species." Introgression is known to occur in junipers, pines, oaks, basswoods, buckeyes, and other genera. An interesting case in which pollinating hummingbirds apparently play an important role in introgression in buckeyes is given by dePamphilis and Wyatt (1989); see also dePamphilis and Wyatt (1990).

Hybridization and introgression between species of a genus form a more inclusive unit of interbreeding called a *syngameon* (i.e., a hybridizing group of species). Examples are in pine, juniper, birch, poplar, buckeye, oak, and others. Some involve only a few species, but others may be highly complex and, for example, include nearly all the white oaks of eastern North America (Fig. 5-2).

For the dendrology student the "take home lesson" from this discussion of variation is to realize that species are not always homogenous, static, typological entities easily pigeonholed in a man-made classification system. Rather, they represent variable,

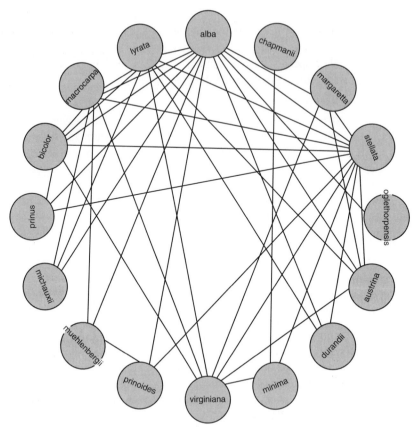

FIGURE 5-2 The white oak syngameon of eastern North America. (*Modified from Journal of the Arnold Arboretum 56:337, Harvard University, 1975, reprinted with permission.*)

dynamic series of populations of individuals that often challenge the plant taxonomist or dendrologist with rather exciting detective work to determine just what an atypical tree really is and how it got that way.

In addition, the recognition, understanding, and use of variation is important in various aspects of forestry. For instance, the success of any tree improvement program depends on a knowledge of variation and its proper utilization. The species that naturally contains the largest genetic variation affords the best opportunity for genetic gains through provenance and trait selection. Knowledge of variation and habitats is also of prime importance in selecting trees for seed orchards or for the most appropriate and successful urban plantings. The understanding and use of variation are becoming increasingly significant in the preservation and protection of natural biodiversity. This assessment of genetic diversity will obviously become more important to the forester in future management planning.

For those interested in more extensive discussions of these topics, see Anderson (1949), Briggs and Walters (1984), Clausen (1951), Grant (1963, 1981), Heiser (1973), Stace (1989), and Stebbins (1950).

6

HABITAT, RANGE, AND COMMUNITIES

Knowledge of the habitat and range of individual species is of great importance in the practice of forestry. Such ecological knowledge is also helpful, in combination with morphological features, for tree identification. Only brief habitat and community descriptions are given in this text, but more complete information can be found in Burns and Honkala (1990), and literature on silvics or forest ecology can be found in Spurr and Barnes (1980).

HABITAT

Factors

Every species of tree is best adapted, by its genetic structure, to a particular combination of environmental factors or conditions. When these conditions are present, the species will grow, develop, successfully compete, and reproduce. The sum of these conditions is known as the *habitat* of the species. The environmental factors which, when combined, produce a particular habitat, are derived from the climate, soils, physiography, and biota present at the site. *Climate* is the product of the interaction between solar radiation, the atmosphere, and the land and water masses of the earth. Climate is regional, the large canvas on which are developed a multitude of habitats or forest sites. The climate of the southeastern United States, for instance, differs in many ways from that of the southwestern states. Climate provides the fluctuating temperature, precipitation, atmospheric humidity, wind, lightning, and atmospheric impurities which contribute to the definition of a habitat. *Soils* provide the moisture and the elements required for growth (save for carbon and oxygen) as well as providing support for the stem and crown. The physical characteristics of a soil, its texture, structure, and depth determine the availability of moisture and air to the trees' roots. The chemistry of a soil determines the availability of mineral nutrients. *Physiography* influences habitat through the effects of elevation, slope, aspect, land shape, and the land–water interface. As elevation increases, average temperature, length of growing season, and usually soil depth decrease while radiation intensity increases. The direction in which a slope faces is known as its aspect. In the latitudes of North America insolation is more intense on south- and west-facing aspects, which causes them to be warmer and often drier than are north- and east-facing aspects. Concave land shapes, because of cold air drainage, can be much cooler at night than adjacent convex land forms. Land areas adjacent to large bodies of water are usually slightly warmer in winter, cooler in summer, and more humid than are inland areas. Elevation and aspect will be described in more detail later. The *biota* is the sum of all living organisms which inhabit an area and exert a positive or negative influence on the suitability of a habitat for a particular species of tree. The relationships between the micro and macro flora and fauna, played on a background defined by temperature and sunlight and by moisture and soil, create the character of a habitat. From bacteria to birds, from predators to herbivores, from algae and fungi to flowering plants, living organisms both result in and are the result of habitats. This contribution is continued, perhaps even accentuated, as the lifeless and decaying remains of all organisms continue to contribute to the maintenance and modification of habitat. It is from its habitat that a tree obtains its resources for seed germination, establishment, growth, and reproduction. If these resources cease to be present, the tree, ultimately, cannot survive.

Very often, the opportunity for seed germination controls the presence or absence of a given species in a particular habitat. In the case of cultivated, urban trees, an established seedling/sapling/older tree may be transplanted and grow perfectly well outside of its natural range and usual habitat.

Elevation and Aspect

The presence of a species is not continuous throughout its range because suitable habitats are not continuous and uniform. The definition of a suitable habitat for a particular species can often be quite sharply defined. The effect of elevation on habitat is an example of this. Quaking aspen, for example, is rarely found above a 3000-ft elevation in the northern part of its range and is abundant only above 10,000 ft in the southern part of its range. In the north it is more common on warmer southern and western aspects while in the south it occurs on the cooler northern and eastern aspects. In each case elevation and aspect, through their direct effect on temperature, are influencing the local presence of this wide-ranging species. Especially in the west, elevation is a limiting factor, and over wide areas certain species are commonly found only in certain elevational belts. The relation between latitude and elevation is also important, and species that occur at sea level in the north are found progressively higher toward the south, until an elevation of 10,000 to 11,500 ft may be reached at the southern limit of distribution.

Tolerance

It has been long known that certain species will grow under varying densities of forest cover, while others grow only in the open. For many years this was interpreted as a reaction to light, and hence an intolerant tree was one which could bear little or no shade. However, Zon (1907) reported the results of root-cutting experiments by Fricke in Germany which seemed to show that the inability of certain species to prosper under old-growth forest was due in large part to excessive root competition. It seems best at present to consider tolerance as the ability of a plant to complete its life history from seedling to adult, under the cover of a dense forest, regardless of the specific factors involved. Or, put more simply, a tolerant tree is one which can survive and grow, if not prosper, under forest competition; when this competition is removed or lessened, the rate of growth and reproduction usually show a marked increase. For a more recent discussion of tolerance, see Decker (1952, 1959).

Tolerance is influenced by site (soil, exposure, climate, etc.) so that the best comparisons are made only between trees growing together under the same set of external conditions. Little is gained in attempting to compare two species of widely separated ranges, growing on different soils and with dissimilar associates. Designations of relative tolerance here follow Burns and Honkala (1990).

Wetland Species

Although some trees are fairly cosmopolitan, most are associated with a characteristic habitat and position along a moisture gradient from wetland to dry upland. For instance, it would be as futile to look for a water tupelo on a dry upland hillside as to expect to find shortleaf pine in a deepwater swamp. Some species cannot survive in saturated soils while others only very rarely can be found elsewhere. In between these extremes there are a multitude of species which are adapted to varying levels and duration of soil saturation. Site relationships are frequently very complicated, and the absence of a certain species in a given habitat may reflect its inability to compete rather than to simply grow there.

This species-specific habitat characteristic is used in the identification of legal or jurisdictional wetlands. In addition to hydric soils which are saturated during some part of the growing season, such sites must support a preponderance of plants adapted to such conditions.

Recent attention has been focused on *wetlands* and their delineation, preservation, and management. Wetlands may be permanently or semipermanently flooded or only temporarily or seasonally flooded. Today it is critical to determine the limits of wetlands because many activities, such as draining, filling, or other disturbances, require federal or state permits. Because plant species are a major determinant of wetlands, it has become increasingly important to classify a plant species into one or more of five categories, based on its usual habitat or range of habitats along a soil-moisture gradient. The five categories are (1) obligate wetland, (2) facultative wetland, (3) facultative, (4) facultative upland, and (5) upland. The U.S. Fish and Wildlife service has compiled a national list of nearly 7000 vascular plants which classifies each species into these categories (P. B. Reed, 1988; see also Tiner, 1991). The trees in this text that are designated as "obligate" or "facultative wetland" in the 10 regions of the contermi-nous U.S. (Fig. 6-1) are indicated in the Table 6-1.

Obligate wetland plants (o) occur *almost always* (probability of 99 percent or more) in wetlands under natural conditions; facultative wetland plants (w) *usually* occur in wetlands (67 to 99 percent probability). Certain species may differ in their designa-tions in different parts of their range. These differences may be ecotypes, parts of a cline, or reflect a broad ecological amplitude. Each species has a characteristic pattern of ecological variation (see Chapter 5).

RANGE

Every tree, indeed every land plant, is restricted in nature to a particular geographical area where conditions of climate and soil are suitable and available for its growth and reproduction and where it has been documented to occur. This area is known as its *natural range.* It may be very large as is the range of quaking aspen which stretches from Newfoundland to Alaska and southward at increasing elevation along the Rocky Mountains to northern Mexico. This represents 111 degrees of longitude and 48 degrees of latitude and is the greatest range of all native North American trees. This vast range is largely defined by growing season moisture stress and high summer tem-peratures. The natural range of Florida torreya, on the other hand, is confined to a small area found in four counties in the panhandle of Florida. Although the warm moist climate found there is common throughout the area, steep shady limestone slopes and ravines are not, and torreya is restricted to that small area where both occur.

The range maps used in this text delineate the larger region in which the species is known to occur naturally. The scale of the maps is too small to show local distribution, but the information given for each species under "Range" does indicate some of the major disjunct areas. Little (1971, 1976, 1977, 1978) and Viereck and Little (1975) show large-scale maps of the various species.

Natural ranges are not fixed but are continually shifting, albeit very, very slowly, in response to environmental changes. Although this may not be immediately apparent, it should be remembered that we are in a postglacial period and that some species are still migrating slowly northward following the retreat of the last great ice sheet. Much is known about species distributions and migrations during the last 12,000 years (FNA, vol. 1, 1993). Spruce and fir trees were the dominant forest type in coastal North Carolina when the ice began to withdraw. As the climate became too warm and dry for these species, they slowly moved northward following cool growing seasons to be replaced first by an oak-dominated forest and then, as the weather continued to warm, by forests of the more drought- and fire-resistant southern pines. Today spruce and fir are found only on a few of the highest peaks of western North Carolina where they linger as a tremulous echo of the ice age.

Global warming due to the greenhouse effect may also create changes in natural ranges of trees. Some believe that the rate of warming is more rapid than that which reduced the ice sheets. As vegetation would have less time to adjust, the magnitude of this change could exceed many fold that caused by the retreating glaciers. Predictions

FIGURE 6-1   Regions of distribution for the National List of Scientific Plant Names. (*From Reed, 1988, U.S.D.I. Biol. Rept. 88(24).*)

TABLE 6-1   WETLAND STATUS OF SELECTED TREE SPECIES

Species	Region									
	1	2	3	4	5	6	7	8	9	10
Abies balsamea			w							
Acer negundo		w	w			w	w	w		w
rubrum	w	o				w				
saccharinum	w	w	w	w	w					
Alnus rombifolia									w	w
rubra										w
Aralia spinosa			w							
Betula nigra	w	w	w		o	w				
Carya aquatica	o	o	o			o				
illinoinensis			w							
laciniosa		w	w							
maristiciformis		w				w				
Celtis laevigata	w	w	w		w					
Fraxinus caroliniana	o	o				o				
latifolia									w	w
nigra	w		w	w						
pennsylvanica	w	w	w		w	w		w		
Gordonia lasianthus		w								
Larix laricina	w		w							
Liquidambar styraciflua			w							
Magnolia virginiana	w	w								
Nyssa aquatica	o	o	o			o				
biflora	w	o				o				
Picea mariana	w		w							
Pinus elliottii		w								
glabra		w								
serotina	o	w								

(Continued)

may be made regarding future migrations which can be expected in response to this climatic change (Critchfield, 1984; Davis, 1976; P. A. Delcourt and Delcourt, 1981; H. R. Delcourt et al. 1983; Jacobson et al. 1987; Wright, 1983).

Mankind has, throughout history, moved trees and plants over long distances bypassing normal barriers to natural range, oceans, mountains, and desserts. When the exotic species are introduced to favorable habitats, they can become *naturalized* and reproduce and develop at least as well as in their native area. Scotch pine from Europe has become naturalized in Canada and the northeastern United States; some species of eucalyptus from Australia are now naturalized in California; mimosa and paulownia from the Middle East have spread throughout much of the southeastern United States; the original distributions of pecan, southern magnolia, and several others were much more limited than their present ranges.

TABLE 6-1   CONTINUED

Species	Region									
	1	2	3	4	5	6	7	8	9	10
Platanus occidentalis	w	w	w							
racemosa										w
wrightii							w			
Populus augustifolia				w	w	w	w		w	w
balsamifera	w		w	w	w			w		w
deltoides							w	w		
fremontii						w	w	w		w
heterophylla	w									
Quercus bicolor	w	w	w		o	w				
laurifolia	w	w				w				
lyrata	o	o	o			o				
michauxii	w	w	w			w				
nigra		w								
nuttallii (texana)		o	o			w				
pagoda	w									
palustris	w	w	w		w					
phellos		w	w			w				
stellata		w				w				
Salix nigra	w	o	o		o	w		o		
Tamarix chinensis				w	w	w		w	w	w
Taxodium distichum	o	o	o			o				
Thuja occidentalis	w		w							
Toxicodendron radicans							w			
vernix	o	o	o							
Ulmus americana	w	w	w							

Regions: See Fig. 6-1.
Status: w = facultative wet; o = obligate wet.

COMMUNITIES

North American biotic communities as we know them today have been structured by processes operative on both evolutionary and ecological time scales. The forest regions present today have not been stable either in composition or in location through very long periods of time. In fact, they are still responding dynamically to changing climate, geological processes, fire regimes, and the progressively increasing impacts of human populations and needs.

When left unhampered, however, trees and lesser vegetation tend to group themselves on the basis of environmental factors and their ability to compete with their associates into *communities*. Thus the *flora* of specific areas and particularly forest communities are often regarded and designated, especially for practical reasons of description and study, as distinct *forest cover types* or *associations* with one or a few dominant species, such as *pinyon-juniper, sugar maple-beech-yellow birch, oak-hickory, longleaf*

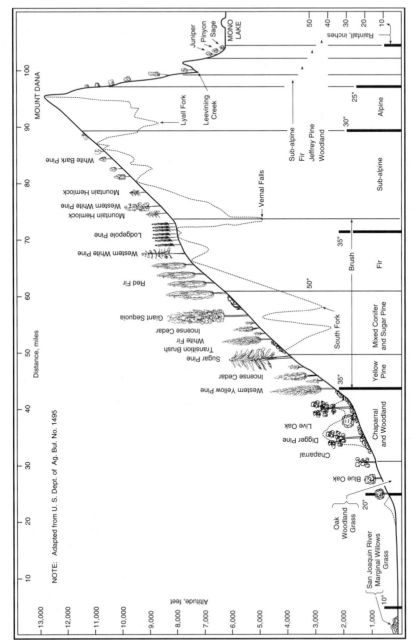

FIGURE 6-2 Profile of the Sierra Nevadas showing the effect of elevation and rainfall on forest distribution.

pine, or *eastern white pine.* The Society of American Foresters has described 145 forest cover types in the United States and Canada (Eyre, 1980). Each of these cover types occupies a particular geographic region and or elevational zone. Each is characterized by the species of trees, shrubs, and forbs which grow together. Each may be permanent as a climax type or transitory as a successional stage. In sharply defined and delimited habitats, the forest communities may also be sharply defined and discontinuous. More often, however, community boundaries are rather indistinct and there is a broad ecotone between two otherwise distinct forest types. An even more gradual change in species composition, a *continuum,* may occur along a very gradual environmental gradient, and specific community types may be impossible to define. Regardless of the community designations or delimitations, each species has a characteristic habitat or ecological range in terms of moisture, shade, and other environmental factors.

Other descriptions of forest communities are in use today. Kuchler (1964) describes 116 plant communities in terms of "potential natural vegetation," meaning what would potentially exist without influence from man. Daubenmire and Daubenmire (1968) developed a different system which is widely used in the West.

Elevational zonation of forest communities may be particularly striking in mountainous areas. For instance, in the Sierra Nevadas of California (Fig. 6-2) one finds an oak woodland below 1000 ft elevation, then several rather distinct forest associations, and finally the whitebark pines of the alpine zone at about 11,000 ft. In the uplands of the southwest, as another example, pinyon-juniper communities dominate from ca. 4500 to 6500 ft of elevation, pine-oak at 6500 to 8000 ft, fir-aspen at 8000 to 9500 ft, and spruce-fir at 9500 to 11,500 ft. These associations are more or less distinct but vary somewhat in their elevational ranges because of latitude and slope direction— higher on the drier and warmer south and southwest exposures and lower on the wetter and cooler north- and northeast-facing slopes and in cool, shaded canyons (Elmore, 1976). Likewise, in the Great Smoky Mountains of eastern Tennessee and western North Carolina, several forest associations occur in rather specific locations with respect to topography, elevation, and moisture; for example, a mixed mesophytic forest in the lower coves to spruce-fir on the peaks and ridges above 6000 ft elevation (Whittaker, 1956). Even in relatively flat topography such as in the Green Swamp area of southeastern North Carolina (Kologiski, 1977), vegetation types are sometimes differentiated on the basis of environmental factors such as soil types, relative periods of flooding, and frequency of fire (Fig. 6-3).

Following disturbance by extensive logging, clear-cutting, or fire, each region has a fairly predictable succession of stages eventually culminating in a climax association characteristic of the climate, soils, and other factors. For example, a general successional pattern (from frequent fire to excluded fire) in the Green Swamp area of North Carolina can be interpreted from Fig. 6-3 (Kologiski, 1977).

On a much broader scale, one or more plant communities with a definite structure or life form (e.g., deciduous forest, conifer forest, or grassland) and which occupy similar habitats are defined as a *formation.* The distribution of recognizable formations of North America is shown in Fig. 6-4.

As indicated, it will be advantageous if you think of habitat and range as important characteristics for understanding and identifying species. It is also useful to think of

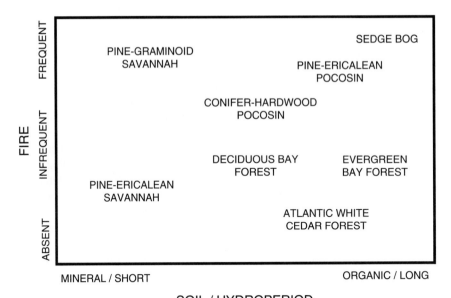

FIGURE 6-3 Relationships among the dominant vegetation types and soil, hydroperiod, and fire in the Green Swamp of North Carolina. (*Modified from Kologiski, 1977, by R. L. Kologiski and T. R. Wentworth.*)

the communities in which a species occurs as either a dominant component or lesser associate. When you learn to recognize a particular community by the dominant species present and also by its general aspect (physiognomy), you will learn to predict the presence of certain other species which are often found in that community.

FIGURE 6-4   Generalized vegetation formations of North America. A = ice; B = Arctic tundra; C = taiga; D = Pacific coastal/Cascadian forests; E = Palouse prairies; F = intermountain deserts, shrub steppes, woodlands, and forests; G = Californian forests and alpine vegetation; H = Californian grasslands, chaparral, and woodlands; I = Mojave and Sonoran deserts; J = Rocky Mountain forests and alpine vegetation; K = central prairies and plains; L = mixed deciduous forests; M = Chihuahuan deserts and woodlands; N = Appalachian forests; O = Piedmont oak-pine forests; P = Coastal Plain forests, bogs, swamps, strand; Q = tropical forests. (*From M. G. Barbour and W. D. Billings, 1988,* North American Terrestrial Vegetation. *Reprinted with permission of Cambidge University Press, New York.*)

7

VEGETATIVE AND REPRODUCTIVE MORPHOLOGY

Before attempting to understand descriptions, comparison tables, or identification keys here or in manuals, or to communicate with others about tree identification, one first has to become familiar with the morphology of vegetative and reproductive parts and descriptive terminology for these parts—the necessary jargon of dendrology. The important terms are explained and illustrated here. For more complete illustrated glossaries, see Jones and Luchsinger (1986), Radford (1986), Radford et al. (1974), Smith (1977), Walters and Keil (1988), Woodland (1991), or Zomlefer (1994).

Sizes of Mature Trees Sizes are very variable and influenced by local conditions of site or by geographical location. For example, some species become shrubby or prostrate at the northern limits of their range or at higher altitudes.

Foresters commonly measure tree diameter at $4\frac{1}{2}$ ft above the ground (dbh, diameter breast high). Diameter at this height is usually above the flaring base of the tree and is a measure of trunk size. On very large trees where butt swell and flaring may extend several feet or more, dbh is measured 18 in. above the butt swell (Avery and Burkhart, 1983).

VEGETATIVE MORPHOLOGY

For tree identification, vegetative parts, including leaves, twigs, and bark, are very important mainly because they are more often present and accessible than reproductive parts.

60

Habit

Trees growing in the open tend to develop characteristic shapes which may be typical of individual species or groups of species (genera); this is well illustrated by the American elm, white oak, Lombardy poplar, or eastern white pine. In general, open-grown specimens have large crowns, which may reach nearly to the ground, and the clear trunk is short, with considerable taper. Under forest competition, the form is very different: the bole is long, more cylindrical, often clear of branches for one-half or more of its length, and the crown small. Certain species, especially those which are extremely tolerant, resist crown restriction, but it may be said that most trees develop typical shapes only in the open; such individuals, of course, are usually less desirable for lumber because of the short clear length and many side branches which would appear as knots in the finished boards.

Because of variation in various habitats, habit (growth form) is of limited use in identification. Yet, with experience, one can learn the shapes of the crown and pattern of branching of many species. Four primary habits are observable: *excurrent,* with a central dominant trunk and symmetrical, conical, or spirelike crown of many conifers and some hardwoods like yellow-poplar; *deliquescent* or *decurrent,* with repeatedly forked stems giving rise to a spreading form such as in oaks, maples, and most hardwood trees; *palmlike,* with an unbranched trunk and leaves only in a top rosette, in palms and most cycads; *yucca-type,* either with a basal rosette of long stiff leaves and a central tall flowering stalk, or an irregularly branched thick trunk as in the treelike yuccas and cacti.

Within the deliquescent habit, there are a number of distinctive architectural forms depending on the relative dominance of the primary trunk, or secondary vertical (orthotropic) branches versus horizontal (plagiotropic) branches (i.e., whether height growth or crown spread is favored). The basic growth form within a species is genetically controlled, but the ultimate architecture is also easily modified by habitat (sun, shade, competition), natural or artificial pruning, or branch damage due to lightning, ice, or insects. For a concise treatment of woody plant form and structure, see Spur and Barnes (1980).

Leaves

General Features (Fig. 7-1)   Leaves are the primary photosynthetic organs of trees. Although they are often the most variable part, each species has a characteristic range of variation, so leaves are still one of the most important means of identification because of the many macro-morphological characters available for observation and comparison. Leaves are formed on stems at regular intervals; and the point on a stem at which one or more leaves arise is called the *node.* The portion of the stem between nodes is the *internode.* The expanded portion of the leaf is the *blade,* or *lamina,* and the supporting stalk is the *petiole.* The petiole (considered part of the leaf) may be either short or long, slender or stout, terete, angular, grooved, or laterally flattened. When the leaf is *petiolate,* the petioles are usually attached to the stem just below an

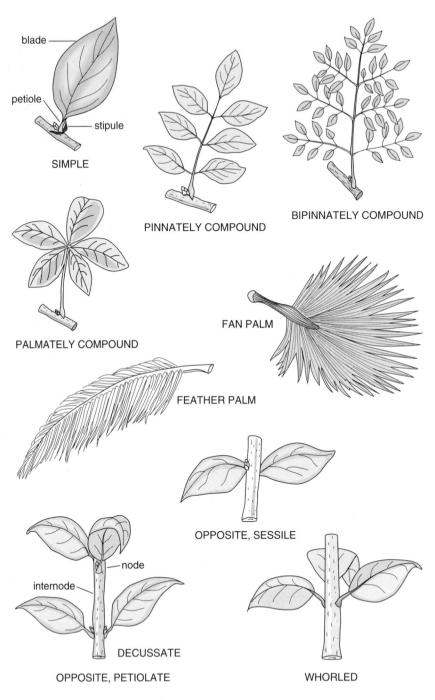

FIGURE 7-1   Leaf morphology, complexity, and arrangement.

axillary bud, but some are swollen at the base and enclose the bud. In some cases the petiole is lacking and the blade is *sessile* (i.e., attached directly to the twig). Some leaves are accompanied by a pair of small scalelike or leaflike structures known as *stipules* which are attached either to the petiole base or to the twig, one on either side of the petiole. These usually drop off as the leaf expands. Plants with stipules are *stipulate;* those without them are *estipulate.*

A given leaf persists on the tree for one season of growth or two or more years and then will eventually drop after development of an *abscission layer* at the junction of stem and leaf. The tree is said to be *deciduous* if all leaves drop after one growing season, or *evergreen* if not all leaves drop at the same season. Some "deciduous" trees keep their leaves in a brown condition into the winter; in this condition the tree is called *marcescent,* particularly noticeable in young beech and some oaks. Some species are deciduous in the northern parts of their range and evergreen southward, such as sweetleaf and laurel oak.

Leaf Complexity (Fig. 7-1)   A leaf with a single blade is *simple.* If the leaf is divided into two or more blades attached to a common stalk, it is *divided,* or *compound,* and the individual blades are *leaflets.* The axis supporting the leaflets is the *rachis.* The lateral bud is still in the axil of the petiole of the compound leaf, not in the axil of the leaflet.

When leaflets are attached laterally along the rachis, the leaf is *pinnately* compound. The leaflets may be sessile on the rachis or on a stalklike *petiolule. Odd* or *even* pinnate indicates whether pinnately compound leaves have odd or even numbers of leaflets, respectively. Leaves are twice pinnate, or *bipinnate,* when the leaflets are attached to a second-order rachis (*rachilla*); an additional division would be *tripinnate.* If the rachis is not elongated, and the leaflets apparently radiate from the top of the petiole, the leaf is *palmately compound.* The "compound" leaves of palms have mechanically split blades either in a pinnate "feather" type, palmate "fan" type, a somewhat intermediate "costa-palmate" type which looks fanlike but has a short midrib (costa), or a twice-pinnate type.

A *trifoliolate* leaf has three leaflets and may be either pinnate if the petiolule of the terminal leaflet is attached to an elongated rachis, or palmate if each of the three leaflets has its petiolule attached at one point.

To distinguish a pinnately compound leaf from a twig with two-ranked, simple leaves, look for the position of the bud in the axil of the leaf (not leaflet). Also, there is usually a color and/or textural difference between the twig and the petiole/rachis.

Leaf Arrangements (Phyllotaxy) (Fig. 7-1)   On normal twigs leaves are usually arranged in one of three definite ways: (1) if they are paired at the same height, one on each side of the twig, they are *opposite;* (2) when more than two are found at the same node, they are *whorled,* or *verticillate;* and (3) where only a single leaf is attached at each node, the leaves are *alternate* and also in spirals up the twig. A modification of this condition is *subopposite* when the leaves appear nearly but not quite opposite. This is characteristic of a few trees such as buckthorn, sweetleaf, or cascara.

With the alternate arrangement the determination of the number of leaves in each complete turn of the spiral is important because it is often the same throughout a genus and sometimes applies to all the members of the same family. In determining spiral phyllotaxy, the twig is held in a vertical position and two leaves are chosen, one of which is directly above the other; twisted, deformed, or very-slow-growth twigs should not be used, and the inspection should be confined to a single season's growth. Do not count the lower leaf of the two chosen, ascend the spiral and count the number of leaves passed, up to and including the upper leaf, and also note the number of complete turns made around the twig. A fraction may then be formed, using the number of turns as the numerator and the number of leaves as the denominator. If this is done, it will be found that one of the following fractions has resulted; ½, ⅓, ⅖, ⅜, ⁵⁄₁₃, ⁸⁄₂₁. . . . (Only the first four are common in broad-leaved trees; the higher fractions occur in some of the conifers.)

The ½ phyllotaxy, typical of elm, hackberry, and basswood, is the simplest and most obvious of the spiral arrangements and is known as two-ranked or *distichous.* The ⅓ type is found in alders, while the ⅖ is found in many trees, including the oaks and poplars. Several relationships are immediately evident in this series. The denominator is the number of vertical rows (or ranks) observable by looking down the stem from the tip, and the fraction (of 360 degrees) indicates the angle between successive leaves in the spiral. If the numerators and denominators, respectively, of the first two fractions are added, the result is the next higher fraction of the series, and this applies to all the rest of the members as one ascends the scale; also the numerator of the third term is the same as the denominator of the first, that of the fourth the same as the denominator of the second, etc. The Italian mathematician *Leonardo Fibonacci* (ca. 1170–1230) recognized the regularity of this, and it is now called the *Fibonacci series.*

In opposite leaved plants, a pair of leaves is often oriented at right angles to the pair above and below, so that there are four vertical ranks. This is known as a *decussate* arrangement, common in several conifers with scale leaves or in maples and other hardwoods. If the opposite leaves form just two ranks (i.e., all in one plane), the arrangement is *distichous.* Privet has this conspicuous arrangement.

Because lateral buds arise in leaf axils, branch arrangement is the same as leaf arrangement (at least if both branches develop in an opposite arrangement). So, if leaf arrangement is difficult to determine because branches are very high above ground, look for the branch arrangement.

Leaf Venation (Fig. 7-2)   There are five basic types of venation. (1) *Pinnate* has a single midrib and secondary veins branching off at intervals. The secondaries form a variety of patterns: they may be more or less diffusely branched, angle straight to the margin, and end there, bend upward near the margin, and sometimes connect to the one above (forming submarginal loops) or the entire secondaries arch upward toward the apex (called *arcuate*). (2) *Pinnipalmate* is somewhat intermediate between pinnate and palmate, in which the lowermost pair of secondary veins, arising at or near the base of the midrib, is slightly larger than the other secondaries and with large tertiary veins going to the lower margins. (3) *Palmate* has three or more primary veins arising at or near the base of the blade and spreading out like a fan, with secondaries off of

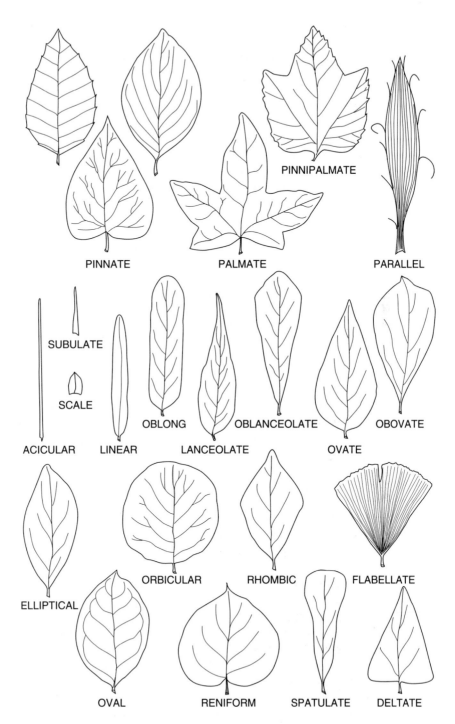

FIGURE 7-2   Leaf venation and shapes.

these. (4) *Parallel,* or *striate,* has many equal veins nearly parallel to each other until they join near the apex. (5) *Dichotomous* has repeated forking or *Y*-branching, as found in ginkgo. In the cycads and conifers, branch veins are rare; in hardwoods, there are smaller and smaller veins that form a netted pattern which is often conspicuous and characteristic of genera and species.

Leaf Shapes (Fig. 7-2)   The overall shape of a leaf or leaflet is usually characteristic of a species, allowing, of course, for a range of variation. The shape of compound or lobed leaves conforms to the outline produced by running an imaginary line around the tips of the leaflets or lobes. In addition to overall shape of the blade, the shapes of apices and bases are important features.

Overall Blade Shapes (Fig. 7-2)

Acicular. Needlelike; very long and slender; variously shaped in cross section

Subulate. Awn or awl shaped; narrow lanceolate, flat, stiff, sharp-pointed, usually less than 12 mm long

Scale. Small, sharp-pointed, broadened at the base, usually appressed and imbricated

Linear. Many times longer than broad; narrow, with approximately parallel sides; flat, triangular, or square in cross section

Oblong. Longer than broad, with parallel sides

Lanceolate. Lance-shaped; several times longer than broad, widest at a point about a third or less of the distance from the base, and tapering to the apex

Oblanceolate. The reverse of lanceolate, with the widest point about a third or less of the distance from the apex and tapering to the base

Ovate. Egg-shaped outline, with the widest point below the middle

Obovate. The reverse of ovate, with the widest point above the middle

Elliptical. Like an ellipse with the widest point at the center

Oval. Broadly elliptical, with the width greater than one-half the length

Orbicular. Circular or nearly so

Reniform. Kidney-shaped; as broad or broader than long with a wide cordate base

Deltate. Delta-shaped; triangular

Rhombic. Diamond-shaped; more or less symmetrical with the widest point at the center and the sides more or less straight to the apex and base

Spatulate. Narrower than obovate; shaped like a spatula with a broad apex and tapering to the base

Flabellate. Fan-shaped

Apices (Fig. 7-3)

Acuminate. Shaped like an acute angle with a long attenuated point

Acute. Shaped like an acute angle but not attenuated

Mucronate. Abruptly tipped with a bristly mucro

Cuspidate. Tip concavely constricted into an elongated sharp, rigid point

Obtuse. Blunt; the sides forming an angle more than 90 degrees

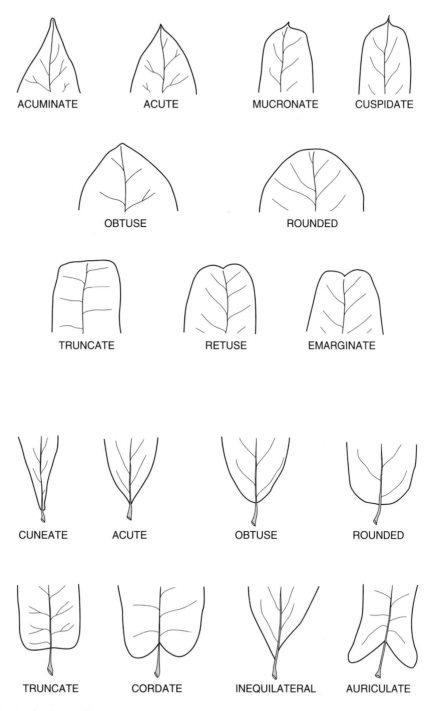

FIGURE 7-3   Leaf apices and bases.

Rounded. Forming a full sweeping arc
Truncate. As though cut off at right angles to the midrib
Retuse. With a shallow, narrow notch
Emarginate. With a shallow, broad notch

Bases (Fig. 7-3)

Cuneate. Wedge-shaped, acuminate; tapering evenly to a narrow base
Acute. Shaped like an acute angle but not attenuated
Cordate. Heart-shaped; inversely indented
Inequilateral, oblique. Asymmetrical
Obtuse. Blunt, narrowly rounded
Rounded. Forming a full sweeping arc
Truncate. As though cut off at right angles to the midrib
Auriculate. With earlike lobes pointing downward

Leaf Margins (Fig. 7-4)   The edge of the leaf is called the margin.

Revolute. Rolled under just at the margin
Entire. Smooth
Repand. Slightly and irregularly wavy
Sinuate. Shallowly indented; wavy in a horizontal plane
Undulate (or *crisped*). Wavy in a vertical plane
Crenate. With rounded to blunt teeth
Crenulate. Small crenations
Serrate. With sharp teeth pointing toward the apex of the blade
Serrulate. Small serrations
Doubly serrate. With the larger serrations again serrated on their margins
Dentate. With sharp teeth pointing outward
Denticulate. Small dentations
Aculeate. Spiny margined with the teeth long and prickly

Leaf Lobing (Fig. 7-4)   When the blade margins are indented one-quarter to one-half the distance to the midrib or base, it is considered a *lobed* leaf; if indented just over one-half, it is *cleft;* and if cut deeply to near the midrib or base, it is *incised.* In general, however, *lobed* is used in a broad sense to include any degree of indentation. Lobing is either *pinnate* if the indentation is toward the midrib or *palmate* if toward the base of the blade. A palmately lobed leaf is usually also palmately veined with a primary vein in each lobe.

Lobing should be considered separately from marginal features or blade shape, as should be obvious from the figures. A lobed leaf may have entire margins such as white oak and sassafras or serrate margins as in red oak and striped maple.

Conifer Leaves (Fig. 7-5)   There are four types of leaves in the conifers: (1) *acicular* (*needle*), which is long and slender (*Pinus, Cedrus*); (2) *linear,* which is shorter than the acicular, narrow, and either flat, triangular, or square in cross section

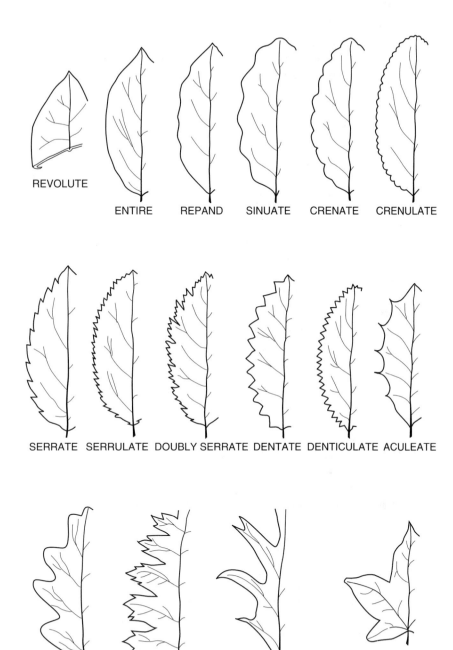

FIGURE 7-4   Leaf margins and lobing.

FIGURE 7-5   Conifer leaves and short shoots.

(*Abies, Picea, Larix, Tsuga, Sequoia, Taxodium*); (3) *subulate* (*awn, awl*), short, nar-row, tapered to a sharp point, flat, and stiff (juvenile leaves of *Juniperus* and other Cupressaceae); and (4) *scale,* small, usually appressed and imbricated (*Thuja, Chamaecyparis, Cupressus, Juniperus*). The distinction between acicular and linear is quite subjective, and various authors may differ in their designations.

In some conifers (Pinaceae), linear leaves are either sessile (*Abies*), sessile on a *peg* (*sterigma*) (*Picea*), petiolate on a peg (*Tsuga*), or petiolate without a peg (*Pseudotsuga*). When pegs are present, the abscission layer is between the peg and leaf blade so the pegs persist on the twig after leaf dehiscence.

In the Cupressaceae, juvenile leaves are often subulate (awl or awn) and the mature leaves scalelike. In *Juniperus virginiana,* for example, leaves of seedlings, vigorous shoots, or spring growth are the stiff subulate ones, those on older or later growth are scales. The subulate leaves are often whorled with 3 at a node; scale leaves are oppo-site and decussate, forming 4 ranks.

The scale leaves of the Cupressaceae are tightly imbricated and completely cover the twig. The twigs (ultimate branchlets) may be terete, angled, or dorsiventrally flattened with two types of scales (and two of each), *lateral,* which cover the sides of the twig and are often keeled (ridged and bent along the center of the leaf), and *facial,* which are flattened or slightly rounded and form the top and bottom of the twig. Scales often have a gland just below the apex on the back (visible) side. The form of these can be important in identification. These branchlets are oriented in either radial (three-dimensional) arrays (*Juniperus, Cupressus*) or are flattened into frondlike *sprays* (*Thuja, Chamaecyparis, Calocedrus*).

In many of the conifers, the linear, subulate, and scale leaves are attached and extend down the stem for some distance below the point of divergence. This is called a *decurrent* leaf base. The pegs of *Picea* and *Tsuga* have decurrent bases. The leaves of *Taxus* also have decurrent bases.

The pine *fascicle,* cluster of one to five needles, is on a very short stem (determinate short shoot) in the axil of a scalelike, *primary* leaf. The needle leaves are therefore *secondary* because they are on a lateral, axillary branch. The fascicle is wrapped initially at the base by closely overlapping bud scales (forming the *fascicle sheath*), which either drops as the needles expand (in soft pines) or persists (in hard pines). The primary leaves in pine also may drop soon (in soft pines) or persist (hard pines).

Surface Features   Several features of the foliar micromorphology are important in identification and classification of trees (Hardin, 1992). The surface of blades is usually not completely smooth if examined with high magnification (40× and above). The primary relief is generally formed by the raised or sunken veins (a condition called *rugose* if very pronounced) or the convexity of the epidermal cell walls. Secondary relief (projections, striations, ridges) may be formed by epidermal cells (papillae) or a thick and sculptured cuticle on the epidermal walls. Tertiary relief, on top of the cuticle, may be formed by a deposit of flaky, white epicuticular wax. Such micromorphological features are best seen with high magnifications (up to 100 to 500×) using a scanning electron microscope (SEM) (Fig. 7-6). A smooth surface usually gives the blade a green, shiny appearance. Added relief, cuticular or epicuticular, increases the reflective surface, and the blade may have a pale color, often found on the lower surface. Epicuticular wax forms a pale or white surface, again usually below, which is called *glaucous* (or *glaucescent* if less). If you can "rub off" this white, it is glaucous or glaucescent.

Hairs (trichomes) on the leaf surface are of numerous types, and their structure is best examined with an SEM (Fig. 7-6). A given species may have a particular type or a complement of types, which is a very stable taxonomic character. The relative density of hairs (*vesticure*) is much more easily observed with the naked eye or a handlens, but it may be variable in relation to season or habitat. The following terms are a few of the many used to describe vesticure character states (Fig. 7-7).

Glabrous. Without hairs of any type; "smooth"
Glabrate. Becoming glabrous or nearly so with age
Puberulent. Minutely hairy as seen with a handlens or dissecting microscope
Pubescent. With fine, soft, short hairs. Often used in a more general way meaning "hairy" without specifying the particular type of vesticure
Villous. With long, silky, straight hairs
Tomentose. With curled, matted, woolly hairs
Scabrous. Rough and "sandpapery" with short bristly hairs
Glandular. With numerous glandular hairs, either sessile or stalked
Lepidote. Covered with minute, scalelike hairs
Stellate. With stellate hairs, each having rays parallel with the surface

FIGURE 7-6 Scanning electron micrographs of leaf surfaces at different magnifications. Top (left to right): yellow-poplar papillae, dogwood cuticle and trichome, magnolia trichomes, and epicuticular wax. Bottom (left to right): trichomes of hickory, basswood, and oak.

FIGURE 7-7 Vesiture types.

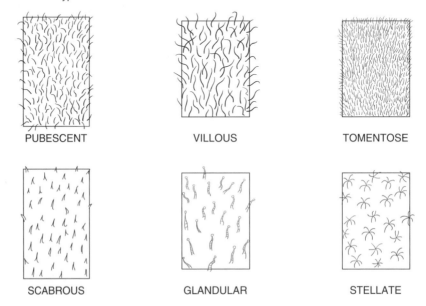

PUBESCENT VILLOUS TOMENTOSE

SCABROUS GLANDULAR STELLATE

Finally, leaf blades may be *coriaceous* (thick and leathery) or *membranous* (thin and pliable).

Twigs (Fig. 7-8)

A *twig*, by definition, is the terminal or last year's growth of a branch, delimited at the base by the terminal bud-scale scars (the position of last year's bud which developed into the twig). This definition is important, for twig characters, and twig keys are based on just this part because the second-year and older branches lose some of the twig features. Twigs offer an excellent means of identifying trees and shrubs throughout the year, except for a short time during the spring when the buds formed the previous season are opening and those for the current season have not yet appeared. The most conspicuous features of twigs are their buds, leaf scars, stipule scars, and pith, although color, taste, odor, and the presence or absence of cork, spur shoots, spines, thorns, prickles, and pubescence are also valuable characters for identification purposes.

Buds   These are conspicuous on most twigs and may be of two sorts: those borne along the twig in the axils of the previous season's leaves are termed *laterals* (*axillary*) while the one at the apex is often larger and is called the *terminal;* it limits further growth in length for the season (ex.: *Acer, Magnolia*). In certain trees, however, a true terminal bud is not formed, and growth continues until checked by external factors. When this occurs, the tender leading shoot dies back to the lateral bud below. This lateral bud assumes the function of the terminal and is called *pseudoterminal.* It is distinguished from the true terminal by its smaller size (it is really a lateral) and the presence of a minute *twig scar* on the side opposite the leaf scar (ex.: *Betula, Tilia*).

If more than one bud appears at a node, the bud directly above the leaf scar is considered to be the true lateral bud, and the others are designated as *accessory buds.* If the accessory buds are arranged on either side of a lateral bud, they are said to be *collateral,* while if they appear above a lateral bud, they are called *superposed.*

Buds are either *scaly* or *naked.* Bud scales are actually modified leaves or stipules and serve to protect the enclosed embryonic axis and its appendages. In some buds the scales are often rather numerous and overlap one another in a shinglelike fashion. Bud scales so arranged are *imbricate.* When buds are covered with two or three scales which do not overlap, the scales are described as *valvate.* In a few genera the buds are covered by a single caplike scale. When the terminal bud opens with the renewal of growth in the spring, the scales slough off, leaving *terminal bud-scale scars. Naked buds* lack scaly coverings and are common to certain trees of tropical climates, but they are relatively rare elsewhere. *Submerged buds,* that is, buds embedded in the callus layer of leaf scars, are featured by a few species. When two sizes of lateral buds occur on the same twig, the larger usually contains the rudiments of flowers and are called *flower buds. Mixed buds* containing twig, embryonic leaves, and flowers are characteristic of some species, in contrast to those enclosing twig and leaves only (*leaf buds*).

Epicormic buds are either newly formed adventitious buds on roots or latent lateral buds of stems that can give rise, upon cutting or damage of the main stem, to stump sprouts or coppice shoots. Coppice is a growth of small trees from root or stump sprouts.

FIGURE 7-8 Twig features.

Leaf Scars   When a leaf falls from a twig, there remains at the point of attachment a *leaf scar*. Leaf scars vary in size and shape with different species and hence are usually diagnostic. On the surface of each leaf scar are found one or more small dots or patches which show where the strands of vascular tissue passed from the twig into the leaf. The size, number, and arrangement of these so-called *vascular bundle scars* are often helpful in identification. It is often necessary to observe these with magnification (10× or more).

Stipular Scars   Stipular scars are not found on all twigs, for many species are *estipulate*. When present, they occur in pairs, one on either side at the top of the leaf scar. As a rule, they are slitlike in shape, and in most instances they are inconspicuous without a handlens (10× or more). In a few species they are fused together and completely encircle the twig.

Lenticels   Lenticels are small, usually lens-shaped patches, sometimes wartlike, consisting of loosely organized tissue, which provide aeration to the tissues beneath. The color, form, orientation, and frequency may be of value.

Pith   The medial or central portion of a twig is composed of *pith*. Pith is usually lighter or darker in color than the wood which surrounds it; hence it is readily discernible in transverse sections of twigs. The shape of the pith when viewed in this section usually conforms to one of several patterns. For example, it is *stellate* (star-shaped) or pentagonal in oaks and cottonwoods, *triangular* in alders, and *terete* (round) in ash, elms, and most others. Pith often varies in color through shades of pink, yellow, brown, or green, to black or white.

A longitudinal cut should be made through the center of the twig to determine composition. In most native trees the pith is *solid* (or *continuous*) and *homogeneous*. A distinct modification of this type is the *diaphragmed* pith, which has more or less regularly spaced disks of horizontally elongated cells with thickened walls. These appear as bars across the pith and are often readily visible to the naked eye. Yellow-poplar and black tupelo are common examples of this type. In a few trees, such as the walnut, the pith is divided into empty chambers by cross partitions and is termed *chambered*. Chambering in certain species does not take place until the fall of the year, and the season's growth is homogeneous until that time. A small portion at the end of each season's growth apparently remains unchambered, and therefore the age of a twig with this kind of pith may be estimated by sectioning it and counting the number of yearly "plugs" present. *Hollow* pith and *spongy* pith characterize some species of woody plants.

Lammas Shoots   It will be observed that a new shoot, or sprout, usually consists of a single stem bearing a number of characteristically arranged leaves. Soon after twig elongation and leaf enlargement have ceased, minute buds appear in the leaf axils. These buds continue to enlarge and by midsummer have attained full growth. Normally they then remain dormant until the following spring. However, in some species such as yellow-poplar, sweetgum, cascara, beech, sassafras, and water tupelo, these newly formed lateral buds often exhibit renewed growth activity. Within a few days after their maturation they become swollen and open and then produce a second shoot subtended by green leaves. These second, or midseason, twigs are known as *lammas shoots,* and while rarely diagnostic, they do occur much more frequently on some species than on others. Lammas shoots are most easily recognized in the late summer or early fall when they still may be seen in the axils of leaves.

Shoot Types   The normal twig, with the leaves and buds spread apart by elongation of the internodes, is called a *long shoot.* These may be entirely preformed within the bud or continue to develop during the season. If there is little growth and almost inconspicuous internode length, the stem is called a *short shoot* or "spur" or "dwarf" shoot or branch. The stem axis and embryonic leaves are preformed in the bud. They may bear only leaves, or leaves and flowers (or the reproductive structures in ginkgo). There are two types of short shoots. One is *indeterminate,* in which there is a functional terminal bud and growth may continue for many years. In this type, the nodes are so close together that otherwise alternate (spiral) leaves may appear whorled. In some cases the "dwarfness" is released and subsequent growth in following years may be a normal long shoot. These are commonly found in apple, pear, birch, mountain ash, ginkgo, larch (Fig. 7-5), and deodar cedar. The second type of short shoot is *determinate,* and as the term implies, growth length is predetermined in the bud, there is no continued growth, and the short shoot drops as a unit with its leaves. This type forms the pine *fascicle* (Fig. 7-5), a short inconspicuous stem (with 1 to 5 needles), the deciduous baldcypress twigs that drop in the fall, and the axis of cones and flowers.

Thorns, Spines, and Prickles (Fig. 7-8)   The presence of these pointed structures is often important in identifying certain genera and species. *Spines* are modified leaves. *Foliar spines* (barberry) are single and have a bud in the axil; *stipular spines* (black locust) are in the position of stipules, therefore one on either side of the leaf scar. *Prickles* (rose, *Aralia*) emerge from the epidermis and cortex and can occur at any location on the twig or leaf. *Thorns* (honeylocust, hawthorn, osage-orange) are modified stems and as such sometimes bear minute leaf scars. They are positioned either above the leaf scar in the position of the bud and may be simple or branched, or terminate a spur branch.

Bark (Fig. 7-9)

Bark features are quite characteristic of tree species but vary with age, growth rate, and habitat and are difficult to describe in words. Yet, bark is still one of the most important features in the identification of large trees, particularly when leaves are absent and twigs inaccessible. Bark characteristics are best learned by actual observation and experience. Beginning students in dendrology often underestimate the value of bark in identification, but with experience, this attitude will change.

On older trunks bark characters to consider are texture, thickness, roughness (smooth, flaky, scaly, shaggy, furrowed, etc.), color of the outer and inner layers, depth and width and configuration of furrows (fissures), width and length and surface of the ridges or plates delimited by the furrows, whether fibrous or not, and horizontal versus

FIGURE 7-9   Bark (left to right): Douglas-fir, Sitka spruce, western hemlock, and western redcedar on the Olympic Peninsula near Willapa Harbor, Washington. (*Photo by Asahel Curtis, Seattle.*)

vertical peeling. On younger trunks, before the furrows or scales develop, color and the form of the lenticels are important features.

Bark is also important economically. The high-energy yields obtained from bark as a fuel have prompted most raw-wood-conversion plants to convert their processes to utilize fully all the heretofore wasted slabs and bark. Dyes, tannins, alkaloids, and some pharmaceutical compounds are extracted from the bark of certain species, and cordage and paper fibers are obtained from others. Vast quantities of bark from Douglas-fir, Rocky mountain white fir, and several yellow pines such as longleaf are used for decoration, mulching, and as a soil conditioner. Mixtures of tupelo, sweet-gum, yellow-poplar, and oak barks are also used for the same purposes. Redwood bark is used in walkways and as an underlay in patios. Pine bark has also proved to be an excellent oil scavenger when particulated and spread around oil spills at sea.

Bark is a common habitat for many corticolous green algae, mosses, leafy liver-worts, and lichens. In rough-barked trees, foliose and fruticose lichens often inhabit the bark fissures which stay moister than the ridges or scales. On smooth-barked trees, such as alder, hornbeam, magnolia, beech, pawpaw, American holly, and young trees of maple, hickory, yellow-poplar, and buckeye, crustose lichens frequently form variously colored blotches on an otherwise gray bark. Some of these are so common, as on American holly, that their presence is a dependable characteristic for identification of the tree without even looking at the leaves.

REPRODUCTIVE MORPHOLOGY

Reproductive features offer the most stable characters and thus are the primary basis for classification of seed plants. In trees, they are often unavailable because they are borne in the upper crown and last for a relatively short time. When available, however, they may be the most definitive features for identification, and it is therefore important to have a basic knowledge of reproductive morphology.

The primary male reproductive structure is the *pollen grain* which carries the *sperm;* the corresponding female structure is the *ovule* with the *egg.* Following the processes of *pollination* then *fertilization,* the ovule develops into the *seed* containing an *embryo.*

There are various levels of sexual differentiation. Some flowers contain both male and female structures and are called *bisexual,* or *perfect* (found in dogwood, cherry, basswood, black locust, and others). A plant with perfect flowers may be called *synoecious* (*syn* = together; *oecious* = house). If the cones or flowers have only one sex, they are *unisexual,* or *imperfect.* If both male and female flowers or cones are on the same tree, then the tree is *monoecious* (one house), as in most conifers, oak, hickory, birch, and so on. If the imperfect cones or flowers are on separate trees, then the tree is *dioecious* (two houses) (e.g., willow, poplar, holly, ginkgo, juniper, ash, boxelder, and a few others). Many trees show developmental or ecological variation in the male/female expression. For instance, a young maple may be male but then switch to female later; or, an ash with male flowers one year may have female flowers and fruits the next, then revert to male again the following year. There also may be a mixture of perfect and imperfect flowers in some trees; for instance, a buckeye inflorescence has a few perfect flowers plus many male flowers.

Gymnosperm Parts (Fig. 7-10)

Gymnosperm ovules are exposed (naked) at the time of pollination. These ovules are either borne on modified leaves (in cycads), on scales in the axils of bracts (in conifers); or on stalks (in ginkgo, podocarpus, yew, and some others). The cycad cone (strobilus) is simple (ovule-bearing leaves attached to a simple stem axis) whereas the conifer seed cone (strobilus) is compound; that is, a central stem axis bearing highly modified lateral branches (the *scales*), each in the axis of a reduced leaf (the *bract*). Pollen cones of all gymnosperms are simple; that is, a stem axis bearing modified leaves, each with two to many pollen sacs.

FIGURE 7-10   Conifer cone structures.

Pollen cones are deciduous soon after the pollen is released and are not important for identification. *Ovulate,* or *seed, cones,* on the other hand, show a number of differences and are very important in the classification and identification of conifers. The scales may be woody, leathery, or fleshy, each one with one or more seeds. They may be spirally borne on the axis (Pinaceae) or opposite and decussate (Cupressaceae). They may be separate from the bract (Pinaceae) or fused with it into a scale/bract complex (Cupressaceae) and either thin or thick, flexible or rigid, flattened or peltate (shield-shaped). In the latter case, the seed cones are more or less oval or spherical. In most of the Pinaceae, in which the scale and bract are separate, the scale is the larger, obvious structure and the bract is much smaller, shorter, and inconspicuous. In some firs and Douglas-fir, however, the bract is longer than the scale.

The exposed portion of the cone scale in a mature unopened cone is known as the *apophysis.* The apophysis is usually lighter in color than the remaining portion of the scale, although this is not always the case. In some species the apophysis is smooth; in others it is wrinkled, grooved, or ridged. In a few species the scale margins are slightly reflexed or revolute, while in others they appear to be eroded (*erose*).

In pine cones, which mature at the end of two, or rarely three, seasons, the apophysis terminates in a small protuberance called the *umbo.* When the umbo is found at the tip of the scale, it is *terminal,* but if it appears on the back or raised portion, it is *dorsal.* Umbos are often wartlike, or with a raised and rounded projection or boss, or they may terminate in a prickle, spine, or claw.

Cones normally open and release seeds fairly soon after maturity or remain closed for a long time and often require fire or a similar level of heat to open. These *serotinous* cones are an adaptation to fire ecology and lead to rapid seed dispersal and seedling development following a fire. Seed cones, open or closed, may persist on the tree for several years. Most cones remain intact when they open, whereas in *Abies, Cedrus,* and *Taxodium* the scales and bracts are deciduous. Most conifers complete their life cycle (pollination to seed development) in one year while others (pines) require two or sometimes three years. In pines, therefore, you can often find small, ovuliferous, first-year (pollination) cones, second-year (fertilization) cones, and the mature seed cones on the same branch.

Seeds are borne at the base of the cone scales. In several species, depressions in the scales denote their original position, while in others minute scars are left after seed dispersal. The number of seeds per cone scale varies with the species, as will be indicated later. Seeds are either terminally winged, laterally winged, or wingless, depending on genus and species.

Angiosperm Parts

Flowers (Fig. 7-11)   A flower is a modified, determinate short shoot with a central stem *axis* (*receptacle*), highly modified sterile leaves (*perianth*), and reproductive leaves. The perianth includes the outer whorl of *sepals* (collectively called the *calyx*) and inner whorl of *petals* (collectively the *corolla*). Undifferentiated perianth parts are called *tepals.* The reproductive leaves are the male *stamens* composed of *anther*

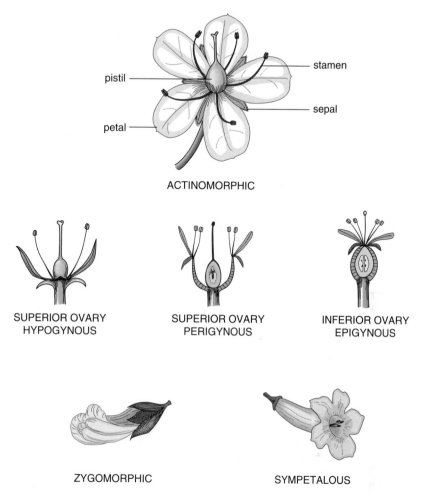

ACTINOMORPHIC

SUPERIOR OVARY
HYPOGYNOUS

SUPERIOR OVARY
PERIGYNOUS

INFERIOR OVARY
EPIGYNOUS

ZYGOMORPHIC

SYMPETALOUS

FIGURE 7-11   Flower parts and variation.

(pollen sacs) and *filament* (stalk), and female *carpels* composed of *ovary* (containing the *ovules*), *style,* and *stigma.* The term *pistil* is used to describe the visible ovary/style/stigma which may be a single carpel or the fusion product of several carpels (a compound pistil). A flower may have several single carpels but never more than one compound pistil. A flower with all four parts (sepals, petals, stamens, pistils) is *complete;* if any one or more are missing, the flower is *incomplete.* If loss of parts involves the perianth, the flower may be *asepalous* or *apetalous* (*a-* means without). If the loss involves functional stamens and pistils, the flower is *imperfect* (rather than perfect) and either *staminate* or *pistillate.*

Several other modifications of the basic floral structure occur such as variation in the number of parts per whorl (usually three, four, or five, or many), symmetry (radial = *actinomorphic* or bilateral = *zygomorphic*), or fusion of parts. Fusion may be *connation* (i.e., lateral fusion between parts within a whorl) or *adnation* (i.e., fusion between parts of different whorls). In the case of connation, separate parts may fuse to form, for example, a *sympetalous corolla,* or *compound pistil.* Adnation between stamens and perianth forms a structure called a *hypanthium.* (In some plants, the hypanthium may be formed by a cup-shaped receptacle rather than by adnation.) This hypanthium may form an open cup-shaped structure, or it may completely envelop and fuse with the ovary wall. Such modifications lead to several different "ovary positions" in the flower. In the simplest case, the ovary is free and above the position of the origin of the perianth and stamens (a *superior ovary*). Even with a cup-shaped hypanthium not fused with the ovary, the ovary is still considered superior. If the hypanthium is fused with the ovary, and thus the ovary appears to be below the perianth and stamens, it is called *inferior.* Terms relative to the position of the perianth with respect to the ovary are: *hypogynous* (perianth below ovary), *perigynous* (hypanthium around but free from ovary), and *epigynous* (perianth above ovary). (The suffix -gynous refers to "gynoecium," the collective term for all the carpels.)

Flowering is the process of floral maturation reaching that point (*anthesis*) when pollination is possible. Because gymnosperms do not have flowers, this term is inappropriate even though frequently heard. *Coning* is correct but less often used.

Pollen and Pollination   Pollen grains are variable in size, weight, shape, number of pores through which the pollen tube may emerge, and outer wall sculpturing. Pollen type is characteristic of family or genus and sometimes species. For some examples of pollen types, as seen by SEM, see Fig. 7-12. For additional information, see Kapp (1969).

FIGURE 7-12   Scanning electron micrographs of representative tree pollens at different magnifications. Top (left to right): pine with air sacs, willow, holly, maple. Bottom (left to right): buckeye, rhododendron tetrad, basswood. (*Those of top row, courtesy of Mr. Stephen B. Bambara and Mrs. Nancy Leidy, Department of Entomology, North Carolina State University, Raleigh.*)

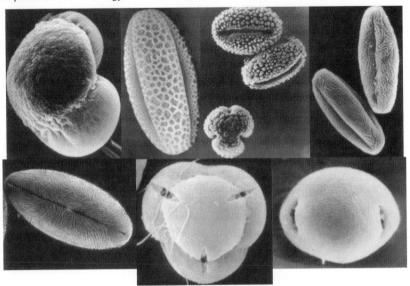

Pollination is the transfer of pollen from the pollen sac to the ovule (in gymnosperms) or stigma (in angiosperms). Among our temperate zone trees, there are three types of pollination mechanisms: wind (*anemophily*), insect (*entomophily*), and bird (*ornithophily*). The usual features of the *anemophilous syndrome* among trees are: small, lightweight, dry pollen in great overabundance; small, reduced flowers generally lacking a perianth and with exposed anthers/stigmas; many pistillate flowers, each with one to few ovules per ovary; and flowering in early spring before the leaves and therefore with maximum airflow among the flowering branches. Many of these pollens are allergenic such as oak, hickory, alder, and others, and cause respiratory and nasal discomfort to many people. The conifers are also anemophilous but much less allergenic. The *entomophilous syndrome* involves a floral morphology correlated with the particular pollinator (beetles, bees, bumble bees, wasps, butterflies, moths): showy perianth; small amounts of large, heavy, sticky pollen grains; usually several to many ovules per ovary; often with a nectar supply used for food (although some insects are pollen feeders); and the flowers generally aromatic. Examples are persimmon, magnolia, yellow-poplar, apple, cherry, sourwood, and locust. *Ornithophilous* flowers are similar, but often red or yellow in color, with a tubular-shaped corolla and an abundance of nectar (e.g., red buckeye, mimosa tree).

Several insect-pollinated trees are important "bee trees" for honey production. Excellent honey comes from sourwood, tupelo, yellow-poplar, apple, holly, basswood, and many others. For additional reading on pollination, see Faegri and van der Pijl (1979) and Proctor and Yeo (1972).

Inflorescence, Infructescence   Flowers may arise from separate buds or in mixed buds with leaves and they may be *terminal* on the twig or *axillary* in leaf axils. They may be single or borne in clusters of several to many. An *inflorescence* is the arrangement of several flowers in a branch system; an *infructescence* is the same for fruits. The stalk of a single flower (as in magnolia) is the *peduncle;* the stalk of an inflorescence (of many flowers) is also the peduncle; the stalk of an individual flower in an inflorescence is the *pedicel.* Pedicels or primary branches arise from a *rachis,* each from the axil of a bract. Successive branches or pedicels may be in the axils of bractlets, and sometimes the pedicels may bear one to two bracteoles below the flower. There are many types of inflorescences, but the main ones found in trees are shown in Fig. 7-13 and described as follows.

Spike. A central rachis bearing a number of sessile flowers (see catkin)

Catkin or *ament.* A dense spike bearing many, apetalous, unisexual flowers; often pendent (staminate flowers in oak, hickory; pistillate flowers in birch)

Raceme. A central axis bearing a number of pedicelled flowers; all the pedicels of about the same length (black locust)

Panicle. Diffusely branched rachises with many flowers, or the primary branches as racemes or cymes (buckeye, sumac)

Umbel. Usually flat-topped, with many pedicels arising from a common point at the top of the peduncle; sometimes compound (ends of panicle branches in devils-walkingstick)

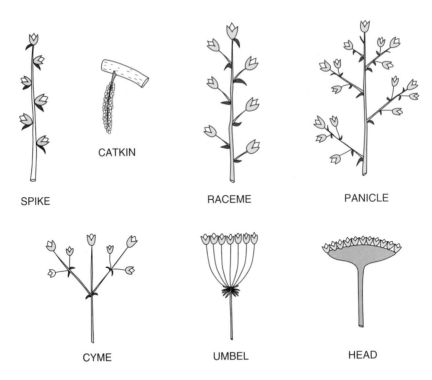

CATKIN

SPIKE   RACEME   PANICLE

CYME   UMBEL   HEAD

FIGURE 7-13   Inflorescence types.

Cyme. A central rachis terminated early by a flower and with lateral branches, arising below and later, either terminated by a flower or leading to successive cymes (alternate-leaf dogwood, basswood)

Head. A number of sessile flowers clustered on a common receptacle which may be flat-topped or more or less globose (flowering dogwood, sycamore)

Fruits and Seeds (Fig. 7-14)   A *fruit* is a ripened ovary, usually with seeds; a *seed* is a ripened ovule, usually with an embryo. Classification of fruits is on the basis of the ovary structure as well as the form of the mature fruit. If the fruit is from a single ovary in a flower, it is a *simple fruit;* if the fruit is formed from several separate ovaries that stay together when mature, it is a *compound fruit.* Both types may be either fleshy or dry. Fleshy fruits are classified on the basis of the differentiation of the fruit wall (*pericarp*). Dry fruits are classified on whether they split open (*dehiscent*) and release the seeds or not (*indehiscent*), the number of carpels, and the general form of the mature fruit. The common types are illustrated and described briefly.

I Simple fruits
  A Dry, indehiscent fruits
    1 *Achene.* Small, one-seeded, unwinged but sometimes plumose (sycamore— multiple of achenes)

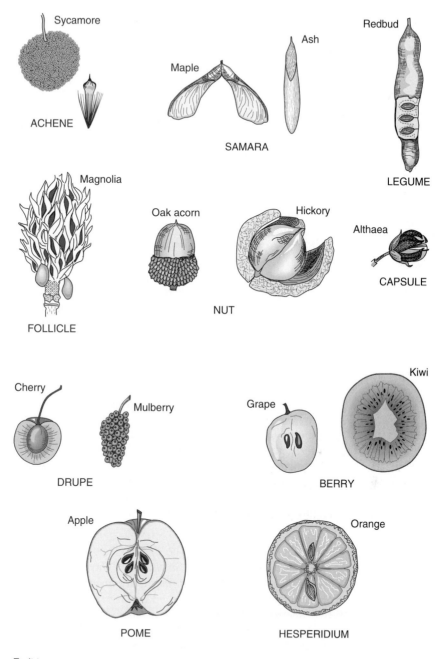

Sycamore

ACHENE

Maple

Ash

SAMARA

Redbud

LEGUME

Magnolia

FOLLICLE

Oak acorn

Hickory

NUT

Althaea

CAPSULE

Cherry

Mulberry

DRUPE

Grape

Kiwi

BERRY

Apple

POME

Orange

HESPERIDIUM

FIGURE 7-14   Fruit types.

    2 *Samara.* Achene-like but winged (elm, maple, ash; yellow-poplar—aggregate of samaras)

    3 *Nut.* Ovary with two or more carpels, but fruit usually one-celled, one-seeded, and with a hard wall (basswood); sometimes partially or entirely encased in a husk (involucre) (walnut, hickory, oak, beech)

B Dry, dehiscent fruit

    1 *Legume.* Product of a simple, one-carpellate ovary, splitting along two lines (or occasionally indehiscent) (black locust, redbud, mimosa tree)

    2 *Follicle.* Product of a simple, one-carpellate ovary, splitting along one line (magnolia—aggregate of follicles)

    3 *Capsule.* Product of a compound ovary, splitting along two or more lines, usually one per carpel (buckeye, sourwood, poplar, willow; sweetgum—multiple of capsules)

C Fleshy fruits

    1 *Pome.* Product of a compound, inferior ovary, the outer hypanthium wall fleshy, the inner pericarp wall (endocarp) papery or woody (apple, pear, hawthorn, serviceberry)

    2 *Drupe.* Product of a simple ovary and usually one-seeded, the outer pericarp walls (*exocarp* and *mesocarp*) fleshy, the inner pericarp wall (*endocarp*) bony; a "stone fruit" (peach, cherry, olive, palm; mulberry—multiple of drupelets or small drupes)

    3 *Berry.* Usually many-seeded (rarely one seed as in avocado), with the entire pericarp fleshy (persimmon, pawpaw, grape, kiwi)

    4 *Hesperidium.* A type of berry with a thick, leathery outer "rind" (exocarp) and many radial sections (orange, grapefruit, lemon, lime)

II Compound fruits

    A *Aggregate.* A cluster of simple fruits from separate pistils of a single flower (magnolia—aggregate of follicles; yellow-poplar—aggregate of samaras)

    B *Multiple.* A cluster of simple fruits from many separate flowers in a compact inflorescence; a coalesced infructescence (sweetgum—multiple of capsules; mulberry—multiple of drupelets; sycamore—multiple of achenes)

Dispersal Mechanisms The dispersed portion (*the diaspore*) of seed plants may be the seed, cone, or fruit. Small, dry, lightweight diaspores (some seeds, achenes, samaras) are generally wind dispersed (*anemochory*). Small, fleshy diaspores of various colors (seeds with fleshy seed coats, berries, drupes, juniper cones) are frequently eaten by birds and small mammals, pass through the digestive tract, and are deposited in the scats (*endozoochory*). Larger, dry diaspores (nuts, large and hard seeds) are often collected by small mammals and the individuals or cache stored or buried and often forgotten (*synzoochory*). Some diaspores (seeds or fruits) have barbs or spines that get caught in feathers or fur and are carried on the bodies of various animals (*exozoochory*). In a few cases (e.g., witchhazel), the seeds are projected out of capsules (*ballochory,* or *autochory*). Large, heavy diaspores (fruits or serotinous cones) may be limited to dispersal by weight (*barochory*). Many diaspores are capable of water dispersal (*hydrochory*) along rivers and streams, during floods, or in ocean currents. Actually, many diaspores may have several means of dispersal, often differing between short-range and long-range dispersal. For a more thorough discussion of dispersal mechanisms, see van der Pijl (1982).

Seed Germination and Seedlings   Seed germination is of two types. *Epigeal* is when the cotyledons are brought above ground level by the elongation of the hypocotyl, as in pine (Fig. 7-15), beech, basswood, maple, and others. The cotyledons then function as either storage with little photosynthesis, or alternatively, photosynthesis with little storage. *Hypogeal* is when the cotyledons are the primary storage or haustorial structures and remain in the seed coat below ground level; the plumule is the first structure to appear above ground, as in oak or hickory. The form of the cotyledons and/or first leaves can be distinctive, and one can learn to recognize genera and sometimes species from these early reproductive stages. Some examples are shown in Figs. 7-16 and 7-17. See Young and Young (1992) for more details.

FIGURE 7-15   Three stages (right to left) in the epigean development of a pine seedling, showing cotyledons and first juvenile leaves. (*Photo by B. O. Longyear.*)

FIGURE 7-16 Some coniferous seedlings: (1) red pine. (2) balsam fir. (3) northern white-cedar. (4) white spruce. (5) eastern hemlock. (6) European larch.

FIGURE 7-17   Some broad-leaved (dicot) seedlings: (1) beech ×¾. (2) basswood ×1. (3) aspen ×3. (4) white ash ×½. (5) white oak ×⅓. (6) sugar maple ×½. (7) yellow birch ×1. (8) American elm ×1.

8

PINOPHYTA (GYMNOSPERMS)

Gymnosperms include many of the world's most interesting and useful trees, and their importance can hardly be overemphasized, especially in the temperate and cold-temperate forests of both northern and southern hemispheres.

Historically the gymnosperms have received much attention because their lineage extends back to the mid-Paleozoic era—the Devonian period about 350 million years ago. They were among the first seed plants and reached their peak of diversity and dominance during the Mesozoic era between 250 and 100 million years ago. Since that time, there has been a steady decline leaving at present only 5 orders, 15 families, some 70 genera, and about 730 species worldwide.

Gymnosperms are seed plants with "naked seeds" (i.e., naked ovules at the time of pollination). This is in contrast with the angiosperms which have ovules (and seeds) enclosed within the carpel. Gymnosperms also have a prezygotic megagametophyte tissue as the storage tissue in the seed whereas the angiosperms have a postzygotic endosperm formed by the process of double fertilization.

Commercially and ecologically, conifers are the most important of the gymnosperms, although cycads, ginkgo, and the yews are used extensively as ornamentals.

Cycadales   Cycads

The cycads (4 families, 10 genera, ca. 100 species) are tropical and subtropical plants that mostly resemble palms or tree ferns. Their trunk is either generally unbranched and 20 to 60 ft tall, or merely a short, tuberous, mostly subterranean stem as in our native *Zàmia* (Zamiaceae). They produce a terminal rosette of large, pinnately divided leaves and seeds borne on modified leaves either clustered around the stem or in a compact cone. The plants are dioecious. Some have very large pollen cones.

Cỳcas (Cycadaceae) is the most frequently used ornamental, but other genera may be seen in botanical gardens and arboreta in southern Florida, southern Texas, and southern California or in greenhouses.

Ginkgoales   **Ginkgoaceae: The Ginkgo Family**

Gínkgo bilòba L. Ginkgo, maidenhair tree

Distinguishing Characteristics (Fig. 8-1). *Leaves* deciduous, alternate, flabellate (fan-shaped), 1 to 2 in. (2.5 to 5 cm) long, 1½ to 3 in. (4 to 7.5 cm) wide, with or without one or more narrow apical sinuses, and with small dichotomous veins; borne on long shoots at the tips of branches, but on older growth, they occur only on short spur branches (indeterminate short shoots); fall color a brilliant pale yellow or orange-yellow, and all leaves drop from a tree within a few days. *Twigs* with scaly buds, terminal present; leaf scars raised, half round with two bundle scars; estipulate; pith homogeneous. *Dioecious;* the male pollen sacs in a catkinlike arrangement on spur branches; the naked ovules in pairs at the end of a long stalk, also from the spur branches. *Seeds* large, ca. 1 in. (2.5 cm) in diameter; outer, fleshy seed coat, upon ripening, has a foul odor, particularly in mass under a tree due to a substance similar to butyric acid or its derivatives (odor of rancid butter, but worse); inner seed coat hard and pale in color.

General Description.   This is a native of China and is the only living representative of a once large group which flourished during the late Mesozoic, about 150 million years ago. It was sacred according to the Buddhist religion and has been cultivated for centuries in the temple gardens of China and Japan and is now used as an ornamental street and yard tree in the United

FIGURE 8-1   *Ginkgo biloba*. Ginkgo. (1) Leaves and catkinlike clusters of male pollen sacs on a spur shoot × ¾. (2) Young leaves and ovules × ¾. (3) Seed × ¾. (4) Seed with outer fleshy layer removed × ¾. (5) Leaf × ½. (6) Twig × ½.

States and Canada and a "nut" tree in Asia. The seed, when boiled, fried, or roasted, is considered a delicacy in the orient (Del Tredici, 1991).

Taxales   Taxaceae: The Yew Family

The yew family comprises five or six genera and about 18 species. *Torreya* and *Taxus* are represented in the American flora (Table 8-1). The other genera are mostly in eastern Asia (one in New Caledonia).

Botanical Features of the Family

Leaves persistent, mostly in spirals (rarely opposite), decurrent, linear, resinous. **Seeds** entirely or partly surrounded by a fleshy aril; plants dioecious or monoecious.

TORREYA Arn.   Torreya

This is a small genus consisting of seven species of trees and shrubs found in North America, China, and Japan. Wooden novelties such as chess pieces, rings, and articles of turnery are manufactured from the Japanese kaya, *Torreya nucifera* (L.) Sieb. and Zucc.

Two species are found in the United States: *Tòrreya taxifòlia* Arn., Florida torreya (stinking-cedar), is rare and local; it is found along the Appalachicola River in western Florida and in southwestern Georgia, but now endangered due to a fungal disease of the stem. *Tòrreya califórnica* Torr., California torreya (nutmeg), is restricted to the west slopes of the Sierra Nevada and central coast region of California. Both are cultivated as ornamental trees or shrubs.

TAXUS L.   Yew

This genus includes 10 species of trees and shrubs of wide distribution through eastern Asia, Asia Minor, northern Africa, Europe, and North America. *Táxus baccàta* L., the English yew, with many cultivars, are commonly used as ornamentals throughout the northern hemisphere. Japanese yew, *T. cuspidàta* Sieb. and Zucc., and its cultivars, and the hybrid of these two, *T. × media,* are similarly employed.

Three species of *Taxus* are native to the United States: *T. canadénsis* Marsh., commonly designated as ground-hemlock or Canada yew, is a low sprawling shrub found in moist, shady situations through the northeastern states and Canada; *T. floridàna*

TABLE 8-1   COMPARISON OF NATIVE GENERA IN THE TAXACEAE

Genus	Leaves	Seeds
Torreya	linear; with 2 narrow, glaucous bands below; stiff	1–1½ in. (2.5–4 cm) long; completely surrounded by a purplish green aril
Taxus	linear; with 2 broad, glaucous bands below; flexible	ca. ¼ in. (6 mm) long; partly surrounded by a scarlet aril

Nutt. ex Chapm., the Florida yew, is a shrub or small tree frequenting river banks and ravines in western Florida; *T. brevifolia* Nutt., the Pacific yew, is a small to medium-size tree of the Pacific Coast and is the only native species of any commercial importance.

Táxus brevifòlia Nutt.   Pacific yew

Distinguishing Characteristics (Fig. 8-2).   *Leaves* ½ to ¾ in. (12 to 19 mm) long, linear and decurrent, appearing distichous, dark yellow-green to blue-green above, paler below, petiolate. *Dioecious;* pollen cones and ovules axillary. *Seed* ovoid-oblong ¼ in. (6 mm) in length, partially surrounded by a scarlet aril. *Bark* dark reddish purple, thin, and scaly.

Range   Southeastern Alaska along the coast to Monterey Bay, California; also in the Sierra Nevada Mountains; eastward through British Columbia and Washington to the west slopes of the Rockies in Montana and Idaho. Elevation: sea level northward to 8000 ft southward. This tree is usually found on deep, rich, moist soils near lakes, rivers, and streams, as well as on protected flats, benches, and slopes of ravines and canyons.

General Description   The Pacific yew is usually a small tree or large shrub 20 to 40 ft high and 12 to 15 in. dbh, although larger trees are occasionally found on the best sites. The crown is large and conical; and even forest trees produce "limby," often fluted, and occasionally con-

FIGURE 8-2   *Taxus brevifolia.* Pacific yew. (1) Twig with arillate seeds and 2-ranked leaves × 1. (2) Pollen cone × 3. (3) Young ovules in leaf axils × 3.

torted boles; the root system is deep and wide-spreading. It ordinarily occurs as an occasional understory tree in old-growth, mixed coniferous forests composed of Douglas-fir, western larch and hemlock, western redcedar, grand and Pacific silver firs, lodgepole and western white pines, western larch, Engelmann spruce, and coastal redwood. It is occasionally found as a much-dwarfed and often sprawling shrub at or near timberline with whitebark pine and Alaska-cedar. The foliage and seeds are poisonous, but the red, juicy aril is edible. The bark contains a compound, taxol, which is a treatment for certain cancers. The wood is used for making archery bows, canoe paddles, and cabinetwork.

Pacific yew produces some seed every year, and large crops occur at irregular intervals. The seeds are largely bird-disseminated, and those falling on wet moss, decaying wood, or leaf litter ordinarily germinate. This species is probably the most tolerant of northwestern forest trees. Growth proceeds very slowly, and maturity is attained in about 250 to 350 years. The largest trunks are usually hollow-butted and often exhibit spiral grain.

Pinales   Conifers

The conifers, with 6 families, about 50 genera, and some 550 species, are of primary value for forest products, ornamentals, and Christmas trees. The Pinaceae and Cupressaceae s. l. are most noteworthy in the northern hemisphere and the only two native in North America (Table 8-2); the Cephalotaxaceae and Sciadopityaceae are found in Asia; the Podocarpaceae and Araucariaceae are preeminent in the southern hemisphere. In the Araucariaceae the monkey puzzle tree and Norfolk Island pine (both species of *Araucaria*) are popular ornamentals, and the kauri-pine, *Agathis australis* Hort. ex Lindl. of New Zealand, is one of the world's most massive trees reaching 200 ft tall and ca. 20 ft dbh. Below a bushy crown, the nearly cylindrical trunk free of branches yields a remarkable amount of valuable wood.

Besides the large amounts of timber and paper pulp produced, the conifers furnish such products as turpentine and rosin (naval stores), pine straw, bark, and Christmas trees, and they also serve to control erosion on the steep slopes of mountains. Also, especially in the cooler portions of the north temperate zone, vast, nearly pure forests of coniferous species are typical and greatly enhance the value of these regions for recreational purposes. The seeds are important wildlife food and several mammals browse the foliage.

TABLE 8-2   COMPARISON OF CONIFER FAMILIES IN NORTH AMERICA

Family	Leaves	Immature ovulate cones	Seed cones
Pinaceae	persistent or deciduous; alternate; acicular or linear	bract and scale distinct and flat; ovules inverted, 2 per scale; monoecious	woody; seeds terminally winged or wingless
Cupressaceae s.l.	persistent or deciduous; alternate, opposite, or whorled; linear, subulate, or scale	bract and scale fused; flat to peltate; ovules erect or inverted; one to many per scale; monoecious or dioecious	woody, leathery, or fleshy; seeds laterally winged or wingless

The various members of this group are known as "conifers," "evergreens," or "soft-woods." In the first instance the common name is obvious, although two families have fleshy seeds not in cones. The name "evergreen" is less satisfactory, because at least five genera (*Larix, Pseudolarix, Taxodium, Metasequoia,* and *Glyptostrobus*) have deciduous leaves while in some species of broad-leaved trees (dicotyledons) the leaves are persistent. The term "softwood" is clearly of lumbermen's origin and is commonly used in distinguishing between the conifers (also Taxales) and the broad-leaved trees, or "hardwoods." It often happens, however, that the wood of a "softwood" (conifer) is harder than that of a "hardwood" (broad-leaved tree); for example, wood of longleaf pine is harder than that of basswood. Even though most of these terms are none too satisfactory, they are all useful provided their limitations are understood.

Pinaceae: The Pine Family

This is the largest and most important timber-producing family of the gymnosperms. It includes 9 genera and about 200 species, mostly distributed through the northern hemisphere from the forests of the tropics to the northern limits of tree growth beyond the Arctic circle.

The genera are placed in two groups on the basis of morphology and anatomy of fossil and extant material and seed proteins (Price et al., 1987). The Pinoid group includes *Pinus, Larix, Picea, Pseudotsuga,* and *Cathaya;* the Abietoid group includes *Tsuga, Abies, Cedrus, Keteleeria,* and *Pseudolarix.* The native conifers of our area include the first four of the Pinoid group and the first two of the Abietoid group (Table 8-3). These are described subsequently in that order. Several of the others are very important as ornamentals. *Cedrus,* particularly, is commonly cultivated. It is an ever-green, having needles spirally arranged on long shoots and indeterminate short shoots, and large, erect, smooth seed cones. *Cedrus atlantica* (Endl.) G. Man. ex Carr. is the Atlas cedar, a native of the Atlas Mountains in northern Africa; *C. deodara* (D. Don) G. Don is the very popular deodar cedar, also a commercially important tree in the western Himalayas; and *C. libani* A. Rich. is the cedar-of-Lebanon. Several cultivars of these species are popular ornamentals.

There is a recent argument that *Pinus* should be alone in the monotypic Pinaceae and that the other genera be classified in the Abietaceae. We follow here the conservative, broader concept of the Pinaceae.

Botanical Features of the Family

Leaves deciduous or persistent; spirally arranged, in certain genera recurring in false whorls on spur shoots developed on older growth; solitary or in fascicles (*Pinus*); acicular (needlelike) or linear.

Cones (juvenile ovulate) with bract and scale distinct, flat; ovules inverted, 2 at the base of each scale; most species monoecious.

Mature cones woody, stalked or sessile, pendent or upright, maturing in one, two, or rarely three seasons, in some genera, disintegrating at maturity; seeds terminally winged or wingless.

TABLE 8-3　COMPARISON OF NATIVE GENERA IN THE PINACEAE

Genus	Leaves	Mature cones
Pinus pine	persistent; acicular; mostly in fascicles of 2 to 5	pendent; bracts shorter than the scales; mostly maturing in 2 (in certain species 3) seasons
Larix larch	deciduous; linear; triangular or 4-sided; on the growth of the season borne singly in remote spirals, on older growth recurring only in clusters on short spur shoots	upright; bracts shorter or longer than the scales; maturing in 1 season
Picea spruce	persistent; linear; usually 4-sided (in certain species flattened); sessile, borne on conspicuous peglike projections from the twig	pendent; bracts shorter than the scales; maturing in 1 season
Pseudotsuga Douglas-fir	persistent; linear; flattened; petioled; borne on moderately raised leaf cushions	pendent; bracts 2-lobed with a central spine and longer than the scales; maturing in 1 season
Tsuga hemlock	persistent; linear; flattened; petiole more conspicuous than in *Pseudotsuga;* often 2-ranked; borne on short peglike projections from the twig	same as *Picea,* but mostly smaller
Abies fir	persistent; linear; flattened (2 species 4-sided), sessile; may or may not appear 2-ranked	upright; scales and bracts deciduous from the cone axis; bracts longer or shorter than the scales; maturing in 1 season

PINUS L.　Pine

This genus, the most important timber-producing taxon of the conifers, includes some 100 species widely scattered through the northern hemisphere from near the northern limits of tree growth in North America, Europe, and Asia southward to northern Africa, Asia Minor, Malaysia, and Sumatra [here one species crosses the Equator (Critchfield and Little, 1966)]. In the New World, pines are found as far south as the West Indies and Nicaragua. Although of primary importance in the production of timber, the wood of most pines is also suitable for pulp and paper manufacture. Turpentine, pitch, pine-wood oils, wood tars, and rosin, collectively known as *naval stores,* are obtained from the wood of several species, notably *P. palustris* and *P. elliottii* of North America, *P. pinaster* Ait. of the Mediterranean basin, and *P. roxburghii* Sarg. (*P. longifolia* Roxb.) of India. The leaf oils of several species are used in the manufacture of medicines, and the seeds of several others are suitable for food. These so-called pine nuts are commonly offered for sale in many cities in the U. S. Needles, gathered as "pine straw," are valuable as mulch.

Natural enemies of the pines are numerous. Because of the resinous nature of the foliage, bark, and wood, fire is always a serious menace, while sawflies, weevils, bark beetles, and tip moths cause considerable damage. White pine blister rust, a fungous disease from Europe, not only destroys true white pines but other five-needle soft pines as well.

About 40 species of *Pinus* are native to the United States, and nearly all the principal timber-producing regions contain one or more important pines. Fifteen species are native to the eastern United States, and the remaining ones are found in the West. Interspecific hybridization and introgression occur naturally and rather extensively among related, sympatric species. See Little (1979) and Burns and Honkala (1990) for the particular hybrids and references.

Botanical Features of the Genus

Leaves of two sorts: (1) primary leaves, scalelike, solitary, spirally arranged, often deciduous or drying within a few weeks after their appearance, bearing in their axils; (2) the secondary fascicled, acicular leaves (needles).* *Needles* triangular, semicircular, or rarely circular in transverse section, borne in fascicles of 2 to 5 (rarely as many as 8, or solitary) usually with several lines of stomata on each surface; *apex* acute; *margin* often sharply serrulate; *basal sheath* deciduous or persistent, composed of 6 to 12 bud scales; *vascular bundles,* 1 or 2; *resin canals,* 2 to many (rarely obscure); needles persistent for 2 to several (exceptionally 17) years, with a pungent aroma when bruised.

Cones (juvenile) unisexual; *pollen cones* axillary, red, orange, or yellow, in clusters of a few to many at the base of the season's growth, consisting of a number of spirally arranged, 2-celled, sessile pollen sacs; *ovulate cones* subterminal or lateral, erect, composed of several to many spirally arranged bracts, each subtending an ovuliferous scale bearing 2 inverted, basal, adaxial ovules; all species monoecious.

Mature cone *woody, cone scales* armed or unarmed; *seeds* obovoid, with terminal wings or wingless; *cotyledons* 3 to 18. The rather remarkable opening mechanism of pine-cone scales has been investigated by Harlow et al. (1962).

Buds scaly, the scales appressed, or free at the ends and then fringed; extremely variable in size, shape, and color, resinous or nonresinous.

Growth habit. Although the growth of a terminal leader and a "whorl" of side branches each year is a feature of several coniferous genera, it is especially typical of the pines. Certain species usually produce a single set of side branches each year, while others are multinodal and develop 2 or 3 such arrangements on the elongating leader during the season. Because the leaf arrangement in *Pinus* is alternate (spiral), so too is that of the branches, and the term *false whorl* should be used for these arrangements.

The pines may be separated into two main groups (subgenera), namely, (1) the "soft pines," and (2) the "hard pines" (see Table 8-4 for comparison). For the complete classification of pines into sections and subsections, see Little and Critchfield (1969). The arrangement here is more geographical for convenience to the student. See Strauss and Doerksen (1990) for a discussion of pine phylogeny.

---

*In seedlings the first foliage to appear consists of a whorl of cotyledons (seed leaves); the growing shoot then develops linear, spirally arranged, serrulate juvenile leaves the first season, and in certain species for several seasons before the adult fascicled needles ultimately develop.

TABLE 8-4 COMPARISON OF SOFT AND HARD PINES

Feature	Soft pines	Hard pines
Needles	in fascicles of 1 to 5, usually 5; cross section of needle shows 1 fibrovascular bundle	in fascicles of 2 to 3 (rarely 5 to 8); cross section of needle shows 2 fibrovascular bundles
Fascicle sheath	deciduous	persistent, rarely deciduous
Cone scales	usually thin at the apex; mostly unarmed	usually thick at the apex; mostly armed with prickle
Wood	soft; transition from early to late wood gradual	hard (with few exceptions); transition from early to late wood abrupt

Subgenus *Strobus*   Soft pines

strobus, monticola, lambertiana, flexilis, strobiformis, albicaulis, cembroides, edulis, monophylla, quadrifolia, balfouriana, aristata

Subgenus *Pinus*   Hard pines (pitch pines or yellow pines)

Western hard pines: *ponderosa, jeffreyi, engelmannii, sabiniana, coulteri, torreyana, radiata, attenuata, muricata, leiophylla, contorta*

Eastern hard pines: *banksiana, virginiana, clausa, resinosa, nigra, sylvestris, palustris, echinata, taeda, glabra, rigida, serotina, pungens, elliottii*

The Soft Pines

There are over a dozen soft pines, one (*P. strobus*) in the East and all the others in western forests (Table 8-5).

Pìnus stròbus L.   Eastern white pine; northern white pine

Distinguishing Characteristics (Fig. 8-3)

Needles 2½ to 5 in. (6 to 13 cm) long, 5 per fascicle, dark bluish green, slender and flexible; persistent until the end of the second season or the following spring.

Cones 4 to 8 in. (10 to 20 cm) long, narrowly oblong-conic, often slightly curved, stalked, with thin scales; usually falling from the tree during the winter or following spring; *apophysis* nearly smooth or slightly lined; *umbo* terminal, unarmed; *seeds* ca. ¼ in. (5 to 8 mm) long, ovoid, reddish or grayish brown, mottled with dark spots, wings ca. ¾ in. (1.5 to 2 cm) long, lined.

Twigs orange-brown, glabrous or sparingly puberulent; *buds* covered with thin reddish or orange-brown scales.

Bark on young stems thin and smooth, dark green, soon furrowed; on old trees 1 to 2 in. (2.5 to 5 cm) thick, deeply and closely fissured into narrow, roughly rectangular blocks, minutely scaly on the surface.

TABLE 8-5   COMPARISON OF THE SOFT PINES

Species	Needles	Seed cones
P. strobus eastern white pine	5 per fascicle, 2½–5 in. (6–13 cm) long, slender flexible	long-stalked, cylindrical, 4–8 in. (10–20 cm) long; scales thin, umbo terminal and unarmed; seed wing long
P. monticola western white pine	5 per fascicle, 2–4 in. (5–10 cm) long, stout, rigid	long-stalked, cylindrical, 5–11(14) in. [13–28(35) cm] long; scales thin, umbo terminal and unarmed; seed wing long
P. lambertiana sugar pine	5 per fascicle, 2¾–4 in. (7–10 cm) long, often twisted, stout, rigid	long-stalked, cylindrical, 11–18 in. (28–46 cm) long; scales relatively thin, umbo terminal and unarmed; seed wing long
P. flexilis limber pine	5 per fascicle, 2–3½ in. (5–9 cm) long, clustered at ends of branches, stout, rigid	short-stalked, cylindrical to ovoid, 3–6 in. (7.5–15 cm) long; scales thick, umbo terminal and unarmed; seeds short-winged or wingless
P. albicaulis whitebark pine	5 per fascicle, 1–2¾ in. (2.5–7 cm) long, clustered at ends of branches, stout, rigid	short-stalked, ovoid-globose, 1½–3¼ in. (4–8 cm) long; serotinous; scales thick, umbo terminal and armed; seeds wingless
pinyon or nut pines	1–5 per fascicle, ¾–2½ in. (2–6 cm) long, incurved, slender and flexible or stout and rigid	short-stalked, ovoid to globose, ¾–3 in. (2–7.5 cm) long; scales thick, umbo dorsal, unarmed or with small prickle; seed barely winged or usually wingless
P. balfouriana foxtail pine	5 per fascicle, ¾–1½ in. (2–4 cm) long, incurved, clustered at ends of branches, stout, rigid	short-stalked, ovoid to cylindrical, 3½–5 in. (9–13 cm) long; scales thick, umbo dorsal, armed with minute prickle; seed wing long
P. aristata bristlecone pine	5 per fascicle, ¾–1½ in. (2–4 cm) long, incurved, clustered at ends of branches, stout, rigid	short-stalked, subcylindrical, 2½–3½ in. (6–9 cm) long; scales thick, umbo dorsal, armed with long, stiff prickle; seed wing long

Range

Northeastern and southern Appalachians (Map 8-1). Local disjuncts in central North Carolina, central Tennessee, eastern Kentucky, west central Indiana, and northern Illinois. Elevation: sea level northward to 4950 ft in the southern Appalachians. Eastern white pine is found on many different sites, even including such extremes as dry, rocky ridges, floodplains, and wet sphagnum bogs. Best development, however, is made on moist, well-drained, sandy loam soils of ridges.

FIGURE 8-3 *Pinus strobus.* Eastern white pine. (1) First year's ovulate cone × ¾. (2) Mature seed cones and foliage × ⅓. (3) Opened seed cone × ¾. (4) Seed × 1. (5) Fascicle of needles × ¾. (6) Cross section of needle × 35. (7) Bark of young tree. (8) Bark of old tree.

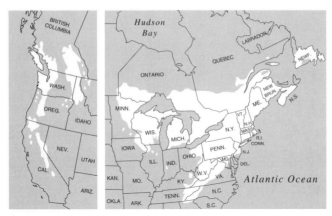

MAP 8-1   (**Left**) *Pinus monticola*. (**Right**) *Pinus strobus*.

General Description

Eastern white pine is the largest of northeastern conifers, and from the beginning of logging in this country it has been a most valuable species, first in New England, then in Pennsylvania and New York, and finally in the lake states where magnificent stands once covered large areas.

This species commonly varies from 80 to 100 ft in height and 2 to 3½ ft in diameter (max. 220 by 6 ft). In the open, young trees produce broadly conical crowns with living branches persisting nearly to the ground; but under forest competition, especially that of hardwoods, a tall cylindrical bole is developed, which is often clear, on older trees, for two-thirds of its length. The crown of middle-aged and old trees consists of several nearly horizontal or ascending branches, gracefully plumelike in outline and very distinctive in comparison with those of associated conifers. The root system is wide-spreading and moderately deep with only the vestige of a taproot; with age, root development nearer the surface may occur.

Especially in the Lake states, moderately moist soils support extensive pure forests, while in drier areas, mixtures with red pine or even jack pine are quite common. On heavier soils the hardwoods compete more successfully, and this pine occurs only as a scattered tree, often reaching, however, large proportions and excellent form in such mixtures.

In Canada pure stands or mixtures with red pine and red spruce frequently occur, while in the northeastern United States, in addition to limited pure groups, eastern white pine occurs on sandy loams with the northern hardwoods, red spruce, and eastern hemlock; here the scattered pines usually tower 40 to 50 ft above the crowns of their associates (Fig. 8-4). Farther south, although reaching large size, they are not so abundant and are found with many of the central hardwoods and eastern hemlocks.

Although extensive logging has removed most of the original pine forests, this species has always been aggressive in reproducing itself. When the exodus from eastern farms began in the late 1860s, many abandoned fields quickly seeded in with this tree, and nearly pure stands have since developed. This process has continued and earned for this species, as well as some others, the local name of "old field pine."

Eastern white pine is intermediate in tolerance, more tolerant than such species as paper birch, the aspens, red pine, and jack pine, but less so than sugar maple, American beech, and hemlock.

FIGURE 8-4 Old-growth eastern white pine.

This pine begins to produce cones at an early age, sometimes when not more than 5 to 10 years old, but good seed production can rarely be expected until the trees are 20 to 30 years old, and under forest conditions from one to two decades later. Large crops usually occur at 3- to 10-year intervals, but a few cones may be produced nearly every year.

After the first two seasons the rate of growth of young trees increases, and when once established, this species makes rapid growth. On the best sites and during favorable seasons, young white pine may grow nearly 4 ft in height and 1 in. in diameter per year. This, however, is exceptional, and average trees usually attain not more than one-half this rate of increase. Between the ages of 50 and 100 years, height growth, especially, decreases, but maturity is not reached for another 100 years, and very old trees have been reported which showed at least 450 growth rings.

This pine develops one horizontal false whorl of side branches each year, a useful feature in estimating the age of the tree.* In contrast, the pitch and jack pines, as well as some of the southern species, often produce two or three such whorls in a single growing season.

*To the count of whorls, add 2 or 3, because as seedlings side branches are not at first developed; this method obviously cannot be used on old trees where the bark has completely obliterated the branch scars.

Because of the demand for the wood, the ease in handling of nursery stock, and the high percentage of survival when properly planted, this tree has been established by the millions throughout the Northeast; in fact, it has been the principal species used in reforestation for many years. Two serious enemies threaten it, however, especially in pure stands: (1) the white pine blister rust caused by a fungus, and (2) the white pine weevil. The former is a bark disease which eventually kills the tree, and the latter deforms the trunk by killing, often repeatedly, the terminal shoots. Open-grown, scattered pasture trees are sometimes successively weeviled to such an extent that they become bushy and totally unfit for good lumber, and even trees in denser stands are badly deformed. Control measures have been applied to each of these enemies, and planting plans modified in an endeavor to lessen the amount of damage incurred. White pine is often damaged by high concentrations of atmospheric sulphur dioxide and ozone.

Although eastern white pine shows certain geographical variations, these are not sufficient to warrant the recognition of races, with one possible exception (Mergen, 1963).

Pinus montícola Dougl. ex D. Don   Western white pine; Idaho white pine

Distinguishing Characteristics (Fig. 8-5)

Needles 2 to 4 in. (5 to 10 cm) long, 5 per fascicle, blue-green, glaucous, slender, flexible, persistent until the third or fourth season.

Cones 5 to 11(14) in. [13 to 28(35) cm] long, narrowly cylindrical, often curved, stalked; *apophysis* yellowish brown to reddish brown, inner surface of scale deep red; *umbo* terminal, unarmed; *seeds* ca. ⅓ in. (7 to 9 mm) long, reddish brown, frequently mottled with black, with a terminal wing ca. 1 in. (2 to 3 cm) long.

Twigs moderately slender, often clothed with orange-brown pubescence during the first season but ultimately becoming dark reddish brown to purplish brown and glabrous; *buds* ca. ½ in. (12 mm) long, cylindrical, blunt, covered by several closely appressed, imbricated scales.

Bark smooth, gray-green to light gray on young trees, thin even on old trunks where it breaks up into nearly square or rectangular, dark gray or purplish gray blocks separated by deep fissures.

Range

Western (Map 8-1). Disjunct in eastern Oregon. Elevation: sea level to 3500 ft northward, 6000–9900 ft southward. Rich, porous, mountain soils of mixed conifer forests and occasionally in pure stands

General Description

Western white pine was first observed along the banks of the Columbia and Spokane rivers in 1831 by the Scottish botanist David Douglas. Reaching a height of 150 to 180 ft, and a dbh of 2½ to 3½ ft at maturity (max. 239 by 8 ft), this tree develops a long, slightly tapered shaft, often clear for 70 to 100 ft or more of its length, and a usually short, symmetrical, and somewhat open crown. Seedlings produce a prodigious taproot which is supplemented in later life by a deep, wide-spreading system of lateral roots which makes the trees unusually windfirm.

Except in the Puget Sound basin, on the Olympic Peninsula of western Washington, and on Vancouver Island, where it occasionally occurs at or near sea level, this species is typically a mountain species. Best development is attained in northern Idaho in moist valleys and on middle and upper slopes and flats of northerly exposure. Here, where nearly 80 percent of the com-

FIGURE 8-5   *Pinus monticola.* Western white pine. (1) Mature seed cone and foliage × ¾. (2) Seeds × 1. (3) Bark of old tree. (*Courtesy of British Columbia Forest Service.*)

mercial timber of the species is found, it is very common. Elsewhere, western white pine occurs largely on poorer and drier soils as an occasional tree or in small groves in mixture with other softwoods, and on such sites it rarely constitutes more than 5 percent of the stand. Its chief associates in the Rocky Mountain region include western larch, Englemann spruce, lodgepole pine, grand and subalpine firs, and occasionally western redcedar. In Washington and Oregon western white pine is frequently found with Douglas-fir, western hemlock, and grand, noble, and Pacific silver firs, and in California with red and Shasta red firs, Douglas-fir, and lodgepole pine.

This species rarely produces large seed crops, but as a rule some seed is released at intervals of 2 or 3 years after the fortieth to sixtieth year. Reproduction is best on a fresh mineral soil, although seeds lodging in humus often germinate and the young trees continue to develop provided they are amply supplied with moisture during the growing season. Rated as intermediate in tolerance, young trees are shade-enduring, but full light is required in later life, and mature trees usually dominate mixed stands. Growth is moderately fast but decreases noticeably after the 125th to 150th year, and maturity is attained in about 200 to 350 years. Jepson (1910) states, "Its extreme age is about 400 years," while Sudworth (1967) indicates that the five-century mark may be reached. The oldest recorded western white pine was a tree in British Columbia with an age of 615 years.

This pine is one of the first tree species to inhabit the peat bogs of the Puget Sound basin. Here the young trees develop with such rapidity that they frequently outstrip those standing on firmer, drier soils nearby.

Western white pine has a number of natural enemies. The bark, even of mature trees, is extremely thin [rarely more than 1½ in. (3 cm) thick], and in consequence the trees are easily damaged by even a light ground fire. White pine blister rust and bark beetles also take a heavy annual toll.

This is an important timber tree. Its wood is used for matches, toothpicks, and lumber.

Pìnus lambertiàna Dougl.   Sugar pine

Distinguishing Characteristics (Fig. 8-6)

Needles 2¾ to 4 in. (7 to 10 cm) long; spirally twisted, 5 per fascicle, blue-green to gray-green, often silvery, persistent until the second and third seasons.

Cones 11 to 18 in. (28 to 46 cm) long, 4 to 5 in. (10 to 13 cm) in diameter when open, cylindrical, stalked; *apophysis* somewhat thickened, yellowish brown, inner surface of scale brown or reddish brown; *umbo* terminal, unarmed; *seeds* ½ to ⅝ in. (1.2 to 1.5 cm) long, dark brown to nearly black, lustrous, with a dark brown or black terminal wing 1 to 1½ in. (2.5 to 4 cm) long.

Twigs rather stout, at first covered with glandular pubescence but later becoming orange-brown to purplish brown and glabrous; *buds* ca. ⅓ in. (8 mm) long, ovoid, sharp-pointed, clothed with several closely appressed, chestnut-brown, imbricated scales.

Bark dark green, thin, and smooth on young stems, grayish brown to purplish brown on old trunks, 1½ to 4 in. (3.5 to 10 cm) or more in thickness, and broken into regular, superficially scaly ridges separated by deep fissures (Fig. 8-7).

Range

Western (Map 8-2). Elevation: 1100 to 5400 ft northward, 2000 to 7800 ft in the Sierras, 4000 to 10,500 southward. Found in moist, cool, mountain soils in mixed conifer forests.

General Description

Sugar pine, another of David Douglas' discoveries, derives its name from a sweet resinous substance found in the canals of both bark and wood and eaten by early Native Americans. It is the tallest and largest member of all the pines and 300-year-old trees on good sites commonly vary from 170 to 180 ft in height and from 30 to 42 in. or more dbh (max. 250 by 11 ft). The boles of forest trees are usually long, clear, and cylindrical and support short crowns composed of sev-

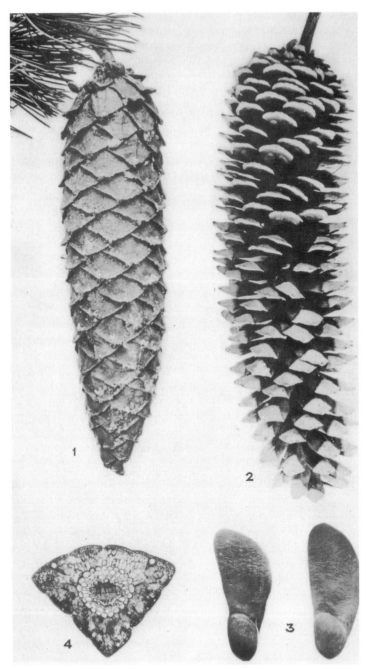

FIGURE 8-6 *Pinus lambertiana.* Sugar pine. (1) Mature seed cone × ½. (2) Open seed cone × ⅓. (3) Seeds × 1. (4) Cross section of needle × 35.

FIGURE 8-7   Bark of old-growth sugar pine.

MAP 8-2   *Pinus lambertiana.*

eral massive, horizontal, or occasionally contorted branches. It is an important source of lumber. The root system is similar to that of western white pine.

Sugar pine never forms pure stands, except in small scattered areas, and while it may occasionally comprise up to 75 percent of a mixed stand, throughout most of its range it seldom occupies more than 25 percent of a forested area. It attains its best development on the granitic and andesitic soils of the west slopes of the Sierra Nevada between the San Joaquin and Feather rivers between elevations of 4500 and 5500 ft. Forest associates within these limits include ponderosa and Jeffrey pines, Douglas-fir, California red, Shasta, and white firs, giant sequoia, and incense-cedar. In southern Oregon and northern California sugar pine is often found with digger and ponderosa pines, Douglas-fir, tanoak, California black oak, bigleaf maple, and Pacific dogwood, usually at elevations of less than 4000 ft. Toward the southern limit of its range, this species invades alpine forests and has been found at elevations of 10,000 ft. This pine is usually found on somewhat cooler and wetter sites than those occupied by most other pines, and to the east of the Sierran crest, where drought and extreme fluctuations in temperature frequently occur, it is very limited.

Sugar pine is not a prolific seeder. Small amounts of seed are usually produced annually, but large crops are normally released only at irregular intervals of from 2 to 7 years after the eightieth to hundredth year. A moist mineral soil covered by a thin layer of humus makes a good seedbed. Pine seeds are eaten by squirrels and other rodents, making natural reproduction in some sections very sparse. Although sunlight is beneficial to the seedlings, protection from extremes of temperature is needed for continued growth, and the most vigorous young trees are usually found under partial shade. The tolerance of this species is intermediate to intolerant.

Sugar pine is the most rapidly growing tree in the Sierras (with the exception of the giant sequoia), and on good sites trees 100 years old may be 140 ft tall and nearly 30 in dbh. It is long-lived and occasionally attains an age of 500 to over 600 years.

Sugar pine is unusually windfirm and is reasonably free from fungous diseases and insect pests, although the white pine blister rust and the mountain pine beetle sometimes cause serious losses. Dwarf mistletoe and fire cause considerable damage to young trees, and fire scars are a major source of culls in mature timber.

Pìnus fléxilis James   Limber pine, Rocky Mountain white pine

Distinguishing Characteristics (Fig. 8-8).   *Needles* 5 per fascicle, 2 to 3½ in. (5 to 9 cm) long, clustered near the branch ends, dark green, stout, rigid, not toothed. *Cones* 3 to 6 in. (7.5 to 15 cm) long, ovoid, the scales thickened, and slightly reflexed at the apex; *seeds* large, with rudimentary wings or wingless. *Bark* on young stems smooth, silvery white to light gray or

FIGURE 8-8 Stone pines. (1) *Pinus flexilis,* open seed cone × ¾. (2) Seeds × 1. (3) *Pinus albicaulis,* fascicle of needles × ¾. (4) Mature seed cone × ¾. (5) Seeds × 1.

greenish gray; that on old trunks dark brown to nearly black, separated by deep fissures into rectangular to nearly square, superficially scaly plates or blocks.

Range. East slopes of the Rocky Mountains in southeastern British Columbia and southwestern Alberta, south along the mountains to northern Arizona and New Mexico; west to the mountains of central and southern California, and east through Nevada, Idaho, and Montana; local in northeastern Oregon, southwestern North Dakota, Black Hills of South Dakota, and western Nebraska. Elevation: 3300 to 12,000 ft. Found on dry rocky slopes and ridges to timberline, often in pure stands.

General Description. Limber pine was first observed near Pike's Peak by Dr. Edwin James, an army surgeon attached to Long's mountain expedition of 1820. Like other relatively inaccessible trees of high altitudes, limber pine is primarily of importance in the protection of valuable watersheds. Ordinarily the tree attains but small proportions, varying from 30 to 50 ft in height and from 15 to 36 in. dbh (max. 85 by 9 ft). The bole is stout, noticeably tapered, and supports a number of large, plumelike, often drooping branches. The result is an extensive crown which may reach to within a few feet of the ground. Young trees develop a long, sparsely branched taproot which is later supplemented by several laterals. It is intolerant, slow growing, and long-lived. There is damage from white pine blister rust, bark beetles, budworms, and several species of dwarf mistletoe.

It is not of prime importance, although used for construction lumber, railroad ties, and poles.

Pìnus strobifòrmis Engelm.   Southwestern white pine

Distinguishing Characteristics. *Needles* 5 per fascicle, 2½ to 3½ in. (6 to 9 cm) long, slender, serrulate at least near tip, bright green. *Cones* 6 to 9 in. (15 to 23 cm) long, cylindrical, yellow brown, short-stalked, the scales slightly thickened, long, the thin apex curving back; *seeds* large, very short-winged, edible. *Bark* gray and smooth, becoming dark gray or brown and deeply furrowed into narrow, irregular ridges.

Range.   West Texas to central New Mexico, east central Arizona, and into northern Mexico. Elevation: 6270 to 9900 ft. Found in canyons and on dry, rocky slopes in high mountains.

General Description.   Straight, conical tree 50 to 80 ft tall and to 3 ft dbh. This is not abundant enough to be of commercial value although it is used locally for fuel and posts. The large seeds were eaten by Native Americans of the southwest.

It is considered by some as *P. flexilis* var. *reflexa* Engelm. See Steinhoff and Andresen (1971) for additional discussion of the variation.

Pìnus albicaùlis Engelm.   Whitebark pine

Distinguishing Characteristics (Fig. 8-8).   *Needles* 5 per fascicle, 1 to 2¾ in. (2.5 to 7 cm) long, similar to those of limber pine, clustered toward the ends of the branchlets. *Cones* 1½ to 3¼ in. (4 to 8 cm) long, ovoid, purplish brown, with thickened apophyses and terminally armed umbos; serotinous. *Bark* on immature trees brownish white to creamy white, smooth or superficially scaly at the base, rarely more than ½ in. (12 mm) thick.

Range.   Western British Columbia in the vicinity of Lake Whitesail south along the Olympic and Cascade Mountains of Washington, the Siskiyou, and Blue Mountains of Oregon, to the Sierra Nevada of California; south through Alberta and eastern British Columbia to northern Montana, northwestern Wyoming, and the Bitterroot Mountains of Idaho. Elevation: 4300 to 7500 ft northward, 8000 to 12,200 ft southward. It occurs in dry, rocky soils on slopes and ridges in the subalpine zone to timberline with other conifers or sometimes in pure stands.

General Description.   This is a small alpine tree which rarely attains a height of more than 30 to 50 ft or 12 to 24 in. dbh (max. 86 by 6 ft). In sheltered places whitebark pine produces an erect, rapidly tapering bole which supports a crown of long, willowy-appearing limbs; these are extremely tough and are rarely damaged by heavy snow or even by the cyclonic winds characteristic of alpine sites. Trees on exposed areas are usually sprawling, or even prostrate and fail to develop anything remotely resembling a central stem. They are generally intolerant, slow growing, and long-lived. Damage occurs from the mountain pine beetle, white pine blister rust, and dwarf mistletoe.

The seeds were eaten by Native Americans and are a main diet of bears. It is of limited commercial importance, but valuable for watershed protection and aesthetics.

Pinyons or Nut Pines

Dominating more than 65,000 square miles in the intermountain region and over 90,000 square miles of the arid southwestern United States. Between the deserts below and the forests above is a major vegetation type composed of small coniferous trees and shrubs (Fig. 8-9) growing in scattered or rather dense mixtures—the "pinyon-juniper woodlands." These woodlands are best developed between 4500 and 6500 ft elevation, although individual species of pinyon pines may be found between 200 and 10,000 ft. This community is expanding into adjacent shrub communities, grasslands, and aspen groves. Past and recent expansions are discussed by Miller and Wigand (1994).

Throughout human history, the pinyon component has made life possible, for both humans and wildlife, in an otherwise harsh environment. The large wingless seeds of these pines were the principal food for the Native Americans who gathered them each autumn in great numbers for winter storage. They are still used for winter food, and these nutritious "pine nuts," "Indian

FIGURE 8-9   Pinyon-juniper woodland. (*Courtesy of U.S. Forest Service.*)

nuts," "pinyon nuts," or "pinyones" find their way to local and gourmet markets and are exported to foreign countries. In addition, the settlers depended on the pinyon and juniper for fuel, fence posts, and building materials. The making of charcoal for Nevada ore smelters was a leading industry of the 1800s.

There are four or five recognized species of pinyons in the southwestern United States and seven more in Mexico, making up a variable group with hybrids. See Lanner (1975) and Malusa (1992) for more detail. The principal species are as follows:

P. cembroìdes Zucc. Mexican pinyon (needles in 3s, rarely 2s)
P. édulis Engelm. Pinyon or Colorado pinyon (needles in 2s, rarely 1 or 3)
P. monophýlla Torr. & Frem. Singleleaf pinyon (Fig. 8-10) (needles 1 per sheath) (incl. *P. californiàrum* D. K. Bailey)
P. quadrifòlia Parl. ex Sudw. Parry pinyon (needles in 4s, rarely 1 to 5)

Foxtail Pines

The foxtail pines, so-called because of the bushy nature of the foliage on young branches, comprise a small group of alpine trees, three of which are found in the western United States. They retain their foliage for many years, the cone scales are dorsally armed, and the seeds have long terminal wings. The trees are very small, rarely attaining a height of more than 30 to 40 ft or 12 to 24 in. dbh (max. 71 by 8 ft). They develop a short, stocky, often malformed trunk which is commonly clothed for the greater part of its length in a dense, narrow, irregular crown. Owing to their inaccessibility, they contribute little or nothing to the nation's timber supply; nevertheless, they provide valuable cover on many of our high western watersheds.

FIGURE 8-10   *Pinus monophylla.* Singleleaf pinyon. Foliage, open seed cone, and wingless seed × ½.

Pìnus balfouriàna Grev. & Balf.   Foxtail pine

Distinguishing Characteristics.   *Needles* in fascicles of 5, bright blue-green, lacking a strong median groove on the abaxial side, ¾ to 1½ in. (2 to 4 cm) long, persisting for 10 to 20 years. *Cones* 3½ to 5 in. (9 to 13 cm) long, ovoid to cylindrical, tapering to a conic base, dark reddish brown, the umbo armed with a minute (0-1 mm), incurved, weak, deciduous prickle (Fig. 8-11).

Range.   Foxtail pine is found locally in northern and central California (Sierra Nevada) between 5000 and 11,550 ft of elevation. It occurs on exposed, dry, rocky slopes, ridges, and high peaks in the subalpine zone to timberline.

General Description.   This tree reaches a height of 20 to 50 ft and 1 to 2 ft dbh with an irregular crown of short, spreading branches. It is shrubby at timberline.

Pìnus longaèva D. K. Bailey [*P. aristata* var. *longaeva* (D. K. Bailey) Little]
Intermountain bristlecone pine

Distinguishing Characteristics.   *Needles* 5 per fascicle, lacking the strong, median groove and with few resin deposits. *Cones* a rich, rusty red, with a rounded base, and the umbo with a slender prickle 1 to 6 mm long.

Range.   These occur in Utah, Nevada, and eastern California at 5600 to 11,200 ft of elevation on rocky ridges and slopes.

General Description.   These are the oldest known trees, with individuals reaching 3000 to ca. 5000 years (Currey, 1965; Schulman, 1958). It is shrubby at timberline or may attain a height of 20 to 40 ft and diameter of 1 to 2 ft with an irregular crown.

FIGURE 8-11   Foxtail pines. (1) *Pinus balfouriana,* open seed cone × ¾. (2) Fascicle of needles × ¾. (3) *Pinus aristata,* open seed cone × ¾. (4) Seed × 1.

Pìnus aristàta Engelm.   Rocky mountain or Colorado bristlecone pine

Distinguishing Characteristics.   *Needles* in fascicles of 5, bright blue-green with small drops and scales of white resin, and with a strong, abaxial, median groove, ¾ to 1½ in. (2 to 4 cm) long, persisting for 14 to 17 years. *Cones* 2½ to 3½ in. (6 to 9 cm) long, subcylindrical, rounded at the base, brown to gray-brown, the umbo armed with a long (6 to 10 mm), slender, stiff, incurved prickle (Fig. 8-11).

Range.   This occurs on the high ridges and slopes in Colorado, northern New Mexico, and northern Arizona. Elevation: 7500 to 11,200 ft. It occurs on exposed, dry, rocky ridges in the subalpine zone to timberline, with mixed conifers or in pure stands. It is intolerant, slow growing, and long-lived.

General Description.   These are among the oldest living trees known, with individual trees reaching 1500 to 2000 years; however, *P. longaeva is* older. *Pinus aristata* is a small tree 20 to 40 ft tall and 1 to 2½ ft dbh.

The Hard Pines

The arrangement of the hard pines is geographical (western and eastern) for convenience.

Western Hard Pines

There are at least a dozen hard or "yellow" pines scattered through the timbered areas of western United States, but only three of them, ponderosa, Jeffrey, and lodgepole pine, are of primary importance (Table 8-6).

TABLE 8-6   COMPARISON OF IMPORTANT WESTERN HARD PINES

Species	Needles	Seed cones
P. ponderosa ponderosa pine	2 and 3(5), per fascicle, 4–8(11) in. [10–20(28) cm] long, stout, dark green	ovoid, 2–6 in. (5–15 cm) long, short-stalked; umbo with short prickle pointed outward
P. jeffreyi Jeffrey pine	3 per fascicle, 5–10 in. (13–25 cm) long, twisted, stout, gray-green	ovoid, 5–10(14) in. [13–25(35)] cm long, short-stalked, umbo with long prickle curved inward
P. contorta lodgepole pine	2 per fascicle, 1¼–3 in. (3–7.5 cm) long, stout, twisted, yellow-green to dark green	ovoid, ¾–2 in. (2–5 cm) long, sessile; umbo with small, slender prickle; usually serotinous and persistent

Pìnus ponderòsa Dougl. ex Laws.   Ponderosa pine

Distinguishing Characteristics (Fig. 8-12)

Needles 3, 5, or 2 and 3 per fascicle on the same tree, 4 to 8(11) in. [10 to 20(28) cm] long, dark gray-green to yellow-green, flexible, persistent until the third season; crushed needles have a turpentine odor similar to that of most other pines.

Cones 2 to 6 in. (5 to 15 cm) long, ovoid to ellipsoidal, sessile, solitary or clustered; usually leaving a few basal scales attached to the twig when shed; *apophysis* dark reddish brown to dull brownish yellow, transversely ridged and more or less diamond-shaped; *umbo* dorsal, with a slender, often deciduous prickle; *seeds* ca. ¼ in. (6 to 8 mm) long, ovoid, slightly compressed toward the apex, brownish purple; wings moderately wide, ca. 1 in. (2.5 cm) long.

Twigs stout, with a turpentine odor when bruised; *buds* usually covered with droplets of resin.

Bark brown to black and deeply furrowed on vigorous or young trees (bull pines); yellowish brown to a cinnamon-red and broken up into large flat, superficially scaly plates separated by deep irregular fissures on slow-growing and old trunks; with an odor of vanilla.

Range

Western (Map 8-3). It is one of the most widely distributed pines in North America. Elevation: sea level to 9900 ft; best developed at 4000 to 8000 ft. Found in the mountains in open, pure stands or mixed conifer forests.

General Description

This is the most important pine in western North America (Fig. 8-13). In the United States it is found in commercial quantities in every state west of the Great Plains. It furnishes more timber than any other single species of American pine, and in terms of total annual production of lumber by species, it is second only to Douglas-fir.

Ponderosa pine is a large tree 150 to 180 ft high and 3 to 4 ft dbh (max. 262 by 9 ft). Even though this species commonly forms open parklike forests, the boles are ordinarily symmetrical

FIGURE 8-12   *Pinus ponderosa.* Ponderosa pine. (1) Mature seed cone × ¾. (2) Open seed cone × ¾. (3) Seed × 1. (4) Pollen cones × 1. (5) Young ovulate cones × 1. (6) Cross section of needle × 35. (7) Bark. (*Courtesy of U.S. Forest Service.*)

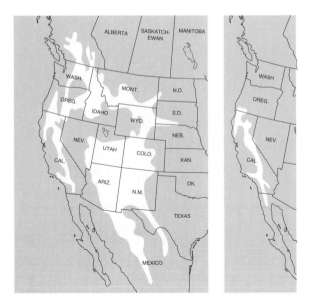

MAP 8-3   (**Left**) *Pinus ponderosa.* (**Right**) *Pinus jeffreyi.*

and clear for one-half or more of their length; short conical or flat-topped crowns are characteristic of old trees. Four-year-old trees may have taproots 4 to 5 ft long. Moderately deep widespreading laterals develop as the trees get older. Ponderosa pine is not exacting in its soil requirements, but trees on thin, dry soils are usually dwarfed. Its occurrence on dry sites with the nut pines and certain of the junipers is indicative of its great resistance to drought. This species attains its maximum development, however, on the relatively moist but well-drained western slopes of the Siskiyou and Sierra Nevada Mountains of southern Oregon and California. Excellent pure forests are found in the Black Hills of South Dakota, the Blue Mountains of Oregon, the Columbian Plateau northeast of the Sierra Nevada, and in northern Arizona and New Mexico. It is also commonly the most abundant tree in mixed coniferous stands; east of the summit of the Cascade Range in Washington and Oregon it occurs with western larch, Douglas-fir, and occasionally lodgepole pine; in the central Rocky Mountains with Douglas-fir; and in California with Jeffrey and sugar pines, incense-cedar, Douglas-fir, and white fir. On the Fort Lewis plains in western Washington, near Puget Sound, ponderosa pine is occasionally found in association with Douglas-fir and Oregon white oak.

Small quantities of seed are produced annually, but there is no dependable periodicity for bumper crops. Over much of its range, effective regeneration depends on a bumper crop of seeds in conjunction with above-average summer rainfall. Seedlings can exist under the canopy of the parent trees, even though they grow quite slowly, and in such situations often attain a height of only 3 to 4 ft during the first 15 to 20 years. Reproduction is best in clearings made by fire or logging. Overstocked stands and subsequent stagnation on poor sites is a problem. The seedlings will grow on sterile sites and have been planted extensively in the Nebraska sand hills and elsewhere. Ponderosa pine is classed as intolerant.

The rapidity of growth has a marked effect on the general appearance of these trees. Young, vigorous specimens commonly develop dense crowns of dark green foliage, and bark which is dark brown to nearly black, more or less corky, and deeply furrowed. In contrast, the foliage of

FIGURE 8-13   Ponderosa pine. (*Courtesy of U.S. Forest Service.*)

old-growth or slow-growing trees is yellow-green, and the bark yellow-brown to cinnamon-red and plated. Those of the first type are commonly called *bull* or *blackjack* pines, and to some woodsmen ponderosa pine and bull pine are different trees. Fast-growth bull pines 150 years of age found near Cle Elum, Washington, measured 30 to 40 in. dbh, while more typical ponderosa pines occurring in the same vicinity were only 10 to 14 in. dbh at the same age. Thus growth of this species varies considerably with locality. In California trees 120 years of age averaged 23 in. dbh, while in Arizona trees of the same age were only 16 in. and in the Black Hills 10½ in. Trees over 500 years of age are seldom encountered. Ponderosa pine is attacked by over 100 different species of insects. Of these, some 16 species of bark beetles may cause widespread damage. Fires kill seedlings and cause considerable damage even to large trees. Severe fires in the past have completely destroyed hundreds of thousands of acres of ponderosa pine forest. Repeated light surface fires cause little if any damage. Other destructive agents include dwarf mistletoe, numerous fungi, and air pollution, particularly ozone.

Previously called western yellow pine, logs of ponderosa pine were also sold under such names as Arizona white pine, California white pine, and western soft pine, because the wood resembles that of the white pines rather than that of the hard, moderately heavy wood of the southern yellow pines. The name ponderosa pine was adopted by the U.S. Forest Service and is now accepted by the industry.

Within the broad geographical range of this species, three races (varieties) have been recognized. The typical var. *ponderosa* is found from sea level to 7600 ft elevation in the mountains of the Pacific Coast region from southern British Columbia to southern California and western Nevada; it has relatively long needles mostly in 3s and large cones. Var. *arizonica* (Engelm.) Shaw (Arizona pine) of 6900 to 8200 ft of elevation in southeastern Arizona has needles mostly in 5s, or 2s and 5s on the same tree. Var. *scopulorum* Engelm. (Rocky mountain ponderosa pine) of 3300 to 9900 ft of elevation in the Rocky Mountains of southwestern North Dakota, Montana, Idaho, south to Arizona, New Mexico, and western Texas, has shorter needles in 2s and smaller cones.

Pìnus jéffreyi Grev. and Balf.   Jeffrey pine

Distinguishing Characteristics (Fig. 8-14)

   Needles 5 to 10 in. (13 to 25 cm) long, in fascicles of 3, or 2 and 3 on the same tree, blue-green, somewhat twisted, persistent until the sixth to ninth seasons. Crushed needles have a violetlike or pineapple odor.

   Cones 5 to 10(14) in. [13 to 25(35) cm] long, ovoid; *apophysis* chestnut-brown, rhomboidal to broadly elliptical, often transversely ridged and occasionally wrinkled; *umbo* dorsal, often chalky white, terminating in a long, stout, incurved, occasionally deciduous prickle; *seeds* ca. ⅓ in. (8 mm) long, yellowish brown, mottled with purple; wings ¾ to 1¾ in. (2 to 4.5 cm) long, broadest below the middle.

   Twigs tinged with purple, often glaucous, with a pineapple or violet aroma when crushed; *buds* only slightly resinous, never covered with resin droplets (a common feature of ponderosa pine).

   Bark similar to that of ponderosa pine, but darker cinnamon-red and commonly tinged with lavender or purple on old trunks (Fig. 8-15).

Range

Western (Map 8-3). Elevation: generally 6000 to 9000 ft, rarely down to 3500 and up to 10,000 ft. It occurs on dry slopes in deep, well-drained soils and either in mixed conifer forests or often in pure stands.

FIGURE 8-14 *Pinus jeffreyi.* Jeffrey pine. (1) Fascicle of needles × ¾. (2) Open seed cone × ¾. (3) Seed × 1. (4) Cross section of needle × 35.

General Description

Throughout its range, Jeffrey pine occurs with ponderosa pine and many of its associates. It can endure greater extremes of climate (Fig. 8-16) than ponderosa pine, and east of the Sierras where conditions are more rigorous, this species occurs in some abundance. The habits of Jeffrey pine are quite similar to those of ponderosa, with which it hybridizes. Seedlings, relative to ponderosa, are somewhat frost-hardy and more suitable for reforesting on sites where low temperatures often prevail.

FIGURE 8-15   Bark of old-growth Jeffrey pine. (*Photo by Emanuel Fritz.*)

Although a stately tree, Jeffrey pine never reaches the proportions of ponderosa. Under favorable growing conditions mature trees will attain a height of 90 to 100 ft and 36 to 60 in. dbh (max. 197 by 8 ft). It is customary to log these two species together, and because of the great similarity of their timbers, no attempt is made to separate them in the trade.

Damage occurs from a needle blight, various rusts, and dwarf mistletoe.

Pìnus engelmánnii Carr.   Apache pine

Distinguishing Characteristics.   *Needles* stout, dull green, borne in fascicles of 2 to 5 (mostly 3), 8 to 12 in. (20 to 30 cm) long. *Cones* 4 to 5½ in. (10 to 14 cm) long, ovoid or coni-cal, light brown; *umbo* with a short, straight or curved spine.

Range.   Apache pine is principally a Mexican species but is found locally in southeastern Arizona and extreme southwestern New Mexico. Elevation: 5000 to 8200 ft. It occurs on rocky ridges and slopes.

General Description.   This is a medium-size tree, 50 to 70 ft tall and to 2 ft dbh, often called the "longleaf pine" of the Southwest. From a distance, the mature trees appear quite simi-lar to those of ponderosa pine, a species with which it is often associated; young trees, however, are very distinctive. The seedling sends down a prodigious taproot which descends to a depth of 6 ft or more during the first few years. In the meantime, the aerial portion grows very slowly and is seldom branched.

FIGURE 8-16 Wind form of Jeffrey pine, growing on Sentinel Dome, Yosemite National Park, California.

Pìnus sabinìàna Dougl.   Digger pine

Distinguishing Characteristics. *Needles* in 3s, gray-green, flexible. *Cones* 6 to 10 in. (15 to 25 cm) long, heavy, subglobose, their reddish-brown scales with irregularly rhomboidal apophyses, each terminating in a stout dorsal claw (Fig. 8-17); *seeds* oblong with very short abortive terminal wings and thick hard coat. *Bark* dark brown with flattened anastomosing ridges.

Range. The coast ranges and west slopes of the Sierra Nevada in California from the Siskiyou Mountains south to the Tehachapi and Sierra de la Liebre Mountains. Elevation: 1000 to 3000 ft, rarely down to 100 and up to 6000 ft. It occurs in high valleys, foothills, and lower mountain slopes and on dry slopes and ridges in the foothills and low mountains.

General Description. Digger pine is restricted to the low fringe forests of California. As a rule, it is a small to medium-size tree 40 to 50 ft high and 12 to 24 in. dbh (max. 160 by 5 ft). The bole is usually short, the crown open and irregular, and the root system moderately deep and spreading. Scattered through the dry foothills and lower mountain slopes it occurs either in pure, open parklike stands or in mixture with one or more of the native oaks. At higher elevations it is occasionally associated with ponderosa pine. It is very intolerant and very susceptible to fire. It is damaged by gall rust and dwarf mistletoe.

The common name refers to the "Digger Indians" who dug roots for food.

Pìnus coùlteri D. Don   Coulter pine

Distinguishing Characteristics. *Needles* 3 per fascicle, 8 to 12 in. (20 to 30 cm) long, blue-green, rigid. *Cones* 8 to 12 in. (20 to 30 cm) long, the heaviest of the conifer cones, when green often weighing 4 to 6 pounds, subcylindrical to oblong-ovoid, short-stalked; *cone scales* with light brownish-yellow, irregularly rhomboidal apophyses, each terminating in a long, sharp, flat claw, those near the base of the cone the longest and exhibiting the greatest curvature (Fig. 8-17); *seeds* ellipsoidal, with extremely thick hard coats, the wings longer than the seeds. *Bark* dark brown to nearly black, with broad rounded ridges separated by deep anastomosing fissures.

FIGURE 8-17   (Left) *Pinus coulteri.* Coulter pine. (1) Open seed cone × ⅕. (2) Seed × ⅔. (Right) *Pinus sabiniana.* Digger pine. (1) Open seed cone × ¼. (2) Seed × ⅔.

Range.   Central coastal California to northern Baja California. Elevation: 3000 to 6000 ft, rarely 1000 to 7000 ft. It occurs on dry, rocky mountain slopes, and ridges in foothills with other conifers.

General Description.   Coulter pine is a medium-size tree, 40 to 50 ft high and 15 to 30 in. dbh (max. 144 by 5 ft), largely restricted to the mountains of southern coastal California and northern Lower California. At low elevations (3000 ft) Coulter pine invades chaparral. Here the trees develop a typical open-grown form, the large crowns often extending to within a few feet of the ground. At higher elevations (3500 to 7000 ft) it occurs on dry, gravelly, or loamy soils in mixture with live oaks, incense cedar, ponderosa and sugar pine, and bigcone Douglas-fir. It is intolerant and slow growing.

It is used for lumber and fuel.

Pìnus torreyàna Parry ex Carr.   Torrey pine

Distinguishing Characteristics.   *Needles* stout, dark gray-green and, unlike other western yellow pines, are borne in fascicles of 5. *Cones* 4 to 6 in. (10 to 15 cm) long, with thick scales with a straight spine; *seeds* large, ovoid, thick-shelled, and short-winged.

Range.   Torrey pine has the distinction of having the most restricted range of any American pine. It occurs only in a narrow strip of coastal land in San Diego County, southern California (subsp. *torreyana*), and also adjacent Santa Rosa Island (subsp. *insulàris* J. R.Haller). Elevation: sea level to 500 ft. It grows on dry, sandy bluffs and slopes in pure stands.

General Description.   Torrey pine is a small to medium-size tree, 30 to 50 ft tall and 1 to 2 ft dbh, with an open, spreading crown; on exposed sites it becomes shrubby. It does well in cultivation and has been propagated with some degree of success in New Zealand for sawtimber. It is intolerant and short-lived.

Pìnus radiàta D. Don   Monterey pine

Distinguishing Characteristics.   *Needles* rich, dark green, slender, flexible, 4 to 6 in. (10 to 15 cm) long, in fascicles of 3. *Cones* large, asymmetrical, and serotinous (Fig. 8-18).

Range.   Monterey pine is restricted to three, small, separated coastal areas of central California in the fog belt to ca. 6 mi. inland. Elevation: 100 to 1350 ft. It grows in dry, coarse soils and sandy loams of slopes in mixed or pure stands.

General Description.   This is a medium-size tree, 50 to 100 ft tall and 1 to 3 ft dbh. It is of little or no commercial value within its range, but it is a common decorative tree in many cities along the Pacific slope and appears to be quite hardy as far north as the Puget Sound Basin. It has been widely planted in New Zealand, Australia, South Africa, Spain, and South America including Chile, where it grows very rapidly and produces saw timber in a relatively short time. Thirty-year-old plantation trees in New Zealand may be from 100 to 140 ft high and 30 in. or more dbh. For a discussion of this pine, see Scott (1960). It is estimated that worldwide, more than 1½ million acres have been forested with Monterey pine.

It is damaged mainly by gall rusts and dwarf mistletoe.

Pìnus attenuàta Lemm.   Knobcone pine

Distinguishing Characteristics.   *Needles* 3 per fascicle, 3 to 7 in. (7½ to 18 cm) long, slender, stiff, and yellow-green. *Cones* 3 to 6 in (8 to 15 cm) long, clustered, narrowly top-shaped, knobby, and serotinous, the umbo with a short spine; *seeds* with a narrow wing.

FIGURE 8-18   *Pinus radiata.* Monterey pine. (1) Mature seed cone × ¾. (2) Seed × 1.

Range.   Largely confined to the mountainous regions of southwestern Oregon and south along the coast ranges and Sierra Nevada to central (sporadically southern) California. Elevation: 1000 to 2000 ft northward, 1500 to 4000 ft southward. It frequents poor soils of dry slopes, rocky spurs, and sun-baked ridges where it may be in pure stands (especially in the north) or mixed with sugar, ponderosa, and Coulter pines and several chaparral oaks.

General Description.   This is a small to medium-size tree, 30 to 80 ft tall and to 2½ ft dbh. It is intolerant, fast growing, and short-lived. Its seeding habits are similar to those of lodgepole pine. Following a fire, scores of viable seeds are released, and the scorched earth is soon again covered with a green mantle of seedlings.

The serotinous cones may remain closed and on the tree for many years and sometimes become embedded in the expanding trunk.

Pìnus muricàta D. Don   Bishop pine

Distinguishing Characteristics.   *Needles* 2 per fascicle, thick, rigid, dark yellow-green, and 4 to 6 in (10 to 15 cm) long. *Cones* small, 2 to 4 in. (5 to 10 cm) long, oblique, commonly borne in clusters of 3 to 5, and with stout, flattened, spurlike prickles, serotinous and persistent for several years.

Range.   In seven widely separated coastal areas from northern California to northern Baja California. Elevation: sea level to 1000 ft. It grows on low hills and plains in the coastal fog belt. A preference is shown for swampy sites and peat bogs, although it also grows on much drier soils.

General Description.   This is a medium-size tree 40 to 80 ft tall and 2 to 3 ft dbh with a rounded or irregular crown. It is moderately tolerant, short-lived, and fast growing. It often forms pure stands but never occurs in sufficient quantity to be of more than local importance.

Pìnus leiophýlla var. *chihuahuàna* (Engelm.) Shaw   Chihuahua pine

Distinguishing Characteristics.   *Needles* 3 per fascicle, 2 to 4 in. (5 to 10 cm) long, stout, stiff, blue-green with white lines on all surfaces, differing from all other American yellow pines in that the fascicle sheaths are deciduous. *Cones* small, 1½ to 2½ in. (4 to 6 cm) long, armed with minute, often deciduous prickles, and unlike all other American pines, require three seasons to mature.

Range.   This pine attains its best development in northern Mexico and is found in the United States only in scattered areas of southwestern New Mexico and east central and southeastern Arizona. Elevation: 5000 to 8200 ft. It occurs on dry, rocky ridges and slopes with other pines.

General Description.   Chihuahua pine is a small to medium-size tree, 30 to 80 ft tall and 1 to 2 ft dbh with an open, spreading crown of upturned branches. It produces vigorous stump sprouts after logging, another feature rare among pines. The typical variety (var. *leiophylla*), with 5 needles per fascicle, occurs in Mexico.

Pìnus contórta Dougl. ex Loud.   Lodgepole pine

Distinguishing Characteristics (Fig. 8-19)

Needles 1¼ to 3 in. (3 to 7.5 cm) long, 2 per fascicle or rarely solitary, dark green to yellow-green, often twisted, persistent until the fourth to sixth seasons.

Cones ¾ to 2 in. (2 to 5 cm) long, subcylindric to ovoid, often asymmetrical at the base, either opening at maturity (especially vars. *contorta* and *murrayana*) or remain-

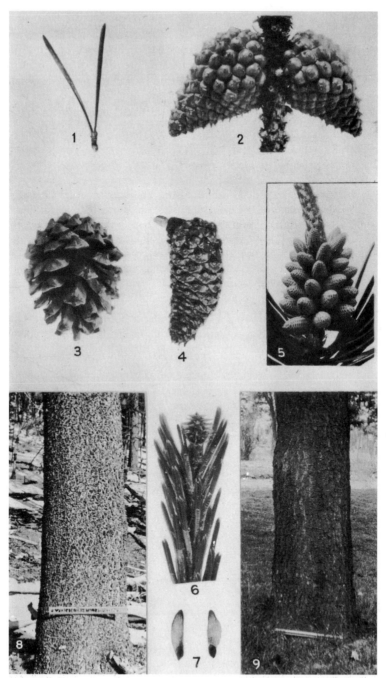

FIGURE 8-19 *Pinus contorta.* Lodgepole pine. (1) Fascicle of needles × ¾. (2) Var. *latifolia,* mature seed cones × ¾. (3) Var. *contorta,* open seed cone × ¾. (4) Mature seed cone × ¾. (5) Cluster of pollen cones × 1. (6) Young ovulate cone and young fascicles × 1. (7) Seeds × 1. (8) Bark (*Photo by H. E. Troxell*). (9) Bark of shore pine.

ing closed for many years; *apophysis* tawny to dark brown, flattened, or those toward the base knoblike; *umbo* dorsal, terminating in a long, recurved, often deciduous prickle; *seeds* ca. ⅛ in. (2 to 3 mm) long, ovoid, reddish brown, often mottled with black; wings ca. ½ in. (1 to 1.5 cm) long.

Twigs moderately stout, dark red-brown to nearly black; *buds* ovoid, slightly resinous.

Bark of coastal trees ¾ to 1 in. (2 to 2.5 cm) thick, deeply furrowed and transversely fissured, reddish brown to black, and superficially scaly; that on mountain trees ca. ¼ in. (6 mm) thick, orange-brown to gray, covered by thin, loosely appressed scales.

Range

Western (Map 8-4). Local disjuncts in the Black Hills of South Dakota and northeastern New Mexico. Elevation: sea level to 2000 ft along the coast, 1300 to 3000 ft inland northward, 7000 to 11,500 ft southward. It occurs in the high mountains in well-drained soils either with other conifers or often in pure stands; Shore pine varieties occur in peat bogs, muskegs, and dry, sandy sites.

General Description

Lodgepole pine is a cosmopolitan tree of wide distribution through western North America. It has the broadest ecological amplitude of any conifer in North America. At least four varieties of the species may be recognized (Critchfield, 1957).

Shore pine. Two of the four varieties, *P. contorta* var. *contorta* and *P. contorta* var. *bolanderi* (Parl.) Vasey (shrubby), are collectively known as shore pine. The latter differs mainly from the

MAP 8-4   *Pinus contorta.*

former in its heavy, knobby, serotinous cones, its complete lack of needle resin canals, and its isolation. It occurs only on a few square miles of highly acid soils in Mendocino County, California. In other respects it is similar to the typical variety, *P. contorta* var. *contorta.* Shore pine is a small tree ordinarily 25 to 30 ft high and 12 to 18 in. dbh. It is characterized by a short, often contorted bole and a dense, irregular crown of twisted branches, many of which extend nearly to the ground; the root system is deep and wide-spreading and includes a persistent taproot, even when growing in bogs or muskegs. The tree is one of the first to invade the peat bogs of Alaska and British Columbia, as well as those of the Puget Sound Basin in western Washington where it may form pure stands. Farther south it is found most abundantly on dry sandy and gravelly sites near the Pacific Ocean to northern California. Here it sometimes mingles with Sitka spruce and occasionally with grand fir. Because of their small size and poorly formed boles, the trees of the coastal form contribute little or nothing to the nation's timber supply. Large stands occasionally retard the migration of sand dunes, but smaller ones have been completely buried by shifting sands.

Lodgepole pine. The two inland varieties are collectively known as "lodgepole pine."* One, Sierra lodgepole pine, *P. contorta* var. *murrayana* (Grev. & Balf.) Engelm. occurs in the Cascade, Blue, and Sierra Nevada mountains. It is characterized by lightweight, symmetrical, nonserotinous cones which are shed soon after opening. Rocky mountain lodgepole pine, *P. contorta* var. *latifolia* Engelm., on the other hand, is found in the Rocky Mountains, and has hard, heavy, asymmetrical, serotinous cones. Aside from other differences in needle width, seedling color, and stomate shape, the two varieties are, in most gross characteristics, quite similar.

Lodgepole pine is a medium-size tree 70 to 80 ft high and 15 to 30 in. dbh (max. 150 by 7 ft), with a long, clear, slender, cylindrical bole and short, narrow, open crown. Best development is attained on a moist but well-drained sandy or gravelly loam, although trees reach commercial proportions on a variety of soil types. Unlike shore pine, which is seldom found far from tidewater, lodgepole pine occurs from 1300 to 11,500 ft of elevation in either pure dense even-aged stands or in mixture with several other conifers. At the lower limits of its elevational range its associates are ponderosa and other western pines, Douglas-fir, and western larch. At higher levels it is found chiefly with Engelmann spruce, subalpine fir, and limber pine in the Rockies, and with limber pine, Jeffrey pine, and California red fir in the Sierra.

This form is one of the most aggressive and hardy of western forest trees and under favorable conditions is capable of fully restocking cutover lands in a remarkably short time. Following fire it quickly forms dense stands and occasionally usurps areas formerly occupied by Douglas-fir, or at higher levels by Engelmann spruce.

The gregarious habit of this species is traceable to a number of factors. The trees are prolific seeders and often produce fertile seed before they are 10 years of age. Heavy seed crops occur at intervals of 2 or 3 years, but instead of releasing all of the seeds at maturity, many of the cones, especially in the Rocky Mountains, remain closed and attached to the branches for as long as 15 to 20 years or more. When the cones remain closed, large quantities of seed are gradually accumulated. The heat of a forest fire sweeping through the stands starts the opening of the cones. After the fire has passed, the scales open fully and release their seeds on the freshly exposed mineral soil. The subsequent reproduction is often so dense that it quickly stagnates. Under normal conditions, growth is rather slow but persistent, and maturity is attained in about 200 years with a maximum of 500 to 600 years. Trees 100 years of age in the Blue Mountains of southern

---

*So-called because of its use for poles by the Plains Indians. The lodge, or tipi, with its movable smoke flaps to control ventilation and its symbolic decorations, is perhaps the most functional and beautiful dwelling ever designed by nomadic people.

Oregon average 70 to 80 ft in height and 12 in. dbh, while trees of the same age in the Sierra are 90 to 100 ft high and 15 to 18 in. dbh. Lodgepole pine is rated as intolerant.

Bark beetles inflict heavy damage in stagnated stands, and Comandra blister rust is a serious fungal disease. Dwarf mistletoe causes some damage, and because of the thin bark of the tree, fire is always a serious menace even though heavy new stands result.

Pinus contorta and the next three species are closely related and constitute subsection Contortae. Their distribution forms a broad, inverted *U*-shape—*P. contorta* in the west, *P. banksiana* in the north, *P. virginiana* in the northeast and east, and *P. clausa* in the southeast. Although *P. contorta* and *P. banksiana* are the only pair that are sympatric (in Alberta, Canada) and hybridize naturally, successful *P. virginiana* × *clausa* crosses can be made artificially.

Eastern Hard Pines

There are 15 hard or "yellow" pines in eastern United States, nine of which are the most important (Table 8-7).

TABLE 8-7   COMPARISON OF IMPORTANT EASTERN HARD PINES

Species	Needles	Seed cones
P. banksiana jack pine	2 per fascicle, ¾–1½ in. (2–4 cm) long, stout, rigid, often twisted, divergent	oblong-conic, 1–2¼ in. (2.5–5.5 cm) long, short-stalked; umbo mostly unarmed; serotinous and persistent
P. virginiana Virginia pine	2 per fascicle, 1½–3 in. (4–7.5 cm) long, stout, twisted	ovoid, 1¼–2¾ in. (4–7 cm) long, short-stalked; umbo with long, slender prickle; persistent, not serotinous
P. clausa sand pine	2 per fascicle, 2–3½ in. (5–9 cm) long, slender, slightly twisted	narrow ovoid, 2–3½ in. (5–9 cm) long, short-stalked; umbo with short, stout prickle; serotinous or not
P. resinosa red pine	2 per fascicle, 4–6¼ in. (10–16 cm) long, slender, flexible, brittle	ovoid, 1½–2⅜ in. (4–6 cm) long, short-stalked; umbo unarmed
P. palustris longleaf pine	3 per fascicle, 8–18 in. (20–46 cm) long, stout, flexible; buds with silvery-white fimbriate scales	conical-cylindrical, 6–10 in. (15–25 cm) long, short-stalked; umbo with small prickle
P. taeda loblolly pine	3 per fascicle, 4–9 in. (10–23 cm) long, stout, rigid	conical-ovoid, 2½–6 in. (6–15 cm) long, short-stalked; umbo with stout prickle; some persisting
P. echinata shortleaf pine	2 and 3 per fascicle, 2¾–4¾ in. (7–12 cm) long, slender, flexible	narrowly oblong, 1½–2½ in. (4–6 cm) long, short-stalked; umbo with small prickle; persistent
P. rigida pitch pine	3(4) per fascicle, 3–6 in. (7.5–15 cm) long, twisted, rigid	ovoid, 1¼–2¾ in. (3–7 cm) long, nearly sessile; umbo with slender prickle; persistent
P. elliottii slash pine	2 and 3 per fascicle, 4–10 in. (10–25 cm) long, stout, rigid; buds with reddish brown, white-ciliate scales	ovoid, 2½–6 in. (6–15 cm) long, short-stalked; umbo with short, stout prickle; persistent for 1 year

Pìnus banksiàna Lamb.   Jack pine

Distinguishing Characteristics (Fig. 8-20)

Needles ¾ to 1½ in. (2 to 4 cm) long, in fascicles of 2 (also 3 near the tip of the leader on young trees), yellow-green, flat or slightly concave on the inner surface, divergent, stout, often twisted; persistent for 2 or 3 years.

Cones 1 to 2¼ in. (2.5 to 5.5 cm) long, oblong-conic, sessile, light brown, usually pointing forward, often strongly incurved, with the scales well developed only on the outer face; opening tardily and often persistent for many years; *apophysis* rounded, smooth; *umbo* dorsal, armed with a minute prickle; *seeds* ca. ⅛ in. (3 to 5 mm) long, triangular, black, and roughened, with wings ca. ⅜ in. (8 to 10 mm) long.

FIGURE 8-20   *Pinus banksiana.* Jack pine. (1) Male cones shedding pollen × 1. (2) Mature seed cones and foliage × ½. (3) Open seed cone and foliage × ¾. (4) Seed × 1. (5) Fascicle of needles × ¾. (6) Cross section of needle × 35.

Bark thin, brown, slightly tinged with red, or dark gray; irregularly divided into scaly ridges.

Range

Northern (Map 8-5). Southern disjuncts in Maine, New Hampshire, Vermont, northern New York, northern Indiana, and northern Illinois. Elevation: sea level to 2600 ft. It occurs on well-drained, sterile, acid, sandy soils of dunes and sand ridges; also rock outcrops, woodlands, and savannas, often in pure stands.

General Description

Jack pine is essentially a Canadian species which reaches its best development north and west of Lake Superior. It is the most widely distributed pine in Canada. It extends southward into the United States in northern New England and the lake states. In these lake states jack pine is one of the most important second-growth species. The growing season over this range is somewhat shorter than that of its associate, red pine, but the extremes in temperature are about the same. Under the most favorable conditions, this pine varies from 70 to 80 ft in height and 12 to 15 in. dbh, but it is usually much smaller (max. 100 by 2 ft). In the open, an irregular rounded crown is produced, the lower branches of which soon die but persist on the trunk for many years; this gives the tree a scraggly appearance unlike that of other conifers of the region (Fig. 8-21). When grown in dense stands, the crown is smaller, but the dead lower branches still prune very poorly. The root system, at least after the first few years, is wide-spreading and only moderately deep.

Serotinous cones are typical of this species, lodgepole pine, knobcone pine and a few others. In jack pine there is considerable variation from one tree to another in the degree of serotiny observed. On some trees, nearly all mature cones remain closed; on others most of them open. When closed cones are subjected to temperatures of 140° F, they subsequently open. Cones extracted with alcohol-benzene also open, and it is presumed that resins and perhaps other substances "glue" the scales together. Scales treated in this way, or whose bonds have been fractured mechanically, behave normally, opening when dried, closing when wet.

Jack pine is very intolerant and occurs in pure stands or open mixtures with quaking aspen and paper birch on dry, sandy, acid soils too poor for such species as red pine or eastern white

MAP 8-5   *Pinus banksiana.*

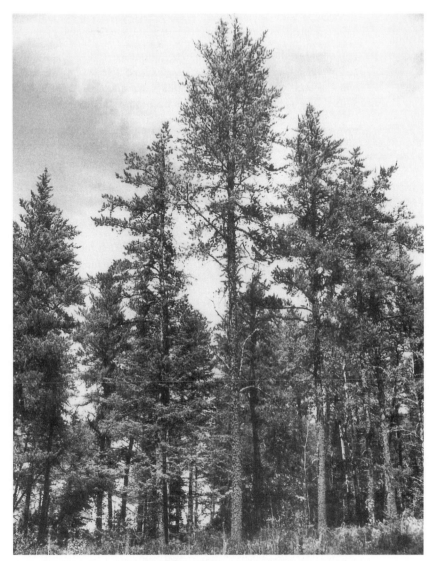

FIGURE 8-21   Jack pine. (*Courtesy of U.S. Forest Service.*)

pine, with which, however, it is often found on the better sites. In fact, much of the land formerly occupied by these two species in the Great Lakes region supports pure stands of jack pine which originated after logging and fire had destroyed the layer of humus, leaving only bare sand. This species serves as a valuable pioneer tree on such areas, but, except on the very poorest, it is eventually replaced by red pine or white pine. On better sandy loam soils these species may in turn yield to hardwoods such as sugar maple, northern red oak, and basswood.

Like the lodgepole pine of the west, which it resembles in many ways, jack pine is very prolific and begins to produce yearly crops of cones at an early age (3 to 15 years) with larger amounts at 3- or 4-year intervals. The cones open irregularly, and many remain closed unless heat is applied; in the former instance they are often engulfed by the trunk or branch to which they are attached. This habit of retaining so many unopened cones explains the rapidity of natural seeding after a fire has swept through a jack pine forest. Interestingly, at the peak of the conflagration, when the cones are on fire and the resin oozing from between the scales is blazing, they do not open (at least not fully). Some time later, when the crown fire has passed, the scales open, and the seeds spiral down or are windblown to land in the now cooling ashes. However, at the southern limits of its range, jack pine may also produce nonserotinous cones.

Perhaps because of its extensive range, jack pine can be host to a very large number of insects and diseases. This is particularly true of seedlings. After the first 4 or 5 years, the young trees make rapid growth, usually developing, like pitch pine, two or three false whorls of branches each year. Jack pine matures in about 60 years and subsequently begins to deteriorate, although trees 150 years of age or older have been found (maximum 230 years).

Pìnus virginiàna Mill.   Virginia pine

Distinguishing Characteristics (Fig. 8-22)

Needles 1½ to 3 in. (4 to 7.5 cm) long, in fascicles of 2, yellow-green to gray-green, twisted, often divergent, persistent until the third or fourth year.

FIGURE 8-22   *Pinus virginiana.* Virginia pine. (1) Open seed cone and foliage × ¾. (2) Seed × 1. (3) Cross section of needle × 35. (4) Bark.

Twigs at first green, becoming purplish glaucous by the end of the season and through the first winter.

Cones 1½ to 2¾ in. (4 to 7 cm) long, usually sessile, ovoid-conic, usually not persistent for more than 3 or 4 years, the scales thin; *apophysis* reddish brown; *umbo* dorsal and armed with a slender prickle; *seeds* ca. ¼ in. (5 to 7 mm) long, oval, light brown, wings terminal, usually broadest near the middle, ca.. ⅜ in. (7 to 9 mm) long.

Bark thin and smooth, eventually scaly-plated, reddish brown.

Range

Eastern (Map 8-6). Local disjuncts in northeastern Mississippi, central Alabama, and eastern North Carolina. Elevation: 50 to 2800 ft in the southern Appalachians. Well-drained sites in mixed forest or in pure stands; often in old abandoned fields, after fires, or poor or severely eroded areas.

General Description

Virginia pine is usually a small, often unkempt-appearing tree about 40 ft high and 12 in. dbh (max. 120 by 3 ft), with persisting side branches and a shallow root system. This pine is found on a wide variety of soils but seems to do best on clay, loam, or sandy loam. It is intolerant and is commonly found as a pioneer tree and eventually replaced by hardwoods; but meantime, it may produce more pulpwood per acre than other pines of the region on such adverse sites. Once considered a "forest weed" it is now considered important because of its rapid spread over extensive areas of neglected and abandoned agricultural land, spoil banks, and strip mines. The tree is also being grown in plantations for pulpwood, lumber, and Christmas trees. It is damaged by heart rot, pitch canker, and a variety of insects.

Pìnus claùsa (Chapm. ex Engelm.) Vasey ex Sarg.   Sand pine

Distinguishing Characteristics.   *Needles* 2 per fascicle, 2 to 3½ in. (5 to 9 cm) long, slender, flexible. *Cones* persisting, open or closed for several years, 2 to 3½ in. (5 to 9 cm) long, narrowly oblong-conic, the scales armed with short, stout spines. *Bark* gray, relatively smooth.

Range.   Southern Georgia to central Florida, west to southern Alabama. Elevation: sea level to 200 ft. Deep, well-drained sands of ridges, coastal dunes, and flatwoods, often in pure stands.

General Description.   Sand pine is generally a small tree reaching 30 to 70 ft tall and with a trunk 1 to 1½ ft dbh. It is cut for pulpwood and grown for Christmas trees. Two varieties are recognized: *P. clausa* var. *clausa* has mostly serotinous cones and occurs in dense, even-aged stands

MAP 8-6   *Pinus virginiana.*

in northeastern to southern peninsular Florida and infrequently in northwestern Florida; *P. clausa* var. *immuginata* D. B. Ward is called the Choctawhatchee sand pine and differs by having the cones consistently open at maturity. It occurs in open, uneven-aged stands of northwestern Florida and southern Alabama. The two occur intermixed in some localities (Ward, 1963).

Pìnus resinòsa Ait.   Red pine

Distinguishing Characteristics (Fig. 8-23)

Needles 4 to 6¼ in. (10 to 16 cm) long, in fascicles of 2, serrulate, dark yellow-green, flexible, straight, breaking cleanly when doubled between the fingers, persistent until fourth or fifth season.

Cones 1½ to 2⅜ in. (4 to 6 cm) long, ovoid-conic, subsessile; *apophysis* chestnut-brown, rounded; *umbo* dorsal and unarmed; *seeds* ca. ¼ in. (5 to 7 mm) long, somewhat mottled, with wings ½ to ¾ in. (12 to 18 mm) long, oblique, chestnut-brown.

Twigs orange-brown, lustrous; *buds* covered with thin, ragged, orange-brown, or reddish-brown scales, often grayish on the margin.

Bark on young trees flaky, orange-red, eventually breaking up into large, flat, reddish brown, superficially scaly plates irregularly diamond-shaped in outline.

Range

Northeastern (Map 8-7). Local disjuncts in Newfoundland, northern New Jersey, eastern West Virginia, northern Illinois, and southeastern Minnesota. Elevation: 650 to 1400

FIGURE 8-23   *Pinus resinosa*. Red pine. (1) Fascicle of needles × ¾. (2) Cross section of needle × 35. (3) Open seed cone × ¾. (4) Mature seed cone × ½. (5) Seed × 1. (6) Bark of old tree.

MAP 8-7 *Pinus resinosa.*

ft northward, to 2700 ft in the Adirondacks, 3100 to 4200 ft in West Virginia. Well-drained soils of flatwoods, ridges, outcrops, and dunes, either in mixed or pure stands.

General Description

Red pine is one of the most distinctive of northern conifers (Fig. 8-24). Even at a considerable distance, the symmetrically oval crown with its tufted dark-green foliage appears very different from that of the ragged, unkempt jack pines or the plumelike tops of the eastern white pine. The

FIGURE 8-24   Old-growth red pine left after logging.

bole of red pine is well formed, long, and cylindrical and is supported by a spreading root system and poorly developed taproot. Although attaining a maximum size of 125 ft tall and 5 ft dbh, most trees vary from 50 to 80 ft in height and 2 to 3 ft dbh.

Best development in the United States was made in the upper Great Lakes region where magnificent pure and mixed stands of this species occurred. On light acid sandy soils too poor for white pine, red pine grew in abundance, and on the better sites was mixed with the former species; occasional trees, often of large size, were found in hardwood mixtures on heavier soils. Following logging and fire, much of the land which had supported red pine became too poor for anything but jack pine, which over large areas established itself as a pioneer tree. In a similar way, red pine occupied former eastern white pine land.

In its soil and moisture requirements and ability to grow under forest competition, red pine is intermediate between jack pine and eastern white pine. Arranged in order of tolerance, eastern white pine is first and jack pine third, while in adaptability to dry sandy soils, this order is reversed. On cutover land, red pine appears to follow jack pine and is often found in mixture with it. Both trees experience great variations in seasonal temperatures, with extremes of -40 to -60° F in winter to 90 to 105° F in summer. The growing season for red pine is from 80 to 160 days.

Seeds may be produced in small quantities each year, but good crops occur only at intervals of from 3 to 7 years. Growth of established unshaded young trees is fast, and during the first two decades they will often outstrip those of eastern white pine. Some 30-year plantations of red pine in New England contain trees with a height of 35 ft and a diameter of 6 in. The maximum age for the species is about 350 years.

Red pine is grown extensively for reforestation purposes and used for lumber, poles, cabin logs, pulp, and Christmas trees. It is also important in ornamental plantings, particularly on light sandy soils. Compared with many other pines, it is lacking in genetic diversity. It occurs mainly in highly fragmented, small populations.

This species is sometimes attacked by the Nantucket pine-tip moth, the European pine-shoot moth, sawflies, and red pine scale. Red pine, growing on acid soils, is remarkably free of serious pathogen damage.

Pìnus nìgra Arnold   Austrian pine or European black pine

This species has been planted extensively in the United States as an ornamental, and it has escaped cultivation locally. Superficially, it is similar to the native red pine, but the needles are stouter and stiffer and do not snap when bent as do those of red pine; the bark is dark brown to black; the buds silvery; and the cones larger, 2 to 3 in. (5 to 8 cm) long, yellowish brown with a short deciduous prickle. It can attain a height of 60 ft and a dbh of 2 ft.

Pìnus sylvéstris L.   Scotch pine

Distinguishing Characteristics.   *Needles* in fascicles of 2 (rarely 3), mostly blue-green, 1½ to 2¾ in. (4 to 7 cm) long, slightly twisted, and sharp-pointed. *Cones* oblong-conical and 1¼ to 2½ in. (3 to 6 cm) long, stalked, reflexed; the apophysis flat, or raised and pyramidal, with a small scarcely armed umbo (Fig. 8-25). *Bark* soon becoming orange in color, and this feature is persistent until the tree reaches nearly full size, at which time it becomes dark and furrowed on the trunk, but remains orange on the branches.

General Description.   This is the most widely distributed pine in the world, spanning much of Europe and Asia (Critchfield and Little, 1966; Mirov, 1967). Because of its centuries of management in European forests, it has been widely used in reforestation, and more recently in Christmas-tree plantations in the United States. It has become naturalized locally in southeastern Canada and in the United States from Maine to Iowa. It reaches 70 ft tall and with a dbh of 2 ft.

FIGURE 8-25 *Pinus sylvestris.* Scotch pine. (1) Mature seed cone and foliage × ¾. (2) Open seed cone × ¾. (3) Seed × 1. (4) Cross section of needle × 35.

Pìnus palústris Mill.   Longleaf pine

Distinguishing Characteristics (Fig. 8-26)

Needles 8 to 18 in. (20 to 46 cm) long, in fascicles of 3 or rarely 4 or 5, bright green, densely tufted at the ends of stout branch tips, persistent until the end of the second season; fascicle sheath to 1⅜ in. (3.5 cm) long.

Cones 6 to 10 in. (15 to 25 cm) long, narrowly ovoid-cylindric, when shed usually leaving a few of the basal scales attached to the twig; *apophysis* reddish brown, weathering to an ashy gray, wrinkled; *umbo* armed with a dorsal prickle which curves toward the base of the scale; *seeds* ca. ½ in. (1 to 1.5 cm) long, somewhat ridged, pale with dark blotches; wings ca. 1¾ in. (4 to 5 cm) long, striped, oblique at the ends.

Twigs stout, orange-brown; *buds* large and very conspicuous, covered with silvery-white, fringed scales.

Bark coarsely scaly, with rough plates on older trees; phellogen layers, ivory-white.

Range

Southeastern (Map 8-8). Elevation: sea level to near 2200 ft in northern Alabama. Well-drained, sandy ridges and flatwoods to wetter flatwoods and savannas, often in pure stands.

General Description

Longleaf pine is one of the most distinctive and important southern conifers. However, only fragments remain of what was one of the most extensive upland forest types in the southeast. It is estimated that only 1 percent of the original presettlement 82 million acres remain in the mid-1990s and nearly all this is second growth. Original longleaf pine stands were heavily impacted

FIGURE 8-26 *Pinus palustris*. Longleaf pine. (1) Mature seed cone and foliage × ½. (2) Terminal bud × ¾. (3) Fringed bud scale × 1½. (4) Open seed cone × ¾. (5) Seed × 1. (6) Fascicle of needles × ½. (7) Cross section of needle × 35. (8) Bark (*Photo by J. C. Th. Uphof*).

MAP 8-8   (**Left**) *Pinus palustris.* (**Right**) *Pinus echinata.*

by naval stores, grazing, disruption of the natural fire regime, logging, and more recently by loss of available habitat due to development and conversion to loblolly plantations. There is now increasing interest and effort in preserving, restoring, and reintroducing longleaf pine forests on public and private lands through plantations or natural and artificial regeneration.

Although it grows best on deep well-drained sands, this species is found on a variety of sites from dry, sterile ridges to wet, low flatwoods, and in sand, loam, or clay. In the poorest sites where a hardpan is near the surface, it maintains itself, even though growth is very slow. Flat land of this character is poorly drained and in spring may be covered with shallow pools of standing water; hence possibly the origin of the name *palustris* (swamp) to longleaf pine. During the summer, however, such areas are exceedingly dry, and only trees like blackjack oak or turkey oak are seen scattered through the open nearly pure forests of pine. On these shallow soils underlain by hardpan, the taproot is poorly developed and wind-thrown trees are common. As indicated, best growth is made on better-drained sandy soils. This growth habit is especially common in the southern part of its range where longleaf often occupies low ridges or knolls while slash or pond pines preempt the moister depressions. It can reach 80 to 100 ft tall and with a dbh of 2 to 2½ ft.

Longleaf is very intolerant but regenerates well under mature trees after fires. Open pure stands are typical with a small accumulation of needles or short grasses on the forest floor. Frequent summer fires, most probably caused by lightning strikes, are common in the range of the species and are thought to have been the primary driving force for development of the reproductive system of longleaf. Seed crops are irregular, with exceptionally high yields every 5 to 7 years.* Seedling survival and growth are enhanced by germination on bare mineral soil. Under natural conditions germination takes place within 2 to 5 weeks after the seeds are released. Fall germination, characteristic of longleaf, is rare in the other southern pines.

It is the nature of longleaf pine to develop very little above ground for the first 3 to 6 years (exceptionally, 20 or more years), but during this time the roots get a firm foothold. Moreover, the young tree does not exhibit annual growth rings but seems to grow intermittently when conditions permit. A dense bunch of green needles is all that appears on the soil surface, and to the inexperienced eye this is often mistaken for grass; hence the so-called "grass stage" of longleaf pine (Fig. 8-27). By the end of this period the root system is well developed, but the aerial stem shows practically no elongation. (This unusual growth habit is also found in south Florida slash pine.) Height and diameter growth then increase rapidly, and trees 25 years old average 45 ft in height and 6 in. dbh. Annual height growth declines markedly after 40 to 50 years. Even at maturity longleaf pine is not often a large tree. Maturity is reached in about 150 years, but old trees sometimes show more than 300 annual rings (Fig. 8-28).

---

*According to Burleigh (1938), such birds as the mourning dove, bobwhite, southern meadow lark, and blackbird consistently eat the seeds. This often makes reproduction by seeding very unsatisfactory or even a failure. It is notable that there are but few birds present in poor seed years.

FIGURE 8-27   "Grass stage" of longleaf pine.

FIGURE 8-28   Longleaf pine stand with an understory of shrubs and scrub oaks as a result of excluded fire. (*Courtesy of U.S. Forest Service.*)

Two-year-old seedlings, so well insulated by the dense cluster of needles, are highly fire-resistant. So too is the thick-barked mature tree. Only during the first 2 or 3 years of height growth is fire a threat. Some ecologists believe the species to be a fire climax throughout much of its range. Observations of hardwood encroachment and failure of longleaf regeneration where fire is excluded support this conclusion. Although longleaf pine is not considered to propagate by sprouting, one reference indicates that some 4-year-old trees cut off just above the root collar produced vigorous sprouts (Garin, 1958). Longleaf is freer from serious pathogen damage than the other major southern pines. Seedlings may be stunted or killed by brownspot disease.

This pine furnishes high-quality lumber, pulp, chipped bark, and pine straw. For hybrids see Burns and Honkala (1990).

Pìnus echinàta Mill.   Shortleaf pine

Distinguishing Characteristics (Fig. 8-29)

Needles 2¾ to 4¾ in. (7 to 12 cm) long, mostly in fascicles of 2, but also in 3s on the same tree (occasionally with the latter number predominant), dark yellow-green, slender, flexible, persistent until the second to fourth seasons, not infrequently occurring from dormant buds along the bole.

Cones 1½ to 2½ in. (4 to 6 cm) long, ovoid-oblong to conical, nearly sessile, usually persistent for several years; *apophysis* reddish brown, rounded; *umbo* dorsal and armed with a small sharp, straight or curved, sometimes deciduous prickle; *seeds* ca. ³⁄₁₆ in. (4 to 6 mm) long, brown, with black markings; wings ca. ½ in. (8 to 12 mm) long, broadest near the middle.

Twigs at first green and tinged with purple, eventually reddish brown and becoming flaky in 3 to 4 years; buds with red-brown scales.

Bark on small trees nearly black, roughly scaly, with small surface pockets or holes; later reddish brown and broken into irregular flat plates, scaly on the surface; phellogen layers ivory-white.

Range

Southeastern (Map 8-8). Elevation: 650 to 3000 ft. Dry, rocky, mountain ridges, old fields, and floodplains, in mixed or pure stands.

General Description

Shortleaf pine is a medium-size to large tree 80 to 100 ft in height and 2 to 3 ft dbh (max. 146 by 4 ft). The clear, well-formed bole supports a small narrowly pyramidal crown and terminates underground in a very deep taproot. Its root system is usually larger than that of the other southern pines.

Although found on many different sites, this species is most common in pure or mixed stands on dry upland soils which are neither highly acid nor strongly alkaline. Its associates include loblolly and Virginia pines, eastern redcedar, black, blackjack, post, and chestnut oaks, and mockernut hickory. In addition, especially on soils containing more moisture, bitternut hickory and sweetgum are included. West of the Mississippi River, shortleaf and longleaf pines are mixed and often attain maximum development together.

In many localities where the ranges of shortleaf and loblolly pines overlap, they are mixed together on dry soils, and because the needles and cones of the latter become somewhat dwarfed under such conditions, differentiating between the two species may be difficult. Generally, how-

FIGURE 8-29   *Pinus echinata.* Shortleaf pine. (1) Open seed cone × ¾. (2) Seed × 1. (3) Mature seed cone and foliage × ½. (4) Fascicle of needles × ¾. (5, 6) Cross sections of needles (3 and 2 per fascicle) × 35. (7) Bark of old tree.

ever, these two trees tend to be complementary, with loblolly pine favoring the heavier, wetter soils, while shortleaf pine prefers the lighter and drier soils. Its best growth is made on well-drained alluvial soils along streams and small rivers.

Shortleaf pine may produce some seed nearly every year (after the fifth to twentieth), with good to excellent amounts at 3- to 10-year intervals. Growth of the young trees is moderately rapid, and as in several of the other southern pines, the terminal shoots are multinodal, developing from two to four false whorls of side branches each year; false growth rings are often concomitant and may be mistaken for true seasonal rings. On good sites trees 35 years old may be 60 ft high and 8 in. dbh; those 60 years old, 80 ft tall and nearly 12 in. dbh.

A remarkable feature of shortleaf pine trees up to 8 or 10 years old is their ability to sprout after their main stems have been destroyed by either fire or cutting. This ability results from the same peculiar juvenile habit mentioned for pitch pine. As reported by Stone and Stone (1943), the stem of shortleaf seedlings may become prostrate as shoot growth begins. It then turns upward from just above the cotyledons. This produces the second part of a double crook and leaves the cotyledonary part of the stem near the ground. If the main axis of the young tree is destroyed, dormant buds in the axils of primary leaves above the cotyledons start to grow and develop new sprouts.

This species may be less tolerant than loblolly pine but will endure suppression for many years and shows greatly accelerated growth when released; it also surpasses longleaf pine in this respect. Maturity is reached in about 170 years, while very old trees may reach the four-century mark.

Young trees are damaged by the Nantucket pine-tip moth, and the southern pine beetle is a serious enemy. The greatest threat is posed by the littleleaf disease. Its high resistance to the damaging fusiform rust is unique among the southern pines.

Shortleaf is used for lumber, plywood, and pulp.

Pìnus taèda L.   Loblolly pine

Distinguishing Characteristics (Fig. 8-30)

Needles 4 to 9 in. (10 to 23 cm) long, in fascicles of 3 (occasionally 2), slender but somewhat stiff, yellow-green, sometimes twisted, persistent until the second autumn.

Cones 2½ to 6 in. (6 to 15 cm) long, ovoid-cylindric to narrowly conical, sessile; *apophysis* rather flattened, wrinkled; *umbo* dorsal and armed with a stout sharp spine; *seeds* ca. ¼ in. (6 to 9 mm) long, dark brown, roughened, with black markings; wings ca. ¾ in. (18 mm) long, usually broadest above the center.

Twigs yellow-brown or reddish brown; *buds* covered with reddish brown scales, free at the tips and not fringed.

Bark variable, on young trees scaly and nearly black, later ¾ to 2 in. (1.8 to 5 cm) thick, with irregular, brownish blocks, or on very old trees, with reddish brown scaly plates similar to those of shortleaf pine or even red pine; phellogen layers slate-gray.

Range

Southeastern (Map 8-9). Elevation: near sea level to 2300 ft. Deep, poorly drained floodplains and old fields to well-drained slopes in mixed or pure stands.

General Description

Loblolly pine, the leading commercial timber species in the southern United States, is a medium-size to large tree 90 to 110 ft in height and 2 to 2½ ft dbh (max. 182 by 5 ft or more). The bole is long and cylindrical, and the crown, although open, is denser than that of the other southern pines. In youth a short taproot is developed, but except on the driest of soils it soon ceases growth in favor of an extensive lateral root system.

This species grows on a very wide variety of soils but does best on those with deep surface layers having plenty of moisture but poor surface drainage and fine-textured subsoils. On such coastal plain sites pure stands are extensive, especially on river bottoms; however, even on the drier soils of the piedmont and inland areas pure stands also develop. Because this pine occurs on so many different sites from wet to dry, the list of associated species is large, including the other important southern pines. Loblolly–hardwood mixtures are also common and include sweetgum, oaks, hickories, and many others. This pine is less tolerant than its hardwood associates but more tolerant than longleaf and slash pines.

When 1- to 3-year seedlings are cut off, they sprout, but older ones do not retain this ability.

FIGURE 8-30   *Pinus taeda.* Loblolly pine. (1) Open seed cone × ¾. (2) Mature seed cone × ½. (3) Seed × 1. (4) Fascicle of needles × ½. (5) Cross section of needle × 35. (6) Bark of old tree.

MAP 8-9   **(Left)** *Pinus taeda.* **(Right solid)** *Pinus elliottii.* **(Right shaded)** *Pinus elliottii* var. *densa.*

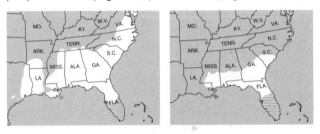

On cutover lands in the south this species has spread to a remarkable degree and is especially aggressive in forming pure stands on old fields; hence the local name of "old field pine." However, most commercial stands are of planted origin. In the south nearly two billion seedlings are planted each year.

Seeds may be produced on 7-year-old trees and in abundance after about the twenty-fifth year. Especially on old fields, open-grown young trees make rapid growth, frequently averaging 3 ft in height and ½ in. or more dbh per year for the first decade, and annual rings nearly 1 in. wide are sometimes produced. Trees 25 years old may be nearly 70 ft tall and 8 to 10 in. dbh, those 70 years of age about 90 ft high and 24 in. dbh. Loblolly pine matures in about 150 years, while old trees may pass the three-century mark.

The problem in producing more loblolly pine in plantations is to extend its original range and to control competing hardwoods which continually invade the pine stands. Besides its importance for lumber, this is a major species in paper making. More than half of United States wood pulp comes from the southern pines, with a large percentage from loblolly.

Widespread pests include the fusiform rust, black root rot and other fungi, and the full range of pine bark beetles.

Loblolly pine hybridizes naturally with longleaf, shortleaf, pitch, slash, and pond pines. For a listing of some hybrids additionally produced by controlled pollination, see Burns and Honkala (1990). Much of the forest-tree genetic research in the south seeks to improve the growth and quality of this species.

Pìnus glàbra Walt.   Spruce pine

Distinguishing Characteristics. *Needles* 2 per fascicle, 1½ to 4 in. (4 to 10 cm) long, very slender, flexible. *Cones* similar to those of *P. echinata,* but more globose when open, often smaller, and the scales nearly unarmed (small weak prickles). *Bark* not plated like that of other southern pines, finely furrowed, and with cross fissures, similar to that of southern red oak and spruce.

Range. Eastern South Carolina to northern Florida, west to southeastern Louisiana. Elevation: sea level to 500 ft. Moist, lowland swamp forests in mixed stands.

General Description. Spruce pine is a medium-size tree 80 ft high and 2 ft dbh (max. 125 by 4 ft). Nowhere abundant, it rarely forms pure stands and is usually seen as a scattered tree among hardwoods and loblolly pine, along stream banks or rich moist hammocks of the coastal plain. It is of very limited commercial value, although used sparingly for lumber, pulp, and Christmas trees.

Pìnus rígida Mill.   Pitch pine

Distinguishing Characteristics (Fig. 8-31)

Needles 3 to 6 in. (7.5 to 15 cm) long, in fascicles of 3, yellow-green, stiff, usually somewhat twisted, standing out at nearly right angles to the twig, often produced on short "water sprouts" or in tufts along the trunk; mostly deciduous during the second season.

Cones 1¼ to 2¾ in. (3 to 7 cm) long, nearly sessile, ovoid, usually persistent for many years and serotinous or not; *apophysis* light brown, smooth; *umbo* dorsal and armed with a rigid prickle; *seeds* ca. ¼ in. (4 to 6 mm) long, triangular to oval, dull black, sometimes mottled with gray, with brownish terminal wings.

Bark at first dark and very scaly; eventually 1 to 2 in. (2.5 to 5 cm) thick at the base of old trees and smoother with brownish yellow, flat plates separated by narrow, irregular fissures.

FIGURE 8-31   *Pinus rigida.* Pitch pine. (1) Fascicle of needles × ¾. (2) Cross section of needle × 35. (3) Open and mature seed cones × ¾. (4) Seed × 1. (5) Bark of old tree.

Range

Northeastern (Map 8-10). Local disjuncts in western Kentucky, northcentral North Carolina, and northcentral Alabama. Elevation: sea level to 2000 ft northward, 1400 to 4600 ft in the southern Appalachians. Slopes and ridges of the mountains, river valleys and swamps elsewhere, in mixed or pure stands.

General Description

Naval stores, which the French harvested first in the northeast, came originally from *P. rigida*, hence the common name. The industry then moved south to *P. palustris* which was much more extensive and more resinous, then later further south to *P. elliottii* when *P. palustris* was all but depleted.

MAP 8-10   *Pinus rigida.*

Pitch pine is a tree of great diversity in form, habit, and development. In the northern part of its range, through New England, it is commonly a small tree growing on the poorest of acid, sandy, sterile soils in company with gray birch and scrub oak (*Q. ilicifolia* Wangenh.). Farther south, especially in Pennsylvania, it reaches its best development and varies from 50 to 60 ft in height and 1 to 2 ft dbh (max. 100 by 4 ft). Populations of dwarf trees (8 to 12 ft tall) occur in the New Jersey pine plains.

The form of the tree is exceedingly variable, and on exposed sites it is often very grotesque, while in better situations a tall columnar bole and small open crown are produced; the root system is deep, and the tree is relatively windfirm until overmature, when shallower roots predominate.

Although pitch pine is extremely hardy in maintaining itself on the driest, most unproductive sites, best growth is made on sandy loam soils with moderate amounts of moisture. Particularly near the coast (New Jersey), this species may be found on peat soils of Atlantic white-cedar swamps. Very little pitch pine is found on the more favorable areas because of its pronounced intolerance to forest competition, especially that of the hardwoods, which usually preempt the better sites. This pine is found naturally in fairly open, pure stands or in mixture with such hardwoods as scarlet, black, and chestnut oak, various hickories, black tupelo, and red maple; best growth is attained in the hardwood mixture.

The production of cones begins very early, at 3 to 4 years, and 12-year-old trees often bear quantities of viable seeds. Good crops may occur at 4- to 9-year intervals; many of the cones remain unopened until midwinter and then gradually release their seeds on the snow, in this way providing food for birds and small rodents. However, the time of seed release varies. On some trees it occurs soon after the cones mature, but on others, the cones may be serotinous. A serotinous-cone ecotype occurs in New Jersey as a result of frequent fires. Serotiny in these cones afford the seeds protection from damaging high temperatures during the fires (Fraver, 1992).

The stems of seedlings often lie nearly flat on the ground. Subsequent growth to an upright position leaves the tree with a double curvature at the base. Evidence of this juvenile habit disappears as the tree becomes older.

On good sites the growth of pitch pine can average 1 ft per year for the first 50 to 60 years. By age 90, height growth essentially ceases (maximum age 200 years). Diameter growth is often made in installments, with false growth rings resulting. Estimates of age made by counting whorls or rings are, therefore, liable to error unless this habit is understood.

Fire is the most serious enemy of this species, even though it is remarkably resistant. Young trees commonly produce sprouts from dormant buds of the stump or main stem after burning or other injury, and these persist for many years, a feature rare among the conifers.

Pitch pine seedlings have been produced in large quantities for forest planting, especially in Pennsylvania, and this species may be of considerable importance, especially on soils too poor for other trees. For hybrids, see Burns and Honkala (1990).

This species is used for construction lumber and pulp and was used earlier for ship building, railroad ties, and naval stores as mentioned.

Pìnus serótina Michx.   Pond pine

Distinguishing Characteristics.   *Needles* 3 (rarely 4) per fascicle, 6 to 10 in. (15 to 25 cm) long and flexible, often in short tufts along the trunk, particularly after fire. *Cones* more nearly globose than those of pitch pine, 2 to 2½ in. (5 to 6 cm) long, and the scales are armed with weak, sometimes deciduous prickles.

Range.   Southern New Jersey and Delaware south to central and northwestern Florida, and southeastern Alabama; local disjuncts in central Alabama. Elevation: sea level to ca. 660 ft. Swamps, pocosins, bays, pond margins, poorly drained flatwoods, often in pure stands.

General Description.   This tree is considered by some writers to be a variety or subspecies of *P. rigida* (Smouse and Saylor, 1973 a and b). The two become sympatric and hybridize in the Delmarva peninsula. The features of serotinous cones and tufted needles along the trunk are shared by both pitch and pond pines, and the latter distinguishes these pines from most other southern pines. It produces prolific sprouts even at advanced ages and can recover from complete defoliation by fire.

Pond pine is a small to medium-size tree, 40 to 70 ft tall and 1 to 2 ft dbh, found in pure stands on wet sites including poorly drained boggy areas on low hills between streams. Such areas of acid organic soils were called "pocosins" (swamp-on-a-hill) by the Indians, and the name persists. This species is increasing in importance as a pulpwood and sawtimber producer.

Pìnus púngens Lamb.   Table mountain pine

Distinguishing Characteristics.   *Needles* 2 per fascicle, 1¼ to 2¼ in. (3 to 6 cm) long, dark yellow-green, rigid, often twisted. *Cones* persisting for many years, 2 to 3½ in. (5 to 9 cm) long, ovoid, heavy, the scales armed with large conspicuous sharp spurs, serotinous. *Bark* reddish brown, plated.

Range.   Pennsylvania south to northeastern Georgia and east Tennessee; local disjuncts in New Jersey, Delaware, and the piedmont of Virginia, North Carolina, and South Carolina. Elevation: 1650 to 4500 ft. Dry, rocky slopes, knobs, and ridges, in mixed or pure stands.

General Description.   This pine is a small to medium-size tree, 20 to 40 ft tall and 1 to 2 ft dbh, and occurs sparingly on dry, often rocky slopes, and granite outcrops of the Appalachians. Especially on the southern tablelands, the tree attains sufficient size and quantity (pure stands) to furnish pulp and timber, although the quality of the lumber is low. It is used locally for firewood and is most important for watershed protection.

Pìnus ellióttii Engelm.   Slash pine

Distinguishing Characteristics (Fig. 8-32)

Needles 4 to 10 in. (10 to 25 cm) long, in fascicles of 2 and 3, dark glossy green, tufted at the ends of tapering branches but extending back some distance along the branch (compare with longleaf pine); persistent until the end of the 2d season; *fascicle sheath* ca. ½ in. (9 to 12 mm) long.

Cones 2½ to 6 in. (6 to 15 cm), ovoid-conic, stalked; usually persistent until the following summer; *apophysis* reddish brown, lustrous, commonly full and rounded; *umbo* dorsal and armed with a sharp spine; *seeds* ca. ¼ in. (6 to 8 mm) long, ovoid, black, ridged; wings ca. 1 in. (2 to 2.5 cm) long, thin, and transparent.

Twigs orange-brown; *buds* covered with reddish brown white-ciliate scales, free at the tips and not fringed.

Bark on young trees deeply furrowed, later becoming plated and ca. 1 in. (2 to 3.2 cm) thick, with thin, papery, purplish layers; phellogen layers ivory-white.

Range

Southeastern (Map 8-9). Elevation: sea level to 500 ft. Low flatwoods, pond margins, swamps, also uplands and old fields.

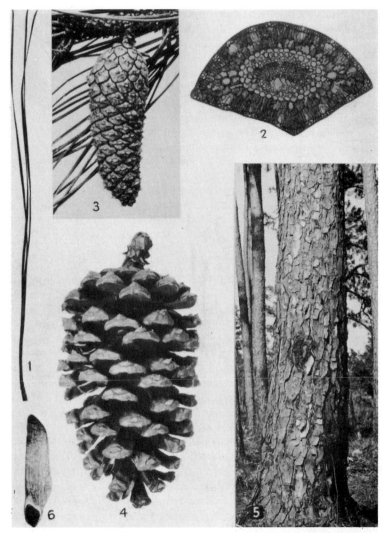

FIGURE 8-32   *Pinus elliottii.* Slash pine. (1) Fascicle of needles × ½. (2) Cross section of needle × 35. (3) Mature seed cone × ½. (4) Open seed cone × ¾. (5) Bark of old tree (*Photo by W. R. Mattoon, U.S. Forest Service*). (6) Seed × 1.

General Description

Slash pine varies from 60 to 100 ft in height and averages about 2 ft dbh (max. 150 by 4 ft). The trunk is straight and erect with a narrow ovoid crown. The root system may reach a depth of 9 to 15 ft or more, unless hampered by the presence of hardpan near the surface.

In virgin forests this tree was found on sandy soils, in depressions, around ponds, or on other low sites with an abundance of moisture in the surface layers. Longleaf pine occupied the drier knolls, and over large areas this alternation of species was frequently seen. Such distribution may have been due in part to the relative susceptibility of slash pine to fire damage. With more recent fire protection, this pine invades the drier soils in mixture with the more fire-resistant longleaf pine (Squillace, 1966). On cutover areas, slash pine is very aggressive and, like loblolly pine, quickly preempts abandoned land, especially where the soil is moist.

Slash pine is less tolerant than loblolly, but more so than longleaf. Trees first produce seed abundantly when about 20 years old, with heavy yields at about 3-year intervals. By the end of the first year young trees are from 8 to 16 in. tall, and subsequent height growth on good sites can average 3 to 4 ft per year for the first 8 to 10 years. Trees of slash pine 25 years of age average 65 ft in height and about 10 in. dbh. Like loblolly pine, young fast-growing trees of this species sometimes show annual rings from ½ to 1 in. wide. Such rapid growth coupled with high-quality fiber has resulted in the establishment of many thousands of acres of plantations, some of which are well outside the natural range of this species such as in southern Brazil (Zobel et al., 1987).

This species, because of its aggressiveness and value for pulp, timber, and naval stores, will undoubtedly remain important in the future, despite the increasing importance of loblolly and longleaf pine. Enemies include red-brown butt rot, fusiform rust, pitch canker, and bark beetles.

Pinus elliottii var. *dénsa* Little Dorman   South Florida slash pine

Distinguishing Characteristics.   This variety differs from the typical slash pine in several ways: the needles are in 2s (rarely 3s also); the seedlings spend 2 to 6 years in a dwarf "grass stage" similar to that of longleaf pine; the bark is somewhat scaly and the trunk divides into large spreading branches forming a flat-topped or rounded crown; the wood is very hard and heavy, with very wide summerwood, and is usually denser than that of the other southern yellow pines.

Range.   The range of south Florida slash pine is south Florida and northward in a narrow strip along both coasts. Over much of its range (Map 8-9) this is the only native pine, occurring both in pure stands and scattered through the grasslands at an elevation of sea level to 35 ft. Typically, this variety is found on dry sites, either sandy flat lands or limestone outcrops (Little and Dorman, 1954).

General Description.   Langdon (1963) showed that between the two coastal "prongs" there is an area in the central part of the state where the ranges of typical slash pine and south Florida slash pine overlap. Squillace (1966) indicated that the variation is essentially continuous or clinal, both within and between varieties. Also, in the northern part of its range, south Florida slash pine may be found on wet sites. This variety is not worked for naval stores.

LARIX Mill.   Larch

Although much larger during previous geological periods, this genus now includes only about 10 species of deciduous trees widely scattered through the forests of eastern and western North America, Europe, and Asia. *Larix decidua* Mill., European larch, is an important continental tree used for reforestation in the eastern United States, where it has now become naturalized. The foliage is yellow-green, the twigs yellowish or straw-colored, and the upright cones are ca. 1¼ in. (2 to 3.8 cm) long (Fig. 8-33). This species also finds use as an ornamental in the United States. The Japanese larch, *L. kaempferi* (Lamb) Carr. [*L. leptolepis* (Sieb. and Zucc.) Gord.] is another exotic similarly cultivated. An interesting hybrid of these two species, the Dunkeld larch, *L. ×eurolepis* A. Henry, promises to be of some importance; this form grows very rapidly and appears to be more resistant to insect or fungal attack than

FIGURE 8-33   *Larix decidua.* European larch. (1) Pollen cone × 1. (2) Ovulate cone × 1. (3) Open seed cones × ¾. (4) Bark of old tree.

either of the parental species. There are three species of *Larix* native to the United States, one in the northeast, and two in the west. Two are important (Table 8-8).

Extensive forests of larch are occasionally destroyed by the larch sawfly.

Botanical Features of the Genus

Leaves deciduous, solitary, and spirally arranged on new growth (long shoots), and on older growth in dense spirals only on lateral spurs (indeterminate short shoots); *shape* acicular, more or less flattened, triangular, or less frequently 4-angled in cross section, keeled below or occasionally above and below, with numerous lines of stomata on all surfaces but most abundant below; *apex* pointed or rounded; base decurrent; fall color yellow.

Cones (juvenile) solitary, terminal, appearing with the leaves; *pollen* cones globose, ovoid, or oblong, sessile or pedicelled, yellow to yellowish green, composed of several to many spirally arranged pollen sacs; *ovulate* cones subglobose, erect, consisting of few to many generally scarlet, sharp-pointed bracts, each subtending a short suborbicular to rectangular scale with two inverted ovules; all species monoecious.

Mature cones short-stalked, erect, subglobose to oblong, maturing in one season; *cone scales* thin, persistent, longer or shorter than the bracts; *bracts* long-acuminate; *seeds* triangular, terminally winged; *cotyledons* 6.

TABLE 8-8   COMPARISON OF IMPORTANT LARCHES

Species	Leaves	Mature cones	Young twigs
L. laricina tamarack	ca. 1 in. (2–3.5 cm) long, blue-green	ca. ⅝ in. (1.2–1.9 cm) long, oblong-ovoid, bracts shorter than scales	glabrous or glaucous
L. occidentalis western larch	ca. 1½ in. (2.5–4.5 cm) long, lustrous green	ca. 1 in. (2.5–4 cm) long, oblong, the bracts exserted	pale pubescent

Twigs with buds small, subglobose, covered by several imbricated scales, non-resinous; leaf scars raised on decurrent base, most occurring on spur shoots, bundle scar 1.

Lárix laricina (Du Roi) K. Koch   Tamarack; eastern larch

Distinguishing Characteristics (Fig. 8-34)

  Leaves deciduous, linear, ¾ to 1½ in. (2 to 3.5 cm) long, flexible, 3-angled, bright blue-green; fall color golden yellow .

FIGURE 8-34   *Larix laricina.* Tamarack. (1) Mature seed cones × ¾. (2) Seed × 1. (3) Foliage showing long shoot above and spur shoots (indeterminate short shoots) below, both with needles × ½. (4) Bark of old tree. (5) Spur shoot in winter × ½. (6) First-year twig (long shoot) in winter × 1½.

Cones ½ to ¾ in. (1.2 to 1.9 cm) long, erect, oblong-ovoid, short-stalked; *scales* slightly longer than broad, sparingly erose on the margin; *bracts* not visible, except near the base of the cone; *seeds* ca. ⅛ in. (3 mm) long, the wings ¼ in. (6 mm) long, light chestnut-brown.

Twigs brownish, marked by many small leaf scars and fewer buds, on older growth showing conspicuous short spurs; *buds* globose, dark red.

Bark thin and smooth on young stems, later becoming ½ to ¾ in. (1.2 to 2 cm) thick, gray to reddish brown, scaly.

Range

Northern (Map 8-11). Local disjuncts in western Maryland, southwestern Pennsylvania, northern West Virginia, westcentral Ohio, and southeastern Minnesota. Elevation: sea level to 4000 ft. Bogs and swamps, lake shores, beach thickets, and also well-drained or drier uplands northward; in mixed or pure stands.

General Description

Tamarack is a small to medium-size tree 40 to 80 ft high and 1 to 2 ft dbh (max. 100 by 4 ft) with a long clear, cylindrical bole, open pyramidal crown, and shallow wide-spreading root system (Fig. 8-35). In the southern part of its range it is usually restricted to cool swamps or sphagnum bogs; but farther north it makes best growth on moist benches and better-drained uplands. Its chief tree associate in bogs is black spruce, while on drier sites it is often found in open mixtures with this species and also balsam fir, quaking aspen, paper birch, and jack pine. Tamarack is exceedingly intolerant and is always a dominant tree under forest conditions.

Seeds are produced annually, with larger crops at 2- to 6-year intervals. Growth of young trees on favorable sites is rapid but decreases after 40 to 50 years; maturity is reached in 100 to

MAP 8-11   (**Shaded**) *Larix occidentalis.* (**Solid**) *Larix laricina.*

FIGURE 8-35   Tamarack. (*Courtesy of U.S. Forest Service.*)

200 years. On Isle Royale in Lake Superior, very long-lived tamaracks have been found, the oldest with an age of 335 years.

Tamarack is not often damaged by fire because of its wet surroundings. Trees of this species past the juvenile stage, in spite of their thin bark and shallow roots, may be fairly fire-resistant even on upland sites. The rare bog fire usually kills or heavily damages trees growing there. Two serious insect enemies are the larch sawfly and the introduced (Europe) casebearer. Where defoliation is severe and repeated from year to year, tree death results.

Tamarack is used as an ornamental and also a source of lumber, pulp, posts, fuel, and dogsled runners.

Lárix occidentàlis Nutt.   Western larch

Distinguishing Characteristics (Fig. 8-36)

Leaves 1 to 1¾ in. (2.5 to 4.5 cm) long, pale green, lustrous, 3-angled; fall color yellow.

FIGURE 8-36   *Larix occidentalis.* Western larch. (1) Foliage on long shoot and spur shoots × ½. (2) Ovulate cones × 1. (3) Pollen cones × 1. (4) Mature seed cone × ¾. (5) Open seed cone × ¾. (6) Seeds × 1. (7) Bark. (*Courtesy of British Columbia Forest Service.*)

Cones 1 to 1½ in. (2.5 to 4 cm) long, purplish red to reddish brown, oblong, short-stalked; *cone scales* broader than long, occasionally finely toothed at the tip of the reflexed apex; *bracts* exserted, shouldered, terminating in a long spike; *seeds* ¼ in. (6 mm) long; the wings ½ in. (13 mm) long, thin, and fragile.

Twigs stout, at first pale pubescent, but soon becoming orange-brown and glabrous; *buds* chestnut-brown.

Bark reddish brown to cinnamon-red, scaly on young stems; 4 to 6 in. (10 to 15 cm) thick on old trunks and then with flat-plated ridges separated by deep irregular fissures.

Range

Northwestern (Map 8-11). Elevation: 1650 to 5300 ft northward, to 7000 ft southward. Mountain slopes and valleys, usually mixed with other conifers.

General Description

This tree was discovered in 1806 by the Lewis and Clark expedition on the upper watershed of the Clearwater River in western Montana. David Douglas also found this larch in northeastern Washington in 1827. He erroneously concluded, however, that he had encountered a natural extension of the European larch into the New World. Thus it was not until 1849, when Thomas Nuttall recognized that the larches in the Blue Mountains of northeastern Oregon did indeed comprise a new species, that the identity of this tree was correctly established.

Western larch is the largest of the American larches and one of the most important trees of the Inland Empire. The boles of mature trees are clear for a considerable length, characteristically tapered, and vary from 140 to 180 ft in height and 3 to 4 ft dbh (max. 210 by 8 ft). The crowns are usually short, open, and essentially pyramidal; in the summer they are distinguishable at a considerable distance by their light, lustrous green foliage and in winter by their bareness. Excellent anchorage is afforded by a deep wide-spreading root system, and the trees are seldom wind-thrown. Western larch attains maximum size on deep, moist, porous soils in high valleys and on mountain slopes of northern and western exposure, although thrifty trees often occur on drier gravelly soils. Nearly pure open forests of western larch are found in northwestern Montana, northern Idaho, and northeastern Washington. It is often the most abundant species in the western larch–Douglas-fir forests of the northern Rockies, where it is also associated with western white pine, and at higher elevations with lodgepole pine, Englemann spruce, and subalpine fir. Its other forest associates include western hemlock, grand fir, ponderosa pine, and occasionally western redcedar.

Small amounts of seeds are released annually, and heavy crops are produced at irregular intervals. Seedling growth is extremely vigorous, and plants only 4 years of age are often 4 ft or more in height. Considering the relatively short growing season, this seems all the more remarkable since Douglas-fir and ponderosa pine on the same site rarely exceed a height of 20 in. and Engelmann spruce seedlings of the same age are usually less than 1 ft high. This height growth advantage of the larch can continue for 10 to 20 years. Western larch is very intolerant throughout life and is dominant in old-growth mixed stands. Maturity is ordinarily reached in 300 to 400 years, but trees from 700 to 900 years of age have been reported. Commercially, this species attains its best development in the Priest River country of northern Idaho.

The bark of old trees is thick and moderately fire-resistant, but young trees are severely damaged by only a light ground fire. Wood-destroying fungi commonly attack overmature timber, and dwarf mistletoe reaches epidemic proportions in some localities. This tree, the most important of the larches, is used for fine veneer, lumber, and pulp. It was also split (rived) for shakes and shingles in earlier times if western redcedar was not available.

Lárix lyállii Parl.   Subalpine larch

Distinguishing Characteristics.   *Needles* 4-angled, pale blue-green. *Cones* erect, elliptical, 1½ to 2 in. (4 to 5 cm) long, with exserted, 3-toothed bracts. *Twigs* densely white woolly.

Range.   Southeastern British Columbia and southwestern Alberta south to western Montana and west to northeastern Washington. Elevation: 5000 to 8000 ft. Rocky soils near timberline; locally in pure stands and also mixed with other conifers.

General Description.   Subalpine larch is a small timberline tree, 30 to 50 ft tall and 1 to 2 ft dbh, with long, willowy, often pendulous branches, found on several high watersheds in the Cascade, Bitterroot, and northern Rocky Mountains. It occurs in pure open groves or intermingled with whitebark pine, mountain hemlock, subalpine fir, and Engelmann spruce. Because of its small size, poor form, and inaccessibility, subalpine larch is of no commercial importance. However, it is aesthetically attractive in the remote, high mountain terrain and also important for watershed protection. It hybridizes with western larch.

PICEA A. Dietr.   Spruce

The genus *Picea* includes about 35 species of trees which are largely restricted to the cooler regions of the northern hemisphere; about half of them are in China. The wood of the spruces is strong for its weight, moderately long-fibered, odorless, but slightly resinous, and is of primary importance in the manufacture of pulp and paper.

The most important European species is *Pìcea àbies* (L.) Karst., Norway spruce. This is a tall tree, readily identified by its dark yellow-green, usually drooping branchlets, somewhat laterally compressed leaves, and large, pendent cones 4 to 7 in. (10 to 18 cm) long (Fig. 8-37). This species, with many cultivars, are popular ornamentals in

FIGURE 8-37   *Picea abies.* Norway spruce. Open cone and seeds × ¾.

many sections of the United States and southeastern Canada. Norway spruce has been also widely used in forest plantations, especially in the east where it grows more rapidly than the native spruces. It has escaped from cultivation in various localities and is naturalized locally. The resinous bark exudations of this tree furnish the so-called Burgundy pitch which is the basic material for a number of varnishes and medicinal compounds, and the new leafy shoots are often used in brewing spruce beer.

In Asia the Himalayan spruce, *Picea smithiana* (Wall.) Boiss., is one of the most important of indigenous softwood species. *Picea jezoensis* (Sieb. and Zucc.) Carr., the yezo or jeddo spruce, and *Picea torana* (K. Koch.) Koehne [*P. polita* Carr.], the tigertail spruce, are two oriental species suitable for decorative purposes in the United States.

The natural enemies of the spruces are rather numerous, and some of them cause considerable damage to immature timber. Because of the thin bark, poor pruning, and flammable foliage, fire is always a serious menace, and damage by wind throw is common. The trees are also subject to periodic attacks of the eastern spruce gall aphid, which lays its eggs at the base of partially developed leaves near the tips of twigs. A large conelike gall soon develops, beyond which all growth ceases. The spruce budworm often destroys whole stands of young timber, while the white pine weevil may damage certain species. Trees growing in large industrial cities are frequently affected by smoke and flue gases.

Seven spruces are native to North America north of Mexico (Tables 8-9, 8-10). The Brewer spruce, *Pìcea breweriàna* S. Wats., a small tree in the Siskiyou Mountains of southern Oregon and northern California, is the only one which is of little or no commercial value. Interspecific hybridization occurs between sympatric species. See Little (1979) for more details.

Botanical Features of the Genus

Leaves spirally arranged, extending from all sides of the twigs or massed toward the upper surface; *shape* linear or nearly acicular; flattened, laterally compressed, or more commonly 4- (rarely 3-) angled, with numerous stomatiferous lines on the lower surfaces, or in many forms on all surfaces; *apex* usually sharp-pointed; persistent for 7 to

TABLE 8-9   COMPARISON OF EASTERN AND TRANSCONTINENTAL SPRUCES

Species	Leaves	Mature cones	Twigs
P. rubens red spruce	shiny, dark yellow-green	1¼–1½ in. (3–4 cm) long, ovoid-oblong; scales rounded on margin, sparingly erose or entire	more or less pubescent
P. mariana black spruce	dull blue-green, more or less glaucous	⅝–1¼ in. (1.5–3 cm) long, ovoid; scales rounded on margin, erose	pubescent
P. glauca white spruce	blue-green, glaucous, more or less fetid when crushed	1¼–2½ in. (3–6 cm) long, oblong-cylindrical; scales truncate on margin, entire	glaucous

TABLE 8-10   COMPARISON OF IMPORTANT WESTERN SPRUCES

Species	Leaves	Twigs	Seed cones
P. sitchensis Sitka spruce	flattened, bright yellow-green above, blue-green below, sharp pointed but not prickly; speading	glabrous; bud scales reflexed	2–3½ in. (5–9 cm) long; scales oblong or elliptical, apex truncate, erose, stiff; persisting 1 year
P. engelmannii Engelmann spruce	4-angled, blue-green, acute but not sharp pointed; usually pointing forward; not pungent to taste	minutely pubescent; bud scales appressed or slightly reflexed	1½–2½ in. (4–6 cm) long; scales rhombic-oblong; apex appressed, truncate to acute, erose, flexible; persisting 1 year
P. pungens blue spruce	4-angled, blue-green, sharp pointed and prickly, stiff; spreading; with pungent taste	glabrous; bud scales reflexed	2½–4 in. (6–10 cm) long; scales rhombic-oblong, apex spreading, truncate or emarginate, erose, flexible; persisting 2 years

10 years, sessile upon conspicuous peglike projections of the *twig*; when bruised frequently emitting an aromatic or fetid odor.

Cones (juvenile): *pollen cones* erect or pendent, stalked, consisting of numerous spirally arranged pollen sacs, appearing from axillary buds on the shoots of the previous season or terminal; *ovulate cones* terminal, erect or nearly so, composed of numerous purple or green scales each of which bears two inverted ovules and is subtended by a bract; all species monoecious.

Mature cones pendent (rarely nearly erect), woody, comprising a number of persistent, unarmed scales, often erose along the margins, and much longer than the bracts; *seeds* 2 to each cone scale, ovoid to cylindrical, often compressed, terminally winged; *cotyledons* 4 to 15.

Buds conic to ovoid, with numerous imbricated scales, resinous or nonresinous.

The Eastern and Transcontinental Spruces

Pìcea rùbens Sarg.   Red spruce

Distinguishing Characteristics (Fig. 8-38)

   Leaves ½ to ⅝ in. (12 to 15 mm) long, linear, 4-sided, shiny yellow-green, apex blunt or acute.

   Cones 1¼ to 1½ in. (3 to 4 cm) long, ovoid-oblong, chestnut-brown at maturity, falling during the first winter or following spring; *scales* rigid, rounded, entire on the margin or very lightly erose; *seeds* ⅛ in. (3 mm) long, dark brown; wings ¼ in. (6 mm) long.

FIGURE 8-38 *Picea rubens.* Red spruce. (1) Foliage × 1/2. (2) Dead twig showing pegs × 2. (3) Mature seed cone × ¾. (4) Seed × 1. (5) Open seed cone × ¾.

Twigs orange-brown, more or less pubescent; *buds* ovoid, reddish brown.

Bark ¼ to ½ in. (6 to 12 mm) thick, separating into close, irregular, grayish to reddish brown scales; inner layers reddish brown (Fig. 8-39).

Range
Northeastern (Map 8-12). Disjuncts in northwestern Connecticut, eastern Long Island, and northern New Jersey. Elevation: sea level northward to 6600 ft in the southern Appalachians. Swamps and bogs northward to mountain tops and ridges southward; often in pure stands or with fir.

General Description
Red spruce is one of the most important of northeastern conifers and is especially characteristic of the mountainous regions in northern New York and New England. In old-growth stands, trees 60 to 70 ft high and 12 to 24 in. dbh are common. Maximum development of the species occurs in the southern Appalachians where humidity and rainfall are especially high during the growing season. There the largest recorded tree was 162 ft high and 57 in. dbh.

Open-grown trees develop a broadly conical crown which extends nearly to the ground; under forest conditions the crown is restricted to the upper portion of the tree and is somewhat pagoda-shaped. The boles of forest-grown trees are long and cylindrical; the root system is shallow and wide-spreading.

Red spruce occurs in pure stands and also in mixture with many other species. It is found in swamps or bogs with black spruce, tamarack, balsam fir, and red maple but grows poorly on

FIGURE 8-39   Bark of old-growth red spruce.

such sites. Faster growth is made on adjacent better-drained flats in company with such species as balsam fir, eastern hemlock, eastern white pine, and yellow birch; while scattered trees occur throughout the neighboring hardwood mixture (sugar maple, yellow birch, and beech), on higher ground, where development is probably best. This species is also found in pure stands on upper slopes where the soil is very thin and rocky. In general, acid sandy loam soils with considerable moisture support the best spruce.

MAP 8-12   *Picea rubens.*

Abundant moisture is also essential for good reproduction, and the most favorable conditions are found under mixed stands of hardwoods and conifers. Open-grown spruce may begin to yield good seed crops when 30 to 40 years old, but in old-growth stands it is usually much later. Good seed years occur at 3- to 8-year intervals. The young trees are very tolerant, more so than those of the associated species, with the possible exception of eastern hemlock, sugar maple, and American beech; but they grow slowly under forest cover (1 ft in height may represent 15 years' growth); and even in the open they do not make rapid growth.

Red spruce is long-lived and scarcely reaches maturity in less than 200 years, and trees with 350 to 400 annual rings have been reported. Because of the shallow root system, red spruce is susceptible to wind throw; it is also severely damaged by fire and defoliated by the spruce budworm. Its decline and mortality since the 1960s are probably due to an interaction of insects, fungi, air pollution, and acid precipitation.

This is an important tree for paper pulp, lumber, musical string instruments, plywood, and flakeboard.

Pìcea maiàna (Mill.) B.S.P.   Black spruce

Distinguishing Characteristics (Fig. 8-40)

Leaves ¼ to ⅝ in. (6 to 15 mm) long, 4-sided, dull blue-green, blunt-pointed; more or less glaucous.

Cones ⅝ to 1¼ in. (1.5 to 3 cm) long, ovoid, purplish, turning brown at maturity; *scales* brittle, rigid, rounded, erose on the margin; *seeds* ⅛ in. (3 mm) long, dark brown; wings ¼ to ⅜ in. (6 to 9 mm) long. The cones persist for many years (20 to 30) and often form large clusters easily seen at a distance.

Twigs pubescent, brownish; *buds* ovoid, somewhat puberulous.

Bark ¼ to ½ in. (6 to 12 mm) thick, broken into thin, flaky, grayish brown to reddish brown scales; freshly exposed inner layers somewhat olive-green.

FIGURE 8-40   *Picea mariana*. Black spruce. (1) Mature seed cone × ¾. (2) Open seed cone × ¾. (3) Bark of old tree. (*Courtesy of Canadian Forest Service.*)

Range

Northern (Map 8-13). Several disjunct populations occur south of the general range. Elevation: sea level to 5000 ft. Acid bogs and swamps, lake shores, and dune ridges; less common in neutral or alkaline swamps.

General Description

Black spruce is a small to medium-size tree 30 to 40 ft high and 6 to 12 in. dbh (max. 100 by 3 ft), with a long, straight, tapering bole, irregularly cylindrical crown, and a shallow, spreading root system. In the southern part of its range, this species is commonly restricted to cool sphagnum bogs; in the far north it is also found on dry slopes but makes its best growth on moist, well-drained alluvial bottoms. Among the conifers, this species is of interest since with white spruce and tamarack it marks "the northern limit of tree growth" and assumes there a prostrate or shrubby habit. Black spruce is especially characteristic as a pioneer tree on the floating mats extending outward from the shores of small ponds which are slowly becoming bogs ("muskegs") through the deposition of plant material. In such situations growth is exceedingly slow, and "trees" 2 in. dbh may show from 80 to 90 growth rings or more in cross section.

Black spruce occurs in dense pure stands or in mixture with such species as tamarack, balsam fir, northern white cedar, black ash, quaking aspen, and paper birch. Like most of the other spruces, it is tolerant, but less so than balsam fir and northern white cedar. Natural pruning is poor, and unless the tree is grown in very dense stands, the side branches persist for many years.

Although most of the good seed is released during the first 4 years, viable seed may come from 15-year-old cones. Fire may start the opening of these semiserotinous cones, and large amounts of seed are then released. Some seed may be produced each year (after the tenth) with larger crops at irregular intervals. Propagation on wet sites also takes place by "layering;" the lower branches become embedded in the moist sphagnum and sprout roots, which eventually

MAP 8-13 *Picea mariana.*

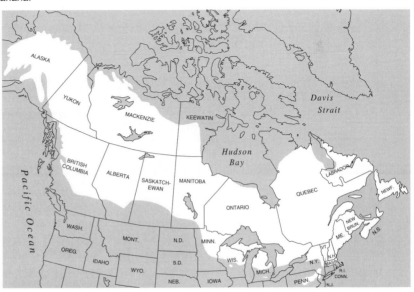

support the erect branch without aid from the parent tree. Black spruce may attain an age of 250 years.

This is the most important pulpwood species in Canada, but it is also used for lumber and Christmas trees. It is damaged by several fungous diseases, spruce budworm, sawflies, and dwarf mistletoe.

Pìcea glaùca (Moench) Voss   White spruce

Distinguishing Characteristics (Fig. 8-41)

Leaves ½ to ¾ in. (12 to 19 mm) long, linear, blue-green, and glaucous; apex acute but not sharp to the touch; tending to be crowded on the upper side of the branch by a twist at the base of those below; crushed foliage often with a pungent odor, hence the common name "cat spruce."

Cones 1¼ to 2½ in. (3 to 6 cm) long, narrowly oblong, light brown; *scales* thin and flexible, usually truncate, rounded, or slightly emarginate at the apex; *seeds* ⅛ in. (3 mm) long, pale brown; wings ¼ to ⅜ in. (6 to 9 mm) long.

Twigs glabrous, somewhat glaucous, orange-brown to gray; *buds* ovoid, with sometimes reflexed scales, ragged, or occasionally ciliate on the margin.

Bark thin, flaky or scaly, ashy brown; freshly exposed layers somewhat silvery.

Range

Northern (Map 8-14). Local disjuncts in central Montana, western South Dakota and northeastern Wyoming, and southeastern Michigan. Elevation: sea level to 4000 ft or timberline. Mesic to wet sites in conifer forests of muskegs, bogs, mountain slopes, and edges of streams or lakes.

General Description

White spruce is one of the most important and widely distributed conifers of Canada and extends southward into several of the northern United States. When grown in the open, it develops a handsome conical crown which extends nearly to the ground. Forest trees are from 60 to 70 ft in height and 18 to 24 in. dbh (max. 184 by 4 ft). The maximum age is more than 200 years.

FIGURE 8-41   *Picea glauca.* White spruce. (1) Mature seed cone and foliage × ¾. (2) Open seed cone × ¾. (3) Bark of old tree. (*Courtesy of Canadian Forest Service.*)

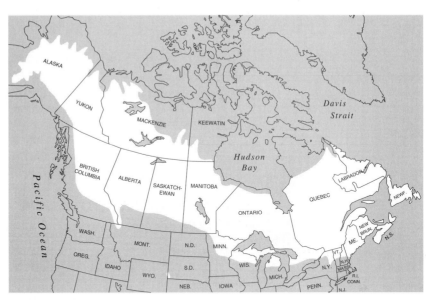

MAP 8-14 *Picea glauca.*

This species forms extensive pure stands but also occurs in mixture with quaking aspen, paper birch, jack and lodgepole pines, balsam fir, and black and red spruces. Best growth is made on moist loam or alluvial soils; and although found on many different sites, white spruce is especially typical of stream banks, lake shores, and adjacent slopes.

In comparison with the preceding species, white spruce is probably shorter-lived and in its early years makes faster growth. It is important for reforestation both in the United States and Canada, and it is used for lumber and pulp, house logs, and musical string instruments. It is also a widely planted ornamental. The pliable roots of white spruce are used by Native Americans for lacing birchbark canoes and making woven baskets.

Along the Canadian Rockies where the ranges of white spruce and Engelmann spruce overlap, certain varieties of white spruce have been recognized, including western white spruce *P. glauca* var. *albertiana* (S. Brown) Sarg. In this region, so much natural hybridization is taking place between white and Engelmann spruces that perhaps varieties should not be recognized (Wright, 1955). There is considerable variation in cone size and scale structure on these spruces.

While white spruce is host to a very wide variety of damaging insects and diseases, the frequency and intensity of wildfire are the primary causes of loss.

The Western Spruces

Pìcea sitchénsis (Bong.) Carr.   Sitka spruce

Distinguishing Characteristics (Fig. 8-42)

Leaves ⅝ to 1 in. (1.5 to 2.5 cm) long, flattened, bright yellow-green above, bluish white, glaucous below, very sharp-pointed, tending to extend outward at right angles from all sides of the twig.

FIGURE 8-42 *Picea sitchensis.* Sitka spruce. (1) Foliage × ½. (2) Pollen cone × 1. (3) Ovulate cone × 1. (4) Open seed cone × ¾. (5) Seed × 1. (6) Bark of old-growth tree (*Photo by J. D. Cress, Seattle*).

Cones 2 to 3½ in. (5 to 9 cm) long, ovoid-oblong, falling in the late autumn and early winter; *scales* thin, papery but stiff, oblong or elliptical, erose at the apex; *seeds* ⅛ in. (3 mm) long, reddish brown, the wings ⅓ to ½ in. (8 to 13 mm) long.

Twigs glabrous, orange-brown; *buds* ovoid, the scales obtuse.

Bark thin, rarely as much as 1 in. (2.5 cm) thick even on the largest trunks, divided at the surface into thin, loosely appressed, concave, and elliptical silvery gray to purplish gray scales.

Range

Northwestern (Map 8-15). Elevation: sea level to 2800 ft or timberline in Alaska, below 1200 ft in California. Coastal fog belt; peat bogs; in mixed or pure stands.

General Description

Sitka spruce, which is also known in the lumber trade as tidewater spruce, is one of the major timber-producing species of the Pacific Northwest. Mature trees on the Olympic peninsula of western Washington vary from 180 to 200 ft in height and from 4 to 5 ft dbh (max. 300 by 18 ft). Many individuals yield from 6000 to 8000 board feet of lumber, and an occasional tree contains as much as 40,000 ft B.M.

Forest-grown trees feature long, clear, cylindrical boles which terminate in short, open crowns with horizontal and ascending branches terminating in pendulous branchlets. The typically shallow wide-spreading root system provides only moderate resistance to wind throw.

Sitka spruce forms extensive pure forests in many parts of its range and also occurs in mixture with several other softwoods and hardwoods. In Alaska and elsewhere its chief associate is western hemlock. In British Columbia, Washington, and northcentral Oregon it mingles with Douglas-fir, western redcedar, Pacific silver and grand firs, red alder, bigleaf maple, and black cottonwood. Occasional associates in southern Oregon include redwood and Port-Orford-cedar. The largest trees throughout its range occur on deep loams of high moisture retention. This

MAP 8-15   (Left) *Picea sitchensis.* **(Right)** *Picea engelmannii.*

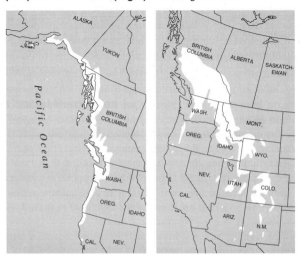

species also invades peat bogs of the Puget Sound region. Trees on such sites, however, are of poor form and rarely attain commercial size. Sitka spruce is a coastal species usually found no more than 30 miles from tidewater and often much closer, as the coastal plain is narrow and the mountains sometimes rise almost directly from the sea. An interesting growth form of this species is found on the dry sandy soils and dunes along the coasts of Oregon and northern California. Here, shaped by the ceaseless westerly winds, individuals may be dwarfed, contorted, sprawling, or prostrate.

Sitka spruce ordinarily produces some seed each fall (after the twentieth year) and usually releases copious crops every third or fourth year. Seedlings become readily established on a variety of soil types. Dependable moisture is required for seedling survival, and those growing on moist organic layers often die during droughts. Growth is vigorous in youth, and the trees soon overtop their forest associates. Their production of epicormic branches is rare among conifers. This spruce is rated as tolerant, but not as much so as western hemlock. Maturity is reached in about 500 years, but occasional forest monarchs 700 to 800 years old have been reported.

Sitka spruce is a source of lumber and pulp. During World War II the famous British "Mosquito" bomber's airframe was crafted of strong, lightweight Sitka spruce. Wind throw and the white pine weevil each cause serious losses.

Pìcea engelmánnii Parry ex Engelm.   Engelmann spruce

Distinguishing Characteristics (Fig. 8-43)

Leaves ⅝ to 1 in. (15 to 25 mm) long, 4-sided, blue-green, flexible, apex often blunt; with a rank odor when crushed; often somewhat appressed and tending to point toward the tip of the twig.

Cones 1½ to 2½ in. (4 to 6 cm) long, ovoid-oblong; *scales* thin and somewhat papery, rhombic-oblong, and commonly erose at the apex, appressed; *seeds* ⅛ in. (3 mm) long, nearly black; wings about ½ in. (13 mm) long, oblique.

Twigs more or less pubescent, light brown to gray; *bud scales* more often appressed than in blue spruce.

Bark very thin, broken into large purplish brown to russet-red, thin, loosely attached scales.

Range

Western (Map 8-15). Local disjuncts from eastern Washington to northern California, northcentral Montana, and southeastern Arizona. Elevation: 2000 to 3500 ft northward, 4000 to 12,000 ft southward. Subalpine zone to timberline (Fig. 8-44); in mixed or pure stands.

General Description

The name of this spruce commemorates Dr. George Engelmann, noted German-American physician and botanist of the middle nineteenth century.

Engelmann spruce is typically a mountain species and under favorable conditions for growth attains a height of from 100 to 120 ft and a dbh of 18 to 30 in., although somewhat larger trees (max. 179 by 8 ft) occur on the best sites. Its general habit is quite similar to that of Sitka spruce, and, like that species, it reaches its maximum size on deep, rich, loamy soils of high moisture content.

Besides occurring in extensive pure stands, Engelmann spruce is found with other species comprising some 14 recognized forest types. The most common associate is subalpine fir.

FIGURE 8-43   *Picea engelmannii.* Engelmann spruce. (1) Foliage × ½. (2) Mature seed cone × ¾. (3) Open seed cone × ¾. (4) Seed × 1. (5) Bud × 1. (6) Bark of old tree. (*Courtesy of Western Pine Association.*)

FIGURE 8-44   Windform of Engelmann spruce near timberline.

Through the central Rocky Mountains, lodgepole, limber, and whitebark pines, Douglas-fir, and quaking aspen may also be included (Burns and Honkala, 1990). Where the ranges of Engelmann and white spruce overlap, a confusing array of natural hybrids is to be found. Both Colorado blue and Sitka spruce produce hybrids with this species.

Engelmann spruce produces large crops of seed every 2 or 3 years (after the twentieth). Seedling development is good in moist duff soils covering the floor of virgin forests. However, seedling development is poorest in both deep shade and full sun. A few trees are also traceable to layering, but individuals produced in this way never attain commercial proportions.

This spruce is tolerant, but among its common associates is less so than subalpine fir and the hemlocks. Trees of all ages are often found under the canopy of old trees, and individuals often suppressed for 50 to 100 years quickly recover upon being released. Growth is restricted by a short summer season, and trees 16 to 22 in. dbh are often 350 to 450 years of age. The average maximum age for Engelmann spruce appears to be in the neighborhood of 400 years. Occasional trees over 600 years of age have been reported.

Periodic outbreaks of the Engelmann spruce bark beetle have been extremely damaging to mature stands in the central Rocky Mountain region. Several wood-rotting fungi and dwarf mistletoe also cause damage. The bark is thin, even on old trunks, and fires cause extensive damage. Wind throw, particularly in partially cut old-growth stands, results in heavy loss.

This spruce is a source of construction lumber, plywood, pulp, and wood for musical string instruments.

Picea púngens Engelm.   Blue spruce; Colorado blue spruce

Distinguishing Characteristics.   *Leaves* 4-sided, ¾ to 1¼ in. (2 to 3.1 cm) long, sharp-pointed, stiff, spreading, dull blue-green or bluish with whitish lines and glaucous when young, with a pungent resinous odor when crushed. *Cones* 2½ to 4 in. (6 to 10 cm) long, cylindrical, sessile or short-stalked, light brown, scales long and narrow, rhombic-oblong, erose, more or less flexible and spreading. *Twigs* glabrous, yellow-brown, stout, bud scales usually reflexed. *Bark* gray to reddish brown, furrowed with scaly round ridges.

Range.   Rocky Mountains of southern and western Wyoming and eastern Idaho, south to northern and eastern Arizona and southern New Mexico. Elevation: 6000 to 9000 ft in the north; 7000 to 10,000 ft in the south. Middle and upper slopes of the mountains.

General Description.   Those who are familiar only with the shapely and beautiful silvery-blue ornamental cultivars of this species would scarcely recognize the blue spruce in its central Rocky Mountain domain. Sculptured by gale-force winds and heavy snows, the trees often bear little resemblance to the carefully nurtured specimens of parks and yards. Even the foliage, except for a brief time in early spring when the needles are coated with a powdery waxy bloom, is dull dark green to blue-green with only an occasional silvery tree. Blue spruce is often 70 to 90 ft tall and 2 ft dbh (max. 126 by 5 ft). It resembles Engelmann spruce, with which it is sometimes associated at lower elevations.

Although not an important timber tree, this species and several of its varieties, because of their habit, beautiful foliage, and ability to withstand drought and extremes of temperatures, are highly prized as ornamentals.

PSEUDOTSUGA Carr.   Douglas-fir

This genus includes five species of trees widely scattered through the forests of western North America, southwestern China, Japan, and Taiwan. While these were originally included under *Abies,* they are readily distinguished by their pointed buds, petiolate leaves, pendent seed cones, persistent cone scales, and exserted 3-lobed bracts. Douglas-fir, *P. menziesii* (Mirb.) Franco, is the only important species in the genus and is one of two found in the western United States.

Botanical Features of the Genus

Leaves spirally arranged; *shape* linear, flattened, grooved on the upper surface and with a broad band of stomata on each side of the midrib below; *apex* blunt to rather sharply pointed; *base* constricted into a very short petiole; persistent for 5 to 8 years and leaving a suborbicular, slightly raised leaf scar upon removal or when shed; having a characteristic odor when crushed.

Cones (juvenile) solitary; *pollen cones* axillary, consisting of a number of spirally arranged, short-stalked, subglobose pollen sacs; *ovulate cones* conical, terminal or in the axils of the upper leaves, composed of several spirally arranged, imbricated, 3-lobed bracts each subtending a small ovate scale with two basal ovules; all species monoecious.

Mature cones ovoid-cylindrical, pendant, maturing at the end of the first season; the conspicuous 3-lobed *bracts* longer than the rounded *cone scales; seeds* more or less triangular, with a large, rounded terminal wing which partially envelops the seed; *cotyledons* 6 to 12.

Buds fusiform, sharp-pointed, covered by several imbricated, shining brown scales.

Pseudotsùga menzièsii (Mirb.) Franco [*P. taxifólia* (Lamb.) Britt.]
Douglas-fir

Distinguishing Characteristics (Fig. 8-45)

Leaves ¾ to 1¼ in. (2 to 3 cm) long, yellow-green or blue-green, standing out from all sides of the twig or with a tendency to be somewhat 2-ranked; *apex* rounded-obtuse or rarely acute, stomatiferous below, persistent for 8 or more years.

FIGURE 8-45 *Pseudotsuga menziesii.* Douglas-fir. (1) Foliage × ¾. (2) Buds × 1. (3) Mature seed cone (var. *menziesii*) × ¾. (4) Ovulate and pollen cones × 1. (5) Open seed cone (var. *glauca*) × ¾. (6) Seed × 1. (7) Bark of old tree.

Cones 2 to 4 in. (5 to 10 cm) long, pendent, ovoid-cylindric, with exserted, 3-lobed, forklike, appressed or strongly reflexed bracts; *seeds* triangular, terminally winged.

Buds fusiform, sharp-pointed, lustrous brown.

Bark on young stems smooth except for resin blisters; becoming 6 to 12 in. (15 to 31 cm) thick on old trees, and then divided into thick, reddish brown ridges separated by deep irregular fissures. In a few instances the bark is "tight" (fine-textured) on old trees and corky on others, particularly those of the mountain form.

Range

Western (Map 8-16). Elevation: sea level to 2000 ft northward and to 6000 ft southward; inland, above 2000 ft northward, 8000 to 10,000 ft southward. Moist soils along the coast; rocky soils on mountain slopes.

General Description

Douglas-fir, monarch of Pacific Northwest forests, was first observed by Menzies on Vancouver Island when he accompanied the British naval captain Vancouver on an expedition to the Pacific Coast in the early 1790s. For more than a quarter of a century this tree was variously classified as a spruce, hemlock, true fir, and even as a pine; in fact logs exported by the Hudson's Bay outpost near the mouth of the Columbia River were listed in European ports as "Oregon-pine," a name which has persisted in the trade to this day, especially in Australia. It remained for David Douglas, a Scottish botanist sent out by the Royal Horticultural Society in 1825, to study this tree and show that it was sufficiently different to be considered as distinct from other previously described conifers; later Carrière coined the new generic name *Pseudotsuga*. This name is a rather unfortunate choice since it literally means "false hemlock." The common name, Douglas-fir, commemorates Douglas and in addition serves to distinguish this species from the true firs (*Abies*).

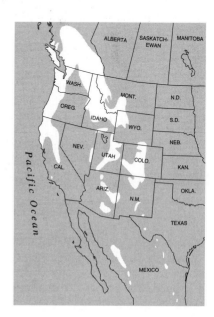

MAP 8-16 *Pseudotsuga menziesii.*

Douglas-fir comprises about 50 percent of the standing timber of our western forests, producing more timber than any other American species. It is also important as a Christmas tree.

Douglas-fir is a dimorphic species with two more or less distinct varieties. One of these is restricted to the forests of the Pacific slope, and the other to the Rocky Mountain region. However, in certain sections, the two types intergrade. Usually the foliage of the Rocky Mountain tree typically is blue-green, and that of the coast form yellow-green. However, atypical colors are found in both areas. The principal botanical difference between these two varieties lies in the structure of their cones. Rocky Mountain trees have small cones rarely 3 in. (7.5 cm) long, with much-exserted and strongly reflexed bracts. By contrast, the cones of the coastal form are often 4 in. (10 cm) long and have straight, more or less appressed bracts. To complicate matters further, there is a "Fraser River" or intermediate Douglas-fir, found in interior British Columbia, which is a form of the Rocky Mountain variety.

Coast Douglas-fir (*P. menziesii* var. *menziesii*).

This is the largest tree in the northwest, and in the United States it is second only to the giant sequoias of California. Trees in virgin forests average 180 to 250 ft in height and 4 to 6 ft dbh, although heights of 325 ft and diameters of 8 to 10 ft may be attained. The tallest reported specimen in the United States, near Mineral, Washington, was supposed to be 385 ft in height and 15 ft dbh. There are many who believe that the height is a great exaggeration, in fact just a lumberjack tale. In Olympic National Park, Washington, a tree was reported to be 221 ft tall and nearly 14 ft dbh.

Old trees are characterized by an exceptionally clear, long, cylindrical bole (Fig. 8-46) and either a rounded or an irregularly flat-topped crown. However, in closed stands of young trees, early natural pruning is poor, and a clear butt log may not begin to develop before the eightieth year. Anchorage is provided by a strong, well-developed, wide-spreading lateral root system. Trees are found on a variety of soils but make their best growth on deep, rich, well-drained, porous loams in regions where there is an abundance of both soil and atmospheric moisture. In youth Douglas-fir forms extensive, pure, even-aged stands, but these are later commonly invaded by other species. In the Pacific Northwest coniferous associates include western redcedar, western hemlock, Sitka spruce, and grand, Pacific silver, and noble firs. Although rated as intermediate in tolerance, Douglas-fir is less so than these associates, with the exception of noble fir. Red alder and Oregon white oak are also found in Douglas-fir forests. In the principal timber belt of the Sierras it occurs chiefly with white fir and ponderosa pine, in the northern coast ranges of California with ponderosa pine, tanoak, and Oregon white oak, and in the redwood belt with redwood.

Seed is produced in quantity after about the twenty-fifth year, with heavy crops at irregular intervals. Dense thickets spring up rapidly after logging, provided fires are excluded. Under favorable conditions trees 10 years of age may be 12 to 15 ft in height and 1 to 2 in. dbh. Pole size is often attained in 30 to 40 years, and saw logs may be harvested in less than 80 years. The trees attain great age and are commonly found with over 700 (max. 1375) growth rings.

Principal enemies are fire, the Douglas-fir bark beetle, certain heart rots and other fungi, and the dwarf mistletoe.

Rocky Mountain Douglas-fir [*P. menziesii* var. *glauca* (Beissn.) Franco].

This variety rarely exceeds a height of more than 130 ft or a diameter of 3 ft. It occurs in both pure and mixed stands with ponderosa pine, western larch, and grand fir. Other associates include western hemlock, western white and lodgepole pines, Engelmann spruce, white fir, and aspen. Douglas-fir is more tolerant than these except the hemlock and spruce.

FIGURE 8-46   Old-growth Douglas-fir. (*Photo by J. D. Cress, Seattle.*)

Although most abundant on moist sites, it is quite drought-resistant and is often found on arid areas with ponderosa pine. It is frost-resistant and hardy in the east and is a common ornamental of that region. The trees are grown for timber in Europe and have been planted successfully in many parts of the world.

Pseudotsùga macrocárpa (Vasey) Mayr   Bigcone Douglas-fir

Distinguishing Characteristics. *Leaves* pointed. *Cones* large, 4 to 6 in. (10 to 15 cm), with rigid, woody scales subtended by longer trident bracts.

Range. Southern California from eastern Santa Barbara County south along the mountains to Lower California. Elevation: 900 to 7875 ft. Dry slopes and canyons.

General Description. This tree never attains the grandeur or stature of the Douglas-fir, which it resembles. Its rapidly tapering bole (max. 173 by 7 ft), usually clothed for the greater part—if not all—of its length in a massive pyramidal crown, is seldom used for the production of lumber in commercial quantities. This tree contributes little or nothing to the nation's timber supply, but it is a valuable cover tree and aids materially in erosion control.

TSUGA (Endl.) Carr.   Hemlock

This genus includes about 10 species of evergreen, usually pyramidal-shaped trees confined to the forests of eastern and western North America, Japan, Taiwan, China, and the Himalaya. Hemlock pollen has been identified in several French and Polish peat bogs, and fossil wood has been unearthed in other sections of Europe, but hemlocks are not found in the modern forests of that continent.

The Japanese hemlocks, *T. sieboldii* Carr. and *T. diversifolia* (Maxim.) Mast., and the Chinese species, *T. chinensis* (Franch.) Pritz., are oriental timber-producing species. They are frequently used for ornamental purposes in other parts of the world, including North America.

Four species of *Tsuga* are indigenous to North America; two in the East and two in the West (Table 8-11). Of these, the western hemlock is at present the most important timber-producing species in this genus. Hemlock bark contains from 7 to 12 percent tannin, and in the United States, bark of the eastern hemlock was one of the principal commercial sources of tannin for many years.

Botanical Features of the Genus
Leaves spirally arranged, but often apparently 2-ranked by a twist of the petioles of the lowest leaves, and those on the upper side of the branchlet short and appressed;

TABLE 8-11   COMPARISON OF IMPORTANT HEMLOCKS

Species	Leaves	Mature cones
T. canadensis eastern hemlock	tapering from base to apex, bands of stomata well defined below	stalked, ⅝–¾ in. (1.5–2 cm) long, oblong-ovoid; scale margins not undulate
T. heterophylla western hemlock	uniform in width from base to apex, bands of stomata poorly defined below, upper surface grooved	sessile, ¾–1 in. (2–2.5 cm) long, ovoid; scale margins undulate

shape linear, flattened or less frequently angular or semicircular in cross section, generally grooved above, with two broad bands of stomata below; *margin* entire or frequently serrulate above the middle; *apex* blunt; conspicuously petioled; persistent for 3 to 6 years; borne on short peglike projections from the twig.

Cones (juvenile) solitary; *pollen cones* axillary, globose, consisting of a number of spiral pollen sacs; *ovulate cones* erect, terminal on the lateral branchlets, consisting of a number of membranous bracts each subtending a nearly orbicular scale with two basal ovules; *bracts* and *scales* of nearly the same length; all species monoecious.

Mature cones pendent, globose to ovoid or oblong, subsessile, maturing in one season; *scales* orbicular to ovate-polygonal, mostly with entire margins, several times longer than the bracts; *bract*s inconspicuous (rarely exserted); *seeds* small, ovoid-oblong, dotted with minute resin vesicles, with obovate, terminal wings; *cotyledons* 3 to 6.

Buds small, ovoid to globose, nonresinous.

Tsùga canadénsis (L.) Carr.   Eastern hemlock; Canada hemlock

Distinguishing Characteristics (Fig. 8-47)

Leaves ⅓ to ⅔ in. (8 to 15 mm) long, tapering from base to apex, dark yellow-green, rounded or slightly emarginate at apex, margin serrulate, marked below with 2 white lines of stomata; persistent until the third season.

Cones ⅝ to ¾ in. (1.5 to 2 cm) long, short stalked, oblong-ovoid; *scales* with suborbicular, smooth margins; shedding their seeds during the winter and often persistent during the next season; *seeds* ca. 1/16 in. (1 to 2 mm) long, with several resin vesicles; wings terminal, broad.

Bark on young trees flaky or scaly; some with wide, flat ridges; on old trees heavily and deeply furrowed; freshly cut surfaces showing purplish streaks.

Range

Northeastern (Map 8-17). Local disjuncts in central North Carolina, northwestern Alabama, western Ohio, and central Indiana. Elevation: sea level to 2400 ft northward, generally 2000 to 6000 ft southward. Cool, moist valleys, coves, and slopes, low ridges, bluffs, lake shores; in mixed or pure stands.

General Description

Eastern hemlock is usually a medium-size tree 60 to 70 ft high and 2 to 3 ft dbh, although in the mountains of West Virginia, North Carolina, and Tennessee it has attained a maximum height of 160 ft and a diameter of 6 to 7 ft. This species is exceedingly graceful in youth, and open-grown trees develop a dense, pyramidal crown, with the lower branches often touching the ground. The slender terminal leader in hemlocks is rare among conifers in that the new growth droops or curves away from the vertical as much as by 90 degrees or more. During the first season, compression wood develops on the under surface of the curve, and straightening begins. Several years may pass before this is completed, and the curved tip is at any season an excellent mark of identification. The crowns of old trees are inclined to be ragged in outline; even in dense stands the lower branches remain alive for many years and, when dead, prune poorly. This causes knots, which in this species are often remarkably hard and flintlike. The bole, except in old trees, shows considerable taper and is supported below by a very superficial, wide-spreading root system. The shallow root system makes it very susceptible to drought damage.

FIGURE 8-47   *Tsuga canadensis.* Eastern hemlock. (1) Ovulate cone × 2. (2) Pollen cones × 2. (3) Mature seed cone × ¾. (4) Open seed cone × ¾. (5) Seed × 1. (6) Foliage × ½. (7) Leaf showing 2 white bands below × 2. (8) Bark of old tree.

This tree is found on many types of soil, and it reaches its best development in cool, moist situations. Eastern hemlock is remarkably tolerant, perhaps more so than any of its associates. Growth rings of trees under heavy shade may be so narrow that a handlens is needed to see them. When such a suppressed tree is liberated by the removal of others around it, the sudden increase in growth is often amazing. Rings 10 times the width of the previous ones may be produced.

In the north common associates of eastern hemlock are eastern white pine, red spruce, sugar maple, American beech, and yellow birch, while farther south additional ones include white ash, yellow-poplar, yellow buckeye, basswood, and several white and red oaks. Eastern hemlock occurs in several forest types with these and other species, and over long periods tends to replace them; pure stands, however, are of limited extent.

Abundant seed is produced at 2- to 3-year intervals, and seedling reproduction is plentiful on moist, shaded humus; in fact, the seeds even germinate on old, partially rotted stumps or logs, and occasionally in the axils of tree branches. In this respect, yellow birch is the chief competitor, both beginning as epiphytes. Although some reproduction may occur on bare, exposed soil,

MAP 8-17 **(Left)** *Tsuga heterophylla.* **(Right)** *Tsuga canadensis.*

this hemlock usually starts under the shade of other species and, growing very slowly, forces its way, during a period of a century or more, into the crown cover overhead. An age of 600 years or more may be attained. The record age is 988 years.

Hemlocks are valued as ornamentals, and young trees may show great variation in form and foliage. About 70 cultivars of the eastern hemlock have been described.This tree is also used for lumber, newspaper pulp, and the bark for tanning. Several fungi, such as root rots and rusts, and many insects may cause damage. The most recent and extreme damage is from the hemlock woolly adelgid which started in the northeast and has spread southward into the Virginia mountains. It may have the potential for extreme destruction to the natural stands.

Tsùga caroliniàna Engelm.   Carolina hemlock

This species is endemic to the upper, dry, rocky slopes, ridges, and ledges of the southern Appalachian Mountains from southwestern Virginia to northeastern Georgia; elevation 2300 to 4000 ft. The cones (Fig. 8-48) and leaves are longer [cone ¾ to 1⅜ in. (2 to 3.5 cm); leaves ⅜ to ¾ in. (10 to 19 mm)] than those of eastern hemlock, the leaves spread in all directions, and the margins are entire. Carolina hemlock is well adapted to relatively drier sites than is eastern hemlock. It is sometimes used as an ornamental. It reaches 40 to 60 ft tall and 2 ft dbh.

Tsùga heterophýlla (Raf.) Sarg.   Western hemlock; Pacific hemlock

Distinguishing Characteristics (Fig. 8-49)

Leaves ¼ to ¾ in. (6 to 18 mm) long, flattened, of uniform width from base to apex, dark shiny green, grooved above, with 2 poorly defined bands of stomata below; mostly rounded or blunt at the apex, margin serrulate, persistent for 4 to 7 years.

Cones ¾ to 1 in. (1.8 to 2.5 cm) long, sessile, ovoid, light brown; *scales* suborbicular, often more or less wavy along the margin; *seeds* ca. ¹⁄₁₆ in. (2 mm) long, ovoid, nearly surrounded by a large straw-colored wing.

FIGURE 8-48 *Tsuga caroliniana*. Carolina hemlock. Open seed cone × ¾.

Bark thin even on the largest trees, separated by deep, narrow fissures into broad, flat, russet-brown ridges; inner bark dark red streaked with purple.

Range
Northwestern (Map 8-17). Elevation: sea level to 2000 ft along coast; to 6000 ft inland. Deep, moist, acid soils on flats and also drier lower slopes.

General Description
Western hemlock is one of the major timber-contributing species in the Pacific Northwest. Largest of the four American hemlocks, this tree varies from 125 to 175 ft in height and 2 to 4 ft

FIGURE 8-49 *Tsuga heterophylla*. Western hemlock. (1) Foliage and seed cones × ¾. (2) Seed × 1. (3) Bark of old tree.

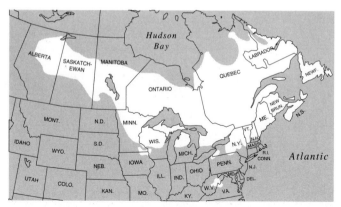

MAP 8-18   *Abies balsamea.* The disjunct area in Virginia and West Virginia is *A. balsamea* var. *phanerolepis.*

dbh (max. 259 by 9 ft). Forest trees produce a long, clear, symmetrical bole and a shallow, wide-spreading root system. The crown is short, open, and pyramidal, and, like the eastern hemlock, features a drooping terminal leader. An abundance of both soil and atmospheric moisture is requisite for rapid growth, and the largest trees are invariably found on moist porous soils in regions where the annual precipitation is at least 70 in. per year. In drier situations the trees are somewhat smaller and slower-growing but do eventually reach commercial proportions. Western hemlock occurs in pure, dense, even-age forests and as an occasional tree in mixed hardwood and coniferous stands, then commonly as an understory species. Nearly pure, extensive forests of western hemlock occur in southeastern Alaska, coastal British Columbia, and western Washington. Those restricted to the middle-upper western slopes of the Cascade and Olympic Mountains usually occur above the Douglas-fir belt. At low elevations hemlock commonly invades forests chiefly composed of Douglas-fir, Pacific silver and grand firs, western redcedar, black cottonwood, bigleaf maple, and red alder. At higher levels its associates include noble fir, Alaska-cedar, mountain hemlock, and western white pine. Western hemlock is a major component of five forest types, and a minor species in eleven others (Burns and Honkala, 1990).

Western hemlock begins to produce seed after the twenty-fifth to thirtieth year, and large crops are borne every 2 to 8 years thereafter. Nearly any sort of soil provides a satisfactory seedbed. Partially rotted stumps and logs are often literally covered with hemlock seedlings, and fresh mineral soil, moist duff, or even sphagnum peat are suitable for seedling development. This species often usurps cutover and burned-over areas formerly occupied by other species when moisture is not a limiting factor. The trees are very tolerant throughout life. Rate of growth compares favorably with that of Douglas-fir, and trees 90 to 100 years of age are commonly 110 to 130 ft high and 15 to 18 in. dbh. The largest trees rarely attain an age of more than 500 years. Western hemlock is susceptible to fire injury, butt rot is prevalent in overmature trees, and dwarf mistletoe is a common parasite.

Western hemlock timber was virtually unknown until the close of World War I, except locally. However, since then it has found a ready market in many of the world's leading lumber centers. It is also a major pulping species in the northwest. The bark of this tree contains tannin (9 to 16 percent), but it is rarely used commercially.

Tsùga mertensiàna (Bong.) Carr.   Mountain hemlock

Distinguishing Characteristics (Fig. 8-50).   *Leaves* ¼ to 1 in. (6 to 25 mm) long, blue-green, semicircular in cross section, margin entire, the upper surface often keeled or grooved;

FIGURE 8-50   *Tsuga mertensiana.* Mountain hemlock. Foliage and mature seed cones × ½.

extending from all sides of the twig or crowded toward the upper side, stomatiferous on all surfaces. *Cones* 1 to 3 in. (2.5 to 7.5 cm) long (the largest cones are found on trees toward the southern limits of the range), oblong-cylindrical, yellow-green to purple, the scales often strongly reflexed after shedding their seeds; *seeds* ⅛ in. (3 mm) long, with one or two resin vesicles; the wings terminal, about ½ in. (13 mm) long. *Bark* dull purplish brown to reddish brown, divided into narrow flattened ridges by deep, narrow fissures.

Range.   Southern Alaska south along the coast ranges of British Columbia, Washington, and Oregon, and inland on the upper slopes of the Sierra Nevada to central California; also in southeastern British Columbia, and south in the Rocky Mountains to northeastern Oregon, northern Idaho, and northwestern Montana. Elevation: sea level to 3500 ft northward, 5500 to 11,000 ft southward. Sheltered valleys, alpine meadows to exposed slopes and ridges, in mixed or pure stands.

General Description.   Mountain hemlock, although one of the largest of alpine trees, is often a low, sprawling, or even prostate shrub on windswept ridges at timberline. Forest trees, however, average 75 to 100 ft in height and 2½ to 3½ ft dbh (max. 125 by 7 ft) and are characterized by a shallow root system which supports a long, clear or limby bole with a narrow pyramidal crown of drooping or even pendulous branches. Trees on the sides of canyons and on very steep slopes are commonly pistol-butted (Fig. 8-51). In open situations, particularly in high alpine meadows, the boles are excessively tapered. Here mountain hemlock forms pure, parklike stands or occurs with subalpine fir, subalpine larch, Engelmann spruce, and whitebark pine. The best stands of this species, however, are found on moist slopes, flats, and heads of ravines of northerly exposure. While pure stands are seldom extensive, mountain hemlock commonly constitutes 85 percent or more of certain mixed coniferous forests. This species reaches its maximum development in southern Oregon, and well-stocked stands are found in the vicinity of Crater Lake National Park.

Seeds are borne at an early age, and regular crops are produced annually after the twenty-fifth to thirtieth year. Seedlings are very tolerant, comparing favorably in this respect with those

FIGURE 8-51   Mountain hemlock. *(Courtesy of U.S. Forest Service.)*

of western hemlock. Dense shade causes suppression, but the trees recover rapidly upon being released. Growth is at no time rapid, and trees 200 to 300 years of age are seldom ever more than 18 to 24 in. dbh on the best sites. Trees 500 years of age or more are rarely found. The laminated root rot which kills in expanding circles is a virulent pathogen of mature stands.

This species is used as an ornamental in a number of European countries, and several cultivars are now known. The bark of mature trees contains large quantities of tannin, but owing to the relative inaccessibility of the trees, it is not used at the present time. Like the subalpine fir, it promises to be a more important timber and pulpwood tree in the future.

ABIES Mill.   Fir

The genus *Abies* includes 42 species of trees, widely scattered through the forests of North and Central America, Europe, Asia, and northern Africa. Trees growing in southern latitudes are usually restricted to the upper slopes of mountains and are commonly found on sites at or near timberline; those in boreal forests, however, are largely confined to regions of relatively low elevations, with only a few forms ascending to the upper limits of tree growth.

This genus comprises a number of important species, although the timber produced is often somewhat inferior to that of the spruces. Several species, including balsam fir, furnish pulpwood. Other forest products traceable to certain of the firs include the oleoresins known to the trade as Canada balsam (Strasburg turpentine) and leaf oils. The former is obtained from superficial pitch blisters on the bark and used chiefly in the manufacture of medicinal compounds and varnishes, as a mounting medium in the preparation of microscope slides, and for cementing lenses in optical instruments. Leaf oils are largely used in the manufacture of pharmaceutical compounds.

Abies pindrow Royle, Himalayan silver fir, is a valuable species indigenous to India. *Abies alba* Mill., silver fir, or "Swiss pine," is an important timber tree of southern and central Europe. Japanese momi and nikko firs, *A. firma* Sieb. & Zucc. and *A. homolepis* Sieb. & Zucc., are two noteworthy trees of Japan, the former being one of its principal pulpwood species. In Central America the wood of the sacred fir, *A. religiosa* (HBK) Schlecht. & Cham., is used, particularly in Mexico and Guatemala, for structural purposes. Siberian fir, *A. sibirica* Ledeb., forms extensive forests through northern and eastern Russia, Siberia, and Turkestan. Some of the timber produced by this species has been offered to the world's trade, and it may become a competitor of the American pulpwood species.

A number of the introduced firs are highly prized for decorative purposes. Spanish fir, *A. pinsapo* Boiss., a tree with sprucelike needles, is a common ornamental in the Pacific Northwest. The stately Greek fir, *A. cephalonica* Loud., Nordmann fir, *A. nordmanniana* (Steven) Spach., and nikko fir are other trees favored for decorative use.

Eleven species of *Abies* are included in the coniferous flora of North America (FNA vol 2, 1993). Nine of these are scattered through the forests of the west (Table 8-12), while two are found in the east. See Robson et al. (1993) for a recent study of the species relationships.

Botanical Features of the Genus
Leaves spirally arranged, often more or less pectinate, sessile; *shape* linear, flattened in cross section, or rarely 4-angled and then grooved above, with numerous lines of stomata on the lower or occasionally all surfaces; *apex* acute, rounded, or shallowly to deeply notched or bifid; persistent for 7 to 10 years; usually with a balsamic, or turpentinelike, odor when bruised.
Cones (juvenile) solitary; *pollen cones* appearing from buds of the previous season, and borne on the underside of the lower crown branches in the axils of leaves, pollen sacs spirally arranged; *ovulate cones* erect, composed of many bracts each subtending a large scale with two inverted basal ovules; strobili axillary on the upper crown branches of the previous season's growth; all species monoecious.

TABLE 8-12   COMPARISON OF IMPORTANT WESTERN FIRS

Species	Lower crown leaves	Mature cones	Bark
A. amabilis Pacific silver fir	ca. 1 in. (2–4 cm) long, flattened, stomatiferous below	ca. 4½ in. (7.5–15 cm) long, the bracts shorter than the scales	silvery white to ashy gray
A. magnifica California red fir	ca. 1 in. (2–3.5 cm) long, 4-angled, stomatiferous on all surfaces	ca. 7½ in. (15–23 cm) long, the bracts shorter than the scales	red-brown
A. procera noble fir	ca. 1¼ in. (2.5–4 cm) long, 4-angled, grooved, above, stomatiferous on all surfaces	ca. 5 in. (10–18 cm) long, the bracts exserted	dark gray, tinged with purple
A. grandis grand fir	ca. 1¼ in. (2–5 cm) long, flattened, stomatiferous below, 2-ranked	ca. 3 in. (5–11 cm) long, the bracts shorter than the scales	gray-brown to reddish brown
A. concolor white fir	ca. 2½ in. (4–7.5 cm) long, flattened, stomatiferous on both sides, obscurely 2-ranked	ca. 4 in. (7.5–13 cm) long, the bracts shorter than the scales	dark ashy gray to nearly black, horny

Mature cones erect, maturing at the end of the first season; *scales* thin, broadly fan-shaped, particularly near the center of the cone, longer or shorter than the bracts; *bracts* apiculate, often shouldered, their margins erose; both scales and bracts together deciduous at maturity, leaving a mostly bare spikelike axis which frequently persists through the winter; *seeds* ovoid to oblong, with conspicuous resin vesicles; the broad terminal wings often delicately tinted with shades of pink, rose, lavender, or brown; *cotyledons* 5 to 7.

Twigs with ovoid to oblong buds, blunt, less commonly pointed, resinous or rarely nonresinous; leaf scars smooth, circular, and light colored.

Eastern Firs

Àbies balsàmea (L.) Mill.   Balsam fir

Distinguishing Characteristics (Fig. 8-52)

Leaves ½ to 1 in. (12 to 25 mm) long, flattened, dark shiny green above, silvery banded below, blunt, or slightly notched at the apex, 2-ranked, tending to crowd toward the upper surface of the twig.

Cones 2 to 3½ in. (5 to 9 cm) long, oblong-cylindrical, green tinged with purple; *bracts* usually shorter than the scales, with rounded erose shoulders and short, pointed tips; *seeds* ca. ⅛ in. (3 mm) long, with broad purplish brown wings.

Buds ⅛ to ¼ in. (3 to 6 mm) long, subglobose, resinous, with orange-green scales.

Bark ½ in. (13 mm) thick, dull green, later with grayish patches, smooth except for numerous raised resin blisters; eventually breaking up into small reddish brown irregular scaly plates.

FIGURE 8-52 *Abies balsamea.* Balsam fir. (1) Foliage × ½. (2) Mature seed cone × ½. (3) Dead twig showing smooth, round leaf scars × 1½. (4) Seed cone with scales partly dehisced × ¾. (5) Seed cone axis remaining after nearly all scales have dehisced × ¾. (6) Abaxial view of scale with subtending bract × 1¼. (7) Adaxial view of scale with 2 winged seeds × 1¼. (8) Bark of old tree.

Range

Northern (Map 8-18, p. 181). Local disjuncts in southwestern Wisconsin, northeastern Iowa, West Virginia, and Virginia. Elevation: sea level to timberline northward, to 5700 ft southward. Swamps to well-drained uplands.

General Description

Balsam fir is a small to medium-size tree 40 to 60 ft high and 12 to 18 in. dbh (max. 125 by 3 ft). It is perhaps the most symmetrical of northeastern trees with its dense, dark green, narrowly pyramidal crown, terminating in a stiff, spikelike tip (Fig. 8-53). The moderately tapering bole usually retains small dead, persistent branches, and is supported by a shallow, wide-spreading root system.

FIGURE 8-53   Balsam fir. (*Courtesy of U.S. Forest Service.*)

Balsam fir is a cold-climate tree, requiring abundant moisture for best development. In swamps it often forms pure stands but does best in association with spruce on the adjacent flats which are better drained; even here pure stands or groups are commonly found. On higher ground, it occurs as a scattered tree in mixture with other northern species. It appears again in dwarfed, matted, pure stands, or entangled with black spruce near the windswept summits of northern mountains where great extremes in temperature occur.

Good seed years occur at about 2-year intervals after the fifteenth, and large quantities of seeds are then produced. It is aggressive in restocking cutover lands, and makes rapid growth if not shaded. Propagation of new fir trees by layering occurs from lower branches in contact with moist soil. Balsam fir is more shade-tolerant than most of its associates, including tamarack, the pines, white spruce, aspens, and white birch. For a complete list of associates and tolerances, see Bakuzis and Hansen (1965).

This fir is short-lived, and although it may reach an age of nearly 200 years, trees over 90 years old show a high percentage of heart rot caused by wood-destroying fungi. The chief insect enemies of balsam fir are the spruce budworm and the balsam woolly adelgid; fire also causes severe loss.

Although the balsam fir was the leading Christmas tree for many years in the eastern United States, its use now has been diminished by plantation-grown fraser fir, various pines, Douglas-fir, and red cedar.

Abies balsamea var. *phanerolepis* Fern., intermediate between *A. balsamea* and *A. fraseri* in cone morphology and also geography, has been variously interpreted as a relict hybrid from an earlier time (Pleistocene) when the species were sympatric, an ecotype or variety of balsam fir, or a relict of an ancient north–south cline (see Clarkson and Fairbrothers, 1970; Thor and Barnett, 1974). The West Virginia population is locally known as Canaan fir and it is grown commercially for Christmas trees in that area.

Àbies fràseri (Pursh) Poir.   Fraser fir; Fraser balsam fir

This species is very similar to *A. balsamea* except for the cone bracts which are longer than the scales and strongly reflexed. It is considered as *A. balsamea* var. *fraseri* Spach by some (Thor and Barnett, 1974). Typical trees have a characteristic appearance and reach a height of 30 to 50 ft. It is a tree of the high mountains in southwestern Virginia, western North Carolina, and eastern Tennessee at 4500 to 6684 ft of elevation.

This species is of particular importance in the Christmas tree trade and is cultivated extensively for this purpose. Nearly all of the natural stands have been severely damaged by the balsam woolly adelgid in combination with acid precipitation. First found on Mount Mitchell, North Carolina, in 1957, the once magnificent stands in such locations as Mount Mitchell and elsewhere in North Carolina and Tennessee are now only dead snags. Reproduction is extensive, however, and the future status of Fraser fir in natural stands is extremely uncertain.

Western Firs

Àbies amábilis Dougl. ex Forbes   Pacific silver fir; Cascades fir

Distinguishing Characteristics (Fig. 8-54)

Leaves ¾ to 1½ in. (2 to 4 cm) long, lustrous dark green above, silvery white (stomatiferous) below; flattened in cross section, deeply grooved above; crowded toward the upper side of the twig, those above often twisted at the base in such a way that they appear to be appressed along the twig; notched or pointed at the apex; those from cone-bearing branches occasionally somewhat thicker and often also stomatiferous on the upper surface at the apex.

FIGURE 8-54   *Abies amabilis.* Pacific silver fir. (1) Foliage × ½. (2) Seed × 1. (3) Mature seed cone × ¾. (4) Abaxial view of cone scale and subtending bract × 1. (5) Bark of old tree.

Cones 3 to 6 in. (7.5 to 15 cm) long, cylindrical to barrel-shaped, deep purple; *bracts* shorter than the scales, with rounded, poorly defined shoulders, and a broad, wedgelike spinose tip; *seeds* ca. ½ in. (13 mm) long, yellowish brown, the wings very broad, straw-colored.

Twigs stout, yellowish brown, puberulous; buds ¼ in. (5 to 7 mm) long, subglobose, dark purple, resinous.

Bark ashy gray, with large, irregular chalky-colored blotches and resin blisters on stems up to 3 ft dbh; superficially scaly on the largest trunks.

Range

Northwestern (Map 8-19). Local disjunct in northwestern California. Elevation: sea level to 1000 ft northward, to 6600 ft southward. Coastal fog belt and interior mountain valleys and slopes.

General Description

Pacific silver fir is the most abundant fir in the Pacific Northwest and forms extensive pure stands in many localities. It attains its largest proportions in the Olympic Mountains in western Washington, where mature trees vary from 140 to 160 ft in height and 2 to 4 ft dbh (max. 245 by 8 ft). The bole and root systems are similar to those of other firs of low altitudes, but the crown, particularly of old trees, is usually pyramidal or even spikelike; hence it is readily distinguished from that of either the noble or grand fir, which are usually domelike. The trees are most abundant on deep moist soil covering slopes of southern and western exposure and grown on a variety of soil types. In mixed stands at low levels this species is commonly associated with Sitka spruce, Douglas-fir, grand fir, western hemlock, and western redcedar, while at higher altitudes it occurs with Engelmann spruce, subalpine and noble firs, Alaska-cedar, western larch, western white pine, and mountain hemlock.

Large seed crops are borne every 3 to 6 years (after the thirtieth). Seedlings become readily established in either a duff or mineral soil and are very tolerant. In fact, this species is considered as tolerant as western hemlock and western redcedar, and it may be that the true climax forest west of the Cascades and in the Olympics is one of Pacific silver fir. Although excessive shade results in extremely slow growth, excellent recovery is made upon release. Even so, growth is not rapid, and forest trees 150 to 250 years of age are often only 15 to 24 in. dbh. Maturity is attained in about 250 years; trees of a much greater age are seldom found (max. 540 years).

MAP 8-19   **(Left)** *Abies amabilis.* **(Right)** *Abies magnifica.*

Because of its beautifully shaped crown and dense lustrous foliage, the silver fir is commonly used ornamentally, particularly in Europe. It is also used for construction lumber, plywood, and pulp. Pacific silver fir and noble fir have long been known as "larch," because that name was once commonly applied to lumber from these two species and shipped to the orient.

Outbreaks of balsam woolly adelgid have reached epidemic proportions and have taken a heavy toll among all age and vigor classes. Wood-destroying and root-rotting fungi are common in overmature timber. Damage also occurs from other fungi, several insects, and dwarf mistletoe. Wood-destroying fungi are common in overmature timber. Fire and wind throw cause much damage.

Àbies magnífica A. Murr.   California red fir; red fir

Distinguishing Characteristics (Fig. 8-55)

Leaves ¾ to 1⅜ in. (2 to 3.5 cm) long, silvery-blue to dark blue-green, on new shoots often silvery white; 4-angled, stomatiferous on all sides, usually pointed at the apex, crowded toward the upper side of the branchlets.

Cones 6 to 9 in. (15 to 23 cm) long, 2 to 3¼ in. (5 to 8 cm) in diameter, cylindrical to barrel-shaped, purplish brown; *bracts* shorter than the scales, with more or less parallel edges and terminating rather abruptly in a spikelike tip; *seeds* ½ to ¾ in. (13 to 19 mm) long, dark brown, with large, broad, reddish purple terminal wings. *Abies magnifica* var. *shastensis* Lemm., Shasta red fir, has bracts longer than the cone scales, but there are intermediate forms.

Twigs light brown; *buds* ¼ in. (6 mm) long, ovoid, dark brown, nonresinous, or slightly resinous.

Bark smooth and chalky on young stems; 4 to 6 in. (10 to 15 cm) thick on old trunks and divided by deep furrows into rounded or plated reddish-colored ridges.

Range

Western (Map 8-19). Elevation: sea level to 4500 ft northward, 5300 to 9000 ft southward. Mountain slopes, ravines, and ridges.

General Description

This is one of the two largest North American firs, and at maturity it varies from 150 to 180 ft in height and 4 or 5 ft dbh (max. 230 by 10 ft). Under forest conditions it is similar in form to noble fir, but it is at once distinguished from that species by its reddish-colored bark. The largest trees are found on cool, moist, gravelly, or sandy soils in sheltered ravines and gulches or in protected mountain slopes, although this species also reaches commercial proportions on much poorer sites. California red fir occurs in pure forests above the white fir belt and in some sections it is a common tree at timberline. In mixed stands it is found with many species; in southern Oregon and northern California these include Douglas-fir, sugar pine, and ponderosa pine at lower altitudes, and mountain hemlock and lodgepole pine at higher levels. In the Sierras it is found with white and Shasta firs, lodgepole, western white, ponderosa, Jeffrey, and sugar pines, incense-cedar, giant sequoia, and mountain hemlock. Trees at high elevations standing on exposed ridges frequently lose their upper crowns from the action of gale-force winds. Such destroyed crowns may be replaced by upsweeping lateral branches from just below the broken top. This replacement growth is often distinctive when silhouetted against the sky.

Red fir produces large seed crops every 2 or 3 years (after the fortieth). Seedlings are hardy and survive well. They are moderately tolerant, but older trees cannot meet intensive forest

FIGURE 8-55 *Abies magnifica.* California red fir. (1) Foliage × ½. (2) Mature seed cone × ¾. (3) Seed × 1. (4) Abaxial view of scale and subtending bract × 1. (5) Bark of old tree.

competition and are intermediate in this respect. Growth is never rapid, and trees 250 to 350 years of age are commonly only 20 to 35 in. dbh. The longevity of this species is not too well-known, but trees in excess of 500 years of age have been reported.

This species is damaged by several insects and fungi, but dwarf mistletoe is the most serious pathogen of California red fir.

Àbies prócera Rehd.   Noble fir

Distinguishing Characteristics (Fig. 8-56)

Leaves 1 to 1⅝ in. (2.5 to 4 cm) long, blue-green, 4-angled in cross section, stomatiferous on all surfaces, grooved above, pointed at the apex, and crowded toward the upper side of the twig; those on sterile branches flexible, somewhat flattened; those on cone-bearing shoots stout, stiff, and nearly equally 4-sided.

Cones 4 to 7 in. (10 to 18 cm) long, 1⅝ to 2⅜ in. (4 to 6 cm) in diameter, cylindrical, olive-brown to purple; *bracts* exserted, strongly reflexed, and imbricate, thus completely ensheathing the cone; *seeds* ½ in. (12 mm) long, dull brown, often tinged with red; wings lustrous light brown to straw-colored.

Twigs slender, reddish brown, finely pubescent; *buds* ⅛ in. (3 mm) long, blunt, oblong-conical, resinous.

Bark 1 to 2 in. (2.5 to 5 cm) thick, gray and smooth for many years, with prominent resin blisters; eventually dark gray, often tinged with purple and broken up into thin, nearly rectangular plates separated by deep fissures on old trunks.

Range

Northwestern (Map 8-20). Elevation: mainly 3500 to 7000 ft, infrequently 200 to 8900 ft. Mountain ridges, slopes, and high valleys.

General Description

Noble fir, the largest (max. 278 by 9 ft) of the Cascade firs and the one producing the best timber, has, unfortunately, the smallest range. It was first discovered in 1825 by David Douglas in the Oregon Cascades near the Columbia River. The finest stands have long since been logged, and those which remain are for the most part relatively inaccessible at the present time. Mature trees produce a long, clear, columnar bole, with an essentially domelike crown, and are anchored by a moderately deep and spreading root system. A deep, moist, cool soil is preferred, although good growth is also made on thin, rocky soils if provided with an abundance of moisture. Noble fir usually occurs singly or in small groups in association with other conifers. Douglas-fir, western hemlock, Pacific silver and subalpine firs, western white pine, and western redcedar are its principal forest associates in northerly portions of its range, while toward the southern limit it also occurs with white fir and sugar pine.

Noble fir is not a prolific seeder. Small quantities of seed may be borne annually, but heavy crops are released only at 3- to 6-year intervals (after the fifteenth). Unlike other firs of the Pacific Northwest, noble fir is intermediate in intolerance. Growth in both height and diameter, although very slow in the seedling stage, is moderately rapid during the first century, as is shown by the fact that trees 100 to 120 years of age are commonly 90 to 120 ft in height and 20 to 24 in. dbh. Maturity is reached in about 350 years, although trees with 500 to 600 annual rings have been reported.

The bark of noble fir is very thin, and trees of all age classes are easily killed by fire. Overmature trees are frequently damaged by one or more species of decay-producing fungi, includ-

FIGURE 8-56 *Abies procera.* Noble fir. (1) Foliage × ½. (2) Mature seed cone × ¾. (3) Seed × 1. (4) Abaxial view of scale and subtending bract × 1. (5) Bark of old tree (*Photo by C. F. Brockman*).

MAP 8-20   **(Left)** *Abies procera.* **(Right)** *Abies grandis.*

ing the Indian paint fungus. Damage by insects is rarely severe. Damage occurs from dwarf mistletoe in the southern part of the range. This fir is used for lumber, Christmas trees, and as an ornamental.

Àbies grándis (Dougl. ex D. Don) Lindl.   Grand fir

Distinguishing Characteristics (Fig. 8-57)

Leaves ¾ to 2 in. (2 to 5 cm) long, flattened, lustrous, dark yellow-green above, silvery (stomatiferous) below, those on sterile side branches 2-ranked, the ones from the upper side shorter than the laterals or those from underneath; often crowded on the upper side of cone-bearing branches; blunt or emarginate at the apex.

Cones 2 to 4¼ in. (5 to 11 cm) long, cylindrical, yellowish green to greenish purple; *bracts* shorter than the scales, the shoulders erose, rounded-truncate or cordate, terminating in a short spikelike tip; *seeds* ⅜ in. (9 mm) long, pale yellow-brown; wings about ¾ in. (19 mm) long, straw-colored.

Twigs slender, brown, puberulous; *buds* ¼ in. (6 mm) long, subglobose, resinous.

Bark smooth, gray-brown with resin blisters and chalky-white blotches on young stems; reddish brown, plated, or more commonly deeply furrowed or divided into flat ridges on old trunks.

Range

Northwestern (Map 8-20). Elevation: sea level to 1500 ft along the coast, to 6000 ft inland. Moist coastal forests, valleys, and mountain slopes.

General Description

Grand fir is one of the two firs found in the northern Rocky Mountain region, and one of four common to the forests of the Pacific Northwest. Trees in coastal forests reach 140 to 160 ft in height and 2 to 4 ft dbh (max. 250 by 7 ft), but in the Rocky Mountains they are rarely more than 120 ft high or 3 ft dbh. Mature trees develop long, clear, columnar boles and domelike crowns (Fig. 8-58); the roots are deep and spreading. Grand fir occurs most frequently on deep, moist alluvial soils in gulches, along streams, and on gentle mountain slopes. While it occasionally forms limited pure stands, it is much more abundant in mixed hardwood and coniferous forests. Douglas-fir, western larch, and ponderosa and lodgepole pines are its common associates in the Rocky Mountains; in the Bitterroot Mountains to the west it occurs with western larch, western white pine, Engelmann spruce, and subalpine fir. At sea level and low elevations

FIGURE 8-57 *Abies grandis.* Grand fir. (1) Foliage × ½. (2) Mature seed cone × ¾. (3) Adaxial side of scale with seeds (above) and abaxial side with subtending bract (below) × 1. (4) Seeds × 1. (5) Bark of old tree.

FIGURE 8-58   Grand fir. (*Courtesy of U.S. Forest Service.*)

in the Cascade Mountains of eastern Washington and Oregon, grand fir occurs with Sitka spruce, Pacific silver fir, western redcedar, western hemlock, Douglas-fir, Oregon ash, red alder, bigleaf maple, and black cottonwood. Redwood is an associated species at the southern limit of its range, and at higher elevations to the south, grand fir occurs with Shasta red, white, noble, and subalpine firs, and western white pine.

The seedling habits of grand fir are similar to those of white fir. Grand fir is a tolerant tree, but it is less so than western hemlock or western redcedar. Early height growth in Idaho often compares favorably with that of western white pine and on the Pacific coast with that of Douglas-fir. Maturity is reached in about 200 years.

Overmature trees are frequent hosts of the brown stringy rot and Indian paint fungi. Young trees are commonly attacked by the eastern spruce budworm and several other insects. It is used for lumber and pulp.

Àbies cóncolor (Gord. and Glend.) Hildebr.   White fir

Distinguishing Characteristics (Fig. 8-59)

Leaves 1½ to 3 in. (4 to 7.5 cm) long, silvery-blue to silvery-green, extending at nearly right angles from all sides of the twig or more or less obscurely 2-ranked; flattened, stomatiferous above and below, rounded or acute at the apex.

Cones 3 to 5 in. (7.5 to 13 cm) long, oblong, olive-green to purple; *bracts* shorter than the scales, with short, broad erose shoulders, and a spikelike tip; *seeds* ½ in. (13 mm) long, yellow-brown, the wings rose-tinted.

Twigs moderately stout, yellowish green to brownish green; *buds* ca. ¼ in. (6 mm) long, subglobose, yellowish brown, resinous.

Bark 4 to 7 in. (10 to 18 cm) thick on old trunks, ashy gray and divided by deep irregular furrows into thick, horny flattened ridges; young stems with conspicuous resin blisters.

Range

Western (Map 8-21). Elevation: sea level to 2000 ft northward, 5500 to 11,200 ft southward. Mountain slopes and ridges.

General Description

White fir has the largest, though fragmented, range of any of the commercial western firs. It attains its maximum development in the Sierras, where it becomes 130 to 150 ft in height and 3 to 4 ft dbh (max. 200 by 9 ft). The Rocky Mountain trees are usually much smaller and rarely attain a height of 100 ft or a diameter of 15 to 30 in. In youth the crown is often elongated and covers a slightly tapered bole from one-half to two-thirds of its length. Older trees usually have a domelike crown unless malformed by the fir dwarf mistletoe. The root system is shallow and wide-spreading. White fir occurs most abundantly on deep, rich, moist but well-drained, gravelly, or sandy loam-covered slopes and benches with a northerly exposure. However, this species requires less moisture than other western firs and possesses a remarkable ability to exist on dry, thin layers of partially decomposed granite or nearly barren rocks. Trees on such sites, however, are small and often malformed.

MAP 8-21   *Abies concolor.*

FIGURE 8-59   *Abies concolor.* White fir. (1) Foliage × ½. (2) Mature seed cone × ¾. (3) Adaxial view of scale with 2 winged seeds × 1. (4) Abaxial view of scale with subtending bract × 1. (5) Bark of old tree (*Photo by Emanuel Fritz*).

Pure stands of white fir are seldom encountered, except as second growth, but forests comprising up to 80 percent of this species are fairly numerous in some parts of the Sierra Nevada. Sugar, ponderosa, and Jeffrey pines, incense cedar, California red fir, and Douglas-fir are common associates. Forests composed of sugar pine and white fir are fairly common, and in the Canadian zone, a red fir–white fir combination occurs quite frequently. White fir–ponderosa pine stands may be found east of the Sierras. White fir is also found with grand fir in the Cascade Mountains of southern Oregon, where intermediate forms exist between the two species, and where identification of either is sometimes difficult.

Little (1979, 1980b) recognizes the Rocky Mountain white fir (var. *concolor*) and California white fir [var. *lowiana* (Gord.) Lemm.], with longer, notched leaves. The latter is considered as a distinct species [*A. lowiana* (Gord.) A. Murr.] by some (FNA vol. 2, 1993).

Good seed crops occur at about 2- to 4-year intervals. The seeds show transient viability, and germination averages about 37 percent. Nearly any soil except heavy clay makes a satisfactory seedbed.

Seedlings develop readily under the canopy of old trees and are even tolerant in later life provided they receive ample moisture. Late spring freezes often decimate seedlings, and reproduction is usually sparse on burnt and logged-off lands because of high insolation until a cover of shrubs and numerous herbaceous species has become well established. Growth in both height and diameter is usually slow for the first 25 to 30 years, but after this period it is comparable to or even faster than that of its associated species. Growth rate gradually diminishes after the first century, and maturity is attained in about 300 years. Trees more than 350 years old are seldom encountered.

White fir is severely damaged by dwarf mistletoe, while the fir engraver beetle causes extremely heavy damage in some areas; heart rots are quite prevalent in others.

This fir is commonly used as an ornamental in many parts of the United States, particularly in the east. Some of the very glaucous cultivars produce a beautiful effect when planted formally with certain of the more somber evergreens. It is also used for construction lumber, plywood, and Christmas trees.

Àbies lasiocárpa (Hook.) Nutt.   Subalpine fir

Distinguishing Characteristics (Fig. 8-60). *Leaves* 1 to 1¾ in. long, flattened, pale blue-green, stomatiferous on both surfaces, spreading nearly in 2 horizontal ranks. *Cones* 2¼ to 4 in. (6 to 10 cm) long, cylindrical, purplish gray to nearly black; *bracts* shorter than the scales, with erose rounded shoulders and long spinelike tips. *Bark* smooth and chalky on young stems; furrowed and scaly on old trunks.

Range. Central Yukon and southeastern Alaska southeast to central Oregon, south to southern New Mexico and southern Arizona; local disjuncts in northwestern California. Elevation: sea level to 3000 ft in Alaska; 2000 to 7000 ft in British Columbia; 2000 to 7900 ft in Washington and Oregon; 8000 to 12,000 ft in the southern Rocky Mountains. Mountain slopes and ridges to timberline.

General Description. Subalpine fir was first observed by Lewis and Clark when they crossed the Bitterroot Mountains in Montana and Idaho in September 1805. It is largely restricted to high western forests, and on exposed sites at timberline it is often reduced to a grotesque shrub of sprawling or prostrate habit. On protected sites of good quality, however, trees attain a height of 60 to 100 ft and 18 to 24 in. dbh (max. 160 by 7 ft), and under average conditions develop dense, narrowly pyramidal crowns (Fig. 8-61) and symmetrical, moderately tapering boles which are often clear for 30 to 40 ft. Open-grown trees, particularly in alpine meadows, feature excessively tapered trunks and dense spirelike crowns of great beauty that commonly extend to the ground.

FIGURE 8-60   *Abies lasiocarpa.* Subalpine fir. (1) Foliage × ½. (2) Mature seed cone × ¾. (3) Abaxial view of scale with subtending bract × 1. (4) Seeds × 1. (5) Bark of old tree. (*Courtesy of British Columbia Forest Service.*)

FIGURE 8-61   Narrow, pyramidal crowns of subalpine firs.

Subalpine fir forms limited pure stands but also occurs in mixed forests. It is an almost constant associate of Engelmann spruce in the Rocky Mountains, although to the north it is also found with mountain hemlock, lodgepole, whitebark and limber pines, and subalpine larch; farther south bristlecone pine, corkbark fir, and quaking aspen are also associated species. In the Bitterroot Mountains of northern Idaho, where it attains a large size if not its maximum development, it mingles with grand fir, western white pine, Engelmann spruce, and western larch. Mountain hemlock, whitebark pine, and Alaska-cedar are its principal associates in high alpine forests along the Pacific Coast.

Because of inaccessibility, subalpine fir, along with Engelmann spruce, was until recently of little commercial importance, except locally, but it serves principally as a cover tree on high watersheds. It is damaged by several insects and fungi.

The more interior populations of the Rocky Mountains have been separated as *A. bifolia* A. Murray (FNA vol. 2, 1993).

Abies lasiocarpa var. *arizónica* (Merriam) Lemm. (*Abies arizonica* Merriam) Corkbark fir

Corkbark fir is a small tree of the southern Rocky Mountains and occurs on thin gravelly or rocky soils at elevations of from 8000 to 10,000 ft. It is readily separated from other firs by its thick, white, corky bark, which is free of resin blisters. The foliage is similar to that of subalpine fir, but the cones of these two sometimes show minor differences. In subalpine fir the cone scales are mostly wedge-shaped, while in corkbark fir they are often halberdlike at the base. There appear to be a number of intergrading forms wherein these differences are not consistent and hence cannot always be relied on for separation.

In southern Colorado, corkbark fir replaces subalpine fir as an associate of Engelmann spruce and as such is logged and distributed as white fir. However, the relative inaccessibility of this species, together with its smaller size and limited distribution, has prevented it from becoming commercially important except locally.

Àbies bracteàta D. Don   Bristlecone fir

Distinguishing Characteristics.   The needles are flat, 1½ to 2¼ in. (4 to 6 cm) long, sharp-pointed, and are arranged in several ranks. The most distinctive features of this species, however, are the cone, which has spiny, long-exserted bracts, 1 to 2 in. (2.5 to 5 cm) long, and the ovoid, nonresinous, tan buds ¾ to 1 in. (18 to 25 mm) long.

Range.   This tree is the rarest of the firs. It is scattered through the dry forests of Santa Lucia Mountains of Monterey County, California, between elevations of 2000 and 5000 ft.

General Description.   Bristlecone fir is a small to medium-size tree, 40 to 100 ft tall and to 3 ft dbh. The very aromatic resin from the trunk has been used as incense in the Spanish missions.

Cupressaceae s. lat.: The Redwood or Cypress Family

The Taxodiaceae (redwood family) and Cupressaceae (cypress family) have long been recognized as distinct. Recent studies, however, have shown that a more realistic classification combines them into one (Brunsfeld et al., 1994; Eckenwalder, 1976; Price and Lowenstein, 1989). The monophyletic Cupressaceae s. str. are derived from within the old Taxodiaceae. Cupressaceae s. lat. include 25 to 30 genera (*Sciadopitys* is in a separate family, Sciadopityaceae) and 110 to 130 species widely scattered throughout the world and in both northern and southern hemispheres. Several genera not native to the United States have become popular ornamentals. Examples are China fir [*Cunninghamia lanceolata* (Lamb.) Hook.], Japanese cedar [*Cryptomeria japonica* (L.f.) D. Don], Oriental arborvitae [*Platycladus orientalis* (L.) Franco], and Dawn redwood (*Metasequoia glyptostroboides* H. H. Hu & Cheng). The Dawn redwood is the most recently discovered. Although known as a widely distributed fossil, it was found growing in central China in the 1940s (Hu, 1948; Li, 1964), introduced into cultivation around the world, and is now widely grown throughout the temperate northern hemisphere. It has the appearance of baldcypress, but the leaves appear opposite rather than alternate on the determinate short shoots, and the seed cone is cylindrical with 4 vertical rows of persistent scale/bracts (Table 8-13).

TABLE 8-13   COMPARISON OF NATIVE GENERA IN THE CUPRESSACEAE S. L.

Genus	Leaves	Branchlets	Seed cones
Sequoia sequoia	alternate, linear, ⅜–¾ in. (10–19 mm) long, 2-ranked; juvenile scalelike, many-ranked; persistent	persistent, spreading	elliptical to subglobose, ½–1⅛ in. (1.2–3 cm) long, remaining intact at maturity; seeds with 2 lateral wings
Sequoiadendron giant sequoia	alternate, scalelike ⅛–¼ in. (3–6 mm) long, many-ranked, persistent	persistent, appressed to spreading	ovoid or oblong, 1¾–2¾ in. (4.5–7 cm) long, remaining intact at maturity; seeds with 2 lateral wings
Taxodium baldcypress	alternate, linear and 2-ranked, ⅜–⅝ in. (10–15 mm) long; or subulate and many-ranked; deciduous	deciduous; horizontal with linear leaves or erect with subulate leaves	globose, ¾–1 in. (2–2.5 cm) diameter, shattering at maturity; seeds triangular, ± winged at the angles
Calocedrus incense-cedar	opposite scales, decussate, appearing 4-whorled, persistent	persistent, flattened	oblong, ¾–1 in. (2–2.5 cm) long, with 6 thin, flattened, woody scales; seed with 2 unequal wings
Thuja thuja	opposite scales, decussate, persistent	persistent, flattened	elliptical, ca. ½ in. (12 mm) long, with 8–12 thin, woody scales; seeds with 2 lateral, equal wings
Cupressus cypress	opposite scales, decussate, persistent	persistent, spreading	globose, ¾–1⅜ in. (2–3.5 cm) diam., with 6–12 leathery, peltate scales; seeds laterally winged; maturing in 2 years
Chamaecyparis white-cedar	opposite scales, decussate, persistent	persistent, flattened	globose, ¼–½ in. (6–12 mm) diam., with 4–8 leathery or dry, peltate scales; seeds laterally winged; maturing in 1 year
Juniperus juniper	dimorphic: opposite scales, decussate; or subulate and mostly ternate; persistent	persistent, spreading	globose, ¼–⅝ in. (6–15 mm) diam., with 3–8 fleshy, peltate scales, fused into berry-like cone; seeds wingless

Botanical Features of the Family

Trees and shrubs evergreen or deciduous, aromatic, resinous.

Leaves alternate, opposite and decussate, or whorled; linear, subulate, or scale.

Cones (juvenile) with bracts and scales partially to completely fused (Fig. 7-10); ovules erect, 2 to 12 on each scale; plants monoecious or dioecious.

Mature cones: *pollen cones* very small; *seed cones* elongated or globose, woody, leathery, or semifleshy; composed of flat, peltate, or wedge-shaped scale/bract complexes; maturing in 1–2 years; *seeds* with 2 or 3 lateral wings, or wingless.

As treated here, *Sequoia, Sequoiadendron,* and *Taxodium* would have been included in the earlier recognized Taxodiaceae; the others would be in the Cupressaceae s. str.

In most members of the Cupressaceae s. str., scale leaves are the mature leaf type and subulate leaves are the juvenile type. Cultivars of several genera, particularly *Thuja* and *Chamaecyparis,* maintain the juvenile forms. All these were at one time placed in the genus *Retinispora* or *Retinospora.* In a few species, such as *Juniperus communis,* the subulate leaf is the mature form.

SEQUOIA Endl.   Sequoia

This group is of ancient lineage and flourished during the Cretaceous and Tertiary periods; about 40 fossil forms have been described. While many forms now extinct were widely scattered through the forests of the northern hemisphere, the modern genus consists of but one species, the coast redwood of California and southwestern Oregon. The name *Sequoia* commemorates Sequoyah, a famous Cherokee Indian who developed an alphabet for his tribe. This was a brilliant achievement and enabled the Cherokee to publish a newspaper and book—something no other Native American tribe could do in 1821.

Sequòia sempervìrens (D. Don) Endl.   Redwood

Distinguishing Characteristics (Fig. 8-62)

Leaves dimorphic, yellow-green; (1) those on lateral branches stiff, ⅜ to 1 in. (10 to 25 mm) long, mostly linear, 2-ranked by a twist of the narrowed leaf base, decurrent, with two lighter colored bands of stomata below; *apex* acute, usually sharp-pointed; (2) leaves on tips of leaders and fertile branchlets ca. ¼ in. (6 mm), long, keeled, oblong to somewhat scalelike, several ranked.

Cones (juvenile) solitary; *pollen cones* ovoid to oblong, composed of a number of spirally arranged pollen sacs; *ovulate cones* consisting of 15 to 20 peltate scale/bracts, each with 2 to 5 erect ovules in a single row; plants monoecious.

Mature cones ½ to 1⅛ in. (1.2 to 3 cm) in diameter, ovoid to subglobose, reddish brown, with 15 to 20 peltate, wrinkled scale/bracts, maturing at the end of one season; *seeds* ⅛ in. (3 mm) long, light brown, with narrow lateral wings.

Buds globose, covered by several acute, imbricate scales.

Bark reddish brown to cinnamon-red, deeply furrowed, fibrous, 3 to 12 in. (8 to 30 cm) thick.

FIGURE 8-62 *Sequoia sempervirens.* Redwood. (1) Foliage × ¾. (2) Pollen cones × 1½. (3) Terminal ovulate cone × 1¼. (4) Open seed cone × ¾. (5) Seeds × 1¼.

Range
Western (Map 8-22). Elevation: sea level to 3000 ft. Alluvial soils on flats, benches, or terraces in the coastal fog belt.

General Description
Redwood is a massive tree (Fig. 8-63) commonly 200 to 275 ft in height and 8 to 12 ft dbh (max. 367 by 22 ft). From a relatively shallow wide-spreading root system rises a clear, impres-

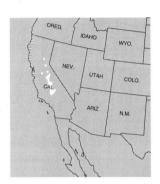

MAP 8-22 **(Shaded)** *Sequoia sempervirens.* **(Solid)** *Sequoiadendron giganteum.*

FIGURE 8-63   Redwoods in the Jedediah Smith Redwoods State Park, Del Norte County, California. (*Photo by Richard St. Barbe Baker.*)

sively tall, buttressed, and somewhat tapering trunk which supports a short, narrow, irregularly conical crown.

Redwood is restricted to a number of separated areas in a narrow strip of coast about 450 miles in length and from 20 to 40 miles in width. Its eastern limits appear to be governed by atmospheric moisture; inland, beyond points where the ocean fogs are cut off by the high coastal mountain ridges, redwood disappears.

Redwood is the dominant species throughout this belt; forests containing 80 percent or more of redwood are extensive, and on moist benches and alluvial bottoms 90 percent or even more of the standing timber is redwood. Douglas-fir, Sitka spruce, grand fir, western hemlock, tanoak, Pacific madrone, red alder, and California-laurel are common associates.

Redwood is a prolific annual seeder (after the fifth to fifteenth year). Although seeds will germinate on moist duff, the young trees can scarcely penetrate it and usually die from drying out. Fresh mineral soil is best. This may result when a large tree falls and the upturned roots strip away the overlying litter and humus. On alluvial flats where the best stands of redwood are found, periodic floods may deposit from several inches to 2 ft of fresh silt, which is soon covered with a thick growth of seedlings. Mature trees may develop new and higher root systems with better aeration in this new, fertile soil. Logging and fire also uncover extensive areas available for new reproduction. Unlike nearly all other conifers, redwood stumps produce vigorous sprouts which reach tree size in a remarkably short time. On the best sites, 20-year-old sprouts attain an average height of 50 ft and a dbh of 8 in. and in 50 to 80 years they commonly reach merchantable proportions. Where coppice growth is removed, a second generation of equally vigorous sprouts soon makes its appearance about the collar of the new stumps, and ultimately they too reach commercial size.

The original redwood forests covered 1,950,000 acres. Only about 5% (93,000 acres) of this remains. In 1994 only 6,000 to 8,000 acres of privately owned old growth remained. This continues to be cut for lumber.

The heaviest stands of timber in the world are found in the redwood belt. On alluvial bottomlands bordering the Smith and Eel rivers through Humboldt and Del Norte counties in north coastal California, where redwood attains its maximum development, mature stands average 125,000 to 150,000 ft B.M. to the acre, and some river flats have yielded as high as 1,000,000 ft of scaled logs per acre. Jepson (1910) reported a single tree which upon being sawn into lumber yielded 480,000 ft B.M. excluding waste.

The rate of growth of redwood both in height and in diameter measurably exceeds that of most American timber-producing species, and research in the second-growth forests indicates that no other species, with the possible exception of eastern cottonwood, is capable of producing as large a tree or as great a volume of wood in the same period of time. Jepson (1910) states that the leaders of open-grown trees 4 to 10 years of age commonly elongate 2 to 6 ft a year and that the annual terminal shoots for these same trees are rarely less than 2 ft in length during the next 20 to 30 years. Redwood is remarkably tolerant, and trees which have been suppressed for protracted lengths of time quickly recover once they are released. This even applies to old trees. It is difficult to ascertain at what age redwood matures, since old trees exhibit from 400 to 2000 growth rings.

Most of the damage in redwood forests is traceable either directly or indirectly to fire. The bark on old trees is very thick (to 12 in.) and offers considerable resistance, but young reproduction is readily killed even by a moderately light ground fire. Most, if not all, of the dry rot found in the basal portions of old trees had its inception near fire scars or seams. Recurring fires are responsible for hollow butts or "goose pens" so common in old growth, and while neither heart rot nor the formation of goose pens actually kill trees, both serve to weaken them materially, and much high-grade saw timber is also destroyed.

Burls, those small to very large excrescences which appear along the bole of many trees, are also a feature of this species. The large ones, if solid, are removed from logs and cut into beautifully figured veneers. Smaller ones are frequently turned on a lathe into trays, bowls, and similar objects or, because of their ability to sprout when placed in water, are offered for sale along with other redwood novelties. A perfume extracted from the leaves is another product of this species offered to the tourist trade.

SEQUOIADENDRON Buchholz   Giant Sequoia; Bigtree

This genus along with *Sequoia* should be considered as "descendants of widely separated genera belonging to a larger group or family of worldwide distribution" (Buchholz, 1939), during the Cretaceous and Tertiary periods.

Sequoiadéndron gigantèum (Lindl.) Buchholz   Giant sequoia

Distinguishing Characteristics (Fig. 8-64)

Leaves blue-green; on lateral and lower branches, ⅛ to ¼ in. (3 to 6 mm) long, ovate, scalelike, appressed; on leaders and young trees, lanceolate, up to ½ in. (12 mm) long, spreading.

Cones (juvenile) similar to those of redwood; *ovulate cones* with peltate to wedge-shaped scale/bracts each with 3 to 9 ovules in one or two rows.

Mature cones 1¾ to 2¾ in. (4.5 to 7 cm) long, ovoid-oblong, reaching full size the first season after emerging from the bud but requiring an additional year for the seed to mature, and persistent, mostly unopened, for a number of years; *cone scale/bracts* woody, 25 to 40, peltate or more nearly wedge-shaped; *apophyses* rugose, depressed; *seeds* ⅛ to ¼ in. (3 to 6 mm) long, straw-colored, laterally broad winged; usually not shed until the next October after maturity, and then irregularly for many years.

Buds naked.

Bark 12 to 31 in. (30 to 79 cm) thick on old trunks, cinnamon-red, fibrous, divided into broad rounded ridges by deep fissures; very fire resistant. When the sky is covered by a white overcast, the great trunks glow rosy red.

Range

Western (Map 8-22). Elevation: 5000 to 8000 ft; infrequently 3000 to 8900 ft. Slopes, canyons, and valleys.

General Description

The giant sequoias, or bigtrees, are numbered among the largest and oldest of living organisms, and some of them may be more than 2500 to 3200 years old. In their presence, all sense of proportion is lost, and trees which may be 4 to 10 ft in diameter appear small by comparison. It is difficult to really appreciate the size of the giant sequoias because the associated trees are also so large. It is small wonder, therefore, that a feeling of reverence comes over one upon entering a grove of these patriarchs whose gigantic red trunks are like the supports of some vast outdoor cathedral. The emotions aroused by the silent ageless majesty of these great trees are akin to those of primitive people for whom they would have been objects of worship, and it is unlikely that centuries of scientific training will ever completely efface this elemental feeling.

Giant sequoia does not attain the height of the redwood but greatly surpasses it in diameter. The General Sherman tree in Sequoia National Park, for example, averages 32 ft in diameter at its base, 27.4 ft at a point 8 ft from the ground, and 17.5 ft at a height of 60 ft. The total height, however, is "only" 275 ft. In general the larger sequoias commonly attain a diameter of 10 to 15 ft and a height of 250 to 311 ft (max. probably about 347 by 37.3 ft). A better appreciation of their size perhaps may be gained when it is discovered that a person of normal height could lie

FIGURE 8-64 *Sequoiadendron giganteum.* Giant sequoia. (1) Mature seed cones and foliage of scale leaves × ¾. (2) Terminal twig with lanceolate leaves × 1½. (3) Seeds × 1¼. (4) Bark of old tree. (*Courtesy of U.S. Forest Service.*)

crosswise on the largest branch (7 ft in diameter) of the General Sherman tree and not be seen from the ground 130 ft below.

The original ancient forest of giant sequoia was 35,452 acres. Of this, 66% (23,400 acres) remains and almost all of this is protected. How much longer the giant sequoia might maintain itself is problematical, as is also the effect of man in clearing the lesser vegetation around certain individual trees. It is known that any general disturbance of the forest litter under the bigtrees results in the death of many small fibrous roots; and their death, if in large numbers, is sooner or later reflected in the effectiveness of the whole anchorage system. Even in the primeval forest it is not certain but that the final overthrow of the largest trees is caused by the gradual shifting of the center of gravity until the balance of the massive tree is upset, because trees have fallen on days when there was little or no wind.

Insects and fungi cause but minor damage. The bark is extremely thick (to 31 in.), which is an effective protection from fire. Lightning, however, causes spectacular damage to certain individuals (Fry and White, 1930).

The principal associates of giant sequoia include sugar, ponderosa, and Jeffrey pines, California red and white firs, and incense-cedar.

Buchholz (1938) in working out the life history of the giant sequoia seed cone, noted that pollination, fertilization, and growth to full size all take place the first season after emergence of the ovulate cone from the bud (the former is present in embryonic form the previous season). While full size is thus attained in one season, a second year elapses before the embryos are developed and the seed matures. Perhaps the most remarkable feature, however, is that the cone remains green and usually closed for as many as 20 years after maturity. During this time the peduncle develops growth rings (with occasional lapses). Few seeds are shed until the cone dies or is detached from the tree.

For so large a tree the seeds might seem to be very small, furnishing a good illustration of the fact that there is no correlation between the sizes of trees and their seeds. Another interesting feature is the presence in the cones of a powdery dark red pigment which is released together with the seeds when the cones are dried artificially. When dissolved in water, this substance furnishes a nonfading writing fluid or ink. The natural function of the pigment, which has a high tannin content, is not well known, but seeds shed normally are always more or less coated with a thin water-deposited layer of this substance. Experiments seem to indicate a slightly higher percentage of germination of seeds treated naturally or artificially with solutions of the pigment while the vigor of seedlings developed from such seeds is somewhat greater than from untreated samples.

Although the giant sequoia produces large quantities of seeds almost every year (after the twentieth), the percentage of germination is low, and bare earth is necessary for seedling development. In the 1930s the trail- and road-building activities of the Civilian Conservation Corps in the giant sequoia belt did much to stimulate natural reproduction, and where mineral soil was laid bare, many young trees appeared.

The securing of seeds in quantity would be a problem were it not for the activities of squirrels, which cut from the trees the otherwise persistent cones. The extracted seeds, especially when treated with the pigment solution and dried, can be stored under proper conditions for 20 years or more without losing their viability.

The seedlings develop a short taproot, but after a few years this ceases to develop; therefore, the tree is characterized by a relatively shallow, wide-spreading system of laterals. The crown of young trees is dense and conical, with the branches reaching to the ground. Later the much-tapered bole clears itself of lower limbs, while the crown still maintains its juvenile shape; eventually very old trees become rounded or irregular in outline.

This species is commonly used ornamentally along the Pacific Coast and also in some of the eastern states and foreign countries.

The wood is exceedingly brittle but, like that of the redwood, durable almost beyond belief, and trees which fell more than a thousand years ago are still perfectly sound, with the exception of the sapwood which soon decays. From trees of this sort have been obtained the oldest records of forest fires; and the story of early climatic conditions as told by a study of the growth rings has been of interest to climatologists the world over.

Although the giant sequoia no longer contributes much lumber, the length of this description seems appropriate, for this species is without doubt the most famous tree of North America, if not of the entire world.

TAXODIUM Rich.   Baldcypress

This genus was once widely distributed in the prehistoric forests of Europe and North America. Now, however, there are but one or two species. *Taxodium distichum* (L.) Rich., baldcypress (deciduous), native to the southeastern United States, and *T. mucronatum* Ten. (*T. distichum* var. *mexicanum* Gordon), Montezuma baldcypress (leaves persistent), found from Guatemala through Mexico to extreme southeastern Texas. A tree of the latter species standing near Oaxaca, Mexico, has a circumference of ca. 115 ft and has been estimated to be 2000 years old. A number of trees of *T. distichum* in North Carolina have been determined to be 1000 to 1700 years old.

Botanical Features of the Genus

Leaves alternate, deciduous or persistent, either (1) linear and 2-ranked, sometimes conspicuously stomatiferous below, or (2) lanceolate (subulate) appressed and overlapping; individual leaves dropping from the terminal long shoots or persisting on and dropping with the short shoots.

Cones (juvenile) unisexual; *pollen cones* in drooping racemes or panicles, each small and globose and composed of several pollen sacs opposite in 2 ranks; *ovulate cones* subglobose, comprising several spirally arranged peltate scale/bracts, each bearing 2 erect, basal ovules; plants monoecious.

Mature cones nearly globose, ¾ to 1 in. (2 to 2.5 cm) in diameter, woody, maturing and shattering in one season, comprising 5 to 10 nearly peltate scale/bracts, each 4-angled in cross section, resinous glandular on the inner surface, and terminating in a short, transverse mucro; *seeds* irregularly 3-angled and wingless or barely winged at the angles.

Buds subglobose, covered with several sharp-pointed, imbricate scales.

Lateral twigs (determinate short shoots) seasonally or annually dehiscent with the leaves.

Taxòdium dístichum (L.) Rich.

This species is treated here as comprising two varieties following Watson (1983) and FNA vol. 2 (1993). However, Godfrey (1988) has a description of the variation and argument for recognizing them as separate species. Duncan and Duncan (1988) also treat them as species. Although the varieties are morphologically and ecologically distinct as extremes, numerous individuals and populations exist that exhibit morphological and/or ecological intermediacy or which show curious admixtures of characters representing the extremes (Watson, 1983). Specimens from saplings, stump sprouts, fertile branchlets, terminal vegetative branchlets, or late-season growth may be very similar and not identifiable to variety.

Taxodium distichum var. *distichum* Baldcypress

Distinguishing Characteristics (Figs. 8-65, 8-66)

Twigs (determinate short shoots) mostly 2-ranked, pendent or horizontally spreading from the branch.

Leaves decurrent, narrowly linear, ¼ to ⅝ in. (5 to 17 mm) long, laterally divergent, the free base contracted and twisted, appearing 2-ranked on the twigs.

Bark fibrous, 1¼ to 1½ in. (3 to 4 cm) in thickness, or scaly and thinner; dark reddish brown to light brown with shallow furrows.

Range

Southeastern (Map 8-23). Elevation: sea level to 530 ft, locally in Texas to 1750 ft. Brownwater rivers, lake margins, swamps, coastal marshes, and river bottoms.

FIGURE 8-65   *Taxodium distichum* var. *distichum*. Baldcypress. (1) Drooping racemes of pollen cones × ¾. (2) Young clusters of pollen cones and ovulate cones × 1. (3) Mature seed cone and foliage of distichous, linear leaves on spreading twigs × ¾. (4) Seeds × 1.

FIGURE 8-66   Old-growth baldcypress with buttress and knee. (*Courtesy of U.S. Forest Service.*)

Taxodium distichum var. *imbricàrium* (Nutt.) Croom (*T. ascendens* Brong.)
   Pondcypress

Distinguishing Characteristics (Fig. 8-67)

   Twigs (determinate short shoot) mostly ascending vertically from the branch.

   Leaves spirally arranged in 5 to 8 or more ranks, narrowly lanceolate (subulate), appressed and overlapping, not contracted or twisted at base.

   Bark brown to light gray, thicker and more deeply furrowed than in var. *distichum.*

Range

Southeastern (Map 8-23). Elevation: sea level to 330 ft. Blackwater rivers, lake and pond margins, swamps, pocosins, shallow depressions in pine flatwoods.

MAP 8-23   *Taxodium distichum.*

FIGURE 8-67   *Taxodium distichum* var. *imbricarium*. Pondcypress. Nearly scale-like, appressed, imbricated leaves on more-or-less erect twigs.

General Description of the species

This species is the most distinctive of southern conifers. In the dim light of an old-growth cypress or cypress-gum forest, the massive, often ashy-gray columnar trunks with their peculiarly swollen, fluted bases, knees, and branches bearded with Spanish moss, produce an unforgettable impression.

Baldcypress is a large tree, 100 to 165 ft high and 3 to 5 (rarely to 13) ft dbh. The trunk of young trees shows considerable taper and supports an open, narrowly pyramidal crown; with age the bole becomes more cylindrical and the crown irregularly flattened. The root system is a very distinctive feature of the tree. It consists of several descending roots providing anchorage, and many shallow, wide-spreading roots from which rise, especially where the water level fluctuates, the peculiar conical structures called "knees." What function these outgrowths may have (if any) is not fully understood. Like the buttresses, they may be a passive development due to the stimulation of a fluctuating water level. The height of both is a good indicator of the local high water level. However, knees can develop in an unexplained manner in a terrestrial habitat.

Best growth of this species is made on deep, fine, sandy loams with plenty of moisture in the surface layers and moderately good drainage. Cypress is rarely found, however, on such areas, presumably because of hardwood competition, and in contrast is typical of wetter areas, where it forms extensive pure stands. In such situations it has few associates, but probably the most common is water tupelo; on slightly higher ground the bottomland hardwood species such as sweetgum, green ash, red maple, American elm, and certain of the oaks are more aggressive, and the cypress eventually disappears. This species, although preeminently adapted to freshwater swamps, extends into the coastal region of brackish tidewater, where it makes poor growth.

Reproduction of seeds is persistent but not widespread, because their weight precludes distribution by wind.

Trees up to 40 to 60 years old sprout vigorously from the stump, and even much older trees often produce a few sprouts. Cypress is considered to be intermediate in tolerance. In deep shade, seeds will germinate, but survival is poor. Growth in partial shade is much slower than in full sun.

Cypress has been considered a slow-growing tree, but studies of old stands do not indicate what may be expected of young trees, which often reach a foot in height the first season, nearly

2 ft the second, and in 10 years as much as 18 ft. Second-growth trees 100 years old are about 100 ft tall and 15 to 20 in. dbh. Because of its great durability (resistance to decay), the wood of cypress is often known in the trade as the "wood everlasting."

Baldcypress and pondcypress have been planted as ornamentals far north of their natural range, in several of the northern states, southern Canada, and Europe.

Small, white, mushroom-shaped growths sometimes seen on leaves are caused by the gall midge, *Taxodiomyia cupressi.*

CALOCEDRUS Kurz   Incense-cedar

For many years, *Libocedrus* was the generic name given to a group of some 10 species scattered widely around the perimeter of the Pacific Ocean. Only one species, the incense-cedar, *L. decurrens* Torr. of California and Oregon, was found in North America. The others were in Chile and Argentina, New Zealand, New Caledonia, New Guinea, southern China, Burma, and Taiwan. Further studies through the years produced evidence for splitting this group into five genera. *Libocedrus* Endl. is applied to five species of New Zealand and New Caledonia; *Calocedrus* Kurz is now the generic name for our native North American incense-cedar. For the names, distribution, and importance of the other genera, consult Dallimore and Jackson (1967). Little (1979, 1980b) still recognizes *Libocedrus* s. lat.

Calocedrus, in addition to the North American incense-cedar, has two other species in south China and along the Burmese border, and in Taiwan. *Calocedrus macrolepis* Kurz, the south China species, now rare, was more common in past geological ages, and perfectly preserved buried tree trunks are "mined" and sawn into boards for making coffins.

Calocèdrus decúrrens (Torr.) Florin   Incense-cedar

Distinguishing Characteristics (Fig. 8-68)

Leaves ⅛ to ½ in. (3 to 12 mm) long scales, lustrous, dark yellow-green, oblong-ovate, 4-ranked, decurrent and adnate to the twigs except at the tips; glandular, having an aromatic odor when crushed; laterals keeled, almost wholly ensheathing the facial pairs, appearing 4-whorled; branchlets flattened into sprays.

Cones (juvenile) terminal; *pollen cones* with 12 to 16 decussate, filamentous, 4-celled pollen sacs; *ovulate cones* composed of 6 scale/bracts, 2 bearing 2 erect basal ovules; trees monoecious.

Mature cones ¾ to 1 in. (2 to 2.5 cm) long, pendent, leathery, 2 of the 6 scale/bracts becoming greatly enlarged and giving to the partially open cone the appearance of a duck's bill; *seeds* ⅛ to ½ in. (3 to 12 mm) long, unequally laterally winged, straw-colored; *cotyledons* 2, rarely 3.

Bark thin, smooth, and gray-green or scaly and tinged with red on young stems; on old trunks 3 to 8 in. (7.5 to 20 cm) thick, yellowish brown to cinnamon-red, fibrous, deeply and irregularly furrowed.

Range

Western (Map 8-24). Elevation: 1000 to 9200 ft. Cool, moist, mountain soils.

FIGURE 8-68   *Calocedrus decurrens.* Incense-cedar. (1) Foliage showing scale leaves × 2. (2) Mature seed cones × ¾. (3) Seeds × 1. (4) Open seed cone and flattened spray × ¾. (5) Pollen cones × ¾. (6) Bark of old tree (*Photo by Paul Graves*).

General Description

Fremont first discovered incense-cedar on the south fork of the American River in California in 1844. Specimens which he collected two years later at the headwaters of the Sacramento River were used by Torrey in compiling the original botanical description of this species.

At maturity this tree attains a height of from 75 to 110 ft and a diameter of 3 to 4 ft (max. 225 by 12 ft). Old trees are usually broadly buttressed at the base and have rapidly tapering trunks

MAP 8-24   *Calocedrus decurrens.*

which are often fluted and clothed for nearly one-half of their length in crowns of lustrous foliage. In youth the crown is typically conical, but that of old trees is more irregular and often deformed by dwarf mistletoe and witches' brooms. Seedlings develop profusely branched root systems, and old trees possess well-developed, moderately deep lateral roots.

Incense-cedar grows best on cool, moist sites in the transition zone. Pure stands are virtually unknown, although it may form up to 50 percent of forests chiefly composed of sugar pine, ponderosa pine, and white fir. It is also a nearly constant associate of the giant sequoia. Ponderosa and Jeffrey pines, together with small amounts of bigcone Douglas-fir and white fir, are its principal associates in southern California; it also occurs in the coast ranges east of the redwood belt with both hardwoods and softwoods. In the Cascades of southern Oregon, incense-cedar invades the mixed coniferous forests composed largely of sugar, ponderosa, and western white pines, white fir, and Douglas-fir.

Good seed years occur about every 3 to 6 years. Reproduction is abundant in moist, organic litter, although good survival may also be found on moist mineral soils. Seedling root development is very slow; consequently this tree is rare where long droughts are common. Incense-cedar exhibits greater tolerance than most of the conifers with which it is associated and grows quite persistently under moderate cover with plenty of soil moisture. Sudworth (1967) observed that reproduction was usually good under old trees and in open situations, but that it was especially abundant in dense thickets under thinned stands where the more tolerant species could not compete. Growth is at no time rapid; trees 200 years of age vary from 90 to 95 ft in height and 25 to 30 in. dbh, while trees twice as old are rarely more than 100 ft high and 40 in. dbh. Maturity appears to be attained in about 300 years, and trees more than 500 years old are rarely encountered.

Pocket dry rot is responsible for considerable damage in old trees. Three species of root rotting fungi account for more mortality than all other pests. A rust fungus and witches' brooms are also prevalent in some sections, but they are relatively unimportant. Incense-cedar mistletoe causes considerable damage. Young trees are quite susceptible to fire.

These trees are used for lumber, pencils, and for ornamentals grown throughout the country.

THUJA L.   Thuja; arborvitae

This is a small genus consisting of 5 species of trees or large shrubs found in the forests of China, Taiwan, Korea, Japan, and North America. The oriental arborvitae and the Japanese "hiba," *Platycladus orientalis* (L.) Franco (*Thuja orientalis* L.)* and *Thujopsis dolabrata* (L.f.) Sieb. & Zucc., respectively, were formerly included in this genus; however, they are each now considered distinct and monotypic.

Two species, one a small to medium-size northeastern tree, the other a large northwestern tree, are the only representatives of *Thuja* in North America (Table 8-14).

Botanical Features of the Genus

Leaves persistent, small scales, decussate; the facial leaves flattened, grooved, and often glandular, the lateral leaves rounded or keeled; on leading shoots ovate to lanceolate and somewhat larger than those on the lateral branchlets; branchlets flattened into sprays.

Cones (juvenile) terminal; *pollen cones* arising from branchlets near the base of the shoot, individual strobili ovoid to globose, consisting of several pairs of decussate pollen sacs; *ovulate cones* appearing at the tips of short terminal branchlets, and comprising 8 to 12 scale/bracts, each bearing 2 or 3 erect ovules; plants monoecious.

Mature cones erect, ovoid-cylindrical, leathery to semiwoody, composed of several thin scale/bracts only a few of which are fertile; cones solitary for the most part and maturing in one season; *seeds* small, laterally 2-winged; *cotyledons* 2.

Thùja occidentàlis L.   Northern white-cedar; eastern arborvitae

Distinguishing Characteristics (Fig. 8-69)

Leaves yellow-green, not lustrous; on leading shoots nearly $\frac{1}{16}$ to $\frac{1}{8}$ in. (1.5 to 3 mm) long, glandular, and long-pointed; on lateral branchlets scalelike and flattened, $\frac{1}{8}$ in. (3 mm) long, obscurely glandular-pitted, the foliage sprays often fanlike.

Cones $\frac{3}{8}$ in. (10 mm) long, erect, oblong; releasing their seeds in the fall, but persisting during the winter, tips of the scale/bracts rounded or with a very minute, inconspicuous prickle; usually 4 scales fertile; *seeds* $\frac{1}{8}$ in. (3 mm) long, wings as wide as the body.

Bark $\frac{1}{4}$ to $\frac{1}{3}$ in. (6 to 8 mm) thick, reddish to grayish brown, fibrous, forming a more or less close network of connecting ridges and shallow furrows, grayish on the surface.

*The oriental arborvitae has numerous cultivars and is much used as an ornamental in the United States. It may be distinguished by somewhat "lacy" foliage and globose cones $\frac{5}{8}$ in. (15 mm) in diameter, leathery becoming woody, the scale/bracts with a distinct curved hook, and seeds wingless. It is not hardy in the northeast during extremely cold winters.

TABLE 8-14   COMPARISON OF IMPORTANT ARBORVITAE

Species	Leaves	Mature cones
T. occidentalis northern white-cedar	dull green, glandular-pitted	with 4 fertile scales, spine tips very minute or lacking
T. plicata western redcedar	dark glossy green, eglandular for the most part	with 6 fertile scales, usually spine-tipped

FIGURE 8-69   *Thuja occidentalis.* Northern white-cedar. (1) Foliage in flattened spray and mature seed cones
× ¾. (2) Pollen cones before and after shedding pollen × 2. (3) Ovulate cone × 2. (4) Open seed
cone × 2. (5) Seed × 2. (6) Bark of old tree.

Range

Northeastern and southern Appalachians (Map 8-25). Disjuncts in northcentral Illinois,
western Pennsylvania, Rhode Island, and eastern Massachusetts. Elevation: sea level
to 3000 ft. Swamps, neutral or alkaline soils on dry, limestone uplands, low stream
borders, in mixed or pure stands.

MAP 8-25   **(Left)** *Thuja plicata.* **(Right)** *Thuja occidentalis.*

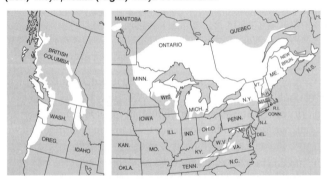

General Description

Trees of northern white-cedar are commonly 40 to 50 ft tall and 2 to 3 ft dbh (max. 125 by 6 ft). The crown, narrowly pyramidal in youth, later becomes irregularly oblong, and the tapering bole is supported by a shallow, wide-spreading root system.

This species occurs on a wide variety of soils but reaches its best development in outlying stations both in the north and in the south, on limestone outcrops. Even though it is in this respect a calcicole, northern white-cedar is also characteristic of shallow sphagnum-covered basins such as those in the Adirondack Mountains, where, however, the growth is very slow, about 1 ft dbh in 200 years. Growth may be from two to three times faster on the best sites.

Some seeds are produced annually (after the twentieth to thirtieth year) with large crops at 3- to 5-year intervals. In suitable locations, especially on swampy ground or limestone areas, extensive pure stands develop. In mixed stands, balsam fir, eastern hemlock, eastern white pine, spruces, tamarack, black ash, yellow birch, and the northern maples are common associates. Northern white-cedar is moderately tolerant. An age of 400 years or more is probably attained; ring counts are not satisfactory, because about 80 percent of old trees are rotten at the heart.

More than 100 cultivars are known (Den Ouden and Boom, 1965), and these may be easily propagated by cuttings. On wet sites, this tree forms new individuals by layering. In much of its range, it is an important source of winter browse, in addition to being a source of lumber, poles, fencing, and shingles. There are no serious insect or fungus pests, but it is susceptible to fire.

Thùja plicàta Donn ex D. Don   Western redcedar;* giant arborvitae

Distinguishing Characteristics (Fig. 8-70)

Leaves lustrous dark yellow-green, usually without glandular pits, similar to those of *T. occidentalis* but somewhat coarser; the foliage sprays long, drooping, and often fernlike, or stringy.

Cones also similar to those of the preceding species, but more often with weakly spine-tipped scale/bracts, 6 of which are fertile; *seeds* ⅛ in. (3 mm) long, the lateral wings about as wide as the seed.

Bark ½ to 1 in. (12 to 25 mm) thick, fibrous, cinnamon-red on young stems, gray on old trunks, and forming a closely interlacing network.

Range

Northwestern (Map 8-25). Elevation: sea level to 3000 ft near the coast and to 6600 ft in the rockies. Slightly acid soil of moist flats and slopes, banks of rivers, swamps, and bogs.

General Description

Western redcedar, the larger of our two American species of arborvitae, was first observed by the Malaspina expedition on the west side of Vancouver Island, British Columbia, near Nootka Sound in 1791. Today it is one of the four most important species of the Pacific Northwest and is the principal timber tree used in shingle manufacture both in the United States and Canada.

Under favorable conditions for growth, forest trees attain gigantic proportions and vary from 150 to 200 ft in height and 4 to 8 ft dbh (max. 250 by 21 ft). A shallow, wide-spreading root system supports a broadly buttressed, often fluted base and rapidly tapering bole. The crown is typi-

---

*Although this is the preferred common name among lumber workers, it unfortunately links the species with *Juniperus virginiana,* or eastern redcedar. The name "giant arborvitae" is seldom used, although it would seem a more logical one for *Thuja plicata* than that now applied.

FIGURE 8-70 *Thuja plicata.* Western redcedar. (1) Foliage in flattened sprays and mature seed cones × ¾. (2) Seed × 2. (3) Open seed cones × ¾. (4) Ovulate cones × 2. (5) Pollen cones × 2. (6) Bark of old tree.

cally irregular and is usually composed of numerous more or less horizontal or drooping branches which bend upward near their tips to form a distinct appearance.

It is seldom found in dry soils, although stunted growth is occasionally found on such sites. Western redcedar seldom occurs in pure stands but often constitutes up to 50 percent of mixed forests. Of its important associates along the Pacific slope are Sitka spruce, western hemlock, Douglas-fir, grand and Pacific silver firs, Pacific yew, red alder, black cottonwood, and bigleaf maple. In Rocky Mountain forests western larch, western white pine, western hemlock, grand fir, Douglas-fir, and Engelmann spruce are its principal associates. Where moisture is plentiful, western redcedar is a tree of great tolerance.

Western redcedar releases large amounts of seed at about 3-year intervals (after the fifteenth to twenty-fifth year), with smaller amounts almost every year. Seedling mortality from drought, fungi, birds, and insects is often excessive, and only a few trees may result from the tremendous number of seeds released. Tree growth is relatively slow, although individuals 80 years old may average 20 in. dbh and 100 ft in height. Maturity is reached in about 350 years, but trees with more than 1000 growth rings have been reported.

Because of its shallow root system and thin bark, western redcedar is readily killed by fire. Pecky heart rot is commonly found in overmature trees, and almost all very old trees are hollow-butted. There is little insect damage.

Western redcedar wood is extremely durable. One old wind-thrown "nurse" tree on the Olympic peninsula was found supporting 14 hemlocks which were over 100 years of age, and while the sapwood of the redcedar had rotted away, the heartwood was sound in every respect.

Several cultivars of this species are now cultivated as ornamentals. It is also used for shingles, siding, poles, lumber, boats, fences, pulp, and for the spectacular totem poles so characteristic of the northwest.

CUPRESSUS L.   Cypress

Cupressus consists of 10 to 26 species of trees and shrubs found in western North America, Mexico, the Mediterranean basin, the Himalaya Mountains, and western China. The Italian cypress, *C. sempervirens* L., is a large and important tree of columnar habit widely scattered through forests of the Mediterranean basin. In this region it is planted extensively as an ornamental, especially along avenues for formal effects. Several species of *Cupressus,* including the Italian cypress, are widely used ornamentals in the warmer portions of this and other countries.

Seven species are native to North America; some of these trees produce timber and Christmas trees used locally.

Botanical Features of the Genus

Leaves persistent, scales (often subulate on juvenile or vigorous growth), decussate in 4 uniform ranks, or the lateral pairs boat-shaped and the facial pairs flattened; finely serrate on the margin and commonly glandular on the back; with irregularly disposed 4-angled branchlets.

Cones (juvenile) terminal; *pollen cones* cylindrical, composed of numerous decussate pollen sacs; ovulate cones consisting of 6 to 12 peltate scale/bracts, each with a terminal mucro and 6 to many basal ovules arranged in 2 or more rows; plants monoecious.

Mature cones globose, woody, or leathery, maturing at the end of the second season; scale/bracts peltate, each with a central boss or mucro; *seeds* 6 to many on each scale; compressed, with narrow lateral wings; *cotyledons* 2 to 5.

Cupréssus arizónica Greene   Arizona cypress

Distinguishing Characteristics (Fig. 8-71).   *Leaves* gray-green, having a fetid odor when bruised. *Cones* ¾ to 1¼ in. (2 to 3 cm) in diameter, subglobose, dark reddish brown, with 6 to 8 bossed scale/bracts. *Bark* breaking into thin irregular scales on young stems, furrowed and fibrous on old trunks.

Range.   Local and rare, western Texas, west to southwestern New Mexico, Arizona, and southern California. Elevation: 2475 to 6600 ft. Coarse, gravelly, rocky soils on mountain slopes and coves of northerly exposure.

General Description.   Under favorable growing conditions, this tree is 50 to 65 ft high and 15 to 30 in. dbh (max. 102 by 5 ft). The bole of mature trees exhibits considerable taper and is covered for half of its length in a dense conical crown composed of short, stout, horizontal branches (Fig. 8-72). Trees on dry, sterile, rocky mountain slopes and canyon walls are small or even dwarfed, but may persist on such sites for many years. This species occurs most abundantly in open pure forests, but it is occasionally observed in mixture with Arizona pine and live oaks.

Seeds are borne in abundance every year, but owing to the fact that much of it never finds conditions suitable for germination, reproduction is usually scanty. The trees are tolerant throughout life. Growth is seldom rapid, and trees 6 to 12 in. dbh frequently show 70 to 100 growth rings; the largest trees are rarely more than 400 years old.

Arizona cypress is used as an attractive ornamental eastward to the Atlantic Coast.

CHAMAECYPARIS Spach   White-cedar; false-cypress

This genus includes 6 or 7 species. Three are indigenous to North America (Table 8-15); one of these, *C. thyoides,* is a coastal species of the East; *C. nootkatensis* and *C. lawsoniana* are important trees of the Pacific Coast. The Japanese Sawara-tree and Hinoki-

FIGURE 8-71   *Cupressus arizonica.* Arizona cypress. (1) Foliage and mature seed cones nearly open × ¾. (2) Seeds × 2.

FIGURE 8-72   Arizona cypress. (*Courtesy of U.S. Forest Service.*)

cypress, *C. pisifera* (Sieb. & Zucc.) Endl. and *C. obtusa* (Sieb. & Zucc.) Endl., respectively, together with many of their cultivars, are favored ornamental trees in many sections of the United States. The remaining species, *C. formosensis* Matsum., is a massive tree native to Taiwan. This tree is said to attain a maximum height of 195 ft, a diameter of 23 ft, and an estimated age of 1500 years (Dallimore and Jackson, 1967).

An artificially made, fertile, intergeneric hybrid between *Chamaecyparis nootkatensis* and *Cupressus macrocarpa* is known as ×*Cupressocyparis leylandii* (A. B. Jackson & Dallim.) Dallim. This Leyland cypress, with several cultivars, has become very popular as a fast-growing, attractive ornamental.

Botanical Features of the Genus
Leaves persistent, scales, decussate, ovate, acuminate, entire on the margin, the lateral pairs boat-shaped, the facial pairs flattened; on terminal shoots linear-lanceolate or

TABLE 8-15   COMPARISON OF THE NATIVE CHAMAECYPARIS

Species	Leaves	Mature cones
C. thyoides Atlantic white-cedar	ca. ¹⁄₁₆ in. (1.5 mm) long, glandular	¼ in. (6 mm) in diameter, somewhat fleshy, maturing in one season; scales terminating in a reflexed boss; seeds 1 or 2 per scale
C. lawsoniana Port-Orford-cedar	same	ca. ⅓ in. (8 mm) in diameter; woody, maturing in 1 season; scales same as above; seeds 2 to 4 per scale
C. nootkatensis Alaska-cedar	ca. ⅛ in. (3 mm) sharp, essentially eglandular	ca. ½ in. (12 mm) in diameter, maturing in 2 seasons, woody; scales terminating in an erect boss; seeds same as *C. lawsoniana*

needlelike, spreading; usually turning brown after the second or third season, but persistent for many years; branchlets flattened into sprays.

Cones (juvenile) of both sexes terminal but on separate branches; *pollen cones* cylindrical, composed of numerous decussate pollen sacs; *ovulate cones* subglobose, usually consisting of 6 to 12 decussate, peltate, ovuliferous scale/bracts, each bearing 2 to 5 erect ovules; plants monoecious.

Mature cones erect, globose, leathery or semifleshy, becoming woody when open, maturing in 1 to 2 years; *cone scale/bracts* peltate, each with a central boss; *seeds* 2 or rarely up to 5 per scale, slightly compressed, laterally winged; *cotyledons* 2.

Chamaecýparis thyoìdes (L.) B. S. P.   Atlantic white-cedar; White-cedar

Distinguishing Characteristics (Fig. 8-73)

Leaves ¹⁄₁₆ to ⅛ in. (1.5 to 3 mm) long, keeled, and glandular on the back, dark blue-green, turning brown the second year, but persistent for several years.

Cones ¼ in. (6 mm) in diameter, somewhat fleshy; at maturity bluish purple, glaucous, later turning brown; *seeds* 1 or 2 for each fertile scale, ⅛ in. (3 mm) long or smaller.

Bark thin, but on old trunks ¾ to 1 in. (19 to 25 mm) thick, ashy gray to reddish brown, somewhat similar in appearance to that of northern white-cedar.

Range

Eastern (Map 8-26). Disjuncts in westcentral Georgia; extending further inland in the North Carolina sandhills. Elevation: sea level to 1650 ft. Peaty, acid soils of low woodlands and swamp forests.

General Description

Atlantic white-cedar on good sites averages 80 to 85 ft in height and 10 to 14 in. dbh (max. 120 by 5½ ft). The bole of mature trees grown in moderately dense stands is long, cylindrical, and

FIGURE 8-73   *Chamaecyparis thyoides.* Atlantic white-cedar. (1) Foliage in flattened sprays and mature seed cones × ¾. (2) Mature seed cone × 2. (3) Seed × 2.

clear of branches for about three-quarters of its length, making it an ideal pole or post timber. The crown of forest trees is small, narrowly conical, and composed of slender limbs with somewhat drooping branchlets; the root system is superficial and wide-spreading.

This species is characteristic of freshwater swamps and bogs, wet depressions, or stream banks and is rarely found except on such sites; extensive pure stands (often extremely dense) are the rule, occurring on shallow peat-covered soils underlain by sand. Because of the extensive north–south distribution of Atlantic white-cedar, the list of associated trees is large. Some of the more common are hemlock, eastern white pine, gray birch, black tupelo, and red maple in the

MAP 8-26   *Chamaecyparis thyoides.*

north; and slash and pond pines, baldcypress, sweetbay, and loblolly bay in the south. Young trees are nearly as tolerant as balsam fir or hemlock, and much more so than the pines or baldcypress; however, they do not survive under the dense cover of older growth, especially hardwoods.

The production of seed in dense stands begins between the ages of 10 and 20 years (earlier in open-grown trees), and good crops are borne nearly every year. The small winged seeds are widely disseminated by wind. Following fires, pure, even-aged stands occur from which merchantable timber can be harvested in 75 to 100 years or less. However, much of the crop is used for posts and prefabricated log cabins.

For a thorough discussion of the distribution, ecology, and variability of Atlantic white-cedar, and recognition of *C. thyoides* var. *henryae* (Li) Little, of the southeastern Gulf Coast, see Clewell and Ward (1987) and Ward and Clewell (1989).

Chamaecýparis lawsoniàna (A. Murr.) Parl. Port-Orford-cedar, Lawson false-cypress, Oregon white-cedar

Distinguishing Characteristics (Fig. 8-74)

Leaves ¹⁄₁₆ in. (1.5 mm) long, yellow-green to blue-green, blunt, glandular, stomatiferous on the lower facial leaves; forming fine, flattened, feathery or lacy sprays; persistent until the third or fourth season.

Cones ³⁄₈ in. (10 mm) in diameter, reddish brown, often glaucous, globose, composed of 3 pairs of peltate scale/bracts each bearing 2 to 4 seeds, maturing in one season; *seeds* ¹⁄₈ in. (3 mm) long, reddish brown, with 2 broad lateral wings.

Bark 6 to 10 in. (15 to 25 cm) thick on old trees, silvery brown, fibrous, divided into thick, rounded ridges separated by deep irregular furrows.

Range

Northwestern (Map 8-27). Elevation: sea level to 5000 ft. Rocky ridges in the coastal fog belt.

General Description

Port-Orford-cedar is a large tree, 140 to 180 ft in height and 4 to 6 ft dbh (max. 239 by 16 ft). The boles of large trees are sometimes buttressed and commonly clear for 150 ft or more of their length. The crown is characteristically short, conical, and composed of numerous more or less horizontal or somewhat pendulous branches; the roots are shallow to moderately deep and spreading.

This species does best in regions where there is an abundance of both soil and atmospheric moisture. It is less exacting in this respect, however, than redwood, and it frequently occurs on drier ridges 30 to 40 miles inland. Except in the vicinity of Coos Bay, Oregon, Port-Orford-cedar is rarely found in pure stands. Although found in a relatively small area, this species spans the floristic transition zone between the trees of California and those of the Pacific Northwest. Common associates in coastal Oregon include Douglas-fir, Sitka spruce, western hemlock, and western redcedar. Farther inland and southward, it is found with such species as western white and sugar pines, incense-cedar, red fir, and red alder.

Port-Orford-cedar reproduces readily on burned or unburned sites with about equal aggressiveness. Large seed crops occur every 3 to 5 years (after the fifth to twentieth year) with smaller amounts annually. Seedling trees grow persistently in either shade or full sunlight, although under very dense cover they are usually suppressed and eventually die. Growth contin-

FIGURE 8-74   *Chamaecyparis lawsoniana*. Port-Orford-cedar. (1) Foliage in flattened sprays × ¾. (2) Ovulate cones × 2. (3) Pollen cones × 2. (4) Mature seeds cones nearly open × 2. (5) Open seed cones × 2. (6) Seeds × 2. (7) Bark of old tree. (*Courtesy of U.S. Forest Service.*)

MAP 8-27   **(Solid)** *Chamaecyparis nootkatensis.* **(Shaded)** *Chamaecyparis lawsoniana.*

ues at a moderate rate, and the trees mature in about 300 to 350 years. The oldest trees are often 500 or more years of age.

Port-Orford-cedar is one of the most commonly used trees for ornamental planting both in North America and Europe. Great variation in color and form have been found, and some 198 cultivars are listed by Den Ouden and Boom (1965). The aromatic wood is used for woodenware, and much is shipped to Japan for this purpose.

This species is relatively free from insect and fungal diseases, but fire causes considerable damage to the thin-barked young trees, and an introduced root rot causes serious damage. Wind throw is also a hazard.

Chamaecýparis nootkaténsis (D. Don) Spach   Alaska-cedar; Nootka false-cypress

Distinguishing Characteristics (Fig. 8-75)

Leaves about ⅛ in. (3 mm) long, acute, blue-green to gray-green, occasionally glandular on the back, appressed, but the apices of the lateral pairs often free, turning brown during the second season but persistent until the third.

Cones ¼ to ½ in. (6 to 12 mm) in diameter, purplish brown to reddish brown, with 4 to 6 peltate, bossed scale/bracts, each bearing 2 to 4 seeds; maturing at the end of the second season; *seeds* about ¼ in. (6 mm) long, the lateral wings about twice as wide as the seed.

Bark thin, grayish brown, scaly on young stems; forming thin, narrow, flattened, interlacing ridges on old trunks.

Range

Northwestern (Map 8-27). Local disjuncts further inland in British Columbia and Oregon. Elevation: sea level northward, 2000 to 7000 ft southward and inland. Wet mountain soils in mixed or pure stands.

FIGURE 8-75   *Chamaecyparis nootkatensis.* Alaska-cedar. (1) Foliage in flattened sprays and mature seed cones × ¾. (2) Seed × 2. (3) Bark (*Photo by Kenneth Walin*).

General Description

This species, known in the trade as Alaska-cypress, yellow-cypress, or yellow-cedar, is typical of the Pacific Northwest region. It is a medium-size tree, 60 to 90 ft high and 2 to 3 ft dbh (max. 175 by 10 ft). In the forest it usually develops a broadly buttressed, often fluted base and rapidly tapering bole which is often clear for about one-half of its length. The conical crown is composed of numerous drooping branches with long, pendulous, flattened sprays of foliage. The root system varies with the site; in moist soils it is shallow, but in drier situations it penetrates to much greater depths.

Alaska-cedar reaches its maximum development on the islands of southeastern Alaska and British Columbia near tidewater, where both soil and atmospheric moisture are abundant. Much of the timber in this region has been logged, however, and the best stands are now located in the humid forests of the Olympic and Cascade Mountains in northern Washington. Here it forms limited pure stands, but it usually occurs in mixture with other conifers. At low elevations, these include western hemlock, Sitka spruce, Pacific yew, Pacific silver and grand firs, and western redcedar; at high altitudes are found subalpine fir, mountain hemlock, western white, and white-bark pines, Engelmann spruce, and western larch. Timberline trees are often reduced to a sprawling shrublike habit, or they may become even prostrate on wholly unprotected sites. This species is considered tolerant, more so than western white pine or western larch, but less than Engelmann spruce, subalpine fir, the hemlocks, Sitka spruce, or western redcedar.

Alaska-cedar may produce a small amount of seed annually, with large crops at irregular intervals of four or more years. The seeds have transient viability, and low germination (about

12 percent), and the percentage of seedling survival is never very great. The seeds are able to germinate in rocky, gravelly, or clay soil, leaf litter, or even moss provided there is an abundance of soil moisture. The seedling, once it has become established, continues to grow very slowly but persistently both in height and in diameter. Pole-size trees may be 100 to 200 years old. This species is one of the longest-lived of western conifers. An age of 1000 years is not uncommon, and one old tree was reported to show 3500 growth rings.

The lumber is used for furniture, boats, and paneling. Most is now exported to Japan.

JUNIPERUS L.   Juniper

The junipers constitute about 60 species of trees and shrubs widely scattered through North and Central America, Japan, Taiwan, China, the Himalaya, the Mediterranean basin, northern Africa, Abyssinia, the Canary Islands, the Azores, and the West Indies.

Juniperus communis L. (common juniper) is a shrub or small tree which is circumpolar in the northern hemisphere. The var. *depressa* Pursh, oldfield common juniper, is a sprawling shrub common to many sections of eastern and western United States and Canada. It is readily recognized by its peculiar bushy habit of growth, its long-subulate, ternate leaves, and its glaucous blue berrylike strobili. Several other varieties of *J. communis* as well as cultivars of many other species are used as ornamentals.

Oil obtained from both the wood and leaves of certain species is used in the manufacture of perfumes and medicines. The leaf oils possess diuretic properties, and cattleraisers exercise particular care in making sure that their grazing livestock do not forage on junipers. Gin derives its characteristic taste from juniper "berries," and they are also used as a flavoring in some cooking.

About thirteen species of *Juniperus* are native to the United States; the most important is *J. virginiana.*

Interspecific hybridization, introgression, clines, and ecotypes have been documented in the junipers. See Flake et al. (1978) and Adams (1986) for examples.

Botanical Features of the Genus

Leaves persistent, opposite or ternate; always subulate on juvenile growth; on older plants (1) wholly subulate and ternate, (2) wholly scalelike and decussate, (3) both 1 and 2 on the same plant; leaves with or without glands; the subulate ones frequently conspicuously stomatiferous and with a single medial resin canal.

Cones (juvenile) terminal or axillary; *pollen cones* composed of several decussate pollen sacs; *ovulate cones* composed of 3 to 8 decussate or ternate, pointed scale/bracts, some or all bearing 1 or 2 basal ovules; plants dioecious or rarely monoecious.

Mature cones red-brown, blue, or blue-black, often glaucous, berrylike, maturing in one, two, or three seasons; *seeds* 1 to 12 ovoid, terete, or angular, unwinged, usually requiring two or more seasons to germinate; *cotyledons* 2, or 4 to 6.

Eastern Junipers

Juníperus virginiàna L.   Eastern redcedar

Distinguishing Characteristics (Fig. 8-76)

Leaves about ¹⁄₁₆ in. (1.5 mm) long, opposite and decussate (rarely ternate), dark green scales, arranged to form a 4-sided branchlet; the long sharp-pointed (subulate)

FIGURE 8-76   *Juniperus virginiana.* Eastern redcedar. (1) Juvenile foliage × ¾. (2) Mature foliage and mature seed cones × ¾. (3) Bark of old tree. (*Courtesy of U.S. Forest Service.*)

juvenile leaves predominate for a number of years and are usually present in small numbers even on old trees.

Cones ¼ to ⅜ in. (6 to 9 mm) in diameter, subglobose, ripening the first season, pale green turning to dark blue at maturity, glaucous; *seeds* 1 or 2, rarely 3 or 4, requiring 2 or 3 years to germinate; cotyledons 2.

Bark ⅛ to ¼ in. (3 to 6 mm) thick, light reddish brown, fibrous, separating into long, narrow, fringed scales; often ashy gray on exposed surfaces.

Range

Eastern (Map 8-28). Local disjuncts in northern Texas, southwestern Kansas, and southwestern North Dakota. The variety *silicicola* is mainly coastal from North Carolina to central and northwestern Florida. Elevation: sea level to 4600 ft in the southern Appalachians. A broad ecological amplitude from sand dunes, dry uplands, old fields, and fence rows to floodplains, hammocks, and swamps; from acid soils to limestone outcrops.

General Description

Eastern redcedar is a small to medium-size tree 40 to 50 ft high and 12 to 24 in. dbh (max. 120 by 5 ft). The crown is dense and pyramidal, columnar (Fig. 8-77) or rather broadly bushy.

Although best growth is made on deep alluvial soils, hardwood competition eliminates most redcedars from such sites. The tree is most common on the poorest of dry soils in pure stands or open mixtures with shortleaf and Virginia pines, or the dry soil oaks, hickories, and other hardwoods. The so-called cedar barrens of Tennessee and northern Alabama have supplied much of the commercial timber produced.

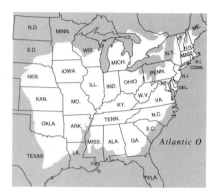

MAP 8-28   *Juniperus virginiana,* not including var. *silicicola.*

FIGURE 8-77   Eastern redcedar, pyramidal (left) and columnar (right) growth forms at approximately the same age.

As treated here, *J. virginiana* includes the southern redcedar, *J. silicicola* (Small) Bailey, recognized by many earlier authors. According to the study by Adams (1986), this is a coastal foredune and sand ridge ecotype and treated as *J. virginiana* var. *silicicola* (Small) J. Silba.

Dispersal of the seeds is primarily by birds, which eat the berrylike cones in large numbers. Seed bearing may begin about the tenth year. Delayed germination is the rule, and the seedlings do not appear until the second or third season after the seeds are sown. Eastern redcedar is a slow-growing, intolerant tree reaching a maximum age of about 300 years.

Seedling variation is pronounced, and many ornamental forms have been propagated vegetatively; in fact, redcedar and its cultivars are among the best of native ornamental evergreens. "Cedar apples," orange galls caused by a fungus, are often conspicuous features particularly after a rain.

The reddish, aromatic wood is used for furniture and paneling, the resistant trunks for fenceposts, and the trees as ornamentals. Redcedar is also browsed by deer and livestock and browse lines about 5 ft above the ground lend a unique aspect to the trees in a field or pasture.

Western Junipers

Most of these species are important components of the pinyon-juniper woodlands of the southwest (see under Pinyon pines; see also Miller and Wigand, 1994). They are mostly large bushy or sprawling shrubs or small stunted trees (sometimes much larger) on poor, dry soils in arid regions. Those which do attain tree size usually have a stout,

FIGURE 8-78   *Juniperus scopulorum.* Rocky mountain juniper. (1) Foliage and young seed cones × ¾. (2) Foliage and mature seed cones × ¾.(3) Bark of tree.

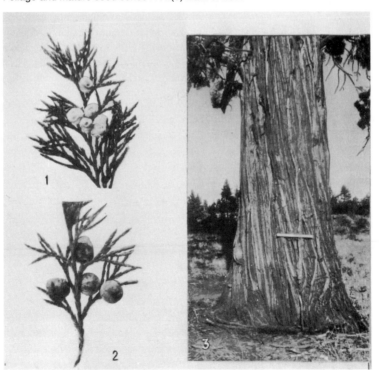

rapidly tapering bole partially covered by a dense pyramidal to subglobose crown of more or less irregular outline. These trees are of little or no value for sawtimber, but they may be used for poles, posts, crossties, and mine props.

The 10 to 12 species of western junipers may be divided into two groups, those with blue cones and those with mostly red-brown cones. Depending on the species, these cones may ripen in one or two growing seasons. The states mentioned in the following summary represent the areas of greatest concentration for each species. Consult Little (1979) or local guides for greater detail.

Blue-coned   Common juniper, *J. communis,* is a tree or shrub with all subulate leaves, as already mentioned, and ranges along the Rockies from British Columbia to New Mexico and Arizona, and in the Cascades to northern California. Oneseed juniper, *J. monosperma* (Engelm.) Sarg., has dark blue cones with a single seed. It is found on semiarid slopes and plateaus of the Rockies at 3000 to 7000 ft elevation, mostly in Arizona, New Mexico, and Colorado. Rocky Mountain juniper, *J. scopulorum* Sarg. (Fig 8-78), reaches 50 ft tall and ranges widely along the Rockies from British Columbia to southern New Mexico, and east to the western Dakotas. Ashe juniper (locally Ozark white cedar), *J. ashei* Buchholz, is mostly in central Texas, south into Mexico and northeastward into Oklahoma and along the Missouri-Arkansas line. Western juniper, *J. occidentalis* Hook., is common at high elevations from southern Washington south to southern California.

Red-brown-coned   Alligator juniper, *J. deppeana* Steud, gets its name from the bark that is divided into squares, or blocks, so that it resembles alligator hide. It is found mostly in Arizona, New Mexico, western Texas, and south into Mexico. Utah juniper, *J. osteosperma* (Torr.) Little, is typical of the Great Basin, mostly in Utah, Nevada, and Arizona. California juniper, *J. californica* Carr., as its name suggests, is largely restricted to the mountains of that state.

9

MAGNOLIOPHYTA (ANGIOSPERMS)

Angiosperms include the flowering plants which are the most common, most complex and highly evolved, and most widely distributed vascular plants now inhabiting the earth's surface. They supply food, clothing, and shelter for both humans and wildlife and also innumerable drugs, oils, dyes, and other products. Numbering some 215,000 species in about 385 families, they are found from the luxuriant, rain-drenched forests of the tropics to the wastes of the tundra in polar regions. Many of them form the only cover on hot, dry soils in arid regions; others occur on mountains to the highest altitudes of plant growth, and still others in aquatic habitats of fresh, brackish, or marine waters. Showing great variation in size and structure, angiosperms range from small, floating disklike bodies with minute flowers to enormous trees 300 ft or more in height. Some complete their life cycle within a few weeks while others may span several centuries.

The origin of the angiosperms was, according to the fossil record, in Lower Cretaceous times about 125 million years ago. They had a progressive but remarkable evolutionary explosion and migration and rapidly became the dominant vegetation over most of the earth. By Eocene of the Tertiary Period (50 million years ago), many modern genera had evolved. See Cronquist (1988) for a review of the early evolution of the angiosperms.

The angiosperms are characterized as seed plants with ovules and seeds enclosed in a modified leaf (carpel). A postzygotic endosperm is the primary food-storage tissue of the developing seed. Frequently, however, cotyledons replace the endosperm as the storage tissue in the mature seed.

Angiosperms are divided into two classes, *Magnoliopsida* commonly called the "dicots," and *Liliopsida* or "monocots". Although common names for these classes indicate the number of cotyledons, there are other differences as indicated in Table

TABLE 9-1   COMPARISON OF THE TWO CLASSES OF ANGIOSPERMS

Class	Cotyledons	Leaf venation	Flower parts	Vascular bundles
Dicots	2 (rarely 1 to 4)	pinnate or palmate	various, often in 4s or 5s	separate or fused, forming a ring around a central pith
Monocots	1	parallel	usually in 3s or 6s, never in 5s	distributed throughout the stem

9-1. The two classes are further divided into a total of 11 subclasses following the system proposed by Cronquist (1988). In the phylogenetic arrangement shown (Fig. 9-1), the monocots arose from primitive dicots, and the relative size of the subclass balloons is roughly proportional to the number of species in each. The characteristics of the subclasses are not given here because of their complexity and because they are based mostly on reproductive morphology. See Cronquist (1988) for these details. This modern classification is being used in many recent books (Elias, 1989; FNA, 1993; Gleason and Cronquist, 1991).

Trees, defined by their habit and having secondary xylem (wood), are only found among the dicots. However, there are several monocots of tree form and size—the palms, bamboos, century plants, and yuccas—but they do not have wood. Trees, in the broad sense then, occur in all the dicot subclasses and three of the monocot subclasses. They represent both primitive and advanced evolutionary types. A list of the 46 families included here, by class and subclass, follows:

FIGURE 9-1   Two classes and eleven subclasses of angiosperms. The phylogenetic arrangement is by Cronquist. (*Reprinted from* The Evolution and Classification of the Flowering Plants, *2d ed., 1988, The New York Botanical Garden, Bronx, N.Y.*)

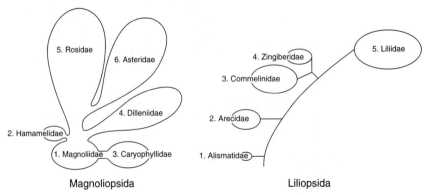

Magnoliopsida—The Dicots

Magnoliidae

Magnoliaceae	Magnolia family	Lauraceae	Laurel family
Annonaceae	Custard-apple family		

Hamamelidae

Platanaceae	Sycamore family	Myricaceae	Waxmyrtle family
Hamamelidaceae	Witch-hazel family		
Ulmaceae	Elm family	Fagaceae	Beech family
Moraceae	Mulberry family	Betulaceae	Birch family
Leitneriaceae	Corkwood family	Casuarinaceae	Beefwood family
Juglandaceae	Walnut family		

Caryophyllidae

Cactaceae	Cactus family

Dilleniidae

Theaceae	Tea family	Sapotaceae	Sapodilla family
Tiliaceae	Linden family	Ebenaceae	Ebony family
Tamaricaceae	Tamarisk family	Styracaceae	Storax family
Salicaceae	Willow family	Symplocaceae	Sweetleaf family
Ericaceae	Heath family		

Rosidae

Rosaceae	Rose family	Sapindaceae	Soapberry family
Mimosaceae	Mimosa family		
Caesalpiniaceae	Caesalpinia family	Hippocastanaceae	Buckeye family
Fabaceae	Bean family	Aceraceae	Maple family
Elaeagnaceae	Oleaster family	Anacardiaceae	Cashew family
Myrtaceae	Myrtle family	Simaroubaceae	Quassia family
Cornaceae	Dogwood family	Meliaceae	Mahogany family
Aquifoliaceae	Holly family		
Rhamnaceae	Buckthorn family	Rutaceae	Rue family
		Araliaceae	Ginseng family

Asteridae

Oleaceae	Olive family	Bignoniaceae	Trumpet-creeper family
Scrophulariaceae	Figwort family		

Liliopsida—The Monocots

Arecidae

Arecaceae	Palm family

Commelinidae

Poaceae	Grass family

Liliidae

Agavaceae	Century-plant family

MAGNOLIOPSIDA—The Dicots

MAGNOLIIDAE

Magnoliaceae: The Magnolia Family

This family not only includes some of the most interesting of our modern trees but also some of the most primitive. Fossils of numerous, now extinct, species have been found, some of which extended northward as far as Alaska and Greenland during the latter part of the Cretaceous Period. The family comprises 12 genera and 220 species of trees or shrubs found in southeast Asia, in the eastern United States southward through Central America, and from the West Indies to eastern Brazil. Two genera and nine species are native in North America (Table 9-2, 9-3).

Botanical Features of the Family

Leaves deciduous or persistent, alternate, simple, stipulate; the stipules enclose the bud and their conspicuous scars encircle the twig.

Flowers large, actinomorphic, perfect (rarely unisexual), terminal or axillary, solitary; *sepals* 3, *petals* 6 or more; *stamens* and *pistils* many, arranged spirally on an elongated receptacle; *ovary* superior; entomophilous.

Fruit a conelike aggregate of follicles or samaras.

MAGNOLIA L.   Magnolia

The trees and shrubs included in this genus are particularly well-known on account of their large, showy, insect-pollinated flowers which, in certain species, are nearly a foot or more in diameter. Many ornamental forms have been developed and are widely used. The genus was named in honor of Pierre Magnol, a celebrated French botanist of the seventeenth century. *Magnolia* numbers some 80 or more species, scattered through southern and eastern Asia, Mexico to Venezuela, and the eastern United States. Eight species are native to this country, but only two are of any importance as timber producers.

Botanical Features of the Genus

Leaves deciduous or persistent, unlobed, entire margined.

Flowers in the native, deciduous species appearing just after the leaves; *sepals* 3; *petals* 6 to 15, in series of 3; *stamens* and *pistils* numerous, spirally arranged.

TABLE 9-2   COMPARISON OF NATIVE GENERA IN THE MAGNOLIACEAE

Genus	Leaves	Flowers	Fruit
Magnolia magnolia	unlobed, apex acute to obtuse	stamens introrse	an aggregate of semifleshy follicles
Liriodendron yellow-poplar	lobed, apex truncate to broadly notched	stamens extrorse	an aggregate of samaras

Fruit a conelike aggregate of spirally placed, 1- to 2-seeded follicles; *seeds* with a scarlet, pulpy outer layer, when mature, suspended by long slender threads; seeds are distributed to some extent by birds.

Twigs somewhat bitter tasting, aromatic, moderately stout, straight or slightly zigzag; *pith* homogeneous or inconspicuously diaphragmed, terete; *terminal buds* usually large and conspicuous, with a single outer scale; *lateral buds* smaller; *leaf scars* crescent-shaped to oval; *bundle scars* conspicuous, scattered or in a double row; *stipular scars* conspicuous, encircling the twig.

Magnòlia acuminàta L.   Cucumbertree; cucumber magnolia

Distinguishing Characteristics (Fig. 9-2)

Leaves deciduous, 4 to 10 in. (10 to 25 cm) long, 3 to 6 in. (7.5 to 15 cm) wide; *shape* broadly elliptical to ovate; *margin* entire or repand; *apex* acute to acuminate; *base* broadly cuneate, rounded, or cordate; *surfaces* glabrous and yellow-green above, glabrous or pubescent below; *fall color* yellow-brown or pale yellow.

Flowers 1½ to 3½ in. (4 to 9 cm) wide, greenish yellow.

Fruit aggregate 1½ to 3 in. (4 to 9.5 cm) long, cylindrical to ovoid, glabrous, rarely over 1 in. (2.5 cm) in diameter; *seeds* ½ in. (12 mm) long, red, after emergence suspended on slender threads.

Twigs moderately stout, reddish brown, becoming grayish brown; *terminal buds* ½ to ¾ in. (12 to 18 mm) long, silvery silky; *lateral buds* smaller; *leaf scars* horseshoe-shaped; *bundle scars* 5 to 9.

Bark brownish gray, fissured into narrow flaky ridges.

Range

Eastern (Map 9-1). Elevation: 100 to 4000 ft. Rich, mesic slopes, ravines, valleys, and along streams.

General Description

Cucumbertree attains heights of 80 to 90 ft and 3 to 4 ft dbh (max. 125 by 6 ft). It has a straight, clear, slightly buttressed bole, pyramidal crown, a deep but wide-spreading root system, and is usually found on moist, fertile soils of loose texture, with the other hardwoods of the region, such as white and red oaks, hickories, black tupelo, American beech, ashes, and yellow-poplar.

TABLE 9-3   COMPARISON OF IMPORTANT MAGNOLIAS

Species	Leaves	Flowers	Fruit	Buds
M. acuminata cucumbertree	deciduous	greenish yellow, 1½–3½ in. (4–9 cm) wide	glabrous	silvery white, silky
M. grandiflora southern magnolia	persistent	snow-white 6–8 in. (15–20 cm) wide	rusty tomentose	rusty brown, pubescent

FIGURE 9-2 *Magnolia acuminata.* Cucumbertree. (1) Twig × 1¼. (2) Flower × ½. (3) Aggregate of follicles with seeds × ¾. (4) Leaf × ½. (5) Bark.

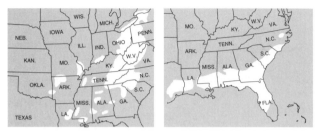

MAP 9-1 **(Left)** *Magnolia acuminata.* **(Right)** *Magnolia grandiflora;* naturalized farther northeast than shown on the map.

Best development is reached at the base of the Appalachians in the Carolinas, Tennessee, and Kentucky, but the tree is nowhere abundant.

The wood is commonly mixed and utilized with that of yellow-poplar. The lumber is used for furniture, interior trim, doors, and boxes.

Magnòlia grandiflòra L.   Southern magnolia; evergreen magnolia

Distinguishing Characteristics (Fig. 9-3)

Leaves leathery, persistent; 4 to 8 in. (10 to 20 cm) long, 2½ to 4 in. (6 to 10 cm) wide; *shape* narrowly oval to ovate; *margin* entire; *apex* bluntly acute or acuminate; *base* cuneate; *surfaces* bright green and very lustrous above, green and puberulent or rusty tomentose below.

FIGURE 9-3   *Magnolia grandiflora.* Southern magnolia. (1) Aggregate of follicles × ¾. (2) Flower opened before anthesis to show tight spiral of stamens and pistils × ¼.

Flowers 6 to 8 in. (15 to 20 cm) wide, fragrant; with 6 or 9 to 12, large creamy white petals; appearing in early summer.

Fruit aggregate 2¾ to 4 in. (7 to 10 cm) long, ovoid or short cylindrical, 1½ to 2½ in. (4 to 6 cm) in diameter; tan tomentose.

Twigs rusty tomentose; terminal buds 1 to 1½ in. (2.5 to 3.5 cm) long, pale or rusty tomentose; lateral buds smaller.

Bark light brown to gray, scaly (Fig. 9-4).

Range

Southeastern (Map 9-1). Elevation: sea level to 400 ft. Upland well-drained soils, mesic slopes, ravines, maritime forests near coasts.

General Description

Southern magnolia is a medium-size tree, commonly 60 to 100 ft high and 2 to 3 ft dbh (max. 135 by 7 ft), with a tall straight bole and somewhat pyramidal crown. It is easily identified in the forest by its persistent (2 years) shiny, dark green leaves, which are often bronze or dark brown below. This magnolia is a southern bottomland species but will not survive long inundations; it is found on moist but well-drained soils in association with American beech, sweetgum, yellow-poplar, white ash, oaks, and hickories. Winter droughts can cause die-back and mortality.

Besides the timber produced and the seeds eaten by various birds and small mammals, southern magnolia is very valuable as an ornamental on account of its large, showy flowers and evergreen leaves. It is planted for this purpose in North America as far north as New Jersey on the Atlantic Coast and along the Pacific Coast northward to British Columbia. More broadly, it is one of America's great gifts to the gardens of the world. It is the state flower of Louisiana and Mississippi.

FIGURE 9-4   Bark of southern magnolia.

Other Native Magnolias

Several other native species, while of little or no importance as timber producers, are worthy of mention on account of their conspicuousness in the forest and because they are in common use as ornamentals throughout the southern states.

Magnòlia virginiàna L.   Sweetbay, sweetbay magnolia

Distinguishing Characteristics.   *Leaves* 2¾ to 6 in. (7 to 15 cm) long, 1⅜ to 2 in. (3.5 to 5 cm) wide, oblong to elliptical, glaucous and white pubescent below, deciduous in the late fall, or persistent until spring. *Flowers* creamy white, cup-shaped, 2 to 3¼ in. (5 to 8 cm) in diameter, very attractive and aromatic. *Aggregate* globose, 1¼ to 2 in. (3 to 5 cm) long.

Range.   Massachusetts to Florida and west to Texas. Elevation: sea level to 500 ft. Swamps, pocosins, bays, and low woods.

General Description.   Trees to a height of 80 ft and dbh of 3 ft. Flowering begins very early, and it is not unusual to see a slender stem only about 2 ft tall with a big flower at the top. These trees are an important deer browse throughout the year. They are also cultivated as ornamental lawn, park, or street trees. The wood is used for furniture, boxes, and tool handles. See the discussion of "bay trees" under *Persea.*

Magnòlia macrophýlla Michx.   Bigleaf magnolia

Distinguishing Characteristics.   *Leaves* deciduous, 10 to 32 in. (25 to 80 cm) long, 6 to 12 in. (15 to 30 cm) wide, broadly elliptical to oblanceolate, white below, cordate or auriculate at the base; fall color yellow. *Flowers* creamy white, often with a purple blotch inside and at the base of the inner petals, 10 to 12 in. (25 to 30 cm) or more in diameter, fragrant. *Aggregate* of follicles globose, over 2 in. (5 cm) in diameter, with 50 or more carpels.

Range.   North Carolina to southern Alabama and Louisiana, north to Kentucky and West Virginia; disjunct in southeastern South Carolina. Elevation: sea level to 1200 ft. This is a relatively infrequent tree found in scattered populations in moist woods of ravines, valleys, and ridges.

Magnòlia áshei Weatherby   Ashe magnolia

Distinguishing Characteristics.   *Leaves* deciduous, 8 to 24 in. (20 to 60 cm) long, 4 to 12 in. (10 to 30 cm) wide, elliptical to oblanceolate, white below, deeply cordate to auriculate at base; fall color yellow-brown. *Flowers* 6¼ to 12 in. (16 to 30 cm) in diameter, whitish with a purple blotch at the inside base of each petal, aromatic. *Aggregate* of follicles cylindrical, less than 2 in. (5 cm) in diameter, with less than 40 carpels.

Range.   Local and rare in northwestern Florida. Elevation: sea level to 200 ft. This is a small tree of upland woods, ravines, and bluffs.

Magnòlia pyramidàta Bartr.   Pyramid magnolia

Distinguishing Characteristics.   *Leaves* deciduous, 7 to 10 in. (18 to 25 cm) long, 2 to 4¾ in. (5 to 12 cm) wide, panduriform to rhombic-spatulate, pale green below, deeply cordate to auriculate at base; fall color yellow. *Flowers* creamy white, 2½ to 3¼ in. (6 to 8 cm) in diameter, fragrant.

Range. South Carolina to northwestern Florida, and west to northeastern Texas. Elevation: sea level to 400 ft. This is a small tree of rich woods, slopes, and river bluffs of the Piedmont and Coastal Plain.

Magnòlia fràseri Walt.   Fraser magnolia

Distinguishing Characteristics. *Leaves* deciduous, 10 to 20 in. (25 to 50 cm) long, 3 to 5 in. (8 to 15 cm) wide, oblanceolate, pale green below, auriculate at base; fall color yellow. *Flowers* creamy white, 6¼ to 8½ in. (16 to 22 cm) in diameter, fragrant.

Range. West Virginia and western Virginia south to northern Georgia. Elevation: 800 to 5000 ft. This is an understory tree of rich woods on slopes and in mountain coves of the southern Appalachians.

Magnòlia tripétala L.   Umbrella magnolia

Distinguishing Characteristics. *Leaves* deciduous, 8 to 16 in. (20 to 40 cm) long, 4 to 8 in. (10 to 20 cm) wide, oblanceolate, often clustered at the ends of branches, pale green below, acuminate at base; fall color yellow. *Flowers* creamy white, malodorous, 10 to 12 in. (25 to 30 cm) in diameter.

Range. Southern Pennsylvania to southern Alabama and Mississippi, and to eastern Oklahoma and the Ohio River valley. Elevation: 100 to 1400 ft. This is an understory tree in moist soils of slopes and ravines and along streams.

LIRIODENDRON L.   Yellow-poplar

Fossil remains indicate that this genus, with several forms, was once widely distributed over North America and the Old World. At present, however, only two species remain, one, *L. chinense* (Hemsley) Sarg. of central China, and the other, *L. tulipifera* of the eastern United States. The common name "yellow-poplar" for the American species is misleading because the true poplars, found in the Salicaceae or willow family, are unrelated to the Magnoliaceae.

Liriodéndron tulipífera L.   Yellow-poplar; tuliptree; tulip-poplar

Distinguishing Characteristics (Fig. 9-5)

Leaves deciduous; 4 to 6 in. (8 to 15 cm) long and wide; *shape* nearly orbicular, mostly 4-lobed; *lobes* rounded to acute and sinuses shallow to deep; *margin* of the lobes entire; *base* and *apex* nearly truncate (or apex often broadly notched); *surfaces* puberulent and pale below; *petioles* slender, 5 to 6 in. (12 to 15 cm) long; *stipules* large and conspicuous, together encircling the twig; *fall color* butter-yellow.

Flowers appearing in spring just after the leaves unfold; 1½ to 2 in. (4 to 5 cm) wide, cup-shaped or tuliplike; *sepals* 3; *petals* 6, in two whorls, light greenish yellow with a conspicuous orange spot at the inside base of each; *stamens* and *pistils* many, spirally arranged.

Fruit an erect conelike aggregate of samaras, 2½ to 3 in. (6 to 7 cm) long, at maturity the upper samaras deciduous from the central, more or less persistent axis (these "cones" are of value in identifying the larger trees at some distance after the leaves

FIGURE 9-5 *Liriodendron tulipifera.* Yellow-poplar. (1) Twig × 1¼. (2) Fruit (samara) × 1. (3) Aggregate of samaras × ¾. (4) Flower × ¾. (5) Leaf × ½. (6) Bark of young tree. (7) Bark of old tree.

have fallen); *samaras* 4-angled, terminally winged, 1 to 1½ in. (2.5 to 4 cm) long, 2-seeded, but commonly 1-seeded by abortion.

Twigs moderately stout, reddish brown, bitter to the taste; *pith* diaphragmed, terete; *terminal buds* ca. ½ in. (12 mm) long, flattened, "duck-billed" in appearance, the scales valvate in pairs, with only the two outer ones visible; *lateral buds* much smaller; leaf scars circular to oval; *bundle scars* small, scattered; *stipular scars* conspicuous, encircling the twig.

Bark on young trees dark greenish or orange-brown and smooth, with small white spots; soon ashy-gray, breaking up into long, rough, interlacing rounded ridges separated by fissures; inner bark bitter and aromatic.

Range

Eastern (Map 9-2). Elevation: sea level to 1000 ft northward, to 4500 ft in the southern Appalachians. Bottomlands in wet to mesic woods, mountain coves, and lower slopes.

General Description

Yellow-poplar is not only one of the most distinctive trees of eastern North America, it is also one of the most valuable timber producers. In the forest this tree presents an unmistakable outline. The tall, clear, almost arrow-straight trunk terminates in a small, rather open, oblong crown. The root system is deep and wide-spreading, and the stumps sprout readily.

Yellow-poplar is intolerant and site-sensitive. On good sites its juvenile height growth, following the first year, is so rapid that it can outstrip its competition. On poor sites, it is dominated by many other species.

Fast-growing trees may be 120 ft tall and 18 to 24 in. dbh at age 50. Maturity is reached in about 200 years, with very old trees attaining the three-century mark. Yellow-poplar is found in some 16 forest types, associated mostly with other hardwoods including oaks and hickories, American beech, sweetgum, maples, sassafras, black cherry, and basswood. Coniferous associates are white pine and hemlock, and, in the South, loblolly pine.

An effective pioneer on disturbed sites, yellow-poplar often persists in climax stands.

Seed production begins at about 15 years and continues beyond two centuries. Seed is produced annually, and bumper crops occur frequently. Pollination is by insects (tuliptree honey is a commercial product), but is often incomplete. This reproductive weakness is overcome by the ability of filled viable seeds to accumulate in the litter for several years and then to produce multitudes of seedlings when conditions for germination are suitable.

There are relatively few insects or pathogens which cause widespread damage. Yellow-poplar is, however, very susceptible to impact basal wounding and subsequent decay. It forms

MAP 9-2   *Liriodendron tulipifera.*

an important deer browse with sprouts, buds, flowers, and seedlings being eaten. The fruits are an important food for birds and small mammals.

Yellow-poplar is a beautiful ornamental tree with its large conspicuous flowers and notched leaves on long petioles that quiver in the slightest breeze. Because of this last feature or perhaps certain wood characters, the name *poplar* became attached to this member of the Magnolia family.

Yellow-poplar is a polymorphic species with chemical, morphological, and ecological differences showing a regional and clinal pattern. See Parks et al. (1994) for a detailed discussion.

Annonaceae: The Custard-apple Family

This family includes 130 genera and over 2300 species of trees, shrubs, and lianas mainly in the tropics except *Asimina* which extends north to Michigan. The family produces several well-known tropical fruits such as custard apple (*Annona reticulata* L.), cherimoya (*Annona cherimoya* Miller), and soursop (*Annona muricata* L.). These fleshy aggregates form by the fusion of carpels and receptacle and have the general appearance of a fleshy cone. There are two genera and four species of trees native in the United States. Only one, pawpaw, is widespread.

Botanical Features of the Family

Leaves persistent or (in ours) deciduous, alternate, simple, estipulate, distichous, entire, aromatic.

Flowers solitary, entomophilous, perfect, regular; *tepals* 6 to 9 in 2 or 3 whorls; *stamens* many; *ovary* 3-carpellate, superior; appearing before the leaves.

Fruit a berry or aggregate of berries; *seeds* large.

Asímina trilòba (L.) Dunal   Pawpaw

Distinguishing Characteristics.   *Leaves* entire, 7 to 12 in. (18 to 30 cm) long, 2¾ to 5 in. (7 to 13 cm) wide, elliptical to usually oblanceolate, acuminate at apex and base, pale below; fall color yellow. *Flowers* to 1½ in. (4 cm) across, maroon, nodding, in early spring before the leaves. *Fruit* a berry, 3 to 6 in. (7.5 to 15 cm) long, 1 to 1½ in. (2.5 to 4 cm) in diameter, yellowish, soft, with several large, shiny brown, oblong seeds. *Twigs* with naked buds covered with reddish hairs; pith diaphragmed the second year. *Bark* light gray-brown, smooth.

Range.   Southern Ontario, southern Michigan, and western New York, south to northwestern Florida, west to eastern Texas, and north to southeastern Nebraska. Elevation: sea level to 4900 ft in the southern Appalachians. Moist soils of floodplains, stream banks, and in the understory of hardwood forests.

General Description.   Pawpaw is a small tree to 30 ft tall and 10 in. dbh or more. The large leaves may appear like Magnolia, but the twig lacks the stipular scars, and the dark chocolate brown, naked buds are conspicuous. The fruit has an unusual but pleasant taste, but is eaten mainly by wildlife and local people who happen to know where the trees occur. Root sprouting is common and many trees form small clones.

Lauraceae: The Laurel Family

The Laurel family includes 45 genera and some 2200 species of trees and shrubs, which are largely evergreen. Most of them are tropical, and although a few extend into the temperate zones, the forests of the American tropics and those of southeastern Asia support a particularly luxurious growth of lauraceous plants.

Many aromatic substances present in the leaves, stems, bark, roots, and fruits of certain species have been investigated and commercially exploited. From "bois de rose," *Aniba rosaeodora* Ducke, is obtained linaloa oil, a compound used in the manufacture of expensive perfumes. Camphor tree, *Cinnamomum camphora* (L.) T. Nees & Eberm., is the source of true camphor of commerce. It is a native of Asia and is commonly planted in the southern United States as an ornamental, evergreen tree of lawns, parks, and along streets. Cinnamon and cassia bark are products of two other Asiatic members of this genus, namely, *C. verum* J. Presl and *C. aromaticum* Nees, respectively. The avocado or alligator pear, now so widely cultivated throughout the tropics, and available in most markets, is the fruit of *Persea americana* Mill., a small tree originally native to the American tropics but now rapidly becoming naturalized in many other tropical countries. *Laurus nobilis* L. of the Mediterranean area provides the bay leaves used in cooking.

A few commercial timbers of the Lauraceae find their way into the lumber markets of the world, but most of them are used only locally. *Endiandra palmerstoni* C. T. White, the Oriental walnut of eastern Australia, resembles black walnut, *Juglans nigra* L. sufficiently (superficially at least) to permit substitution for this species. *Ocotea rodiaei* (R. Schomb.) Mez., the British Guianan greenheart, long since has proved its worth in marine construction; this is exported in quantity, particularly to European ports, and small amounts are utilized along the American seacoasts; the gates of the Panama Canal locks were originally fabricated with this wood. The South African stinkwood, *Ocotea bullata* E. Mey., because of its strength, durability, color, and pleasing figure is a cabinet wood and building timber of recognized merit.

Four or five genera have arborescent forms in the United States, but these are of only minor importance. *Nectandra coriacea* (Sw.) Griseb., Florida nectandra, with entire, persistent leaves, is native to southern Florida. *Lindera benzoin* (L.) Blume, spicebush, is a common large shrub of the eastern states; it has deciduous, entire, aromatic leaves, yellow flowers, and small clustered buds. The remaining genera, *Umbellularia* (monotypic), *Persea,* and *Sassafras,* are worthy of a more detailed description.

Botanical Features of the Family

Leaves persistent or deciduous, alternate (rarely opposite), simple, often glandular-punctate, usually aromatic, estipulate.

Flowers perfect and imperfect (some species polygamous), regular, entomophilous; *tepals* 6-parted; *stamens* in 3 or 4 whorls of 3 each; *pistils* 1, ovary superior, 1-celled and with a solitary ovule.

Fruit a 1-seeded berry or drupe.

Umbellulària califórnica (Hook. & Arn.) Nutt.   California-laurel; Oregon-myrtle

Distinguishing Characteristics (Fig. 9-6).   *Leaves* evergreen, coriaceous, 2 to 5 in. (5 to 13 cm) long, ½ to 1½ in. (1.2 to 4 cm) wide, lanceolate to elliptical, entire, pungent-spicy when crushed. *Flowers* perfect, yellowish green, in axillary umbels, appearing from January to March

FIGURE 9-6   *Umbellularia californica.* California-laurel. (1) Leaf × ¾. (2) Flowers × ¾. (3) Fruit (drupe) × 1. (4) Bark (*Photos 2 and 4 by W. I. Stein, U.S. Forest Service*).

before the new leaves. *Fruit* an acrid, yellow-green to purple drupe. *Twigs* yellow-green, terminal bud present, pith homogenous. *Bark* brown, with thin appressed scales.

Range.   Coos Bay region of southwestern Oregon southward through the Coast Ranges and lower Sierras to southern California. Elevation: sea level to 1500 ft in the north; 2000 to 6000 ft in the south. Dry, rocky soils on slopes and bluffs; also in moist bottomlands.

General Description.   California-laurel is the only lauraceous species in western North America. In moist sites in southwestern Oregon it is a large tree 100 to 175 ft in height and 3 to 10 ft dbh, although elsewhere in its range it is usually a small or medium-size tree 40 to 80 ft high and 18 to 30 in. dbh. In drier sites it is commonly shrubby, and along the windswept bluffs of the Pacific Ocean it often becomes prostrate and forms a spreading network of thickly matted branches. The bole, even under forest conditions, occasionally divides near the ground into several ascending limbs resulting in a broad, dense, round-topped crown; the root system is usually deep but wide-spreading.

Large burls or smaller excrescences are often formed on the trunks of older trees, and those devoid of defects command a high price in the trade. The smaller ones are often turned into many sorts of fancy articles of woodenware, while the large ones are shipped to veneer plants where they are carefully cut into thin sheets of intrinsic value and beauty.

The evergreen leaves have a strong, camphorlike odor when crushed or bruised. In spite of this, goats are known to forage on them during the winter months when more suitable browse is extremely sparse or lacking. The fruits and seeds are eaten by various wildlife.

The aromatic properties of all parts of the tree have been used in primitive medicine. Seeds are produced in abundance after 30 to 40 years; they mature in one season and germinate within a few weeks after dispersal. Seedlings often form dense clumps under partial shade and develop quite rapidly; this species also sprouts from the root collar.

SASSAFRAS Nees and Eberm.   Sassafras

There are three species of *Sassafras;* one is found in central China, another in Taiwan, and the third in the eastern United States.

Sássafras álbidum (Nutt.) Nees   Sassafras

Distinguishing Characteristics (Fig. 9-7).   *Leaves* 3 to 5 in. (7.5 to 13 cm) long, 1½ to 4 in. (4 to 10 cm) wide, variable in shape. On the same tree three different forms of leaves may be found: entire and (1) somewhat elliptical and unlobed (typical of older trees), (2) mitten-shaped (either right- or left-handed), and (3) three-lobed, rarely 4-5 lobed; fall color yellow to orange or

FIGURE 9-7   *Sassafras albidum.* Sassafras. (1) Fruits (drupes on thickened pedicels) × ¾. (2) Three-lobed leaf × ½. (3) Unlobed leaf × ½. (4) Two-lobed or mitten-shaped leaf × ½. (5) Twig × 1¼.

red. *Flowers* imperfect (plants dioecious), yellowish, appearing before the leaves. *Fruit* a blue drupe on a thickened, reddish pedicel. *Twigs* green, aromatic, buds scaly, bundle scar 1, stipular scars lacking, pith homogeneous. *Bark* deeply furrowed, reddish-brown, spicy, and aromatic.

Range.   Southern Ontario, east to southwestern Maine, south to central Florida, west to eastern Texas and eastern Oklahoma, north to central Michigan. Elevation: sea level to 5000 ft in the southern Appalachians. Disturbed sites and in dry to mesic forests, clearings, fence rows, and old fields.

General Description.   This is usually a small to medium-size tree but may reach a maximum of 100 ft tall and 6 ft dbh. It is intolerant, and it is common as a pioneer tree.

The very durable wood, often mixed with that of black ash, is used for furniture. Sassafras may be of greater importance in the future, because in certain parts of its range it is, by means of root sprouts as well as seeds, rapidly restocking abandoned farm lands. Oil of sassafras is used in the preparation of certain soaps and flavorings for medicines, candy, root beer, and sassafras tea. The young leaves, dried and powdered, are quite mucilaginous and are used to both thicken and flavor creole dishes.

Damage occurs from several insects and fungi. It forms an important deer browse during spring, summer, and winter, and the seeds are important food for various wildlife.

PERSEA Mill.   Persea

This is a mostly tropical genus with about 150 species including the avocado mentioned earlier. There are two species of native trees, to 25 ft tall, in the southeastern Coastal Plains. Both are recognized by their *leaves*—alternate, simple, elliptical, 3 to 6 in. (7.5 to 15 cm) long, ¾ to 1½ in. (2 to 4 cm) wide, evergreen, entire, estipulate, and aromatic as in the "bay leaf" of commerce; *flowers* small and rather inconspicuous; *fruits* dark blue to black drupes, ¼ to ½ in. (7 to 12 mm) in diameter. They are of some importance for browse and the fruits are eaten by birds and small mammals.

Persèa borbònia (L.) Spreng.   Redbay

Distinguished by its scattered straight hairs, barely visible and appressed to the lower leaf surface; the twig and petioles are sparsely pubescent or glabrous. It is a common tree in mesic to xeric woodlands and coastal dunes from North Carolina to Florida and west to southeastern Texas.

Persèa palústris (Raf.) Sarg.   Swampbay

The underside of the leaves have curved hairs not appressed to the surface, and twigs and petioles are usually pubescent. It is common in wet woodlands, hammocks, bay forests, and edges of marshes from Delaware south to Florida and west to southeastern Texas. These species are sometimes considered varieties of *P. borbonia* (Little, 1979).

"Bay Trees"

There are three genera of bay trees which are evergreen, often grow together in "bay" forests of the southeastern Coastal Plain, and which are often confused when flowers or fruits are lacking. The red and swamp bays (***Persea***, Lauraceae) have aromatic, entire leaves, green below and estipulate; sweetbay (***Magnolia virginiana***, Magnoliaceae) has aromatic, entire leaves but with stipular scars around the twig, and the leaves white below; loblolly bay (***Gordonia lasianthus,*** Theaceae) has leaves which are not aromatic when crushed, pale green on the back, estipulate, and bluntly serrulate on the margin.

HAMAMELIDAE

Platanaceae: The Sycamore or Planetree Family

This is a monotypic family with the single genus, *Platanus,* with six or seven species; three are native to North America, one of the eastern states, the other two of the west. The foreign species are found in Mexico, and from southeastern Europe to India.

PLATANUS L.   Sycamore; planetree

Botanical Features of the Genus

Leaves deciduous, alternate, simple, palmately 3- to 7-lobed; *petioles* enlarged at the base and enclosing the lateral bud; *stipules* leaflike and very conspicuous, encircling the twig and often persisting.

Flowers imperfect (plants monoecious), anemophilous, appearing with the leaves, in separate globose heads at the ends of a long peduncle; individual flowers minute; *staminate* with 3 to 8 sepals, petals, and stamens; *pistillate* with 3 to 8 sepals, petals, and carpels.

Fruit a globose head (multiple) of narrowly elongated achenes, each surrounded at the base by a circle of erect brown hairs and usually bearing at the apex a minute curved spur; long persistent on a tough, fibrous peduncle until the multiple shatters.

Twigs conspicuously zigzag; *pith* homogenous, terete; *terminal buds* lacking; *lateral buds* divergent, resinous, with a caplike outer scale; *leaf scars* encircling the buds; *bundle scars* several; *stipular scars* encircling the twig.

Plátanus occidentàlis L.   Sycamore; American planetree

Distinguishing Characteristics (Fig. 9-8)

Leaves 4 to 8 in. (10 to 20 cm) in diameter; *shape* broadly ovate to orbicular, 3- to 5-lobed, sinuses broad and usually shallow; *margin* of lobes sinuately toothed; *apex* acuminate; *base* cordate to truncate; *surfaces* glabrous above, hairy throughout below but later only along the veins; *petioles* stout, 2 to 3 in. (5 to 7 cm) long, hollow at the base; *fall color* yellow to brown.

Fruit heads ¾ to 1¼ in. (2 to 3 cm) in diameter, borne singly on slender peduncles 3 to 6 in. (7.5 to 15 cm) long; usually persistent on the tree during part of the winter.

Twigs moderately slender, dark orange-brown, conspicuously zigzag; *pith* homogeneous, terete; *leaf scars* nearly surrounding the bud; *stipular scars* distinct, encircling the twigs; *terminal buds* lacking; *lateral buds* divergent, resinous, and with a single visible caplike scale.

Bark on young branches brownish; soon characteristically mottled (brown, green, and white) by the exfoliation of the outer bark which exposes the lighter creamy-white inner layers; bark on the lower trunk of older trees often entirely brown and scaly.

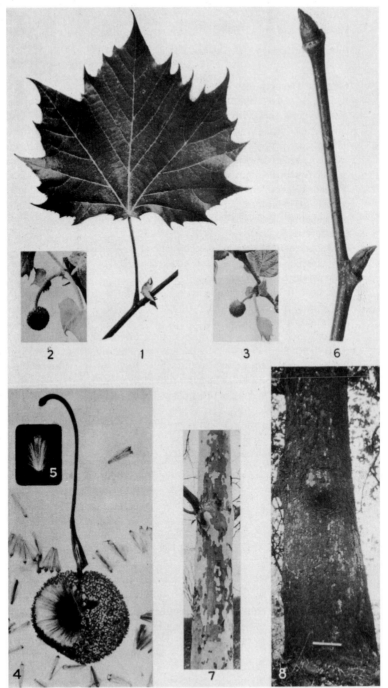

FIGURE 9-8   *Platanus occidentalis*. Sycamore. (1) Leaf and stipules × ½. (2) Head of pistillate flowers × ½. (3) Head of staminate flowers × ½. (4) Head (multiple) of achenes × ¾. (5) Achene surrounded by hairs × 1. (6) Twig × 1¼. (7) Bark of young tree. (8) Bark of old tree.

Range

Eastern (Map 9-3). Elevation: sea level to 300 ft. Alluvial soils of river bottoms and lake shores.

General Description

Sycamore is one of the largest (perhaps the greatest dbh) of eastern hardwood trees and commonly attains a height of over 100 ft and a dbh of 3 to 8 ft (max. 175 by 11 to 14 ft). Even at a considerable distance this tree can hardly be mistaken for any of the associated species. The mottled bark is very striking in appearance, while the open, spreading crown with its somewhat crooked smaller branches is also characteristic. The root system is superficial. Its associates include American elm, soft maples, water and Nuttall oaks, river birch, cottonwood, sweetgum, bitternut hickory, and willows. Sycamore is usually rated from intermediate to intolerant and occurs as a pioneer tree in small, nearly pure groves that are transitional. As competition from more tolerant species increases, sycamore remains only as a scattered tree in a number of forest climax types.

Seeds are usually produced each year and are shed irregularly throughout the fall, winter, and early spring. Growth is fast, and first-year seedlings may reach 8 ft in height. Sycamore may attain an age of 500 to 600 years.

Except for frequent defoliation by anthracnose, sycamore in natural stands is not seriously impacted by insects or diseases. However, damage by a number of diseases can be serious in intensively managed plantations.

Long used for lumber and veneer, sycamore is now much used for wood pulp. Established either as seedlings or cuttings in intensively cultivated and fertilized plantations ("short-rotation forestry"), its volume growth is outstanding. Vigorous sprouting permits two or three short coppice rotations. It is of little value to wildlife.

Although this species is often planted as an ornamental, the London planetree is the more commonly cultivated as a street or park tree. The London planetree, *P. × acerifolia* (Ait.) Willd., is presumably a hybrid between *P. occidentalis* L., sycamore, and *P. orientalis* L., the Oriental plane. It is similar in appearance to the native sycamore except that the bark is more olive-green in color and the fruit heads may occur in 2s and 3s rather than singly.

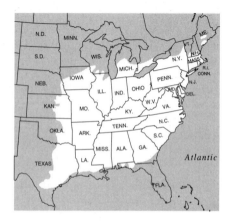

MAP 9-3   *Platanus occidentalis.*

Western Species

Two western sycamores, occurring in widely separated regions, commonly form dense cover along streams or on precipitous slopes and aid materially in controlling erosion.

Plátanus wrìghtii Wats.   Arizona sycamore

Probably the most abundant broad-leaved tree in the southwest, it occurs generally along stream banks and canyon walls in southern Arizona and southwestern New Mexico. The tree is readily distinguished by its deeply 5- to 7-lobed leaves (the lobes over half the length of the blade), with cordate base, and heads of achenes borne in racemose clusters of 2 to 4.

Plátanus racemòsa Nutt.   California sycamore

Medium-size, broadly buttressed tree of wide distribution along stream banks in the Coast Ranges and in the foothills along the west slopes of the Sierra Nevada Mountains in California. It is identified by its narrowly 3- to 5-lobed leaves (the lobes about half the length of the blade), with cuneate (rarely cordate) bases, and heads of achenes in racemose clusters of 2 to 7.

Hamamelidaceae: The Witch-hazel Family

This family includes 26 genera and about 100 species of trees and shrubs scattered through the forested regions of eastern North America and Mexico to Central America and also South Africa, Madagascar, Australia, Asia, and the Malayan archipelago.

Commercial storax, a balsam used in the manufacture of soaps, perfumes, and pharmaceutical preparations, is obtained from the resinous exudations of the bark of *Liquidambar orientalis* Mill. of Asia Minor.* Burmese storax, a similar but somewhat inferior compound, comes from the resinous constituents of *Altingia excelsa* Noronha and is used locally in the preparation of incense and medicinal compounds. *Altingia, Bucklandia,* and *Liquidambar* are the principal timber-contributing genera of this family.

Three genera are represented in the eastern United States: *Fothergilla* with two or three shrubby species, is confined mostly to the Atlantic Coastal Plain from North Carolina southward; *Hamamelis* (two species) is found in the east; and *Liquidambar* is an important hardwood of the south (Table 9-4).

*Storax may also be prepared in commercial quantities by wounding trees of the native sweetgum, but for economic reasons it will probably not compete with that from abroad, except when the foreign supply is interrupted.

TABLE 9-4   COMPARISON OF IMPORTANT GENERA IN THE HAMAMELIDACEAE

Genus	Leaves	Flowers	Fruit	Buds
Liquidambar sweetgum	lobed	imperfect	multiple	scaly
Hamamelis witch-hazel	unlobed	perfect	borne singly	naked

Botanical Features of the Family

Leaves deciduous or persistent, alternate, simple, stipulate, often with stellate hairs.
Flowers perfect or imperfect (plants monoecious), anemophilous or entomophilous; *calyx* 4- or 5-parted or 0; *petals* 4, 5, or 0; *stamens* 4, 5, or more; *pistils* 1 with a 2-celled ovary enclosing 1 or more ovules in each cell.
Fruit a 2-celled capsule, borne singly, or in multiple heads; seeds winged or wingless.

LIQUIDAMBAR L.   Sweetgum

The genus *Liquidambar* has about four species; only one, *L. styraciflua,* is native to the New World; the other species are found in Asia. *Liquidambar formosana* Hance, Formosan sweetgum, is cultivated as an ornamental in North America.

Liquidámbar styracíflua L.   Sweetgum; American sweetgum

Distinguishing Characteristics (Fig. 9-9)

Leaves deciduous, 3 to 6 in. (7.5 to 15 cm) in diameter; *shape* orbicular, star-shaped, deeply and palmately 5- to 7-lobed; *margin* finely serrate; *apex* of the lobes acuminate; *base* truncate or slightly cordate; *surfaces* bright green and lustrous above, pubescent in the axils of the veins below; somewhat fragrant when crushed; *petioles* long and slender; stipulate; *fall color* yellow or deep red to purple.

Flowers imperfect (plant monoecious), both types in heads, anemophilous; *staminate* heads in racemes, *pistillate* terminal and solitary; *staminate* flowers lacking calyx and corolla, stamens indefinite in number; *pistillate* flowers with a minute calyx, no corolla, 4 nonfunctional stamens, and a 2-celled ovary; appearing with the leaves.

Fruit a woody, globose head (multiple) of 2-celled, beaked capsules, 1 to 1¼ in. (2.5 to 3 cm) in diameter, persistent during the winter; *seeds* 2 in each capsule, ca. ⅜ in. (8 to 12 mm) long, terminally winged, also with many, small, abortive ovules.

Twig shiny, green to yellowish brown, slender to stout, somewhat angled, or terete, aromatic, with or without corky wings (Fig. 9-10) which sometimes appear the first year; *pith* homogeneous, stellate; *terminal buds* ovate to conical, ¼ to ½ in. (6 to 12 mm) long, with several, shiny, orange-brown scales; *lateral buds* similar but smaller; *leaf scars* crescent-shaped to triangular; *bundle scars* 3, conspicuously white with a dark center; *stipular scars* slitlike and inconspicuous even with magnification.

Bark grayish brown; deeply furrowed into narrow, somewhat rounded, flaky ridges.

Range

Southeastern (Map 9-4). Elevation: sea level to 3000 ft in the southern Appalachians. Mesic, upland woods, slopes, ravines, floodplains, and stream banks.

General Description

Sweetgum at its best is a large tree 80 to 120 ft high and 3 to 4 ft dbh (max. 200 by 6 ft) with a long, straight, often buttressed bole, small oblong or pyramidal crown, and shallow wide-spreading root system.

Sweetgum is one of the most widespread trees in the southern forest. It is an important though intolerant member of four forest-cover types, and a component of 24 others; these are

FIGURE 9-9   *Liquidambar styraciflua.* Sweetgum. (1) Twig × 1¼. (2) Staminate and pistillate flowers × ½. (3) Multiple of capsules × 1. (4) Winged seed × 1. (5) Leaf × ½. (6) Bark. (*Courtesy of U.S. Forest Service.*)

FIGURE 9-10   Sweetgum branch with corky wings × ½.

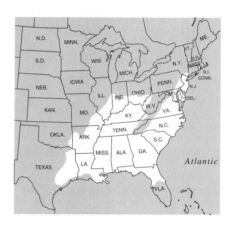

MAP 9-4   *Liquidambar styraciflua.*

mostly hardwoods, but southern pines and baldcypress are also included. It is found on a wide variety of sites, but always develops best on rich, moist alluvial soils. Its growth is retarded on dry sites, and prolonged drought may cause extensive dieback. Maturity is reached in 200 to 300 years.

Although its flowers are frost-sensitive, viable seed production is normally abundant. As the buoyant seed is not exacting in seedbed requirements, sweetgum is an aggressive pioneer of disturbed sites, particularly old fields. The pure even-aged stands which often develop on such sites can be quite dense. Only on very fertile sites is individual stem growth exceptional, and here the total volume growth is very high.

Sweetgum stumps sprout prolifically. In addition, an individual stem, particularly a young one, when weakened, cut, or top-killed, can produce an abundance of fast-growing root suckers.

This capacity is in part responsible for much of the regeneration of the species, and many stands are of sprout origin.

Sweetgum has few insect and disease problems. Sweetgum blight, associated with protracted drought, has caused decline and mortality throughout most of its range. Many species of rodents girdle young stems, and lush vine growth may override slow-growing saplings. It is very fire-sensitive, and top-kill or decay often follow even light fires.

This species is a desirable ornamental in the milder portions of the north because of the attractive shape and brilliant autumnal coloration of the leaves, and the peculiar corky outgrowths on the twigs. It is hardy at least as far north as central New York and will exist even in dry, heavy clay soils.

Sweetgum is one of the more important commercial hardwoods of the United States, especially in the manufacture of utility and decorative plywood panels. Its use by the southern paper industry as an intensively managed plantation species increases yearly. The seeds are eaten by birds and small mammals.

HAMAMELIS L.   Witch-hazel

Witch-hazel, although of little or no importance commercially, is so common and widely distributed that it deserves at least brief mention. No more distinctive shrub or small tree can be found in the eastern United States (Fig. 9-11). *Leaves* are simple and alternate, broadly elliptical, with margin irregularly and coarsely repand or sinuate; fall color yellow. *Flowers* conspicuous, with their 4 long, yellow, straplike petals borne in late fall, often after the leaves have dropped, or early spring before the leaves. *Fruit* maturing the following season into a 2-valved woody capsule, from which the shining, black, wingless seeds are ejected forcibly to a distance of several feet or more from the tree. *Twig* with tawny buds, naked except for two small scales.

Witch-hazel is said to be especially prized by "water diviners," some of whom prefer twigs cut from this tree. An alcoholic extract prepared from the bark or small branches is a well-known rubbing lotion. The seeds are eaten by various wildlife.

FIGURE 9-11   *Hamamelis virginiana.* Witch-hazel. (1) Flowers × 1. (2) Fruit (capsule) and seeds × ¾. (3) Bud × 2. (4) Leaf × ½.

Hamamèlis virginiàna L.

Found from New Brunswick to Iowa, south to Georgia and southern Arkansas. It flowers late in the fall. A second species, *H. vernális* Sarg., is a shrub of the Ozark region flowering in early spring. Two or more other species are native to Japan and China. These are sometimes cultivated as ornamentals.

Ulmaceae: The Elm Family

The Elm family includes 18 genera and ca. 150 species of trees and shrubs, widely distributed throughout the temperate regions of both hemispheres, with a few species in the tropics. Four genera are represented in this country, but only two include common trees (Table 9-5).

Botanical Features of the Family

Leaves deciduous (rarely persistent), alternate, simple, stipulate, pinnately veined, usually serrate, often inequilateral at the base.

Flowers perfect or imperfect (plants polygamo-monoecious), anemophilous; *calyx* 4- to 9-lobed or parted; *corolla* none; *stamens* 4 to 6; *ovary* superior, usually 1-celled with a single ovule; *styles* 2.

Fruit a samara, drupe, or nut.

ULMUS L.   Elm

This genus includes some of the most useful and well-known forest and ornamental trees of the northern hemisphere. The 18 to 20 species are scattered throughout eastern North America, Europe, and Asia, and in many regions are important constituents of hardwood forests. The wood is important commercially, and the tough bark fibers were sometimes used by primitive peoples for making rope and coarse cloth; the inner mucilaginous bark of certain species is used in medicine, or occasionally as emergency food. Many elms are highly regarded as shade and ornamental trees, and some are perhaps unsurpassed in form and general usefulness for this purpose. However, their future use must be evaluated in terms of the rapid spread of the lethal Dutch elm disease. Several foreign species, with many cultivars, have been introduced for ornamental planting. One is Scotch or Wych elm, *U. glabra* Huds. The bark of this tree remains fairly smooth even on large trunks. A common grafted form, Camperdown

TABLE 9-5   COMPARISON OF IMPORTANT NATIVE GENERA IN THE ULMACEAE

Genus	Leaves	Flowers	Fruit
Ulmus elm	doubly serrate (American species)	perfect	samara
Celtis hackberry	entire or singly serrate	perfect and imperfect	drupe

TABLE 9-6   COMPARISON OF IMPORTANT ELMS

Species	Flowers	Fruit	Twigs
U. americana American elm	in long-pedicelled fascicles	ca. ½ in. (12 mm) long, deeply notched at apex, ciliate on margin	brown, glabrous or sparingly pubescent; buds brown, acute but not sharp
U. rubra slippery elm	in short-pedicelled fascicles	ca. ¾ in. (18 mm) long, emarginate at apex, pubescent only on outside of seed cavity	ashy gray, scabrous; buds nearly black
U. thomasii rock elm	in racemose cymes	ca. ¾ in. (18 mm) long, rounded at apex, generally pubescent, ciliate; outside of seed cavity indistinct	reddish brown, glabrous or puberulous, at length corky; buds brown, sharp-pointed

elm, 'Camperdownii' is the familiar "umbrella elm" often seen in parks and yards. In certain areas, **U. pumila** L., Siberian elm, and **U. parvifolia** Jacq., Chinese elm, are common small-leafed ornamentals. The Siberian elm has escaped from cultivation. Of the six native species, three are of considerable importance and will be described in detail (Table 9-6).

Botanical Features of the Genus

Leaves alternate, simple, usually doubly serrate, short-petioled, inequilateral at base, distichous.

Flowers perfect, appearing before the leaves unfold, or in some species autumnal; borne on slender pedicels in fascicles or cymes (sometimes racemose); *ovary* flattened, surmounted by a deeply 2-lobed style.

Fruit maturing in the late spring, or in some species autumnal; a flattened, oblong to suborbicular samara; seed cavity encircled by a thin, membranous or papery wing, which is often notched above, and subtended below by the persistent remnants of the calyx; *seed* lacking endosperm.

Twigs slender to stout, in some species corky, slightly zigzag; *pith* terete, homogeneous; *terminal buds* lacking; *lateral buds* medium-size, with the scales imbricate in 2 ranks; *leaf scars* 2-ranked, small semicircular; *bundle scars* conspicuous, depressed, 3 or more; *stipular scars* small, at times indistinct.

Úlmus americàna L.   American elm; white elm

Distinguishing Characteristics (Fig. 9-12)

Leaves 3¼ to 6 in. (8 to 15 cm) long, 1 to 3 in. (2.5 to 7.5 cm) wide; *shape* oblong-obovate to elliptical; *margin* coarsely doubly serrate; *apex* acuminate; *base* conspicuously inequilateral; *surfaces* glabrous or slightly scabrous above; usually pubescent below; *fall color* bright yellow.

FIGURE 9-12 *Ulmus americana.* American elm. (1) Twig × 1¼. (2) Inflorescence × ¾. (3) Flower × 4. (4) Fruit (samara) × 1. (5) Leaf × ½. (6) Bark. (7) Section through bark showing alternating brown and white layers (compare with that of slippery elm).

Flowers appearing before the leaf buds open, long-pedicelled, in fascicles of 3 or 4.

Fruit maturing in the spring, as the leaves unfold; ⅜ to ½ in. (10 to 12 mm) long, oval to oblong-obovate, deeply notched at apex, margin ciliate.

Twigs slender, zigzag, brown, glabrous or slightly pubescent; *lateral buds* ca. ¼ in. (6 mm) long, ovoid, acute but not sharp-pointed, smooth or sparingly downy, chestnut-brown.

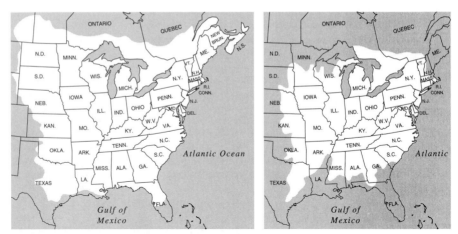

MAP 9-5   **(Left)** *Ulmus americana.* **(Right)** *Ulmus rubra.*

Bark on older trees typically divided into grayish, flat-topped ridges, separated by roughly diamond-shaped fissures, but sometimes rough and without a definite pattern; the outer bark when sectioned shows irregular, corky, buff-colored patches interspersed with the reddish-brown fibrous tissue.

Range
Eastern (Map 9-5). Elevation: sea level to 2500 ft. River bottoms, swamps, disturbed fields, road sides, cutover forests.

General Description
Probably no other North American tree is more easily recognized from a distance. When grown in the open, the trunk usually divides near the ground into several erect limbs strongly arched above and terminating in numerous slender, often drooping branchlets, the whole forming a vase-shaped crown of great beauty and symmetry (Fig. 9-13). At times the branches are more wide-spreading and give rise to the so-called oak form of this tree. In the forest the buttressed, columnar trunk, 2 to 4 ft dbh, may rise to a height of 50 to 60 ft before branching and is topped by a small crown of arching branches (max. 160 by 11 ft).

The root system of American elm is extensive but shallow, and the tree is a common inhabitant of wet flats where standing water may accumulate in the spring and fall; in such places its associates include the soft maples, some of the swamp oaks, willows, poplars, and black ash. The fastest growth and maximum size, however, are attained on better-drained, rich bottomland soils, in association with sweetgum, basswood, green ash, and other hardwoods. In the western portion of its range, American elm is a common tree along water courses in company with box-elder, green ash, and cottonwoods. This elm, when planted in the deep dry soils of the Great Plains region (shelterbelts), may send down quite deep taproots to the water table. Because it is a component of no less than 26 forest-cover types, the complete list of associates is large.

On a tolerance scale, American elm may be rated as intermediate. Seeds are produced annually (May to June) in extremely large numbers, and they germinate on moist soil within a few days of being released. They may be wind-carried for a quarter of a mile or more, and waterborne over much greater distances. Maturity is reached in about 150 years, but old trees may be twice this age.

FIGURE 9-13   Open-grown form of American elm.
(*Courtesy of U.S. Forest Service.*)

Much of the American elms, once the favorite shade tree of innumerable yards, parks, streets, and university campuses, has been destroyed by Dutch elm disease since 1930. This is caused by a vascular fungus vectored by bark beetles introduced to the United States presumably in elm veneer logs arriving from Europe. Other native elms are also susceptible to Dutch elm disease but to a lesser extent. In addition to Dutch elm disease, American elm is plagued by an impressive number of fungi, viruses, and insects. The David elm, *U. davidiana* Schneid., from northern China, has been introduced into the U.S. It is resistant to Dutch elm disease and may be an appropriate substitute for the American elm as an urban tree.

The fruits are important as wildlife food, and the saplings are frequently browsed by deer and rabbits.

Úlmus rùbra Mühl.   Slippery elm; red elm

Distinguishing Characteristics (Fig. 9-14)

Leaves 4 to 7 in. (10 to 18 cm) long, 2 to 3 in. (5 to 7.5 cm) wide; *shape* elliptical to obovate, or oval; leaf often creased along the midrib; *margin, apex,* and *base* as for

FIGURE 9-14   *Ulmus rubra.* Slippery elm. (1) Twig × 1¼. (2) Leaf × ½. (3) Samara × 1. (4) Bark. (5) Section through bark showing brownish layers only (compare with that of American elm).

the preceding species; *surfaces* very scabrous above, soft pubescent below; *fall color* yellow.

Flowers appearing before the leaves, in short-pedicelled fascicles.

Fruit maturing when the leaves are about one-half expanded, ½ to ¾ in. (12 to 18 mm) long, suborbicular in shape, emarginate at apex, margin and surface of wing smooth, outer surface of seed cavity pubescent.

Twigs stouter than in American elm, ashy gray to brownish gray, scabrous; *lateral buds* dark chestnut-brown to almost black, pubescent; *flower buds* larger, often with an orange tip; inner bark mucilaginous and "slippery."

Bark dark reddish brown, and, in contrast to that of both American and rock elms, it does not show buff-colored corky patches or streaks when sectioned with a knife; bark fissures not diamond-shaped in outline, ridges more nearly parallel than in American elm, often coarsely scaly or with vertical plates; with declining vigor, bark composed of flat, thin, gray plates; inner bark mucilaginous, with a somewhat aromatic flavor.

Range

Eastern (Map 9-5). Disjuncts in southern Maine, southern Louisiana, Kansas, southwestern Nebraska, and eastern North Dakota. Elevation: sea level to 2000 ft. Mesic to moist soils of slopes and bottomlands, or drier in calcareous soils.

General Description

Slippery elm is a medium-size tree 60 to 70 ft high and 18 to 30 in. dbh (max. 135 by nearly 7 ft); it resembles American elm in general appearance except for a greater clear length of bole and a tendency of the twigs to be ascending. These features give individuality to slippery elm, and while they are not striking, with a little practice one may learn to identify the tree at some distance by observing them.

This elm makes best growth on moist, rich bottomland soils, along streams, and on lower slopes. Associates include red and white oaks, butternut, ashes, basswood, hickories, maples, black cherry, and yellow-poplar. While somewhat less susceptible to Dutch elm disease than American elm, it is also killed by elm phloem necrosis. It stump-sprouts readily.

Slippery elm was well-known to the early pioneer woodsmen on account of its mucilaginous inner bark, which was chewed to quench thirst, and when steeped in water produced a common remedy for throat inflammations and fever; the powdered bark was recommended for poultices. Native Americans used the wood for tomahawk handles. It is used now for furniture, paneling, and boxes. The saplings are browsed by deer and the fruits eaten by various wildlife.

Úlmus thómasii Sarg.   Rock elm; cork elm

Distinguishing Characteristics (Fig. 9-15)

Leaves 2 to 4 in. (5 to 10 cm) long, ¾ to 2 in. (2 to 5 cm) wide; *shape* obovate to elliptical; *margin* coarsely doubly serrate; *apex* acuminate; *base* often nearly equilateral; *surfaces* usually glabrous, often somewhat lustrous above, slightly pubescent below; *fall color* yellow.

Flowers appearing before the leaves, on slender pedicels, in racemose cymes.

Fruit maturing when the leaves are about half grown, ⅜ to ¾ in. (9 to 18 mm) long, oval to obovate, pubescent, more or less rounded at apex, ciliate on the margin, seed cavity indistinct.

Twigs light reddish brown, glabrous or slightly puberulent, after a year or two often developing conspicuous corky ridges; *lateral buds* similar to those of American elm but longer and more sharply pointed, downy-ciliate.

Bark somewhat similar to that of American elm but often darker and more deeply and irregularly furrowed, especially on younger trees.

Range

North central (Map 9-6). Disjuncts in several states around the normal range. Elevation: 200 to 2500 ft. Mesic forests, moist, well-drained uplands, rocky ridges, and flatwoods, also limestone bluffs.

General Description

Rock elm, so-called because of its extremely hard, tough wood, is a medium-size to large tree which, in virgin stands, attains a height of some 80 ft and dbh of 3 to 4 ft (max. 103 by 6 ft). In contrast to the two preceding species, the tall straight trunk extends unbranched for some dis-

FIGURE 9-15   *Ulmus thomasii.* Rock elm. (1) Samara × 1. (2) Corky outgrowths on twig × 1¼. (3) Leaf × ½. (4) Inflorescence × ¾. (5) Twig × 1¼. (6) Bark.

MAP 9-6   (Left) *Ulmus thomasii.* **(Right)** *Celtis occidentalis.*

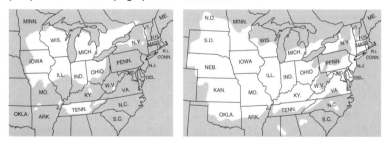

tance into the narrow oblong crown. It stump-sprouts easily. Best development is made on moist, loamy soils of lower Michigan and Wisconsin. It is intermediate in tolerance but shows a dramatic ability to respond to release. Rock elm occurs with many other hardwoods, including beech, ashes, maples, basswood, butternut, oaks, hickories, and black cherry. Drastic cutting has greatly reduced the original supply of rock elm timber, which was never very large, but used for implements and tool handles. It is an important wildlife food.

Southern Elms

Úlmus alàta Michx.   Winged elm

Leaves 1¼ to 2½ in. (3 to 6 cm) long; *twigs* very slender, with or without 2 corky wings nearly ½ in. (12 mm) wide. This species is usually a small to medium-size tree found equally on dry gravelly uplands and on fertile bottomlands from southeastern Virginia to southern Missouri, south to central Florida and eastern Texas. Perhaps it is the least tolerant of the native elms. Flowering in spring.

Úlmus crassifòlia Nutt.   Cedar elm

This is another small-leafed species found in Mississippi, southern Arkansas, and Texas; the *twigs* often bear 2 corky wings which are only about half as wide as those of winged elm. Flowering in late summer.

Úlmus serótina Sarg.   September elm (red elm)

Leaves 2 to 3½ in. (5 to 9 cm) long (larger than those of the last two species); *twigs* often with 2 or 3 corky wings. September elm occurs only sporadically on alluvial soils and limestone hills from eastern Kentucky to southern Illinois, south to northeastern Georgia and eastern Oklahoma. Flowering in the fall.

CELTIS L.   Hackberry

Celtis, with about 75 species, is found in many of the temperate and tropical regions of the world. Some of these species, because of their variability, are not well defined, and the genus is much in need of additional study. There are possibly seven species native in North America. Throughout the world, several species supply valuable lumber, the drupes are consumed by wildlife and to a lesser extent by humans, and some species are cultivated as ornamental and shade trees. A number of Asian species have been introduced into North America as ornamentals.

Botanical Features of the Genus

Leaves deciduous (persistent in a few tropical forms), alternate, distichous, simple, singly serrate or sometimes entire, with more-or-less inequilateral base.

Flowers perfect and imperfect (plants polygamo-monoecious) appearing just before or with the leaves; the *staminate* borne below, in fascicles, the *perfect* and *pistillate* flowers above, solitary in the leaf axils; *calyx* 4- to 6-lobed; *stamens* 4 to 6.

Fruit a thick-skinned, thin-fleshed, ovoid or globose drupe; pit surface with a reticulate (netlike) pattern.

Twigs slender, zigzag; *pith* terete, very finely chambered at the nodes, homogeneous elsewhere; *terminal buds* lacking; *lateral buds* small, closely appressed; *leaf scars* 2-ranked, oval to crescent-shaped; *bundle scars* 3; *stipular scars* minute.

Céltis occidentàlis L.   Hackberry

Distinguishing Characteristics (Fig. 9-16)

Leaves 2 to 5 in. (5 to 13 cm) long, 1½ to 2½ in. (4 to 6 cm) wide; *shape* ovate to ovate-lanceolate; *margin* sharply serrate (often entire below the middle); *apex* acuminate, falcate; *base* inequilaterally cordate; *surfaces* glabrous, or slightly scabrous above; smooth or sparingly hairy below; *fall color* pale yellow.

Flowers appearing in spring with or soon after the leaves.

Fruit borne on peduncles ½ to ¾ in. (12 to 18 mm) long, ¼ to ⅜ in. (6 to 10 mm) in diameter, subglobose or ovoid, dark red or purple; flesh thin, edible; ripening in September and October, often persistent for several weeks; pit conspicuously reticulate.

Twigs slender, zigzag, reddish brown, somewhat lustrous; *lateral buds* small, acute, closely appressed.

Bark grayish brown, with characteristic corky warts or ridges, later somewhat scaly.

Range

Northeastern (Map 9-6). Local disjuncts in several Provinces and States around the continuous range. Elevation: sea level to 5000 ft. Stream banks, bottomlands, rocky slopes and bluffs, also calcareous soils.

FIGURE 9-16   *Celtis occidentalis.* Hackberry. (1) Twig × 1¼. (2) Flower × 3. (3) Fruit (drupe) × ¾. (4) Pit showing reticulations × 1. (5) Leaf × ½. (6) Bark.

General Description

Hackberry is usually a small tree 30 to 40 ft high and about 16 in. dbh (max. 130 by 6 ft). Best growth is made on rich, moist, alluvial soils, but especially in the northeast the tree is commonly found on limestone outcrops and other droughty sites. Hackberry occurs as a scattered tree in mixture with other hardwoods. Seed dispersal is mainly by birds, and sprouts from young trees often persist. It exhibits a wide range of growth rates and tolerance ratings, both of which are related to site conditions.

Certain varieties of hackberry are used to some extent as ornamentals and seem to succeed even under adverse conditions of soil and moisture. Long overlooked by the wood-using industry, both hackberry and sugarberry are of increasing importance in the manufacture of paneling, furniture, boxes, and plywood. The fruits are eaten by birds and small mammals.

Céltis laevigàta Willd.   Sugarberry; sugar hackberry

Sugarberry is a medium-size tree 60 to 80 ft high and 2 to 4 ft dbh. It ranges along the Coastal Plain from Virginia to southern Florida, west to the valley of the Rio Grande, and north in the Mississippi valley through eastern Oklahoma, Missouri, western Tennessee, and Kentucky to southern Illinois and Indiana. The leaves are narrower than those of hackberry, only slightly serrate to entire, and the fruit is borne on shorter pedicels; the otherwise smooth bark is marked by conspicuous warty excrescences. It is a tree of bottomlands where the fruits are important to wildlife, especially birds.

Moraceae: The Mulberry Family

This is a family of 48 genera and 1000 species of trees, shrubs, vines, and herbs, distributed for the most part in the warmer regions of the world, but with a few species in the temperate zone. The sap is milky, and in certain genera, notably *Ficus* and *Castilla,* it is a source of rubber. Three genera are represented in North America, and a fourth, *Broussonetia,* paper-mulberry, has been introduced and has become naturalized. They all are small or medium-size trees of little value as timber producers, but they are often used ornamentally. Other genera are a source of valuable timbers, edible fruit, paper fibers, and dyes.

Botanical Features of the Family

Leaves deciduous or persistent, alternate, simple, stipulate.
Flowers imperfect, the plants monoecious or dioecious; *sepals* 4; *petals* 0; *stamens* 4; *ovary* superior or inferior, 2-carpellate; anemophilous except for the entomophilous *Ficus.*
Fruit a small drupe or achene, usually in multiples.

MORUS L.   Mulberry

Of the 10 species of mulberry, two are native to the United States and two others have become naturalized. The fruit, a multiple of drupelets, resembles a blackberry and is a very important food for birds and small mammals.

Botanical Features of the Genus
Leaves deciduous, alternate, simple, to 7 in. (18 cm) long, elliptical to suborbicular, venation pinnipalmate or palmate, unlobed or 2 or 3-lobed, the margin crenate-serrate, the base cordate or truncate; milky juice evident in broken petiole of very young leaves; stipulate; *fall color* yellow.
Flowers unisexual, the tree monoecious or dioecious, each flower small and in compact, cylindrical, or globose racemes or spikes, appearing with the leaves.
Fruit a cylindrical or nearly globose multiple of drupelets, ¾ to 1¼ in. (2 to 3 cm) long, each drupelet globose and white to purple or black in color.
Twigs with some milky juice, slender, brown, smooth; *leaf scars* semicircular or nearly circular; *bundle scars* many; pseudoterminal and lateral *buds* ovoid, acute, light brown, ca. ³⁄₁₆ in. (5 mm) long, appressed to the twig, and with 3 to 6 outer scales; *stipular scars* narrow and unequal; *pith* solid and homogeneous, round.
Bark thin, dark brown, scaly, and furrowed.

Mòrus rùbra L.   Red mulberry

This is an eastern tree to 40 ft tall and 18 in. dbh of floodplains, river valleys, and moist hillsides; leaves scabrous-pubescent above and soft pubescent below, 2½ to 5 in. (6 to 13 cm) long; fruit dark purple and edible (Fig. 9-17). It seldom occurs as a weed in cities and other disturbed areas, as does white mulberry.

Vegetatively, red mulberry is sometimes mistaken for basswood (*Tilia*). However, *Tilia* has 2 (rather than 3 to 6) bud scales; the twig is more zigzag and lacks milky juice; the leaf margin is more sharply serrate with a thickened tip on each tooth; the leaf surface is not scabrous and often has stellate or fasciculate hairs.

Mòrus microphýlla Buckl.   Texas mulberry

Texas mulberry grows in the southwest (Oklahoma west to eastern Arizona and south into Mexico) along streams, in mountain canyons, and on dry hills, at 2100 to 6600 ft of elevation. It is similar to red mulberry, but the leaves are smooth above and smaller, 1 to 2½ in. (2.5 to 6 cm) long, and the fruit is subglobose and nearly black.

Mòrus álba L.   White mulberry

A native of China, this tree was introduced in colonial times in attempts to establish the silkworm industry in this country; although the attempt failed, the tree is now naturalized locally throughout the United States and has become weedy in disturbed areas, particularly in cities and towns. The leaves are lustrous and smooth above; the fruit is white, pink, or violet. The Russian mulberry, *M. alba* 'Tatarica', was introduced about 1875 and has become widely distributed in the western United States. It is the hardiest of all mulberries, grows rapidly in sandy or clay soils, and is used in shelterbelts or for the production of farm timbers.

Mòrus nìgra L.   Black mulberry

Black mulberry, probably a native of Persia, was introduced in the Pacific and southeastern states for its large, dark-colored juicy fruit. It is naturalized locally in the southern United States. The leaves are scabrous above, deeply cordate at base, and the fruit nearly black.

FIGURE 9-17   *Morus rubra.* Red mulberry. (1) Staminate flowers × ½. (2) Pistillate flowers × ½. (3) Multiple of drupelets × ¾. (4) Twig × 1¼. (5–7) Leaves showing variation in lobing × ½.

MACLURA Nutt.   Osage-Orange

This genus is monotypic, and the single species, *Maclùra pomífera* (Raf.) C. K. Schneid., originally restricted to southern Arkansas, southern Oklahoma, and northeastern Texas, is now planted for hedges or as an ornamental throughout the United States. *Leaves* 2½ to 5 in. (6 to 13 cm) long, entire, oblong-lanceolate to ovate, with a narrow, pointed apex, and dark green and shiny above. *Fruit* a peculiar and very distinctive, spherical, semi-fleshy, yellow-green multiple of drupes, 3½ to 5 in. (9 to 13 cm) in diameter; when crushed, it exudes a bitter milky juice (Fig. 9-18). *Twigs* armed with sharp thorns. The *wood* is of a characteristic bright orange color and is used for bows, hence the origin of the name "bois d'arc," or bowwood, which is often applied to this species; the wood yields a yellow dye extracted with hot water.

FICUS L.   Fig

This is a large genus (about 800 species), chiefly tropical, and in the United States it is restricted to two arborescent species, *Fìcus aùrea* Nutt., Florida strangler fig, and *F. citrifòlia* Mill., short-

FIGURE 9-18   *Maclura pomifera.* Osage-orange. (1) Leaf × ½. (2) Twig with thorn × 1¼. (3) Multiple of drupes × ½.

leaf fig, both natives of southern Florida. The commonly cultivated, edible fig, *F. cárica* L., is grown for its fruit in the southern states and sometimes escapes. Rubber may be produced from the latex of the India rubber tree, *F. elástica* Roxb. ex Hornem., but most of it comes now from *Hèvea brasiliénsis* (Willd. ex A. Juss) Muell. Arg. (Euphorbiaceae) or by synthetic processes.

Leitneriaceae: The Corkwood Family

Although of no commercial importance, this monotypic family is of interest botanically and also because it produces the lightest wood grown in the United States (specific gravity of about 0.21; compared with cork, 0.24 and balsa wood, 0.12).

The single species, corkwood, **Leitnèria floridàna** Chapm., is a shrub or small deciduous tree native to swamps and riverbanks in scattered areas of the Gulf Coastal Plain and lower Mississippi valley. The leaves are alternate, 2½ to 6¾ in. (6 to 17 cm) long, oblong to elliptic-lanceolate, and pubescent below. The flowers are unisexual on separate trees, and the fruit is a dry drupe.

Juglandaceae: The Walnut Family

The Juglandaceae include seven genera and ca. 60 species of trees and large shrubs which are widely distributed through the forests of the north temperate zone and to a lesser extent in the tropical forests of both the northern and southern hemispheres. The importance of this family lies chiefly in the many valuable timber trees which it includes. The genera *Juglans, Engelhardtia,* and *Pterocarya* produce cabinet woods, while the wood of *Carya* is extremely tough and suitable for many purposes where strength is required. The nuts of several species of *Carya* and *Juglans* are used as wildlife and human food in many localities; and the bark and fruit husks of a few species are sources of yellow dyes and tannic compounds. Two genera and 17 species of this family are found in the United States (Table 9-7).

Botanical Features of the Family

Leaves deciduous, mostly alternate, pinnately compound, estipulate, more or less aromatic.

Flowers imperfect (plants mostly monoecious), anemophilous, appearing with or after the leaves; *staminate* in drooping axillary aments, the individual flowers consisting of 3 to many often nearly sessile stamens surrounded by a 3- to 6-lobed calyx and subtended by a bract; *pistillate* solitary or in few-flowered spikes terminating the new growth, the individual flowers with a 1- to 4-celled pistil, short style, and 2 plumose stigmas, the ovary inferior, covered by a 3- to 5-lobed or parted calyx and subtended by an adnate involucre consisting of a bract and 2 bracteoles.

Fruit a bony nut encased in a semifleshy or woody, dehiscent or indehiscent "husk;" *seed* lacking endosperm but with large, convoluted cotyledons.

JUGLANS L.   Walnut

The walnuts, although numerous and widely distributed during past geological periods (Tertiary), now have only about 20 species. These are found in the forests of North, Central, and South America, the West Indies, southern Europe, and southern and eastern Asia. The French, Turkish, Italian, and Circassian walnut timbers are produced by *Juglans regia* L., which is also an important timber-contributing species of India. The so-called English walnuts are the fruits of this tree, and in recent years, large plantations have been developed in both Oregon and California.

Six species of *Juglans* are native to the United States, but only two of them (*J. nigra* and *J. cinerea*) are important for lumber. *Juglans hindsii* Jeps. ex R. E. Smith and *J. californica* Wats. are California species. The former is used as a stock for English walnut cultivation along the Pacific slope and occasionally as a shade tree. Little walnut, *J. microcarpa* Berlandier, the fifth species, is a small tree native to Texas, Arizona, and northern Mexico, and the remaining southwestern species is Arizona walnut, *J. major* (Torr.) Heller (Table 9-8).

TABLE 9-7   COMPARISON OF NATIVE GENERA IN THE JUGLANDACEAE

Genus	Flowers	Fruit	Pith
Juglans walnut	staminate aments unbranched; stamens, 7 to 105	shell of nut corrugated or rugose; husk indehiscent	chambered after the first season
Carya hickory	staminate aments 3-branched; stamens, 3 to 7	shell of nuts smooth although generally ribbed; husk usually dehiscent along 4 sutures	homogeneous

TABLE 9-8 COMPARISON OF IMPORTANT WALNUTS

Species	Leaves	Fruit	Pith	Bark
J. nigra black walnut	with 9 to 23 ovate-lanceolate leaflets	globose; nut corrugations rounded	buff-colored	dark brown to black, with thin anastomosing ridges
J. cinerea butternut	with 11 to 17 oblong-lanceolate leaflets	oblong-ovoid; nut corrugations sharp	chocolate-colored	ashy gray, with broad, anastomosing ridges

Botanical Features of the Genus

Leaves odd- or even-pinnately compound, consisting of 9 to 23 sessile or nearly sessile *leaflets,* the central ones longest; *leaflets* more or less oblong-lanceolate, each with an acute to acuminate apex, inequilateral base, and finely serrate margin; *petiole* and *rachis* stout, usually pubescent.

Flowers (Fig. 9-19) imperfect (plant monoecious); *staminate* aments preformed, appearing as small, scaly, conelike buds, unbranched; stamens 7 to many; *pistillate* in 2- to 8-flowered spikes, the individual flowers consisting of a 2- to 4-celled pistil sur-

FIGURE 9-19 *Juglans.* Walnut. (1) Pistillate and staminate flowers × ½. (2) Staminate flower, face view × 3. (3) Pistillate flower × 3. (4) Staminate flower, rear view × 3.

mounted by a short style and 2 divergent, plumose stigmas; appearing with or just after the developing leaves.

Fruit a nut with a semifleshy, indehiscent husk; nut thick-walled, rugose or deeply corrugated; seed sweet, often oily.

Twigs stout, with an acrid taste, pubescent or glabrous; *pith* chambered after the first season except between the seasons' growth, stellate in cross section; *terminal buds* few-scaled, often appearing naked; *lateral buds* commonly superposed; *leaf scars* obcordate to obdeltate, slightly 3-lobed, with three *U*-shaped bundle scars.

Júglans nìgra L.   Black walnut; eastern black walnut

Distinguishing Characteristics (Fig. 9-20)

Leaves 12 to 24 in. (30 to 61 cm) long, with 9 to 23 nearly sessile leaflets attached to a stout puberulent rachis, the terminal leaflet often suppressed; *leaflets* 2¼ to 5 in. (6 to 13 cm) long, 1 to 1¼ in. (2.5 to 3 cm) wide, ovate-lanceolate; *margin* finely serrate; *apex* acute to acuminate; *base* inequilateral; *surfaces* lustrous, dark yellow-green and glabrous above, pale green and pubescent below; *petiole* very short, puberulent; *fall color* yellow.

Flowers appearing in late May and early June; *staminate* with 17 to 50 nearly sessile stamens.

Fruit 1½ to 2½ in. (4 to 6 cm) in diameter, globose or nearly so, solitary or in clusters of 2 or 3; with a thick, semifleshy, yellowish-green, pubescent husk; nut corrugated, with rounded ridges; *seed* sweet, oily.

Twigs stout, light brown to orange-brown, lenticellate; *pith* chambered, with thin diaphragms, buff-colored; *terminal buds* short, blunt, covered by a few pubescent scales; *lateral buds* much smaller, often superposed; *leaf scars* elevated, obcordate, without a hairy fringe on the upper margin.

Bark dark brown to grayish black, divided by deep, narrow furrows into thin ridges, the whole forming a roughly diamond-shaped pattern.

Range

Eastern (Map 9-7). Disjuncts in western and central New York, and western Vermont. Elevation: sea level to 4000 ft. Mesic woods, slopes, and along streams.

General Description

Black walnut is not only first in importance among the native species of *Juglans,* but it is also one of the most highly valued of North American hardwoods. Although usually a medium-size tree 70 to 90 ft high and 2 to 3 ft dbh, it may reach a maximum height of 150 ft and a dbh of 8 ft.

This species is very intolerant, and under forest competition develops a tall, well-formed clear bole, with a small, open crown which is always dominant in the stand; the root system is deep and wide-spreading, with a definite taproot, at least in early life.

Small amounts of seed may be produced every year, with large crops at 2- or 3-year intervals; rodents are the chief means of dispersal, although they also use many of the nuts for food.

On deep, rich, moist soils, of alluvial origin, young seedlings may grow 3 ft in height the first season and double this figure the second year; logs 10 in. dbh may be produced in 35 years.

FIGURE 9-20 *Juglans nigra*. Black walnut. (1) Leaf × ⅕. (2) Bark. (3) Nut with husk × ¾. (4) Nut with husk removed × ⅓. (5) Cross section of nut with husk × ¾. (6) Twig × 1¼ showing dark chambered pith.

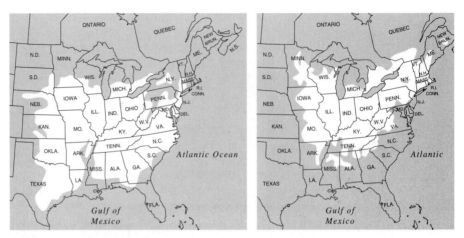

MAP 9-7　(**Left**) *Juglans nigra.* (**Right**) *Juglans cinerea.*

This species, however, is very sensitive to soil conditions and grows much more slowly on poorer sites; large pure stands are rare, but walnut groves are frequently found, apparently from seeds buried by squirrels. The chief associates of black walnut include yellow-poplar, white ash, black cherry, basswood, American beech, numerous oaks, and hickories. Black walnut matures in about 150 years, but its life span may embrace two and one-half centuries.

The supply of black walnut timber has been greatly depleted, but efforts have been made to popularize the planting of this valuable species. Besides the timber which it produces, highly prized for furniture, gunstocks, and so on, the fruit is sold locally, and new varieties with thinner shells are being developed.

Black walnut is one of the most notorious of allelopathic trees, inhibiting growth of some other plants under and around the trees. For additional information on this subject, see the term "allelopathy" in the Glossary and also Waller (1987).

Júglans cinèrea L.　Butternut, white walnut

Distinguishing Characteristics (Fig. 9-21)

Leaves 15 to 24 in. (38 to 61 cm) long, with 11 to 17 nearly sessile leaflets, attached to a stout, pubescent rachis; *leaflets* 2 to 4½ in. (5 to 11 cm) long, 1¼ to 2⅜ in. (3 to 6 cm) wide, oblong-lanceolate; *margin* serrate; *apex* acute to acuminate; *base* inequilateral and rounded; *surfaces* yellowish green, rugose above, paler and soft pubescent below; *petioles* extremely short, pubescent; *fall color* yellow or brown.

Flowers appearing in late May or early June; *staminate* with 7 to 15 nearly sessile stamens.

Fruit 1½ to 2½ in. (4 to 6 cm) long, oblong-ovoid, in clusters of 2 to 5, or solitary; with a semifleshy, greenish-bronze, indehiscent husk clothed with glandular pubescence, sticky to the touch; nut deeply corrugated, with sharp ridges; *seed* sweet and very oily.

Twigs stout, greenish gray to reddish brown, lenticellate; *pith* chambered, with thick diaphragms, dark chocolate-brown to nearly black; *terminal buds* somewhat elongated, blunt, covered by a few pubescent scales, the outer ones lobed; *lateral buds*

FIGURE 9-21   *Juglans cinerea*. Butternut. (1) Twig × 1¼ showing chambered pith and velvety ridge above leaf scar. (2) Nut with husk × ¾. (3) Cross section of nut with husk × ¾. (4) Nut with husk removed × ¾. (5) Leaf × ⅕. (6) Bark.

much smaller, often superposed, covered by rusty-brown tomentum; *leaf scars* elevated, obcordate with a velvety ridge along the upper margin.

Bark light gray, divided by shallow to moderately deep fissures into broad, flat ridges, later more closely furrowed with a roughly diamond-shaped pattern.

Range
Eastern (Map 9-7). Disjuncts in central and eastern North Carolina, northern Alabama, northern Mississippi, and Arkansas. Elevation: sea level to 4800 ft. Mesic slopes, ravines, coves, river banks, floodplains, also dry, rocky soils over limestone.

General Description
Butternut is a small to medium-size tree, 40 to 60 ft high and 12 to 24 in. dbh (max. 110 by 5 ft). The bole is often short and divides into a few stout, ascending limbs which form a broad, open, somewhat irregular, flat or round-topped crown. The root system comprises a taproot and a number of deep-seated but wide-spreading laterals; however, the roots of trees growing on shallow soils are superficial and devoid of anything resembling a taproot.

Butternut never occurs in pure stands, but rather is found occasionally in mixed hardwood forests with black cherry, basswood, hickories, American beech, oaks, yellow-poplar, and elms. At the northern limits of its range it is frequently mixed with sugar maple and yellow birch, and much more rarely with eastern white pine.

The silvical features of butternut are similar to those of black walnut, but it is shorter-lived, usually not reaching a greater age than 75 years. There has been a decline in butternut throughout its range to the point where it is now rare. A canker-producing fungus, first found in 1967, is a major cause. There is no resprouting when the crowns and trunks are killed by the canker.

In addition to the timber used for cabinetwork and novelties, the tree provides nuts used for food and a sweet sugary syrup obtained by boiling down the sap; the green husks liberate a dye which colors cloth orange or yellow, and the dried inner bark of the roots contains natural substances used in medicine.

CARYA Nutt.   Hickory

It is known that numerous species of *Carya* were included in the ancient floras of Europe, northern Africa, Asia, and North America prior to the Glacial Epoch. Many of them since have become extinct, until today there remain only about 16 species. A few are found in southeastern Asia. The remaining ones range through eastern and southern United States; several of these are also found in adjacent Canada, and one is confined to Mexico.

Hickories are a somewhat difficult group due to variability of leaves and fruits and interspecific hybridization. Trichome morphology and vesture are important characters for identification of hickories (Hardin and Stone, 1984) and should be combined with bark, leaflets, twig, and fruit characters for positive identification.

Hickories produce heavy, strong, especially shock-resistant wood with high fuel value; pecan hickory, besides furnishing timber, is valuable for its edible fruit. Hickory nuts of several species were used by Native Americans as an important food, and they continue to be an important food for various wildlife.

Botanical Features of the Genus
Leaves odd-pinnately compound, consisting of 3 to 17 sessile or nearly sessile leaflets; in the true hickories, the terminal one is often the largest and the lowest pair the small-

est; in the pecan hickories, all the leaflets are more similar in size; *leaflets* ovate to obovate, with acute to acuminate apices, inequilateral bases, and finely serrate margins; variously pubescent; *petiole* and *rachis* usually stout, and glabrous or pubescent.

Flowers (Fig. 9-22) imperfect (plants monoecious); *staminate* in 3-branched aments, in clusters on the new growth or near the summit of the previous season's; individual flowers with 3 to 7 stamens, and a 2- or 3-lobed calyx; *pistillate* flowers in 2- to 10-flowered terminal spikes; the individual flowers with a bract and three bracteoles and a 1-celled ovary surmounted by 2 sessile stigmas; appearing just before or just after the leaves.

Fruit an ovoid, pyriform, or globose nut, sometimes flattened, encased in a semi-woody "husk" which completely or partially splits along 4 sutures; *nut* ribbed, smooth, or slightly rugose, with a thick or thin shell; *seed* sweet or bitter.

Twigs stout to moderately slender, dark brown, gray, or orange-brown; *terminal buds* much larger than the laterals, covered by numerous imbricated or few valvate scales; *leaf scars* 3-lobed or obdeltate, the *bundle scars* many mostly in 3 *U*-shaped clusters; *pith* homogeneous, somewhat stellate.

The species of native hickories are grouped into two sections, "true hickories" (Sect. *Carya*) and "pecan hickories" (Sect. *Apocarya*) (Table 9-9).

True Hickories (Table 9-10)

Cárya ovàta (Mill.) K. Koch   Shagbark hickory

Distinguishing Characteristics (Fig. 9-23)

Leaves 8 to 14 in. (20 to 36 cm) long, with 5 (rarely 7) ovate-lanceolate to obovate, sessile or nearly sessile leaflets; *terminal leaflets* 5 to 8 in. (12.5 to 20 cm) long, 2 to 3 in. (5 to 7.5 cm) wide, larger than the lateral leaflets; *margin* finely serrate, ciliate with

FIGURE 9-22   *Carya.* Hickory. (1) Pistillate and staminate flowers × ½. (2) Pistillate flowers × 3. (3) Staminate flower × 3.

TABLE 9-9   COMPARISON OF SECTIONS OF *CARYA*

Section	Leaves	Fruit husks	Bud scales
True hickories (*Carya*)	with 3 to 9 (mostly 5 to 7) leaflets	unwinged, occasionally ribbed at the sutures	imbricate with more than 6 scales
Pecan hickories (*Apocarya*)	with 5 to 17 (mostly more than 7) commonly falcate leaflets	usually broadly winged at the sutures	valvate with 4 to 6 scales

a subterminal tuft of white hairs on the teeth; *apex* acute to acuminate; *base* cuneate; *surfaces* dark yellow-green, glabrous above; pale yellow-green, glabrous or puberulent below; *rachis* stout, grooved, glabrous or puberulent; *fall color* golden yellow.

Fruit 1¼ to 2½ in. (3 to 6 cm) in diameter, solitary or paired, subglobose, depressed at the apex; nut subglobose, brownish white to pinkish white, 4-ribbed, with a reddish-brown to nearly black, readily dehiscent husk, ¼ to ½ in. (6 to 12 mm) thick; *seed* sweet.

Twigs stout, gray-brown to reddish brown, usually somewhat pubescent, lenticellate; *terminal buds* ½ to ¾ in. (12 to 18 mm) long, broadly ovoid to ellipsoidal, obtuse, covered with 3 or 4 visible dark brown, loosely fitting pubescent scales; *lateral buds* somewhat smaller, ovoid, divergent; *leaf scars* slightly elevated, somewhat obdeltate to semicircular; *bundle scars* scattered or in 3 clusters.

TABLE 9-10   COMPARISON OF IMPORTANT TRUE HICKORIES

Species	Leaves	Fruit	Bark
C. ovata shagbark hickory	usually with 5 leaflets; essentially glabrous	1¼–2½ in. (3–6 cm) in diameter; husk ¼–½ in. (6–12 mm) thick; nut 4-ribbed, thick-shelled	broken into long, thin plates, the split ends curling away from the trunk
C. laciniosa shellbark hickory	usually with 7 leaflets; velvety beneath	1¾–2½ in. (4.5–6 cm) in diameter; husk same; nut 4- to 6-ribbed	similar, but plates more often straight
C. tomentosa mockernut hickory	aromatic, usually with 7 or 9 leaflets; pubescent beneath, and on the rachis	1½–2 in. (4–5 cm) in diameter; husk ⅛–¼ in. (3–6 mm) thick; nut 4-ribbed	dark with interlacing ridges; shallowly furrowed
C. glabra pignut hickory	with 5 or 7 leaflets; pubescent with many scales	1–2 in. (2½–5 cm) long, pyriform to oval; husk thin and dehiscent or partly dehiscent; nut rounded or 4-ribbed	dark and deeply furrowed or lighter and scaly

FIGURE 9-23 *Carya ovata.* Shagbark hickory. (1) Twig × 1¼. (2) Leaf × ¼. (3) Nut with dehiscing husk × ⅓. (4) Nut × ⅓. (5) Cross section of nut × ⅓. (6) Bark.

Bark smooth and gray on young stems, soon breaking up and becoming shaggy with large vertical plates which curve away from the trunk at the ends.

Range

Eastern (Map 9-8). Elevation: sea level to 2000 ft northward, to 3000 ft in the southern Appalachians. Dry to mesic woods, floodplains, valleys, upland slopes, and limestone flatwoods and glades.

General Description

Shagbark hickory is a medium-size tree, 70 to 80 ft high and 12 to 24 in. dbh (max. 132 by 4 ft). In the forest it develops a clear, straight, cylindrical bole with a small, open crown; if given sufficient space, however, the crown is typically oblong, and this shape characterizes many of the hickories grown in the open. Seedlings of shagbark hickory develop a large and remarkably deep taproot which may penetrate downward 1 to 3 ft the first season with a corresponding top growth of only a few inches; this feature is typical of most of the hickories except those found on wet soils.

This species varies greatly over its range in the kind of site occupied; in the north it is often found on upland slopes and flatwoods with other hickories and oaks, while farther south it is more common in deep, moist soils of alluvial origin with the hardwoods of that region. This shift in common site conditions occurs in other hickories and also in other genera. Shagbark hickory, at least in youth, will stand considerable forest competition and may be rated as moderately tolerant.

Large crops of seed are produced nearly every other year, especially by trees in the open, and it is not unusual to obtain 2 to 3 or more bushels of nuts from a single large tree. These are distributed by squirrels and other rodents. Squirrels fail to claim some of their buried nuts, and the following year young hickory seedlings spring up, often in the most unlooked-for places. Young trees produce vigorous sprouts when cut, and root suckers, especially from older trees, are also common.

MAP 9-8   **(Left)** *Carya ovata.* **(Right)** *Carya laciniosa.*

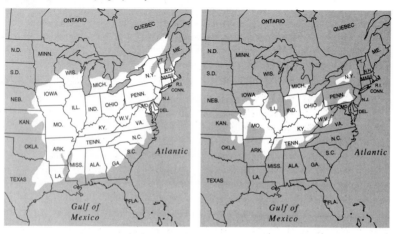

Although one of the fastest-growing hickories, shagbark is still a slow-growing tree and attains an age of 250 to 300 years. The shaggy bark makes it picturesque as a specimen tree when used ornamentally, but the litter of husks and nuts does not recommend it for city planting. Like most hickories, this tree is highly susceptible to damage by fire.

Cárya carolìnae-septentrionàlis (Ashe) Engl. & Graebn. [*Carya ovata* var. *australis* (Ashe) Little]   Carolina hickory; southern shagbark hickory

This species resembles *C. ovata* except for its smaller leaves and fruit, slender twigs, and smaller, nearly glabrous, black or brownish black cylindrical buds. It reaches commercial proportions and is very abundant in the Piedmont and ranges from central North Carolina to northern Georgia and northeastern Mississippi, and west through eastern and central Tennessee. It occurs most frequently in basic soils or around limestone glades. Although treated as a variety by Little (1979) and some other authors, it is considered a distinct species by those who know it well in the field.

Cárya laciniòsa (Michx. f.) Loud.   Shellbark hickory; bigleaf shagbark hickory

Distinguishing Characteristics (Fig. 9-24)

Leaves 12 to 20 in. (30 to 50 cm) long, with 5 to 9 (usually 7) ovate, oblong-lanceolate, or obovate, sessile or nearly sessile leaflets; *terminal leaflets* 5 to 9 in. (12.5 to 23 cm) long, 3 to 4 in. (7.5 to 10 cm) wide, larger than the laterals; *margin* finely serrate, but the teeth lack the subterminal tuft of hairs; *apex* acute to acuminate; *base* cuneate or inequilaterally rounded; *surfaces* dark green, lustrous above, pale yellow-green to yellowish brown, velvety pubescent below; *rachis* stout, grooved, glabrous or pubescent; *fall color* yellow-brown.

FIGURE 9-24   *Carya laciniosa.* Shellbark hickory. (1) Twig × 1¼. (2) Side view of section of husk after dehiscence × ½. (3) Nut × ½.

Fruit 1¾ to 2½ in. (4.5 to 6 cm) long, solitary or paired, ellipsoidal to subglobose, depressed at the apex, with an orange to chestnut-brown husk, ¼ to ½ in. (6 to 12 mm) thick; *nut* subglobose to obovoid, yellowish brown to reddish brown, 4- to 6-ribbed; *seed* sweet.

Twigs stout, orange-brown, prominently orange lenticellate; *terminal buds* ¾ to 1 in. (18 to 25 mm) long, ovoid, obtuse, covered with 6 to 8 visible dark-brown, loosely fitting scales; *lateral buds* smaller, ovoid-oblong, divergent; *leaf scars* obcordate.

Bark similar to that of *C. ovata,* but usually with straighter plates.

Range
East central (Map 9-8). Disjuncts in several outlying states. Elevation: sea level to 1000 ft. Floodplains, mesic woodlands.

General Description
This hickory, as its common name indicates, is very similar to shagbark hickory. It is, however, much more frequently found on wet alluvial bottoms in neutral or alkaline soils where it attains greater size and age. It often occurs in nearly pure groves, or mixed with other bottomland hardwoods, on areas which are inundated for several weeks during high water. Some of the common associates include bur, swamp chestnut, cherrybark and pin oaks, red maple, American elm, and sweetgum. It is very tolerant of low light intensities. The growth rate is perhaps slower than that of other hickories. The maximum measured size of shellbark is 145 ft tall and 4 ft dbh.

Cárya tomentòsa (Poir.) Nutt.   Mockernut hickory

Distinguishing Characteristics (Fig. 9-25)

Leaves 8 to 20 in. (20 to 50 cm) long, with 7 or 9 (rarely 5) sessile or nearly sessile, lanceolate to obovate-oblanceolate, glandular-resinous, fragrant leaflets; *terminal leaflets* 4 to 8 in. (10 to 20 cm) long, 2 to 3 in. (5 to 8 cm) wide, larger than the lateral leaflets; *margin* finely to coarsely serrate; *apex* acute to acuminate; *base* inequilaterally rounded or cuneate; *surfaces* dark yellow-green, lustrous above, pale yellow-green to orange-brown, densely pubescent below with fascicled hairs; *rachis* stout, grooved, pubescent; *fall color* golden-brown.

Fruit 1½ to 2 in. (4 to 5 cm) long, solitary or paired, obovoid to ellipsoidal, deeply 4-channeled from the base to the depressed apex, with a dark red-brown husk, ⅛ to ¼ in. (3 to 6 mm) thick; *nut* light reddish brown, 4-ribbed, somewhat laterally compressed; *seed* sweet.

Twigs stout, reddish brown to brownish gray, pubescent; *terminal buds* ½ to ¾ in. (12 to 18 mm) long, subglobose, reddish brown, tomentose, the outer scales soon deciduous, showing the paler, silky ones beneath; *lateral buds* smaller, somewhat divergent; *leaf scars* 3-lobed to obcordate.

Bark dark gray, firm, close, with low, rounded interlaced ridges and shallow furrows.

Range
Eastern (Map 9-9). Elevation: sea level to 3000 ft in the southern Appalachians. Well-drained, fertile uplands, dry to mesic slopes, and floodplains.

FIGURE 9-25 *Carya tomentosa.* Mockernut hickory. (1) Leaf × ¼. (2) Portion of tomentose petiole × 2. (3) Twig × 1¼. (4) Nut × ⅓. (5) Cross section of nut × ⅓. (6) Nut with dehiscing husk × ⅓. (7) Bark.

General Description

Mockernut hickory is a small to medium-size tree, 40 to 60 ft high and 10 to 20 in. dbh, but it may attain a maximum size of 146 ft by 4 ft. It is found on many soil types with varying amounts of moisture. This tree is the common hickory on dry, sandy soils in the pine forests of the southern Coastal Plains. Mockernut is common on terraces in the second bottoms along the Mississippi and reaches its best development in Arkansas, Missouri, and the lower Ohio River Valley. Most of the commercial mockernut is found on fertile uplands. Hardwood associates

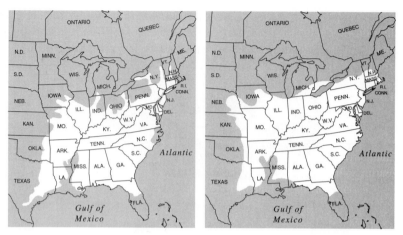

MAP 9-9   **(Left)** *Carya tomentosa.* **(Right)** *Carya glabra* including var. *odorata.*

include other oaks and hickories, sweetgum, maples, American beech, and many others depending on the site. Mockernut's growth rate is slow, and although intolerant, it responds quickly to release.

The wood is used extensively for furniture, flooring, barrels, tool handles, baseball bats, skis, veneer, charcoal, and pulp.

Cárya glàbra (Mill.) Sweet var. *glabra*   Pignut hickory

Distinguishing Characteristics (Fig. 9-26)

Leaves 6 to 10 in. (15 to 25 cm) long, 5 or 7 (mostly 5 but variable from tree to tree) leaflets sessile or nearly sessile, lanceolate to oblanceolate or obovate; *terminal*

FIGURE 9-26   *Carya glabra* var. *glabra*. Pignut hickory. (Left) Pear-shaped nut showing incomplete dehiscence of husk (compare with var. *odorata*) × ½. (Right) Bark.

leaflets 4 to 6 in. (10 to 15 cm) long, 1½ to 2 in. (4 to 5 cm) wide, somewhat larger than the lateral leaflets; *margin* finely serrate; *apex* acute to acuminate; *base* cuneate or inequilaterally rounded; *surfaces* dark yellow-green, glabrous above, more or less pubescent to glabrous below; *rachis* slender, glabrous, green; *fall color* golden yellow.

Fruit 1 to 2 in. (2.5 to 5 cm) long, obovoid or pyriform, the smooth, somewhat shiny husk tardily dehiscent about halfway to the base, often not releasing the nut until after it falls to the ground; *nut* smooth, not ribbed; *seed* bitter.

Twigs slender, lustrous reddish brown, glabrous; *terminal buds* ¼ to ½ in. (6 to 12 mm) long, ovoid to subglobose, obtuse to acuminate, covered by a few reddish brown, glabrous scales, the outer usually deciduous; *lateral buds* smaller, somewhat divergent; *leaf scars* obdeltate to obcordate.

Bark on young trees smooth, eventually developing close, rounded interlacing ridges, medium to dark gray.

Cárya glàbra var. *odoràta* (Marsh.) Little [*Carya ovalis* (Wangenh.) Sarg.]
Red hickory

Distinguishing Characteristics (Fig. 9-27)

Leaves similar to var. *glabra* but with 7 leaflets, less often also 5 on the same tree, petiole reddish.

Fruit 1 to 1½ in. (2.5 to 4 cm) long, oval to subglobose, with a dull (not shiny) granular-textured husk, thin, splitting freely to the base; *nut* brownish white, thin-shelled, 4-ribbed above the center; *seed* usually sweet.

Bark light gray, at first smooth, later somewhat platy or shaggy; eventually closely and deeply furrowed with interlacing ridges, scaly or ragged on the surface.

Range of the species

Eastern (Map 9-9). Elevation: sea level to 4800 ft in the southern Appalachians. Xeric to mesic forests, uplands, slopes, and ridges.

General Description

Pignut hickory and red hickory are usually medium-size trees 50 to 60 ft high and 12 to 24 in. dbh (max. 145 by 4 ft). They are important upland species occurring in mixture with black, red, and white oaks and mockernut hickory.

The treatment of these pignuts has been problematical and variable for many years—from recognition as two separate species, *C. glabra* and *C. ovalis,* or varieties as treated here, to no distinction at all between the two. Although the extremes are distinct morphologically and ecologically, intergradation is so extensive throughout the range that many trees can be identified only as *C. glabra.*

Cárya pállida (Ashe) Engl. & Graebn.   Sand hickory; pale hickory

Sand hickory is similar to *C. glabra.* It is found on dry soils from southern New Jersey through the Piedmont and Coastal Plains to western Florida and Louisiana. The leaflets are narrow, conspicuously silvery below, with fascicled hairs on the petiole and rachis but not on the back of the leaflets, and the crown is denser than that of the other associated hickories; the nut is pear-shaped like *C. glabra* var. *glabra,* but the husk is dehiscent to the base.

FIGURE 9-27 *Carya glabra* var. *odorata*. Red hickory. (1) Twig × 1¼. (2) Leaf × ⅓. (3) Subglobose nut showing full dehiscence of husk (compare with var. *glabra*) × ¾. (4) Cross section of nut × ¾. (5) Nut × ¾. (6) Bark.

Cárya texàna Buckl.   Black hickory

The black hickory is found on dry, often rocky, hillsides, sandy uplands, and along creeks mainly west of the Mississippi River from Missouri to Texas. This is a pignut type like *C. glabra* but with usually 7 leaflets, and the buds and leaflet backs covered with dense rusty-brown hairs and yellow-brown scales.

Cárya floridàna Sarg.   Scrub hickory or Florida hickory

This is similar to the black hickory but confined largely to the scrub vegetation of coastal dunes and sand ridges of north-central peninsular Florida. It has 3 to 7 leaflets and many brownish scales on the leaflet backs.

Pecan Hickories (Table 9-11)
Cárya illinoinénsis (Wangenh.) K. Koch   Pecan

Distinguishing Characteristics (Fig. 9-28)

   Leaves 12 to 20 in. (30 to 50 cm) long, with 9 to 17 sessile or nearly sessile, lanceolate to oblanceolate, usually falcate leaflets; *leaflets* 2 to 7 in. (5 to 18 cm) long, 1 to 3 in. (2.5 to 7.5 cm) wide; *margin* serrate or doubly serrate; *apex* acute to acuminate; *base* cuneate or inequilaterally rounded; *surfaces* dark yellow-green, glabrous or nearly so above, pale yellow-green, glabrous or pubescent below; *rachis* slender, glabrous or pubescent; *fall color* yellow.

   Fruit usually in clusters of 3 to 12, ellipsoidal, 1¼ to 2 in. (3 to 5 cm) long; with a dark-brown husk, 4-winged from apex to base; *nut* ellipsoidal, bright reddish brown, smooth or slightly 4-ridged; *seed* sweet.

   Twigs moderately stout, reddish brown, dotted with orange-brown lenticels, usually more or less pubescent; *terminal* buds ¼ to ½ in. (6 to 12 mm) long, acute, somewhat 4-angled, valvate, yellowish brown, scurfy and appearing naked; *lateral buds* smaller, often divergent; *leaf scars* obovate.

   Bark on mature trees light brown to brownish gray, divided into interlacing, somewhat scaly ridges separated by narrow fissures (Fig. 9-29).

Range

Southeastern (Map 9-10 illustrating the native range). The present-day distribution extends east to the Atlantic coast, being naturalized from pecan groves. Elevation: sea level to 1600 ft. Bottomlands.

TABLE 9-11   COMPARISON OF IMPORTANT PECAN HICKORIES

Species	Leaves	Fruits
C. illinoinensis pecan	9 to 17 lanceolate (often falcate) leaflets	ellipsoidal; husk 4-winged from base to apex; seed sweet
C. cordiformis bitternut hickory	7 to 11 oblong-lanceolate leaflets	subglobose; husk 4-winged above the middle; seed bitter

FIGURE 9-28 *Carya illinoinensis.* Pecan. (1) Twigs × 1¼, fast-growing (left) and slow-growing (right). (2) Nut with husk × ¾. (3) Nut × ¾. (4) Cross section of nut × ¾. (5) Leaf × ¼.

FIGURE 9-29 Bark of pecan.

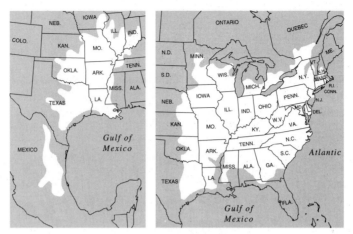

MAP 9-10 **(Left)** *Carya illinoinensis;* now naturalized eastward to eastern North Carolina. **(Right)** *Carya cordiformis.*

General Description

Pecan is said to be the largest of the native hickories and varies from 110 to 140 ft in height and 2 to 4 ft or more dbh (max. 180 by 7 ft). This species is found as a scattered tree on moist but well-drained ridges in river bottoms in company with sycamore, sweetgum, American elm, willow and water oaks, persimmon, poplars, hackberries, black willow, and other bottomland hardwoods. It is the least tolerant and the fastest growing of the hickories.

The timber produced from the pecan hickories is not as strong or heavy as that of the "true hickories," but it is suitable for flooring, veneer, and furniture. Pecan is valuable chiefly for its fruit, which is produced in large amounts and used widely in the United States. Efforts to improve the size and quality of the nuts have been successful (hence "papershell pecans"), and fruit from large planted groves of these trees is harvested on a commercial scale; pecan is now found planted and naturalized through all the southern states as far north as Virginia.

The spelling of the specific epithet has varied over the years: *illinoensis, illinoiensis,* and *illinoinensis.* The last of these is the original spelling and has been designated as the correct one.

Cárya cordifórmis (Wangenh.) K. Koch Bitternut hickory

Distinguishing Characteristics (Fig. 9-30)

Leaves 6 to 10 in. (15 to 25 cm) long, with 7 to 11 sessile or nearly sessile, lanceolate or ovate-lanceolate to oblong-lanceolate leaflets; *terminal leaflets* 3 to 6 in. (7.5 to 15 cm) long, 1 to 1¼ in. (2.5 to 3 cm) wide, slightly larger than the lateral leaflets; *margin* finely to coarsely serrate; *apex* acuminate; *base* cuneate to unequally rounded; *surfaces* bright green, lustrous, glabrous above, pale green, pubescent or glabrous below; *rachis* slender, slightly grooved, pubescent; *fall color* golden yellow.

Fruit ¾ to 1¼ in. (2 to 3 cm) long, solitary or paired, subglobose, with a yellowish green, often minutely scurfy husk, 4-winged above the middle; *nut* subglobose, light reddish brown or gray-brown, thin-shelled; *seed* bitter.

Twigs moderately stout, greenish brown to gray-brown, more or less pubescent, lenticellate; *terminal buds* ⅓ to ¾ in. (8 to 18 mm) long, cylindrical or somewhat 4-

FIGURE 9-30   *Carya cordiformis*. Bitternut hickory. (1) Twig × 1¼. (2) Leaf × ⅓. (3) Nut with husk × ¾. (4) Nut × ¾. (5) Cross section of nut × ¾. (6) Bark.

angled, valvate, sulfur-yellow, and scurfy pubescent; *lateral buds* smaller, often short-stalked, divergent; *leaf scars* 3-lobed, obcordate; *pith* brownish white.

Bark close and firm, remaining smooth for many years, eventually with shallow furrows and low, narrow, interlacing ridges, sometimes slightly scaly on the surface.

Range

Eastern (Map 9-10). Elevation: sea level to 2000 ft. Mesic forests, alluvial bottomlands, valleys, and stream banks, also dry uplands northward.

General Description

Bitternut hickory, the only member of the pecan group in the north, is a medium-size tree and commonly attains a height of 60 to 80 ft and 12 to 24 in. dbh (max. 171 by 4 ft). Like mockernut hickory it is found on many soil types, from those of dry, gravelly uplands to rich, moist bottomlands. Bitternut hickory is associated chiefly with other hickories and oaks, but many other hardwoods may also be in the mixture. It is usually more tolerant than its associates.

Probably the most abundant and uniformly distributed of the hickories, it reaches its largest size in the bottomlands of the lower Ohio basin; it is also the common hickory of Kansas, Nebraska, and Iowa, where it occurs on gravelly ridges bordering streams. It is an important source of lumber and pulp.

Cárya aquática (Michx. f.) Nutt.   Water hickory; bitter pecan

This species is common in swamps and on other low wet sites through the Coastal Plains from Virginia to Florida, west to eastern Texas, and north in the Mississippi valley to southern Illinois. It is most similar to *C. illinoinensis* but differs in its fruit, which is a shorter, flattened, obovoid, 4-ribbed nut with a bitter seed, 5 to 13 narrow, often falcate leaflets, and shaggy bark. In the absence of the nut, it is often difficult to separate the two species. Water hickory, although of minor importance, will grow on sites too poor for the better-grade hardwoods, and hence merits some consideration. Its most common associates include overcup and Nuttall oaks, green ash, American and cedar elms, waterlocust, and hackberries.

Cárya myristicifórmis (Michx. f.) Nutt.   Nutmeg hickory

Nutmeg hickory tends to have fewer leaflets (7 or 9, sometimes 5) than other pecan hickories. The thin husk is ridged along the sutures from apex to base, and the shape of the broadly ellipsoidal to obovoid nut suggests that of a nutmeg; the seed is sweet; the bark is thin and finely scaly. This hickory is found in swamp forests, along stream banks, or elsewhere on rich, moist soils. Although reaching 80 to 100 ft by 2 ft dbh, it is of minor importance because of its rare, scattered occurrence. Small, widely separated populations are found in South Carolina, Alabama, Mississippi, Arkansas, Louisiana, Oklahoma, and Texas.

Myricaceae: The Waxmyrtle Family

This family includes three genera and about 50 species of evergreen shrubs and small trees found usually in swamps or on dry sandy soils in the temperate and warmer parts of the world. The leaves are alternate, simple, aromatic, and bear minute, yellow-orange or black resin dots, visible with a handlens. The flowers are unisexual and in rather short, inconspicuous aments, appearing in early spring. *Comptonia peregrina*

(L.) Coult. with pinnatifid, fernlike, linear-lanceolate leaves is the common, shrubby "sweet-fern" of the northeast. The myricas, or bayberries, have leaves with entire or toothed margins. The waxy covering of the fruit of *Myrica pensylvanica* Loisel. (northern bayberry) furnishes most of the bayberry wax used for candles. For a description of candlemaking, see Dengler (1967). Both of the following species are cultivated as ornamentals. The fruit is eaten by small birds.

Mỳrica cerífera L.   Wax myrtle or southern bayberry

A common, large shrub or small tree of the Coastal Plain from New Jersey south to southern Florida, west to eastern Texas and southeastern Oklahoma. It is found in moist habitats and often forms dense thickets. The leaves are oblanceolate with yellow-orange glands mainly on the backs and coarse teeth only above the middle.

Mỳrica califórnica Cham.   Pacific bayberry

Occurs quite abundantly on low hills, sand dunes, and riverbanks near the coast from southwestern Washington to southern California, from sea level to 500 ft of elevation. The leaves have black glands below.

The roots of *Myrica* have a symbiotic relationship with actinomycetes (moldlike bacteria) which form root nodules and have the capacity to convert atmospheric nitrogen into a form usable by plants. This capacity for nitrogen fixation is generally associated with legumes, but *Myrica, Alnus, Elaeagnus, Casuarina,* and *Ceanothus* are notable additions. This process is of major ecological significance, for great quantities of nitrogen compounds are added to the soil.

Fagaceae: The Beech Family

The Beech family includes nine genera and about 800 species of trees and shrubs scattered throughout both hemispheres, but is most characteristic of the forests in the north temperate zone. The importance of this group to American forestry can hardly be overemphasized, for in this country it takes first place among the hardwoods in the production of lumber and other forest products. The most important genus is *Quercus* (oak).

Five genera with about 75 species are found in North America. Two, *Lithocarpus* and *Castanopsis,* are confined to the Pacific coast region; *Castanea* and *Fagus* are restricted to the east, and *Quercus* is widely distributed over a large portion of the United States and southern Canada, with the exception of the Great Plains (Table 9-12).

Botanical Features of the Family

Leaves persistent, or deciduous and often marcescent; alternate, simple, stipulate, usually pinnately veined, and short-petioled.

Flowers anemophilous, imperfect (plants monoecious) and borne in one of several ways. *Staminate* flowers usually in aments, but in *Fagus* they form a globose head; the aments pendent or erect, the flowers variously grouped on the axis; *staminate* flowers have a 4- to 7-lobed calyx and 4 to 8 (rarely more) stamens. *Pistillate* flowers borne in short few-flowered spikes on new growth (*Fagus* and *Quercus*), or in clusters near the base of the smaller staminate aments (*Castanea, Castanopsis, Lithocarpus*). When

TABLE 9-12   COMPARISON OF NATIVE GENERA IN THE FAGACEAE

Genus	Leaves	Flowers	Fruit
Fagus beech	deciduous	staminate in heads, pistillate in short 2- to 4-flowered spikes	a nut, triangular in section, occurring usually in 2s within a bur covered with weak, unbranched spines; fruit maturing in one season
Castanea chestnut	deciduous	in erect, unisexual and bisexual aments	a rounded nut, occurring singly or in 2s or 3s within a bur covered with sharp, rigid, branched spines; maturing in one season
Castanopsis chinkapin	persistent	similar to those in *Castanea*	similar to that of *Castanea* but requiring 2 seasons to mature
Lithocarpus tanoak	persistent	similar to those of *Castanea*	an acorn, maturing at the end of the second season
Quercus oak	deciduous or persistent	staminate in aments, pistillate in several-flowered spikes	an acorn, maturing in one or two seasons

such bisexual aments occur, there are also others of the purely staminate type present; *pistillate* flower consists of a 4- to 8-lobed calyx adnate to a 3- (rarely 6-) celled ovary with a style for each cell, containing 1 to 2 ovules, only one of which matures.

Fruit a nut with an outer cartilaginous coat, and partially or wholly encased in an involucre; *nut* 1-seeded by abortion, seed lacking endosperm; cotyledons large and fleshy, and as in *Juglans, Carya,* and certain other genera with large seeds, always remaining (with the exception of *Fagus*) within the seed coats upon germination.

FAGUS L.   Beech

There are 10 species of *Fagus,* all in the northern hemisphere. Besides the one North American species (eastern United States, Canada, and Mexico), one is European, another is in the Caucasus, and the others range through temperate eastern Asia.

European beech, *Fagus sylvatica* L., is an important timber tree of Europe, where it is grown in pure or mixed stands under forest management. It is distinguished by the leaves which have 5 to 9 pairs of secondary veins in contrast to 9 to 14 pairs in *F. grandifolia*. The leaves, buds, and bark of *F. sylvatica* are also darker than those of the American species. The fruit, known as *beech mast,* is used in Europe for fattening hogs and as a source of vegetable oil. There are numerous cultivars of this species which are very widely cultivated as beautiful ornamental lawn, street, or park trees.

The name "beech" has a very ancient origin and signifies "book." It is said that the early writings of the Germanic peoples were inscribed upon tablets made of this wood. Gutenberg printed the first Bible from movable type carved from beech wood.

The bluish-gray, smooth bark of the beech is a most distinctive feature, but often, and almost characteristically, made very unsightly by initials, hearts, and dates carved on its surface.

Young trees of some oaks, and particularly beech, characteristically hold their brown or tan leaves until spring. Trees with this very conspicuous feature during the winter are called *marcescent.*

Fàgus grandifòlia Ehrh.   American beech

Distinguishing Characteristics (Fig. 9-31)

Leaves deciduous, 2½ to 6 in. (6 to 15 cm) long, 1 to 3 in. (2.5 to 7.5 cm) wide; *shape* elliptical to oblong-ovate; *margin* remotely serrate with sharp, incurved teeth; *apex* acuminate; *base* broadly cuneate; *surfaces* silky at first, becoming glabrous above and various degrees of puberulent below plus tufts of hairs in the vein axils, secondary veins parallel to each other; texture of the leaf somewhat papery to the touch; *petiole* short; *stipules* ¾ to 1¾ in. (2 to 4 cm) long, narrow and straplike, membranous to papery; *fall color* yellow to bronze.

Flowers appearing after the unfolding of the leaves in the spring; *staminate* in globose heads, each flower with a 4- to 8-lobed calyx and 8 to 16 stamens; *pistillate* in 2- to 4-flowered spikes, surrounded by an involucre, each flower with a 4- to 5-lobed calyx attached to a 3-celled ovary.

Fruit an edible nut, ½ to ¾ in. (12 to 18 mm) long, triangular in cross section; paired or in 3s within a woody, 4-parted involucre or bur covered with weak, unbranched spines.

Twigs slender, at times slightly zigzag; *pith* homogeneous, terete; *pseudoterminal buds* ¾ to 1 in. (18 to 25 mm) long, slender, lance-shaped, sharp-pointed, often appearing and interpreted as a true terminal; scales numerous and imbricated in 4 ranks; *lateral buds* similar; *leaf scars* small, inconspicuous; *stipular scars* narrow, nearly encircling the twig.

Bark thin, smooth, light blue-gray in color, often mottled and not changing appreciably as the tree grows older.

Range

Eastern (Map 9-11). Elevation: sea level to 3000 ft northward, to 6000 ft in the southern Appalachians. Moist, rich uplands and lowlands.

General Description

American beech is one of the most distinctive and common trees of the eastern hardwood forest, and its smooth blue-gray trunk and marcescent condition are easily recognized even at some distance. The tree averages 70 to 80 ft in height and 2 to 3 ft dbh (max. 161 by 6 ft). In the open it is featured by a short, stocky bole with a wide-spreading crown, while under forest conditions a clear, straight, massive trunk and smaller crown are developed. The root system is shallow and extensive and has a tendency to produce sprouts. Such root suckering is very characteristic of beech, and old trees are often surrounded by thickets of young growth, mostly of this origin rather than from seed. It is doubtful whether these root sprouts ever attain much size, at least during the life of the parent tree. Also stump and root collar sprouts, except from stumps under 4-in. diameter, are short-lived.

FIGURE 9-31   *Fagus grandifolia.* American beech. (1) Twig × 1¼. (2) Staminate flowers × ½. (3) Leaf × ½. (4) Fruit (nuts) in a spiny husk × ¾. (5) Nuts in partly opened husk × ¾. (6) Bark.

American beech is found on a wide variety of soils from the sandy loams of the northeast to the alluvial bottoms of the Ohio and Mississippi valleys. Beech requires much more moisture for growth than many other hardwoods. Trees are not usually found on soils where the surface layers dry out quickly or are subject to prolonged flooding. This species may be the most tolerant of northern hardwoods, and with sugar maple and yellow birch it forms the typical maple–beech–birch forest of that region. Other associates include red spruce, white pine, hemlock, black cherry, northern red oak, and white ash. Several of these are also southern associates,

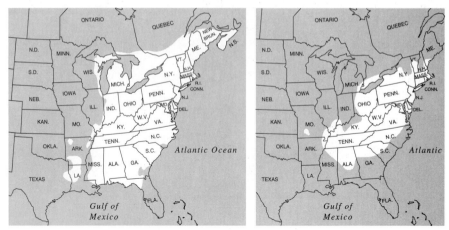

MAP 9-11   **(Left)** *Fagus grandifolia.* **(Right)** *Castanea dentata.*

and to them may be added such species as southern magnolia, basswood, sweetgum, oaks, and hickories.

American beech reaches its largest size on the better-drained sites of alluvial bottoms in the Ohio and Mississippi valleys and in the western half of the southern Appalachians. However, even under the best conditions growth is slow.

Large crops of seed may be produced at 2- to 3-year or longer intervals. This species may attain an age of 300 to 400 years, but old trees are usually affected by butt rot. The thin bark and shallow root system make beech very susceptible to damage by fire.

American beech is a variable species and shows at least three different races (Camp, 1950; Cooper and Mercer, 1977; Hardin and Johnson, 1985). The northern form is "gray beech" found from Nova Scotia to the Great Lakes, and on the higher mountains of North Carolina and Tennessee mainly on neutral to alkaline soils. "White beech" is found on the southern Coastal Plains and northward on poorly drained acid sites. Between these two forms, mainly on well-drained acid sites and mixing with them, is "red beech." The beech of much of the glaciated area is a mixture derived in various combinations from the three basic forms. Careful studies are needed to clarify this variation on a local basis, for each stand is not only variable but also has a "norm" often differing from that of adjacent sites.

The wood is used for flooring, furniture, veneer, butcher's blocks and cutting boards, and plywood. The nuts are an important source of mast for wildlife.

CASTANEA Mill.   Chestnut; chinkapin

This is a small genus with about 10 species found in southern Europe, northern Africa, southwestern and the eastern Asia, and the eastern United States. Because the superior flavored nuts of the blight-stricken American chestnut are no longer available, three other species are used. Spanish or European chestnut, *C. sativa* Mill.; Japanese chestnut, *C. crenata* Sieb. & Zucc.; and Chinese chestnut, *C. mollissima* Bl., are all important in their native lands. The United States imports the nuts but also has a few groves of the better varieties for local production, especially in Georgia and Maryland. These are also used as ornamental yard or park trees.

Pollination in *Castanea* has been described as anemophilous, entomophilous, or a combination of both. The anemophilous syndrome is generally expressed by a monoecious condition, flowering before the leaves, large quantities of smooth, light-weight pollen, and pistillate flowers inconspicuous and lacking both odor and nectar. The entomophilous syndrome normally includes flowering after the leaves appear, less amounts of heavier, sticky pollen, and flowers showy and aromatic. Johnson (1988) found that the American species of *Castanea* are primarily wind-pollinated. Any role played by insects is a passive, indirect one by dislodging pollen from the anthers, but they do not visit the pistillate flowers. The combination of anemophilous and entomophilous features in these species may reflect an intermediacy between ancestral entomophily and the derived anemophily characteristic of other Fagaceae.

Botanical Features of the Genus

Leaves deciduous, serrate, stipulate.

Flowers borne in ascending, staminate, and also bisexual aments, appearing in late spring when the leaves are nearly full grown; *staminate* in clusters of 3 to 7 along the elongated and conspicuous ament axis, each with a 6-lobed calyx and 10 to 20 long-stalked stamens; *pistillate* solitary or in clusters of 2 to 3, in an involucre at the base of special, short, staminate aments (bisexual aments); calyx 6-lobed, adnate to a 6-celled ovary bearing occasionally a few abortive stamens.

Fruit a lustrous-brown, rounded, edible nut borne singly or in clusters of 2 or 3 in a 2- to 4-valved bur covered with needle-sharp branched spines.

Twigs slender to moderately stout, usually brown, glabrous or tomentose; *pith* stellate; *terminal buds* lacking; *lateral buds* with 2 or 3 visible scales; *leaf scars* half round; *bundle scars* 3 or more; *stipular scars* present.

Castànea dentàta (Marsh.) Borkh.   American chestnut

Distinguishing Characteristics (Fig. 9-32)

Leaves 5 to 9 in. (13 to 23 cm) long, 1½ to 3 in. (4 to 7.5 cm) wide; *shape* oblong-lanceolate; *margin* coarsely and sharply serrate, with bristle-tipped or hair-tipped teeth; *apex* acuminate; *base* acute; *surfaces* dull yellow-green and glabrous; phyllotaxy variable, usually ½ or ⅖; *fall color* yellow to orange-yellow.

Fruit 2 to 2½ in. (5 to 6 cm) in diameter, covered with sharp, branched spines; *nut* ½ to 1 in. (12 to 25 mm) wide, nearly flat on one side, borne 2 or 3 in each bur.

Twigs somewhat lustrous, chestnut-brown; *lateral buds* ca. ¼ in. (6 mm) long, ovoid, brown.

Bark dark brown, shallowly fissured into broad, flat ridges.

Range

Eastern (Map 9-11). Elevation: sea level to 4400 ft in the southern Appalachians.

General Description

The American chestnut was a highly valued tree; its growth was rapid, the wood durable, and the flavorful roasted nuts contributed to the food supply. In the forest the nuts were an important wildlife food. Tannin was extracted from both bark and wood. All things considered, chestnut

FIGURE 9-32   *Castanea dentata.* American chestnut. (1) Twig × 1¼. (2) Leaf × ½. (3) Inflorescence × ⅓. (4) Portion of staminate inflorescence showing clusters of flowers × 1. (5) Base of inflorescence showing pistillate flower × 1. (6) Nut × 1. (7) Nut in partly opened spiny husk × ¾. (8) Chestnut sprouts.

may well have been the most important hardwood of North America. However, in 1904, a chestnut blight disease, caused by the fungus *Cryphonectria parasitica,* presumably brought in from eastern Asia, was first noticed on a few trees at the Bronx Zoo. Within 50 years the blight had spread over the entire range of the chestnut, causing wholesale destruction. The standing-dead trunks were important for the highly prized "worm-eaten chestnut" lumber until the 1960s. Its ability to sprout vigorously after the trunk is dead helps the species to persist in spite of continued attacks by the fungus dispersed from cankers present on other trees. These sprouts occasionally have fruit, but no resistant form has been found.

With the beginning of the chestnut blight, scientists began a vigorous program of hybridization and, in the 1970s, experimented with a strain of the fungus of reduced virulence. Thus far, however, there is no prospect of the American chestnut again becoming a significant forest tree. Its original dominance on many sites has been replaced by various oak and hickory species.

Castànea pùmila Mill.   Chinkapin

Chinkapin (or chinquapin) differs from the American chestnut in its smaller, tomentose leaves; smaller, single-seeded burs; and usually tomentose twigs. It is a small tree or shrub of dry soils from Pennsylvania to Florida and west to Oklahoma and Texas. The nuts are eaten by people and wildlife. Although quite variable in habit and other features, Johnson (1988) found that the most realistic classification was to recognize only a single species (including *C. alnifolia* Nutt. and *C. ozarkensis* Ashe).

CASTANOPSIS (D. Don) Spach   Chinkapin; evergreen chinkapin

This genus includes about 100 species of evergreen trees and shrubs, the majority of which are scattered through the forests of China, India, and the Malayan archipelago. The American flora includes but two species, both native to the Pacific Coast. *Castanopsis sempervirens* (Kell.) Dudl. (Sierra chinkapin) is a small, timberline shrub common in the Coast Ranges and the high Sierra Nevada of California.

Botanical Features of the Genus
Leaves persistent, coriaceous, entire or dentate, stipulate.
Flowers in erect, unisexual or bisexual aments; *staminate* in cymose clusters of three along the amentiferous stalk, the individual flowers similar to those of chestnut; *pistillate* solitary or in clusters of two or three, the ovary 3-celled; appearing in early summer.
Fruit a large, lustrous, brown to yellowish brown nut borne solitary or in clusters of two or three and encased in a 4-valved husk with branched spines, maturing at the end of the second season (American species).

Castanópsis chrysophýlla (Dougl.) A.DC.   Giant chinkapin

Distinguishing Characteristics (Fig. 9-33)
Leaves lanceolate to oblong-ovate, 2 to 5 in. (5 to 13 cm) long, ⅝ to 1½ in. (1.5 to 4 cm) wide, entire, often slightly revolute, dark green above, covered with minute golden-yellow persistent scales below; *fall color* yellow.

Flowers like those of chestnut.

Fruit densely covered with branched spines, the husk containing one or two edible nuts which mature at the end of the second season.

Twigs at first covered with golden-yellow scales, becoming reddish brown and somewhat scurfy.

Bark initially dark gray and smooth, maturing to very wide reddish brown plates, bright red within.

FIGURE 9-33 *Castanopsis chrysophylla.* Giant chinkapin. (1) Leaf × ¾. (2) Nut with spiny husk × 1. (3) Nut × 1. (4) Bark (*Photo by E. Fritz*).

Range

Southwestern Washington, south from the Columbia River along the west slopes of the Cascades through Oregon to central California, along the Coast Ranges to the San Jacinto Mountains. Elevation: sea level to 1500 ft; shrub form to 6000 ft. Gravelly and rocky slopes, canyons, and dry ridges.

General Description

The giant chinkapin, which is never more than a large shrub in Washington, attains tree size in Oregon and California. Under average conditions for growth it will reach a height of 60 to 80 ft and 3 ft dbh, although trees up to 150 ft high and 8 ft dbh have been observed in the moist valleys of northern coastal California. Under forest conditions this species develops a clear bole for one-half to two-thirds of its length, and a dense, ovoid to conical crown; the crown of open-grown trees is generally large and wide-spreading. A taproot is developed by juvenile trees, but this gives way in later life to a well-developed lateral system of anchorage. It is very tolerant when young but requires full sunlight for adequate mature growth.

Considerable seed is produced at frequent intervals, and natural regeneration by this means is generally satisfactory. Some renewal is also traceable to stump sprouts. Growth is moderately rapid, and maturity is reached in about 200 to 500 years.

This species is quite gregarious on poor, dry soils and often forms pure stands over wide areas. The tree also appears as an understory species in stands of redwood and Douglas-fir, or mixed with western juniper, Jeffrey pine, canyon live oak, and as a component of chaparral.

The wood is used for furniture, paneling, veneer, and cabinetwork. The nuts are an important source of mast for birds and small and large mammals.

LITHOCARPUS Blume   Tanoak

Lithocarpus numbers 300 species of evergreen trees and shrubs. The genus is widespread through southeastern Asia and Indonesia but is not found elsewhere except for a single species indigenous to western North America. The Asiatic forms will not endure cold winters, and hence their use as ornamentals is not possible in the cooler regions of the temperate zone. A few species have been successfully introduced into southern United States, but they are rarely used for decorative purposes. The fruits of *L. edulis* (Mak.) Nakai and *L. corneus* (Lour.) Rehd. of Japan and south China, respectively, are rather sweet and edible. Botanically, this genus is very interesting, because its flowers are nearly identical with those of either *Castanea* or *Castanopsis,* while its fruit resembles that of *Quercus.*

Botanical Features of the Genus
Leaves persistent, stipulate.
Flowers similar to those of *Castanea* or *Castanopsis;* appearing in early spring or sometimes in the fall.
Fruit a nut (acorn), partially or rarely wholly enveloped by a cuplike involucre; maturing at the end of the second season.

Lithocárpus densiflòrus (Hook. & Arn.) Rehd.   Tanoak; tanbark-oak
Distinguishing Characteristics (Fig. 9-34)
Leaves oblong to oblong-lanceolate, 2 to 5 in. (5 to 13 cm) long, ¾ to 2¼ in. (2 to 6 cm) wide, repand-dentate to entire-revolute, rounded-truncate at the base, light green above, brownish to golden woolly pubescent in early summer below, ultimately becoming bluish white and sparsely pubescent toward the end of the season; *petiole* tomentose.
Flowers similar to those of *Castanopsis.*
Fruit a bitter acorn, ¾ to 1¼ in. (1.8 to 3 cm) long, the cup shallow, with narrow, spreading scales, tomentose, lined with lustrous red pubescence.
Twigs at first densely pubescent but later dark reddish brown and often covered with a glaucous bloom.
Bark broken into heavy rounded ridges separated by deep narrow fissures.

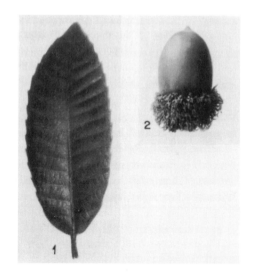

FIGURE 9-34 *Lithocarpus densiflorus.* Tanoak. (1) Leaf × ¾.
(2) Acorn × 1.

Range

Southwestern Oregon, south along the Coast Ranges to southern California; south in the Sierras to Mariposa County. Elevation: sea level to nearly 5000 ft. Moist valleys and mountain slopes in mixed evergreen and redwood forests.

General Description

Tanoak is a moderately large tree 70 to 90 ft in height and 24 to 36 in. dbh but reaching some-what larger proportions (max. 150 by 9 ft) under the most favorable conditions. The boles of forest trees are clear, but often asymmetrical, and support narrow pyramidal crowns of ascending branches; open-grown trunks are short and often disappear in a mass of widespread limbs which form broad, nearly globose crowns. The anchorage consists of a deep, well-developed taproot and a number of short laterals. Best development is reached on deep, rich, moist, but well-drained, gravelly and sandy soils with redwood, Douglas-fir, Oregon white oak, giant chinkapin, and California black oak. At elevations of 3500 to 4500 ft along the middle-west slopes of the Sierra, tanoak occurs in mixture with California black oak, Pacific madrone, bigleaf maple, white fir, sugar pine, ponderosa pine, and Douglas-fir. Fairly extensive, nearly pure stands of coppice growth appear on cutover areas.

Viable seed is borne in abundance after 30 to 40 years. The growth of seedlings proceeds at a moderate rate, and the trees reach maturity between 200 and 300 years. Tanoak can exist under forest cover throughout its life, and the rapidity with which suppressed trees often develop upon being released from dense shade is remarkable.

The bark of tanoak contains appreciable amounts of tannin and at one time was an important commercial source of this material for the western states. It is now used for fuel and pulp. Acorns are a very important mast for a wide variety of wildlife.

QUERCUS L.   Oak

The oak genus with its many species is the most important aggregation of hardwoods found on the North American continent, if not in the entire northern hemisphere; in fact, the central and southern hardwood forests of the United States may be thought of as oak forests, with the other broad-leaved species playing a secondary role. An interesting discussion of the development of oak forests is given by Abrams (1992). Oaks furnish more native timber annually than any other group of broad-leaved trees, and the amount is surpassed only by the conifers, which occupy first place in this respect. Other products of lesser importance but widespread use include cork from two southern European species,* tannin from the bark of certain others, and ink derived from the insect leaf galls of a few Old World species; the sweet acorns of several North American oaks were used extensively for food by Native Americans. Indeed, throughout its vast range, this genus has historically been an important food source for primitive people. It continues to be of major importance to many forms of wildlife.

The sturdy qualities and appearance of many of the oaks, together with their longevity in comparison with other hardwoods, have made them from very ancient times the objects of admiration and worship among the early people of the Old World. This feeling still persists in a modified form, and many of the historic as well as ornamental trees of the United States and other countries are oaks of one species or another.

From the botanical standpoint, oaks are of great interest because of their intrinsic variation as well as hybridization and introgression. For an example of variation, see Baranski (1975) and for a discussion of oak hybrids, see Cottam et al. (1982), Hardin (1975), Little (1979), Manos and Fairbrothers (1987), Palmer (1948), Rushton (1993), and Tucker (1993).

The oaks are widely distributed throughout the temperate regions of the northern hemisphere and extend southward at higher elevations to the tropics (Colombia in the western hemisphere; northern Africa and Indonesia in the eastern hemisphere). The total number of species is 500 to 600, with 250 in the New World. There are about 60 species native to the United States, and according to Little (1979), 58 of these reach tree size.

Because of the size and complexity of this genus, only the most important or characteristic are fully described in this text. Other species of ecological interest are mentioned briefly. Identification of local species can be accomplished with the aid of local or regional field guides to trees.

Botanical Features of the Genus
Leaves deciduous or persistent; lobed or not; *margin* crenate, serrate, or entire; *shape* and *size* often very variable even on the same tree; *stipules* usually deciduous, at times persistent at the upper nodes; phyllotaxy ⅖.
Flowers (Fig. 9-35) imperfect (plants monoecious), appearing on the old or new growth, before, with, or after the unfolding of the new leaves; *staminate* aments pendent, clustered; individual flowers with a 4- to 7-lobed calyx which encloses 6 stamens (rarely 4 to 12); *pistillate* flowers solitary or in few- to many-flowered spikes from the axils of the new leaves; individual flowers consist of a 6-lobed calyx surrounding a 3- (rarely 4- to 5-) celled ovary, the whole partly enclosed in an involucre.

---

*The world's cork supply is obtained chiefly from *Q. suber* L. of southern Europe and northern Africa. See Cooke (1946) and Fowells (1949) for reports on attempts at growing these trees in the United States.

FIGURE 9-35   *Quercus*. Oak. (1) Spring twig × ½ showing flowers and young leaves. (2) Pistillate flowers × 4. (3) Staminate flower × 4.

Fruit an acorn maturing in 1 or 2 seasons; *nut* partially enclosed by a scaly cup (the modified involucre); usually 1-seeded by abortion.

Twigs stout to slender, straight, commonly angled; *pith* homogeneous, stellate; *buds* clustered at the ends of the twig; *terminal* bud present, with many scales imbricated in 5 ranks; *lateral buds* similar but smaller; *leaf scars* semicircular; *bundle scars* scattered, numerous; *stipular scars* minute.

Infrageneric Classification

On the basis of similarities in leaf, flower, pollen, and fruit characteristics, morphology of foliar trichomes (Hardin, 1979a), molecular data, and interspecific hybridization, oaks are classified into two subgenera and three sections. The classification followed in earlier editions of this text was based on a single characteristic of summer wood anatomy (Williams, 1939) which is now considered to be an artificial classification (Tillson and Muller, 1942). Although the early classifications by Trelease (1924) and Camus (1938) were fairly realistic, there are a number of exceptions to most differences between subgenera, and none of the classifications is entirely satisfactory. The classification of subgenera and sections used here follows Nixon (1993). Much more research is needed to determine species relationships among the oaks. An outline of the groupings used here follows.

Outline of Subgenera, Sections, and Smaller Groups

I. Subgenus *Cyclobalanopsis.* The cycle-cup oaks. Asian
II. Subgenus *Quercus.* The scale-cup oaks. Northern Hemisphere
    A. Section *Quercus* (= *Leucobalanus*). The white oaks (leaves lacking spinose teeth or bristle-tipped lobes; often with stellate hairs and lacking multiradiate

hairs; acorns maturing in one season; acorn cup scales basally thick; inner pericarp glabrous; seed sweet)

   1. True white oaks (leaves deciduous; more or less deeply lobed). *Q. alba,
   macrocarpa, lyrata, stellata, margarettiae, douglasii, garryana, lobata,
   gambelii*
   2. Chestnut oaks (leaves deciduous; crenate, coarsely toothed, or sinuate). *Q.
   michauxii, prinus, bicolor, muehlenbergii*
   3. Live oaks (leaves persistent; usually unlobed). *Q. virginiana, geminata, arizonica, oblongifolia*

   B. Section *Lobatae* (= *Erythrobalanus*). The red and black oaks (leaves mostly
   with bristle-tipped lobes, if unlobed, the margins, apices, or both, often with
   spines or bristles; often with multiradiate hairs and lacking stellate hairs;
   acorns usually maturing in two seasons; acorn cup scales rarely thick; inner
   pericarp tomentose; seed bitter)

   1. True red and black oaks (leaves deciduous; lobed). *Q. rubra, velutina, shumardii, falcata, pagoda, coccinea, palustris, ellipsoidalis, texana, marilandica, laevis, kelloggii*
   2. Willow, laurel, and water oaks (leaves deciduous or tardily so; unlobed). *Q.
   phellos, nigra, hemisphaerica, laurifolia, imbricaria, incana*
   3. Western live oaks (leaves persistent; unlobed). *Q. wislizeni, agrifolia,
   emoryi*

   C. Section *Protobalanus*. The intermediate oaks (leaves persistent, often with aristate teeth; stellate or multiradiate hairs present; acorns maturing in two seasons;
   acorn cup scales more-or-less thick, tomentose; inner pericarp tomentose appearing glabrous). *Q. chrysolepis, palmeri, cedrosensis, tomentella, vaccinifolia*

True White Oaks

Deciduous; leaves more or less deeply lobed; eastern and western species (Table 9-13).

Quércus álba L.   White oak

Distinguishing Characteristics (Figs. 9-36)

   Leaves deciduous, 4 to 9 in. (10 to 23 cm) long, 2 to 4 in. (5 to 10 cm) wide; *shape*
oblong-obovate; *margin* entire, 7- to 9-lobed, with deep to shallow sinuses extending
evenly toward the midrib, sometimes with secondary lobes; *apex* rounded; *base*
cuneate; *surfaces* glabrous or puberulent, bright green above, slightly paler below; *fall
color* yellow, red, or purplish brown.

   Fruit solitary or paired, sessile or short-stalked; *nut* ⅜ to 1¼ in. (1 to 3 cm) long,
ovoid-oblong, enclosed for one-quarter of its length in a light chestnut-brown, bowl-
like cup with thickened, warty scales.

   Twigs moderately stout, purplish gray to greenish red; *terminal buds* ⅛ to 3⁄16 in. (3
to 5 mm) long, globose to broadly ovoid, reddish brown, glabrous.

   Bark light ashy gray, very variable in appearance; on young to medium-size trees
often broken up into small, vertically aligned blocks, scaly on the surface; later irregularly plated, with the plates attached on one side or deeply fissured, with narrow

TABLE 9-13 COMPARISON OF IMPORTANT TRUE WHITE OAKS

Species	Leaves	Fruit
Q. alba white oak	deeply to shallowly lobed, sinuses narrow; green and glabrous below	⅜–1¼ in. (1–3 cm) long; nut ovoid-oblong; cup bowl-like with warty scales
Q. macrocarpa bur oak	irregularly lobed, the center pair of sinuses the deepest; pale below	¾–½ in. (2–5 cm) long; nut broadly ovoid; cup deep, conspicuously fringed on the margin
Q. lyrata overcup oak	deeply lobed, with broad irregular sinuses; green or pale below	½–1 in. (1.2–2.5 cm) long; nut subglobose, almost wholly enclosed in a deep, thin, unfringed cup
Q. stellata post oak	cruciform; tawny tomentose below	½–1 in. (1.2–2.5 cm) long; nut ovoid-oblong; cup bowl-like with thin scales
Q. garryana Oregon white oak	evenly and deeply lobed; orange-pubescent below	1–1¼ in. (2.5–3 cm) long; ovoid to obovoid; cup shallow with pubescent scales

rounded ridges. (Figure 9-36, pts. 5 and 6, shows the amount of variation to be expected, with pt. 5 the more common except on very old trees.)

Range

Eastern (Map 9-12). Elevation: sea level to 5500 ft in the southern Appalachians. Dry to mesic woods.

General Description

This tree is the most important species of the white oak group and is said to furnish nearly three-fourths of the timber harvested as white oak. Any estimate, however, is subject to error because only white oak and red oak are recognized in the trade; each type includes the wood of a number of species which lose their identity when the logs are manufactured into lumber or other forest products.

White oak at its best is a large tree 80 to 100 ft high and 3 to 4 ft dbh (max. 150 by 9 ft). In the open it is characterized by a short stocky bole and a wide-spreading crown of rugged appearance; this outline with some variation is a feature of most oaks. Under forest conditions, white oak develops a tall straight trunk with a small crown.

The oaks as a group are noted for their deep root systems, and at the end of the first season, white oak seedlings with but 3 to 4 in. of slender top growth terminate below in a prodigious taproot ¼ to ½ in. in diameter at the surface and extending 1 ft or more into the ground (Fig. 7-17, pt. 5).

Although white oak is found on many types of soil, it reaches its best development in coves or on the higher bottomlands where the soil is deep and moist, with good internal drainage. Common associates include hickories, other oaks, basswood, white ash, black cherry, yellow-poplar, and sweetgum; a complete list would include a much larger number of species (see Burns and Honkala, 1990). Some of the finest old-growth white oak was in central New York in

FIGURE 9-36   *Quercus alba.* White oak. (1) Twig × 1¼. (2, 3) Variation in leaf lobing × ½ (see also Fig. 5-1). (4) Acorn × 1. (5, 6) Barks.

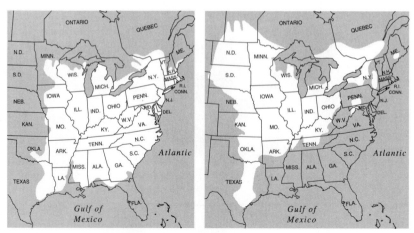

MAP 9-12   (Left) *Quercus alba.* **(Right)** *Quercus macrocarpa.*

mixture with eastern white pine, eastern hemlock, sugar maple, and hickories. Although often found in uneven-aged mixed hardwood forests, this oak, after clear-cutting, may form even-aged stands. The ability to complete many cycles of growth, its declining vigor, and the death of the aerial portions of a seedling while its roots increase both in size and stored energy are characteristics of this and most other oaks. This is in part responsible for much successful oak regeneration and the maintenance of these less than tolerant species in so many climax forest types. These stool and small-stump sprouts can respond dramatically to release and produce trees of excellent form and quality. Sprout growth from high stumps is often affected by heart rot.

White oak is often a prolific seeder, but good seed years do not occur regularly, and locally several years (4 to 10) may pass without any crop whatever. Like many of the white oak group, the acorns of this species germinate in the fall soon after they are released. This is a disadvantage northward because the roots often do not have time to penetrate the soil before they are frozen.

The growth of white oak is not fast, and like many slow-growing trees it may attain a considerable age, in some instances a maximum of 400 to 500 years. This species, like a number of other oaks, is intermediate in tolerance, with a tendency to become more intolerant with age.

This oak is used as an ornamental tree and the wood for furniture, flooring, cabinets, veneer, shakes, railroad ties, and tight cooperage. White oak casks for aging whisky are well-known, and the discarded ones are often cut in half and used as planters.

White oak is a wide-ranging species in terms of latitude and elevation and is quite variable in leaf shape (see Fig. 5-1), acorn size, and other features. Much of this variation is intrinsic (Baranski, 1975), but added variation is due to introgression from the other associated species of the white oak section (Hardin, 1975).

Quércus macrocárpa Michx.   Bur oak; mossycup oak

Distinguishing Characteristics (Fig. 9-37)

Leaves deciduous, 4 to 12 in. (10 to 30 cm) long, 3 to 6 in. (8 to 15 cm) wide; *shape* obovate to oblong; *margin* entire, 5- to 9-lobed, the two center sinuses usually reaching nearly to the midrib; *apex* rounded; *base* cuneate; *surfaces* dark green and lustrous above, pale and pubescent below; *fall color* yellow or brown.

FIGURE 9-37   *Quercus macrocarpa.* Bur oak. (1) Twig × 1¼. (2) Leaf × ½. (3) Acorn × ¾. (4) Bark.

Fruit solitary, usually stalked, variable in size; *nut* ¾ to 2 in. (2 to 5 cm) long, broadly ovoid, downy at the apex, enclosed one-half or more in a deep cup which is conspicuously fringed on the margin.

Twigs stout, yellowish brown, usually pubescent; after the second year often with conspicuous corky ridges; *terminal buds* ⅛ to ¼ in. (3 to 6 mm) long, mostly obtuse, usually tawny pubescent.

Bark similar to that of *Q. alba* but darker and more definitely ridged vertically.

Range

Northeastern and central (Map 9-12). Local disjuncts in several states. Elevation: 300 to 3000 ft. Dry to mesic ravines, ridges, flatwoods, savannas, bottomlands, or upland on calcareous soils.

General Description

Bur oak is a medium-size to large tree 70 to 80 ft high and 2 to 3 ft dbh (max. 170 by 7 ft) with a massive trunk and broad crown of stout branches. On dry upland soils the root system is remarkably deep; the taproots of 8-year-old saplings may be more than 14 ft in length. Over its very extensive range, this oak is found mixed with numerous hardwoods on many types of soil from sandy plains to moist alluvial bottoms. Bur oak is noted for its resistance to drought; invading the grasslands of the prairies and Great Plains, it may form extensive open, parklike stands.

Besides its value as a timber producer, the distinctive leaves, fringed acorns, and corky twigs make it a popular ornamental; it is also more resistant to city smoke and gas injury than most other oaks.

Quércus lyràta Walt.   Overcup oak

Distinguishing Characteristics (Figs. 9-38 and 9-39)

Leaves deciduous, 5 to 8 in. (13 to 20 cm) long, 1½ to 4 in. (4 to 10 cm) wide; *shape* oblong-obovate; *margin* entire and very variable, mostly with 5 to 9 lobes separated by broad irregular sinuses; *apex* acute; *base* cuneate; *surfaces* dark green and glabrous above, green and nearly glabrous, or silvery white and downy below; *fall color* yellow, red, or brown.

Fruit solitary or paired, sessile or stalked; *nut* ½ to 1 in. (1.2 to 2.5 cm) long, the diameter usually greater than the length, subglobose to ovoid, two-thirds to almost entirely enclosed in a deep, thin, unfringed cup.

FIGURE 9-38   *Quercus lyrata.* Overcup oak. (1) Bark. (2) Twig × 1¼. (3) Acorn × 1. (4) Leaf × ½.

FIGURE 9-39   Leaf variation in one tree of overcup oak.

Twigs slender, gray; *terminal buds* about ⅛ in. (3 mm) long; ovoid to globose, and covered with light chestnut-brown, somewhat tomentose scales; stipules often persistent near the tip of the twig.

Bark somewhat similar to that of *Q. alba,* but brownish gray and rough, with large irregular plates or ridges; trunk frequently with a twisted appearance.

Range
Southeastern (Map 9-13). Disjuncts in central Tennessee and northwestern Georgia. Elevation: sea level to 500 ft. River banks, floodplains, adjacent lower slopes, and swamp edges.

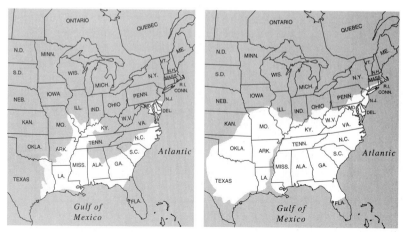

MAP 9-13 **(Left)** *Quercus lyrata.* **(Right)** *Quercus stellata.*

General Description

Overcup oak perhaps more nearly resembles bur oak than any other associated species, because of its deeply cupped acorns and somewhat similar leaves. It is usually of poor form with a short, often crooked or twisted bole and a large, open crown with crooked branches and relatively few smaller branchlets. Overcup oak may attain a height of 126 ft and a dbh of 7 ft, but it is commonly much smaller.

This species is not abundant or important except in the main bottomlands of the lower Mississippi and the lower valleys of its tributaries. Here overcup oak is one of the most common swampland trees growing on wet, poorly drained clay soils, and it is better adapted to withstand prolonged inundation than most of the accompanying species. Common associates are water hickory, willow and Nuttall oaks, American and cedar elms, green ash, water locust, persimmon, sugarberry, water tupelo, and baldcypress.

Overcup acorns are often disseminated by flood waters and, unlike most others of the white oaks, may remain dormant until spring when the waters recede. Its seedlings, however, may be killed by prolonged inundation. Although overcup oak usually produces timber of poor quality, it merits consideration because of its abundance over large areas and its ability to grow on the poorest of the bottomland sites.

Quércus stellàta Wangenh.   Post oak

Distinguishing Characteristics (Fig. 9-40)

Leaves deciduous, thick, somewhat leathery, 4 to 6 in. (10 to 15 cm) long, 3 to 4 in. (7.5 to 10 cm) wide; *shape* oblong-obovate; *margin* entire and usually deeply 5-lobed, the two middle lobes squarish, nearly opposite and at right angles to the midrib, giving the leaf a cruciform appearance; *apex* rounded; *base* cuneate; *surfaces* dark green with scattered stellate-pubescence above, tawny tomentose below; *fall color* brown, yellow, or red.

Fruit solitary or paired, sessile or short-stalked; *nut* ½ to 1 in. (1.2 to 2.5 cm) long, ovoid-oblong, sometimes slightly striped, smooth or pubescent at the apex; enclosed

FIGURE 9-40   *Quercus stellata.* Post oak. (1) Twig × 1¼. (2) Acorn × 1. (3) Leaf × ½. (4) Bark.

for about one-third of its length in a bowl-shaped cup with thin scales (less often warty like those of white oak).

Twigs somewhat tawny-tomentose; *terminal buds* about ⅛ in. (3 mm) long, subglobose to broadly ovoid, covered with chestnut-brown pubescent scales.

Bark similar to that of *Q. alba* but darker often reddish brown and with more definite longitudinal ridges and less scaly.

Range
Southeastern (Map 9-13). Elevation: sea level to 3000 ft. Upland dry ridges to more mesic flatwoods.

General Description
Unlike the two preceding species, post oak is typically found on dry, gravelly or sandy soils and on rocky ridges. It is a small to medium-size tree 40 to 50 ft high and 12 to 24 in. dbh (max. 105 by 5 ft), but it may attain only shrubby proportions under adverse conditions. The crown usually consists of fewer large branches than in white oak, and they are characteristically gnarled or somewhat twisted in appearance. The associates of post oak on the so-called barrens or in sand-plain country include black, blackjack, and scarlet oaks, upland hickories, pitch and shortleaf pines, and eastern redcedar. Post oak is an intolerant species of very slow height growth which survives and reproduces in part because of its great drought resistance. Post oak is susceptible to the chestnut blight fungus (*Cryphonectria parasitica*), which has caused considerable damage in some localities.

The common name *scrub oak* is frequently used collectively for several species of oaks (*Q. stellata, Q. margarettiae, Q. laevis, Q. marilandica, Q. incana*) which form an often dense, scrubby layer under a canopy of longleaf or slash pine, particularly when fire is excluded for many years.

On the driest, deepest sands or occasionally loamy soil is another species, closely related to post oak, ***Q. margarétiae*** Ashe ex Small or sometimes considered as *Q. stellata* var. *margarettiae* (Ashe ex Small) Sarg. Sand post oak is distinguished by glabrous or puberulent twigs, smaller leaves with lobes more rounded and less cruciform, acorn cup scales generally thinner, and winter buds larger and more acute. It is found from southeastern Virginia, south to Florida, west to central Texas, and north to Missouri.

In the lower Mississippi Valley on the silty loam soils of the second bottoms or terraces is the closely related delta post oak, ***Q. símilis*** Ashe (*Q. stellata* var. *paludosa* Sarg.) with puberulent twigs and less cruciform leaves. The usual associates of this bottomland form include several other oaks (*Q. michauxii, Q. lyrata, Q. alba, Q. nigra, Q. pagoda*), sweetgum, elms, ashes, hickories, and occasionally loblolly pine.

Quércus douglásii Hook. & Arn.   Blue oak; mountain white oak

Distinguishing Characteristics.   *Leaves* deciduous, blue-green, oblong to oval, 1¼ to 4 in. (3 to 10 cm) long, ¾ to 1¾ in. (2 to 4.5 cm) wide, with entire, sinuate and/or toothed to lobed margins. *Fruits* ¾ to 1¼ in. (2 to 3 cm) with shallow, bowl-like cups (Fig. 9-41).

Range.   Northern to southern California in the Coast Ranges and Sierras. Elevation: 3000 to 3500 ft. Low valleys and foothills where it forms pure groves or mixed forests with digger pine and several other oaks.

General Description.   Mature trees may exceed a height of 80 ft and dbh of 30 in., but they are usually much smaller. The geographical range has been reduced by clearing in recent years, and the remaining woodlands show poor reproduction. It is used locally for fuel and fenceposts.

Quércus garryàna Dougl. ex Hook.   Oregon white oak

Distinguishing Characteristics (Fig. 9-42)

Leaves deciduous, 3 to 6 in. (7.5 to 15 cm) long, 2 to 4 in. (5 to 10 cm) wide; *shape* oblong to obovate; *margin* entire, with 5 to 7 rounded lobes separated by moderately deep sinuses, often more or less revolute; *surfaces* lustrous dark green and glabrous above, pale green and with orange-brown pubescence below; *petiole* ca. ¾ in. (18 mm) long, stout, pubescent; *fall color* red.

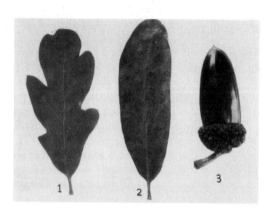

FIGURE 9-41   *Quercus douglasii.* Blue oak. (1, 2) Leaf variation × 1. (3) Acorn × 1.

FIGURE 9-42   *Quercus garryana.* Oregon white oak. (1) Twig × 1¼. (2) Leaf × ½. (3) Acorn × 1.

Fruit solitary or paired, sessile or short-stalked; *nut* 1 to 1¼ in. (2.5 to 3 cm) long, ovoid to obovoid, light brown, enclosed only at the base in a shallow bowl-like cup with pubescent or tomentose free-tipped scales.

Twigs stout, orange-red, densely pubescent during the first winter; *buds* ¼ to ½ in. (6 to 13 mm) long, covered with rusty-brown tomentum.

Bark (Fig. 9-43) smooth on young stems; on old trunks broken up into thin, gray-brown or gray scaly ridges, separated by narrow, shallow fissures.

Range

Northwestern (Map 9-14). Elevation: sea level to 3000 ft northward, 1000 to 5000 ft southward. Dry, rocky slopes or alluvial soils.

General Description

This, the only oak indigenous to the Pacific Northwest, is a medium-size tree seldom more than 50 to 70 ft high and 2 to 3 ft dbh (max. 120 by 8 ft). The bole, even under forest conditions, is usually short and rather crooked. It rises above a well-developed lateral root system and merges into a wide-spreading, round-topped crown. Oregon white oak grows on almost any kind of soil, commonly on hot, dry, grassy but rocky slopes in a region where rainfall averages 35 in. annually. Best development is attained on the alluvial soils of Washington and Oregon. There, limited pure stands are found, but the tree usually occurs as an individual or in small groves mixed with such species as Douglas-fir, ponderosa and digger pines, California black oak, and Pacific madrone.

FIGURE 9-43
Bark of Oregon white oak.

MAP 9-14
Quercus garryana.

Large crops of seeds are produced every few years, but reproduction by this means is usually poor, owing to the inability of the germinating seeds to penetrate the heavy sods on which they are so frequently disseminated. Stump sprouts and root suckers are vigorous, and these afford the best means of natural regeneration. Growth is slow. Trees 3 ft dbh may be 250 years old, but a life span of 500 years may be attained. This oak is usually rated as intolerant and eventually dies when overtopped by Douglas-fir.

It is the most important of the western oaks, and it is used for furniture, construction lumber, cabinetwork, interior trim, fenceposts, locally for fuel, and as an ornamental.

Quércus lobàta Née   Valley oak; California white oak

Distinguishing Characteristics.   *Leaves* deciduous, 2 to 4 in. (5 to 10 cm) long, 1¼ to 2½ in. (3 to 6 cm) wide, oblong, elliptical, or obovate, 7- to 11-lobed, both surfaces finely pubescent. *Fruit* 1¼ to 2¼ in. (3 to 6 cm) long, elongated-conic, one-third enclosed in a deep bowl-like cup, the cup scales free at their tips and forming a fringe about the cup. *Twigs* slender, pubescent. *Bark* with the appearance of alligator leather.

Range.   Northern to southern California, from the Sierra Nevada Mountains to the Coast Ranges. Elevation: mostly below 2000 ft, but occasionally to 5000 ft. Valleys and slopes.

General Description.   This white oak is largely restricted to low valley sites in western California. It is the largest of California oaks and attains a height of 90 to 125 ft or more and a dbh of 3 to 5 ft (max. 139 by 10 ft). Through the central portion of the state it forms nearly pure open groves. The bole is usually short, but massive, and merges into a large widespread hemispherical to subglobose crown with the ends of the branches drooping. Best development is reached on deep rich loams, although the tree also occurs on poor, dry, sandy, and gravelly sites.

This tree grows with greater rapidity than any other California oak and usually attains large size in a comparatively short time. The oldest trees are commonly defective (heart rot being quite prevalent) and hence are of little value except for fuel. Ring counts of large stumps indicate that an age of more than 200 to 250 years is rarely attained. Because of large-scale clearing, the range has been dramatically reduced in recent years.

Quércus gambélii Nutt.   Gambel oak; Rocky mountain white oak

Distinguishing Characteristics. *Leaves* deciduous, elliptical or oblong, rounded at apex, acute at base, deeply 5- to 9-lobed, 2 to 6 in. (5 to 15 cm) long, 1¼ to 3¼ in. (3 to 8 cm) wide; shiny dark green above, paler below with soft pubescence; fall color yellow or reddish. *Fruit* short-stalked, ½ to ⅞ in. (1.2 to 2.1 cm) long, oval, with thick, scaly cup enclosing ¼ to ⅓ of the nut.

Range. Northern Utah, east to southern Wyoming and western Oklahoma, south to western Texas, west to southern Arizona; local disjunct in southern Nevada. Elevation: 5000 to 8000 ft. Slopes and valleys in the foothills.

General Description. Tree 20 to 70 ft tall with rounded crown forming dense groves, or a thicket-forming shrub on dry slopes and valleys, in mountains, foothills, and plateaus. It is the common oak in the Rockies and a frequent associate of ponderosa pine. It was named for its discoverer, William Gambel, a naturalist from Philadelphia who made important collections in the southern Rockies in the 1840s.

Chestnut Oaks

Deciduous; leaves crenate, coarsely toothed, or sinuate; eastern species (Table 9-14).

Quércus michaùxii Nutt. (*Quercus prinus* L. sensu some authors)   Swamp chestnut oak; cow oak; basket oak

Distinguishing Characteristics (Fig. 9-44)

Leaves deciduous, 4 to 9 in. (10 to 23 cm) long, 2 to 5½ in. (5 to 14 cm) wide; *shape* broadly obovate to oblong-obovate; *margin* deeply crenate to coarsely dentate, often with large glandular-tipped teeth; *apex* acute or slightly obtuse; *base* cuneate; *surfaces* dark green and lustrous above, pale green to silvery white and pubescent below; *fall color* dark red or brown.

TABLE 9-14   COMPARISON OF IMPORTANT CHESTNUT OAKS

Species	Leaves	Fruit
Q. michauxii swamp chestnut oak	obovate, crenate-dentate	sessile or nearly so, cup thick, the scales wedge-shaped
Q. prinus chestnut oak	elliptical or nearly so, crenate	long-stalked, cup thin, the scales more or less fused

FIGURE 9-44   *Quercus michauxii.* Swamp chestnut oak. (1) Twig × 1¼. (2) Acorn × 1. (3) Leaf × ½. (4) Bark.

Fruit solitary or paired, sessile or nearly so; *nut* 1 to 1½ in. (2.5 to 4 cm) long, ovoid to oblong, enclosed for not more than a third of its length in a thick bowl-shaped cup, with distinct, somewhat wedge-shaped scales.

Twigs moderately stout, reddish brown to orange-brown; *terminal buds* ¼ in. (6 mm) long, acute, covered with thin, red, puberulous scales, pale on the margin.

Bark irregularly furrowed or scaly, ashy gray, tinged with red; freshly cut surfaces reddish brown.

Range
Southeastern (Map 9-15). Disjuncts in northeastern Tennessee and southern Kentucky. Elevation: sea level to 1000 ft. Bottomlands, ravine slopes, flatwoods over limestone.

General Description
Swamp chestnut oak is probably the most important species of this group. It is a well-formed tree with a straight massive trunk and narrow crown, averaging 60 to 80 ft tall and 2 to 3 ft dbh (max. 152 by 9 ft). This oak, at least in the lower Mississippi Valley, is somewhat irregular in occurrence, but when present, it is frequently abundant.

Swamp chestnut oak is found on the best, relatively well-drained, loamy ridges and silty clay and loamy terraces in bottomlands. Principal associates are cherrybark, Shumard, white, and delta post oaks and blackgum; other bottomland hardwoods are also present.

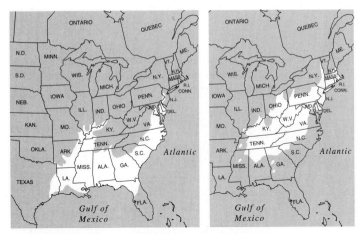

MAP 9-15 **(Left)** *Quercus michauxii.* **(Right)** *Quercus prinus.*

The quality of the wood is second only to that of the best white oaks, and for this reason, the tree has suffered excessive cutting in many localities; the name "basket oak" undoubtedly originated from its use for basket splits.

Quércus prìnus L. (*Quercus montana* Willd.)   Chestnut oak; rock oak

Distinguishing Characteristics (Fig. 9-45)

Leaves deciduous, 4 to 8 in. (10 to 20 cm) long, 1½ to 4 in. (4 to 10 cm) wide; *shape* obovate to elliptical, or nearly lanceolate; *margin* coarsely crenate, or repand-crenate; *apex* rounded; *base* cuneate; *surfaces* yellowish green and lustrous above, paler and often finely pubescent below; *fall color* yellow to orange.

Fruit solitary or paired, stalked; *nut* ¾ to 1⅜ in. (2 to 3.5 cm) long, ovoid to ellipsoidal, very lustrous, enclosed at the base, or more often from one-half to one-third of its length, in a thin cup with somewhat fused scales; inner surface of the cup only moderately curved vertically.

Twigs orange to reddish brown; *terminal buds* ¼ in. (6 mm) long, usually acute or acuminate, covered with bright chestnut-brown scales.

Bark brownish gray to nearly black, on older trees very deeply and coarsely furrowed.

Range

Northeastern (Map 9-15). Elevation: 1500 to 5000 ft. Xeric, rocky ridges and upper slopes, also more mesic sites.

General Description

Chestnut oak is a medium-size tree 50 to 60 ft tall and 2 ft dbh (max. 100 by 7 ft). It is found typically on poor dry upland rocky sites where it may form pure stands. On somewhat better soils, common associates include white and pitch pines, eastern redcedar, white, scarlet, and black oaks, sweetgum, red maple, and numerous other hardwoods.

FIGURE 9-45   *Quercus prinus (Q. montana).* Chestnut oak. (1) Twig × 1¼. (2) Leaf × ½. (3) Acorn cup showing thin wall × 1. (4) Acorn × 1. (5) Bark.

Chestnut oak can produce many stump and root collar sprouts which are initially capable of very rapid growth, and much of its regeneration on cutover or burned land is of sprout origin. Best growth is made in well-drained coves and other moist sites. The bark of chestnut oak contains about 11 percent tannin.

The name *Q. prinus* L. is now completely confused in the botanical and ecological literature because it has been used for both chestnut oak and swamp chestnut oak for many years by various authors. It is safer to use *Q. montana* and *Q. michauxii* for these, or at least give the common name when using *Q. prinus* (Hardin, 1979b).

Quércus bicolor Willd.   Swamp white oak

Distinguishing Characteristics (Fig. 9-46).   *Leaves* deciduous, 4 to 7 in. (10 to 18 cm) long, 2 to 4½ in. (5 to 11 cm) wide, obovate, shallowly lobed or coarsely toothed; fall color red. *Fruit* ¾ to 1¼ in. (2 to 3 cm) long, usually paired, borne on a slender peduncle. *Twigs* straw-brown, dull, terminal buds ¹⁄₁₆ to ⅛ in. (2 to 3 mm) long, orange-brown, essentially glabrous. *Bark* on the upper limbs peeling off in ragged, papery scales; deeply furrowed below into flat scaly ridges or blocky, dark brown.

Range.   Southern Ontario, east to southern Quebec and southern Maine, south to northern Virginia, west to Missouri, north to southeastern Minnesota; local disjuncts in North and South Carolina, Tennessee, southern Missouri, and northeastern Kansas. Elevation: sea level to 1000 ft, locally to 2000 ft. Low, wet bottomlands, edge of swamps and streams.

General Description.   Swamp white oak is a medium-size tree 60 to 70 ft high and 2 to 3 ft dbh (max. 100 by 7 ft), often with a poorly pruned bole and irregular crown. This species is not abundant except locally where it occurs along stream banks or on moist or peaty flats and along

FIGURE 9-46   *Quercus bicolor.* Swamp white oak. (1) Tip of twig × 1¼. (2) Leaf × ½. (3) Acorn × 1. (4) Bark.

swamp margins. It is highly tolerant of poorly aerated soils. When present at all, the supply may be large, and even though the quality of the timber is often inferior, it is harvested and used with that of the other white oaks.

Quércus muehlenbérgii Engelm.   Chinkapin oak

Distinguishing Characteristics (Fig. 9-47).   *Leaves* deciduous, 4 to 6 in. (10 to 15 cm) long, 1½ to 3 in. (4 to 7.5 cm) wide, obovate to oblong-lanceolate, coarsely serrate with glandular-tipped teeth; *fall color* reddish. *Fruit* sessile or short stalked, ½ to 1 in. (1.2 to 2.5 cm) long, with a thin bowl-shaped cup. *Twigs* slender, orange-brown, terminal buds ⅛ in. (3 mm) long, orange-brown. *Bark* ashy gray, more or less rough and flaky.

Range.   Southern Michigan and southern Ontario, east to western Vermont, south to northwestern Florida, west to central Texas, north to Iowa and southern Wisconsin; local disjuncts in southeastern New Mexico and western Texas. Elevation: 400 to 3000 ft. Limestone outcrops and calcareous soils, dry slopes or bluffs, moist bottomlands, and river banks.

General Description.   This oak is rare over most of its range and hence is of little commercial value. It is usually a small to medium-size tree found on dry limestone outcrops and alkaline soils. In the Ohio and Mississippi valleys, it is found on moist soils in the higher bottoms; here it averages 60 to 80 ft tall and 2 to 3 ft dbh (max. 160 by 6 ft).

Live Oaks

Evergreen; leaves usually unlobed; eastern and western species of the white oaks.

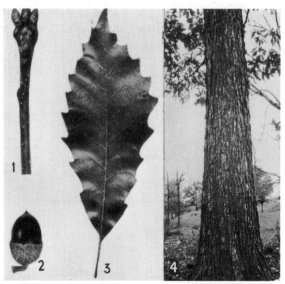

FIGURE 9-47   *Quercus muehlenbergii.* Chinkapin oak. (1) Twig × 1¼. (2) Acorn × 1. (3) Leaf × ½. (4) Bark.

Quércus virginiàna Mill.   Live oak

Distinguishing Characteristics (Fig. 9-48)

Leaves persistent until the following spring; ¾ to 5 in. (2 to 13 cm) long, ⅜ to 2 in. (1 to 5 cm) wide; *shape* oblong, elliptical, or rarely obovate; *margin* usually entire (sometimes sparingly toothed) and very slightly revolute; *apex* obtuse; *base* cuneate or acute; *surfaces* dark glossy green above, paler below and densely covered with fused-stellate hairs which are closely appressed to the surface and barely obvious even with a handlens.

Fruit usually in clusters of 2 to 5 on a peduncle of varying length; maturing in one season; *nut* ⅝ to 1 in. (1.5 to 2.5 cm) long, dark brown to nearly black, ellipsoidal, one-third enclosed in a turbinate cup; seed sweet.

Bark dark reddish brown, slightly furrowed, with small surface scales.

Range

Southeastern (Map 9-16). Local disjuncts in southern Oklahoma. Elevation: sea level to 300 ft and to 2000 ft in Texas. Mixed low woodlands, hammocks, borders of salt marshes, coastal dunes, and maritime forests.

General Description

This species is generally considered to be the only important "live oak" of eastern North America, although laurel oak holds its leaves so late in the spring that they are almost evergreen. Live oak is usually a medium-size tree 40 to 50 ft high and 3 to 4 ft dbh. The short, enlarged, but-

FIGURE 9-48   *Quercus virginiana.* Live oak. (1) Leaves × ½. (2) Acorns × 1. (3) Bark.

tressed trunk, sometimes 6 to 8 ft through (max. 78 by 11 ft), divides into three or four wide-spreading, horizontal branches; the crown is close, round-topped, and in the largest open-grown trees may be upward of 125 to 150 ft across (Fig. 9-49).

Live oak is a dry sand-plain species but found on a variety of sites including hammocks. On moist locations, some common associates are southern magnolia, redbay, sweetgum, American holly, laurel and water oaks, and hickories.

Live oak is extremely difficult to kill. When a tree is cut or girdled, numerous sprouts spring up from the root collar and surface roots. When these sprouts are cut, many more appear.

When grown ornamentally, especially on rich soils, growth is fast, and one tree in Georgia reported by Coker and Totten (1945) attained a diameter of about 4½ ft in less than 70 years. Although very large trees are supposed to be many centuries old, studies have shown that the largest specimens now standing are about 200 to 300 years of age.

Certain individual trees yield acorns much sweeter and more edible than others, and it is said that the Native Americans produced an oil somewhat comparable to olive oil from them.

The wood is exceedingly strong and one of the heaviest of native woods. During the era of "wooden ships and iron men" it was utilized in building frigates and other naval vessels. The

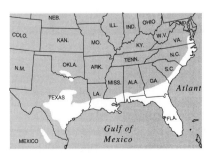

MAP 9-16   *Quercus virginiana* and *Q. geminata.*

FIGURE 9-49 Live oak showing typical spreading form of an old, open-grown tree. (*Courtesy of U.S. Forest Service.*)

earliest planting and intensive management of forest trees for timber in North America centered around this naval demand for ships' knees from live oaks.

Quércus geminàta Small   Sand live oak

The sand live oak, sometimes considered *Q. virginiana* var. *geminata* (Small) Sarg., is distinguished from *Q. virginiana* by a more revolute leaf margin, the lower surface with more raised and conspicuous fused-stellate hairs, reticulate venation conspicuous above, and flowering 2 to 3 weeks later than *Q. virginiana* in the same area. It is the common form of live oak on coastal dunes along the Atlantic and Gulf coasts and inland areas in central Florida on light-colored sands. It occurs from southeastern North Carolina to central Florida and west to southeastern Louisiana (Map 9-16).

Quércus arizónica Sarg.   Arizona white oak

This tree with persistent, spinose, blue-green leaves (Fig. 9-50), 1½ to 3 in. (4 to 7.5 cm) long, and plated bark is common to moist benches and canyon walls in the southwest. Under favorable growing conditions it attains a height of 40 to 60 ft and a dbh of 24 to 36 in. and develops a short trunk which supports a massive round-topped crown. It is usually dwarfed at timberline. Arizona white oak ranges through southern New Mexico and Arizona and northern Mexico between elevations of 5000 to 10,000 ft.

Quércus oblongifòlia Torr.   Mexican blue oak

This is a small tree rarely attaining a height of more than 30 ft and a dbh of 30 in. It occurs in association with *Q. arizonica* and *Q. emoryi,* and its foliage (Fig. 9-50), 1 to 2 in. (2.5 to 5 cm)

FIGURE 9-50   Leaves of southwestern evergreen oaks × ½. (1) *Quercus emoryi*, Emory oak. (2) *Q. arizonica*, Arizona white oak. (3) *Q. oblongifolia*, Mexican blue oak.

long, usually entire and blue-green, is a source of forage for range stock. It is somewhat more restricted in elevation, however, and rarely occurs over 6000 ft. This southwestern tree is found in extreme western Texas, southwestern New Mexico, southeastern Arizona, and into northern Mexico.

True Red and Black Oaks

Deciduous or tardily so; leaves lobed with bristle tips; eastern and western species (Table 9-15).

Quércus rùbra L.   Northern red oak

Distinguishing Characteristics (Fig. 9-51)

Leaves deciduous; 4 to 9 in. (10 to 23 cm) long, 3 to 6 in. (7.5 to 15 cm) wide; *shape* oblong to obovate; *margin* with 7 to 11 often toothed lobes separated by regular *U*-shaped sinuses extending about halfway to the midrib; *apex* acute to acuminate; *base* obtuse to broadly cuneate; *surfaces* somewhat lustrous, or dull above, glabrous below except for occasional often inconspicuous axillary tufts; *fall color* dark red.

Fruit solitary or paired; *nut* ⅝ to 1⅛ in. (1.5 to 2.8 cm) long; variable in shape, but usually subglobose, enclosed at the base in a flat, thick, saucerlike cup; *cup scales* pubescent, their tips appreciably darkened.*

Twigs moderately stout, greenish brown to reddish brown, glabrous; *terminal buds* ¼ in. (6 mm) long, ovoid, pointed, terete, covered by numerous reddish-brown, more or less hairy scales.

Bark smooth on young stems, greenish brown; ultimately brown to nearly black and broken up into wide, flat-topped ridges, separated by shallow fissures; on very old trees more narrowly ridged or corrugated; inner bark light red or brownish red.

---

*Figure 9-51, parts. 3 and 4, show the variation to be expected in acorns from different trees. Previously, trees bearing the shallow-cup type were designated as a separate variety. Because intergradations are found, and the two forms do not appear to breed true, there seems to be no good reason for continuing to keep them separate.

TABLE 9-15   COMPARISON OF IMPORTANT TRUE RED AND BLACK OAKS

Species	Leaves	Fruit
Q. rubra northern red oak	oblong-obovate, 7- to 11-lobed, with narrow, regular sinuses; glabrous except for inconspicuous axillary tufts below	variable, but mostly subglobose, ⅝–1⅛ in. (1.5–2.8 cm) long; nut usually enclosed only at the base by a flat, thick, saucerlike cup
Q. velutina black oak	obovate to ovate, 5- to 7-lobed, with sinuses of varying depth; more or less scurfy and yellowish to copper-colored below; axillary tufts white to rufous	ovoid-oblong, ⅝–¾ in. (1.5–1.9 cm) long, nut ⅓ to ¼ enclosed in a bowl-like cup; cup scales dull (not shiny), free at the tips
Q. shumardii Shumard oak	obovate to oval, 7- to 9-lobed, with many bristle tips and moderately deep sinuses; glabrous except for axillary tufts below	oblong-ovoid, tapering toward the apex, ⅝–1⅛ in. (1.5–2.8 cm) long; nut enclosed only at the base by a flat, thick, saucerlike cup
Q. falcata southern red oak	polymorphic; lower crown leaves usually 3-lobed at apex; middle and upper crown foliage 5- to 7- (often falcate) lobed; grayish or rusty tomentose below	subglobose, ½–⅝ in. (1.2–1.5 cm) long; nut enclosed only at the base by a flat, saucerlike cup
Q. pagoda cherrybark oak	more or less uniformly 5- to 11-lobed, the lobes pointing outward	same as above
Q. coccinea scarlet oak	ovate to oval, deeply 5- to 9-lobed, the sinusus nearly circular; glabrous except for axillary tufts below	depressed-globose, ½–1 in. (1.2–2.5 cm) long, usually with several concentric rings below the apex; nut ½ enclosed in bowl-like cup with shiny, appressed scales
Q. palustris pin oak	same as *Q. coccinea* except the sinuses broadly *U*-shaped or squarish	hemispherical, ⅜–⅝ in. (0.9–1.5 cm) long; nut enclosed only at the base by a flat, saucerlike cup with free-tipped scales
Q. texana Nuttall oak	same except with yellowish axillary pubescence below	oblong-ovoid, ¾–1¼ in. (2–3 cm) long; nut ⅓ enclosed in a bowl-like cup

Range

Eastern (Map 9-17). Elevation: sea level to 5500 ft. Mesic, well-drained slopes, coves, and drier ridges.

General Description

This species, probably the most important and widespread of northern oaks, is a medium-size to large tree 60 to 80 ft high and 2 to 3 ft dbh (max. 160 by 8 ft). Although developing a short massive trunk with an extensive crown in the open, this tree when grown in the forest produces a tall, straight, columnar bole which supports a small rounded crown. The root system, although deep like that of many other oaks, is often lacking in a well-developed and persistent taproot which develops less rapidly than the laterals after the seedling stage.

FIGURE 9-51   *Quercus rubra.* Northern red oak. (1) Twig × 1¼. (2) Acorns at end of first season × 2. (3, 4) Variation in mature acorns × 1. (5) Leaf × ½. (6) Bark of young tree. (7) Bark of old tree.

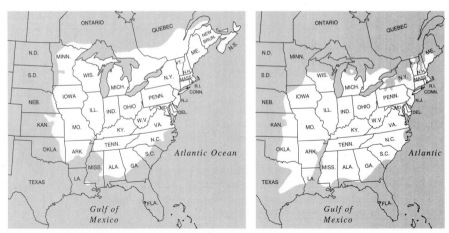

MAP 9-17 **(Left)** *Quercus rubra.* **(Right)** *Quercus velutina.*

Northern red oak may be found on sandy loam soils in mixture with other northern hardwoods and with white pine. Best development, however, is usually made on fine-textured, well-watered soils with good surface drainage, associated with such species as basswood, black cherry, ashes, hickories, other oaks, yellow-poplar, and sweetgum. Northern red oak forms nearly pure stands at high altitudes in the southern Appalachians, but it is also listed as a component in more than 20 forest-cover types, and therefore the number of associated species is very large. On a tolerance scale, this oak, like many others, is intermediate.

Good seed crops occur at 2- to 5-year intervals. Germination of red oak acorns does not take place until the following spring, and many of the acorns are destroyed by insects. Growth of seedlings is fast, and on the best soils nursery stock sometimes attains a height of nearly 3 ft the first season. This oak is also a prolific sprouter, both as a seedling and as a young tree, and quickly restocks cutover areas by this means. Although not so long-lived as white oak, this species may live up to two to three centuries.

Northern red oak is widely used as an ornamental because of comparative ease in transplanting, the autumnal coloration of the leaves, and the symmetrical form of the tree. The wood is used for flooring, furniture, railroad ties, posts, and pulp.

Quércus velùtina Lam.   Black oak

Distinguishing Characteristics (Fig. 9-52)

Leaves deciduous; 4 to 9 in. (10 to 23 cm) long, 3 to 6 in. (7.5 to 15 cm) wide; *shape* obovate to ovate; *margin* with 5 to 7 often toothed lobes separated by oval or *U*-shaped sinuses of variable depth; *apex* acute to acuminate; *base* broadly cuneate to nearly truncate,* *surfaces* exceedingly lustrous and dark green above, yellow-green to coppery-colored below, and more or less scurfy pubescent with conspicuous axillary tufts; *fall color* dark red.

*This species illustrates a characteristic of several of the red oak group: heteromorphic foliage. The narrow-lobed form (Fig. 9-52, part 3) is common in the upper crown of mature trees, while the broad-lobed form (Fig. 9-52, part 2) is common in the lower crown or on immature trees.

FIGURE 9-52 *Quercus velutina.* Black oak. (1) Twig × 1¼. (2, 3) Variation in leaf lobing × ½. (4) Variation in acorns × 1. (5) Bark.

Fruit solitary or paired; *nut* ⅝ to ¾ in. (1.5 to 1.9 cm) long, ovoid to hemispherical, often striated, light red-brown, one-fourth to one-third enclosed in a deep bowl-like cup; *cup scales* loosely imbricated above the middle, dull chestnut-brown, tomentose.

Twigs stout, reddish brown, glabrous; *terminal buds* ¼ to ½ in. (6 to 12 mm) long, ovoid, sharp-pointed, angular, covered with numerous, hoary tomentose scales.

Bark thick, nearly black on old stems, deeply furrowed vertically, and with many horizontal breaks; inner bark bright orange-yellow.

Range
Eastern (Map 9-17). Elevation: sea level to 5000 ft. Xeric, upland ridges and slopes, also mesic woodlands.

General Description
Black oak, a tree 50 to 60 ft high and 2 to 3 ft dbh (max. 150 by 8 ft), is one of the commonest of eastern upland oaks. Although making its best growth on moist, rich, well-drained soils, where it approaches red oak in stature, it is sensitive to competition on such sites and is found more often on poor, dry, sandy, or heavy glacial clay hillsides. Black oak is featured by a deep taproot, a somewhat tapering, often limby bole, and an irregularly rounded crown. It is intermediate in tolerance, and although pure stands may occur, this oak is usually found in mixture with a large number of other species. These include pignut and red hickories, post, scarlet, southern red, blackjack, and chestnut oaks, and less often white and red oaks. In the south it is commonly found in the shortleaf pine belt and occasionally in the bottoms, where it occupies the highest and best-drained areas with loblolly pine, southern red oak, and sweetgum.

Black oak is a persistent sprouter; good seed years may occur at 2- to 3-year intervals, although as with all oaks this periodicity can be very irregular. Growth is slower than in red oak but faster than in most other associated oaks; trees over 200 years old are rarely found.

Quércus shumárdii Buckl.   Shumard oak

Distinguishing Characteristics (Fig. 9-53)
Leaves deciduous; 3 to 8 in. (8 to 20 cm) long, 2½ to 5 in. (6 to 13 cm) wide; *shape* obovate to oval; *margin* with 5 to 9 lobes again divided near their ends and with many bristle tips, the lobes separated by moderately deep oval or *U*-shaped sinuses; *apex* acute to acuminate; *base* obtuse to nearly truncate; *surfaces* dark green and lustrous above, paler and glabrous below except for axillary tufts; *fall color* red or brown.

Fruit solitary or in pairs; *nut* ⅝ to 1¼ in. (1.5 to 3 cm) long, oblong-ovoid, slightly tapering toward the apex, enclosed at the base in a thick, shallow, saucer-shaped cup; *cup scales* appressed, pale pubescent or nearly glabrous.

Twigs slender to moderately stout, gray to grayish brown, glabrous; *terminal buds* ¼ in. (6 mm) long, ovoid, pointed, usually angled, covered by gray to gray-brown, downy, or nearly glabrous scales.

Bark on old trees very thick, broken into pale to whitish scaly ridges by deep, much darker-colored furrows.

Range
Eastern (Map 9-18). Disjuncts in southern Pennsylvania, western West Virginia, northeastern Tennessee, and northern Virginia. Elevation: sea level to 2500 ft. Mesic woodlands, hammocks, bluffs, ravines, river banks, and limestone hills.

General Description
This species, one of the largest of the southern red oaks, may attain a height of 100 to 125 ft and a dbh of 4 to 5 ft (max. 180 by 8 ft). A long, clear, symmetrical bole rises above a slightly but-

FIGURE 9-53 *Quercus shumardii.* Shumard oak. (1) Twig × 1¼. (2) Acorn × 1. (3) Leaf × ½. (4) Bark (*Courtesy of U.S. Forest Service.*)

tressed base and moderately shallow root system, while the crown is usually open and wide-spreading. The tree never occurs in pure stands but rather as an occasional individual or in small groves in mixture with other hardwoods, particularly swamp chestnut, cherrybark, and delta post oaks, black tupelo, green ash, and hickories. This oak will grow on a number of soil types, but it is mostly a bottomland species and develops best on river terraces and small-stream flood-plains. On such sites it may make very rapid radial growth. It is intolerant, and full light is needed for satisfactory reproduction. Its sparse distribution is somewhat puzzling but occurs

MAP 9-18 **(Left)** *Quercus shumardii.* **(Right)** *Quercus falcata.*

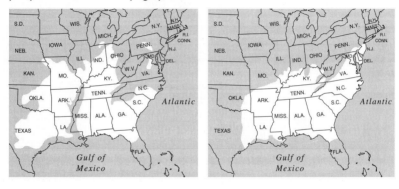

perhaps because it is shade-intolerant and has erratic regeneration. It grows to a large size in the Coastal Plain and Mississippi valley regions, but is nowhere very abundant.

It has been stated that the wood of this species is mechanically superior to that of many other red oaks. However, it is mixed with other red oak timbers and is not sold as Shumard oak.

Quércus falcàta Michx.   Southern red oak

Distinguishing Characteristics (Figs. 9-54 and 9-55)

Leaves deciduous; 4 to 9 in. (10 to 23 cm) long, 2 to 6 in. (5 to 15 cm) wide; *shape* obovate to ovate; *margin* either shallowly 3-lobed at the apex, or more or less deeply 5- to 7-lobed, often falcate, the terminal lobe much longer than the laterals; *apex* acuminate or falcate; *base* rounded, *U*-shaped, or rarely cuneate; *surfaces* dark lustrous green above, grayish green to tan and tomentose below, turning rusty upon drying; *fall color* red to brown.

Fruit solitary or paired; *nut* ½ to ⅝ in. (1.2 to 1.5 cm) long, subglobose, orange-brown, sometimes striated, more or less stellate pubescent, enclosed one-third or less in a thin, shallow cup; *cup scales* reddish brown, appressed, pubescent except on the margins.

Twigs dark red, pubescent, or nearly glabrous; *terminal buds* ⅛ to ¼ in. (3 to 6 mm) long, ovoid, acute with reddish-brown, puberulent scales.

FIGURE 9-54   *Quercus falcata.* Southern red oak. (1) Twig × 1¼. (2) Acorns × 1. (3) Leaf from upper part of large tree × ½. (4) Bark.

FIGURE 9-55   Trilobed leaf of young southern red oak.

Bark dark brown to nearly black, thick, the rough ridges separated by deep, narrow fissures; inner bark only slightly yellow (otherwise similar to that of *Q. velutina*).

Range
Eastern (Map 9-18). Elevation: sea level to 2500 ft. Well-drained, fertile, dry to mesic uplands.

General Description
This species is one of the most common of upland southern oaks and is particularly characteristic of the drier, poorer soils of the Piedmont region; it is rare in the bottomlands of the Mississippi Delta. However, throughout its range, the largest trees are found on fertile stream bottoms. Its occurrence in the various pine types of the Coastal Plains is sporadic. It is a medium-size tree 50 to 80 ft tall and 1 to 2½ ft dbh (max. 128 by 9 ft) with a deep root system, a short trunk, and an extensive rounded crown which even under forest conditions is composed of large branches. This oak is similar in its silvical features to black oak and is found with it and other dry-soil oaks and hickories, black tupelo, sweetgum, southern magnolia, and shortleaf and Virginia pines. It is used for lumber and fuel.

This species, even more than black oak, is characteristically heteromorphic. Leaves of saplings and the lower crown of older trees are trilobed near the apex (Fig. 9-55); those of the upper crown or throughout older trees are 5- to 7-lobed with a prolonged terminal lobe (Fig. 9-54).

Quércus pagòda Raf. (*Q. falcata* var. *pagodifolia* Ell.)   Cherrybark oak

Distinguishing Characteristics (Fig. 9-56)
Leaves more uniformly 5- to 11-, shallow-lobed than those of *Q. falcata,* with the margins of the lobes more nearly at right angles to the midrib; *base* broadly cuneate; *fall color* red.

Bark smooth, soon with narrow, flaky, or scaly ridges; otherwise similar to that of *Q. falcata.*

FIGURE 9-56 *Quercus pagoda.* Cherrybark oak. (1) Leaf × ½. (2) Acorn × 1. (3) Bark.

Range
Southeastern (Map 9-19). Elevation: sea level to ca. 800 ft. River banks, well-drained bottomlands, terraces, and slopes.

General Description
This oak is a more massive, better-formed tree than the southern red oak and often reaches heights of 100 to 130 ft and dbh of 3 to 5 ft (max. 130 by 9 ft), which classes it among the largest of southern oaks. The tree is found in a number of different bottomland types, but it develops best on well-drained loamy bottomland soils, where its associates include swamp chestnut oak, wetland hickories, green ash, and sweetgum. On higher ground, including the rich well-drained soil of old fields, to white ash and sweetgum may be added American beech, southern magnolia, black tupelo, yellow-poplar, and others.

Cherrybark oak has medium tolerance and is usually dominant or codominant in the stand. It is especially plentiful in the lower Mississippi Valley, and on account of its fast growth, clear bole, and the superior quality of the wood it has been rated as the best red oak of this region, and it is often used for furniture and trim.

Quércus coccínea Muenchh.   Scarlet oak

Distinguishing Characteristics (Fig. 9-57)
Leaves deciduous; 3 to 7 in. (7.5 to 18 cm) long, 2 to 5 in. (5 to 13 cm) wide; *shape* ovate, obovate, or oval; *margin* deeply 5- to 9-lobed, with wide nearly circular sinuses; *apex* acute to acuminate; *base* truncate to broadly cuneate; *surfaces* bright lustrous green above, paler and glabrous below except for axillary tufts; *fall color* scarlet.

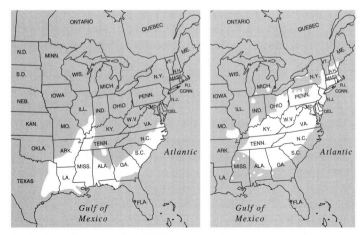

MAP 9-19   **(Left)** *Quercus pagoda.* **(Right)** *Quercus coccinea.*

FIGURE 9-57   *Quercus coccinea.* Scarlet oak. (1) Twig × 1¼. (2) Leaf × ½. (3) Acorn × 1. (4) Top of acorn showing concentric rings × 3. (5) Bark.

Fruit solitary or paired; *nut* ½ to 1 in. (1.2 to 2.5 cm) long, oval to hemispherical, or depressed-globose, reddish brown, rarely striated, usually with concentric rings near the apex, one-third to one-half enclosed in a deep bowl-like cup; *cup scales* appressed, reddish brown, lustrous.

Twigs slender, reddish brown, glabrous; *terminal buds* ⅛ to ¼ in. (3 to 6 mm) long, ovoid, often angled, covered by dark reddish-brown scales often pale pubescent above the center of the bud.

Bark on mature trees dark brown to nearly black, broken up into irregular ridges separated by shallow fissures of varying width; often flaky on the upper branches; otherwise similar to that of *Q. velutina,* except inner bark red.

Range

Eastern (Map 9-19). Disjuncts in southwestern Georgia, southern Alabama, southwestern Mississippi, northern Indiana, southern Michigan, western New York. Elevation: sea level to 5000 ft. Xeric uplands and slopes.

General Description

Scarlet oak is a medium-size tree 70 to 80 ft high and 2 to 3 ft dbh (max. 102 by 5 ft). Its ability to make rapid growth on dry soils of ridges and upper slopes makes it an important component of the climax forests of the Appalachians and eastward. In this region it may grow in nearly pure stands or in mixture with other oaks and hickories, also with pitch, shortleaf, and Virginia pines.

Scarlet oak is quite intolerant, and although its growth on good sites may rival that of yellow-poplar and red oak, it is usually excluded from such sites by more tolerant species. Though quite sensitive to the frequent fires on upland sites, it sprouts vigorously following fire. This oak is often used as an ornamental because of its general hardiness and brilliant autumnal leaf coloration. It may reach an age of nearly 400 years.

Quércus palústris Muenchh.   Pin oak

Distinguishing Characteristics (Fig. 9-58)

Leaves deciduous; 3 to 5 in. (7.5 to 13 cm) long, 2 to 4 in. (5 to 10 cm) wide; *shape* obovate to broadly oval; *margin* 5-, less commonly 7- to 9-lobed, with irregular wide to narrow often angled sinuses extending two-thirds or more to the midrib, the median lobes nearly perpendicular to the midrib; *apex* acute to acuminate; *base* truncate to broadly cuneate; *surfaces* bright green and lustrous above, paler below and glabrous except for axillary tufts; *fall color* red.

Fruit solitary or clustered; *nut* ⅜ to ⅝ in. (0.9 to 1.5 cm) long, nearly hemispherical, light brown, often striated, enclosed only at the base in a thin, saucerlike cup; *cup scales* appressed, red-brown, puberulent, dark-margined.

Twigs slender, lustrous, reddish brown; *terminal buds* ⅛ in. (3 mm) long, ovoid, acute, with reddish-brown scales.

Bark grayish brown, smooth for many years, eventually with low, scaly ridges separated by shallow fissures.

Range

Northeastern and Northcentral (Map 9-20). Disjuncts in southwestern Ontario, western Vermont, and central North Carolina. Elevation: sea level to 1000 ft. Wet to mesic bottomlands or upland flats.

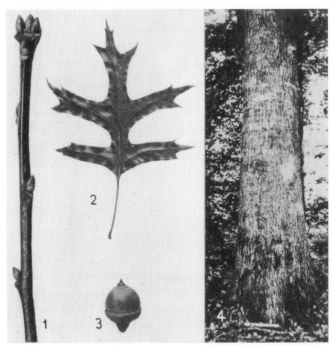

FIGURE 9-58   *Quercus palustris.* Pin oak. (1) Twig × 1¼. (2) Leaf × ½. (3) Acorn × 1. (4) Bark.

General Description

Pin oak is a medium-size tree 70 to 80 ft high and 2 to 3 ft dbh (max. 135 by 7 ft). The root system is shallower than in many of the other oaks and supports a trunk more or less studded with small tough branchlets which do not prune readily; these are also characteristic of the larger limbs; hence perhaps the common name "pin oak." The crown of open-grown trees is broadly pyramidal, with slightly drooping lower branches; together with the deeply cut leaves, this presents a very pleasing appearance, especially in the fall when autumnal coloration is at its height. These features recommend pin oak as an ornamental yard or street tree.

Pin oak makes good growth on wet clay flats, where water may stand for several weeks during late winter and spring. The prolific mast produced on such sites is an important game food, particularly for waterfowl. It is also found on better-drained soils in the bottoms, but here its

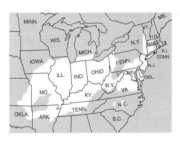

MAP 9-20   *Quercus palustris.*

intolerance gives other species an advantage. Common associates include sweetgum, overcup and bur oaks, elms, green ash, and red maple.

Quércus ellipsoidàlis E. J. Hill   Northern pin oak; jack oak

Distinguishing Characteristics.   Very similar to those of pin oak except for the ellipsoidal acorn one-third to one-half enclosed in a deep bowl-shaped cup.

Range.   Southern Manitoba and Minnesota, east to northcentral Wisconsin, and central Michigan, south into northwestern Ohio, northern Indiana, northern Illinois, and Iowa. Elevation: 600 to 1300 ft. Dry, upland woods, near ponds, and along streams.

General Description.   This is a medium-size tree reaching 65 ft tall and 3 ft dbh. The wood is hard, heavy, and strong and used for flooring and furniture.

Quércus texàna Buckley (*Q. nuttallii* Palmer)   Nuttall oak

Distinguishing Characteristics

Leaves deciduous; 4 to 8 in. (10 to 20 cm) long, 2 to 5 in. (5 to 13 cm) wide; *shape* obovate; *margin* usually 5- to 7- (rarely 9-) lobed, lobes rather broad, separated by deep sinuses; *apex* acute to acuminate; *base* truncate to broadly cuneate; *surfaces* dull, dark green above, paler below, glabrous except for axillary tufts; *fall color* brown.

Fruit (Fig. 9-59) solitary or clustered; *nut* ¾ to 1¼ in. (2 to 3 cm) long, oblong-ovoid, reddish brown, often striated, one-fourth to one-half enclosed in a stalked, deep, thick cup; *cup scales* appressed, or free at the rim.

Twigs moderately slender, gray-brown to reddish brown, glabrous; *terminal buds* nearly ¼ in. (6 mm) long, ovoid, slightly angled, with numerous gray-brown, glabrous or slightly downy scales (similar to those of *Q. shumardii*).

Bark dark gray-brown, smooth; on older trees broken into broad flat ridges divided by narrow lighter-colored fissures (similar to that of pin oak).

Range

Southcentral (Map 9-21). Disjuncts in southeastern Oklahoma and eastern Texas. Elevation: sea level to 500 ft. Poorly drained alluvial woodlands of river and stream bottoms.

General Description

When Thomas Nuttall explored the Arkansas bottomlands more than a century ago, he listed among other species *Q. coccinea,* scarlet oak. Not until 1927 was it discovered that what he presumed to be this tree was probably the species which now is called Nuttall oak. The species,

FIGURE 9-59   Acorn of *Quercus texana,* Nuttall oak × ¾.

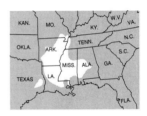

MAP 9-21 *Quercus texana.*

long called *Q. nuttallii,* is now considered the same as *Q. texana* and when combined, the latter name has priority over the former (Dorr and Nixon, 1985).

Nuttall oak is a medium-size tree attaining, however, in virgin stands a height of 100 to 120 ft and a dbh of 5 ft. It is commercially important for railroad ties, fuel, and charcoal, and is one of the few noteworthy species found on poorly drained clay flats in the first river bottoms. Its very rapid growth on such sites and the ability of its seedlings to tolerate some shade recommend its intensive management for lumber production. Reproduction is consistently good, and second-growth trees reach merchantable size (2 ft dbh) in about 70 years. The common associates include sweetgum, American elm, green ash, red maple, and overcup, willow, and water oaks. It is often used as an ornamental.

Quércus marilándica Muenchh.   Blackjack oak

Distinguishing Characteristics (Fig. 9-60).   *Leaves* deciduous, coriaceous, 2½ to 5 in. (6 to 13 cm) long, 2 to 4 in. (5 to 10 cm) wide, variable but typically obovate, and shallowly 3-lobed at the apex; lustrous above, tawny pubescent below; fall color yellow or brown. *Fruit* ⅝ to ¾ in. (15 to 19 mm) long, oblong, one-half enclosed in a thick bowl-shaped cup with loose, red-

FIGURE 9-60   *Quercus marilandica.* Blackjack oak. (1) Twig × 1¼. (2) Acorns × 1. (3) Leaf × ½. (4) Bark.

dish-brown scales. *Twigs* stout, somewhat scurfy-pubescent; buds often more than ¼ in. (6 mm) long, angled, similar to those of *Q. velutina* but usually more reddish brown and more rounded in cross section. *Bark* black, very rough, and "blocky."

Range.   Long Island, New Jersey, and central Pennsylvania, south to northwestern Florida, west to southeastern and central Texas, north to southern Iowa. Elevation: near sea level to 3000 ft. Open, dry woodlands, ridges, slopes, and sandy flatwoods.

General Description.   Blackjack oak is a small, poorly formed tree characteristic of dry, sterile soils where it is associated in open mixtures with such species as post, black, and southern red oaks, mockernut hickory, and eastern redcedar. It is not common in the north, but very abundant southward, and in the southeast comprises a large part of the forest growth on the poorest of sites. Although of value chiefly as a cover crop, this oak is utilized locally as mine props, fuel, charcoal, and railroad ties.

Quércus laèvis Walt.   Turkey oak

Distinguishing Characteristics (Fig. 9-61).   *Leaves* deciduous, 4 to 8 in. (10 to 20 cm) long, 3 to 6 in. (7.5 to 15 cm) wide, very variable in size and shape, commonly much dissected and with 3 to 5(7) spreading, slender, falcate lobes; lustrous above, glabrous below except for axillary tufts; fall color red. *Fruit* ¾ to 1 in. (2 to 2.5 cm) long, oval, one-third enclosed in a thin bowl-shaped and top-shaped cup, with the scales extending slightly over the rim. *Twigs* stout, usually glabrous; buds to ½ in. (13 mm) long, narrow and tapering, rusty pubescent above the middle. *Bark* rough, on old trees nearly black.

Range.   Coastal Plain from southeastern Virginia to central Florida and west to southeastern Louisiana. Elevation: near sea level to 500 ft. Well-drained sandy ridges and flatwoods.

General Description.   Turkey oak is a small tree found in the coastal pine belt of the south. The leaves are very distinctive and are not readily mistaken for those of other associated species. The plane surfaces of the leaves are oriented more-or-less vertically, an adaptation to the hot sun and highly reflective, white, sandy soil.

FIGURE 9-61   *Quercus laevis.* Turkey oak. (1) Leaf × ½. (2) Twig × 1¼. (3) Acorn × 1.

FIGURE 9-62   *Quercus kelloggii.* California black oak. (1) Leaf × ⅓. (2) Acorn × 1.

Quércus kellóggii Newb.   California black oak

Distinguishing Characteristics (Fig. 9-62). *Leaves* deciduous, 5- to 7-lobed, 3 to 8 in. (7.5 to 20 cm) long, 2 to 5 in. (5 to 13 cm) wide, elliptical, dark green above and pale pubescent below; fall color yellow. *Acorn* oblong-ellipsoidal, 1 to 1½ in. (2.5 to 4 cm) long, with deep bowl-like cups. *Bark* gray to black and deeply fissured.

Range. McKenzie River basin in central Oregon, south over the Cascade and Siskiyou Mountains, along the Coast Ranges and western slopes of the Sierra to southern California near the Mexican border. Elevation: 1000 to 8000 ft. Dry sandy and gravelly soils of canyon floors, benches, and moist mountain slopes.

General Description. This tree is typical of the transition zone in California. Its most common associates include Douglas-fir, digger and ponderosa pines, Pacific dogwood, and canyon live oak. At elevations above 4000 ft it is also found with sugar pine, incense-cedar, giant sequoia, and white fir. It is a tree of moderate proportions sometimes attaining a height of 80 ft with a broad, rounded crown; the bole is usually short, often crooked, and in old trees, highly defective.

Willow, Water, and Laurel Oaks

Deciduous or tardily so; mature leaf form unlobed; eastern species (Table 9-16).

TABLE 9-16   COMPARISON OF WILLOW, WATER, AND LAUREL OAKS

Species	Leaves	Fruit
Q. phellos willow oak	deciduous, mostly linear-lanceolate	⅜–½ in. (10–12 mm) long; nut greenish brown, hemispherical, enclosed at the base by a saucer-shaped cup
Q. nigra water oak	deciduous; very variable, spatulate, obovate, oblong or linear, pinnatifid-lobed or 3-lobed at the apex	⅜–⅝ in. (10–15 mm) long; nut black or nearly so; subglobose; cup similar to above
Q. hemisphaerica laurel oak	finally deciduous, but persistent until early spring, elliptical to oblong-ovate	¼–½ in. (6–12 mm) long; tan; shape and cup as above

Quércus phéllos L.   Willow oak

Distinguishing Characteristics (Fig. 9-63)

Leaves deciduous, often tardily so; 2 to 5 in. (5 to 13 cm) long, ⅜ to ¾ in. (1 to 2 cm) wide; *shape* linear to linear-lanceolate, occasionally oblanceolate; *margin* entire; *apex* and *base* acute; *surfaces* glabrous above, glabrous or rarely tomentose below; *fall color* yellow-brown.

Fruit solitary or paired; *nut* ⅜ to ½ in. (10 to 12 mm) long, subglobose, more or less pubescent, light yellowish or greenish brown, enclosed at the base in a saucerlike cup; *cup scales* thin, hoary tomentose, with a somewhat greenish-red tinge.

Twigs slender, glabrous, red to reddish brown; *terminal buds* ⅛ in. (3 mm) long, ovoid, sharp-pointed, covered by chestnut-brown scales paler on the margin.

Bark smooth and steel-gray on young stems, ultimately breaking up into thick rough ridges separated by deep, irregular fissures and becoming nearly black on mature trees.

Range

Southeastern (Map 9-22). Disjuncts in northeastern Florida and southeastern Georgia, eastern Missouri, and western Illinois. Elevation: sea level to 1000 ft. Bottomlands or low flatwoods and upland old fields.

General Description

Willow oak is a medium-size to large tree, 80 to 100 ft high and 3 to 4 ft dbh (max. 130 by 7 ft), although much smaller in the northern part of its range. Open-grown trees are very distinctive with their dense oblong to oval crowns and bright green willowlike leaves. In the forest, the crown, although less developed, is still more or less full or rounded, and the slender lower branches do not prune readily. Numerous spurlike branchlets throughout make this tree similar in appearance to pin oak, which it is often called in some sections of the South.

Willow oak is a bottomland tree. Growth is best on well-drained loams and poorest on poorly drained heavy clays. Common associates are laurel, cherrybark, Nuttall, overcup, and

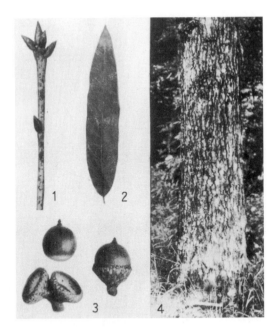

FIGURE 9-63 *Quercus phellos.* Willow oak. (1) Twig × 1¼. (2) Leaf × ½. (3) Acorns × 1. (4) Bark.

swamp chestnut oaks, sweetgum, American elm, cedar elm, green ash, and water hickory. As an ornamental, willow oak has few if any superiors throughout the southern part of its range, and in many southern cities it is the most widely planted shade and street tree. This use has probably led to the natural spread of the tree to a number of more upland sites.

Quércus nìgra L.   Water oak

Distinguishing Characteristics (Fig. 9-64)

Leaves deciduous, but many remain green and attached to the tree until late winter; size variable, but usually 2 to 5 in. (5 to 13 cm) long, and ¾ to 2 in. (2 to 5 cm) wide;

MAP 9-22 **(Left)** *Quercus phellos.* **(Right)** *Quercus nigra.*

FIGURE 9-64 *Quercus nigra.* Water oak. (1) Twig × 1¼. (2) Leaf variation × ½. (3) Acorns × 1. (4) Bark *(Photo by R. A. Cockrell).*

shape spatulate, obovate, and oblong; *margin* very variable, usually entire and not lobed or slightly 3-lobed at the apex; or on sprouts, saplings, or vigorous growth, deeply 3-lobed at the apex or variously pinnatifid-lobed; *apex* acute to obtuse; *base* mostly acute to cuneate; *surfaces* glabrous except for occasional axillary tufts below; *fall color* yellow.

Fruit solitary or paired; *nut* ⅜ to ⅝ in. (10 to 15 mm) long, hemispherical, black or nearly so, often striated, minutely tomentose or glabrous, enclosed at the base by a thin, saucerlike cup; *cup scales* appressed, tomentose except on the often darker margins.

Twigs slender, dull red, glabrous; *terminal buds* ⅛ to ¼ in. (3 to 6 mm) long, ovoid, sharp-pointed, angular, with reddish-brown scales.

Bark gray-black, relatively close, often with irregular patches, eventually with rough, wide, scaly ridges.

Range

Southeastern (Map 9-22). Elevation: sea level to 1000 ft. Mixed upland woods, bottomlands, hammocks, and old fields.

General Description

In the forest, water oak is a medium-size tree 60 to 70 ft high and 2 to 3 ft dbh (max. 125 by 6 ft) with a tall, slender bole and a somewhat symmetrical, rounded crown of ascending branches.

This tree is a bottomland species although also found on moist uplands; between these limits it is exceedingly cosmopolitan, occurring in most bottomland types with the exception of permanent swamps. Best development is made on the better-drained loamy or clay ridges in the bottoms with sweetgum, although, because of the diversity in site, the number of associates is very large. On old fields in the bottomlands, especially in the lower Mississippi Delta, second-growth water oak is one of the commonest of trees and together with cherrybark oak often comprises nearly 80 to 90 percent of the stand; growth is fast, and trees 50 to 70 years old are merchantable. This species is a favorite ornamental in many southern cities. It is also used sometimes for timber, fuel, and plywood.

Quércus hemisphaèrica Bartr. ex Willd.   Laurel oak; Darlington oak

Distinguishing Characteristics (Fig. 9-65)

Leaves rather coriaceous and opaque, semi-evergreen or tardily deciduous and falling during early spring just before the new leaves appear, or earlier in severe winters; 1 to 3 in. (2.5 to 8 cm) long, ⅝ to 1¼ in. (1.5 to 3 cm) wide; *shape* predominantly oblanceolate although variably elliptical to oblong-obovate but usually widest above the middle; *margin* entire to repand or undulate, sometimes undulate or irregularly lobed on saplings or vigorous shoots; *apex* acute, often obtuse but apiculate, or occasionally rounded and aristate; *base* narrowly rounded or broadly cuneate; *surfaces* lustrous green above, paler and only minutely puberulent below and with a more or less conspicuous yellow midrib.

Fruit sessile or subsessile, usually solitary; *nut* ovoid to hemispherical, tan and short pubescent, ¼ to ½ in. (7 to 11 mm) long, one-fourth or less enclosed in a thin, saucerlike cup; *cup scales* red-brown, pale pubescent, appressed.

Twigs slender, brown to gray, glabrous; *terminal buds* ⅛ to 3/16 in. (2 to 4 mm) long, ovoid to oval, acute, covered by lustrous, red-brown scales.

Bark dark gray and moderately smooth on young stems but ultimately black and divided by deep furrows into broad, flattened ridges.

FIGURE 9-65   *Quercus hemisphaerica.* Laurel oak. (1) Upper acorn × 1. (2) Leaf × ½. *Quercus laurifolia.* Swamp laurel oak. (1) Lower acorn × 1.

Range

Southeastern (Map 9-23). Disjuncts more inland in several states including southern Arkansas, southcentral Tennessee, and northwestern Mississippi. Elevation: sea level to 500 ft. Well-drained woodlands, terraces along rivers and streams, hammocks, maritime forests.

General Description

Laurel oak may be 60 to 70 ft high and 2 to 3 ft dbh (max. 148 by 7 ft), but it is usually much smaller. Common associates include willow, live, and Nuttall oaks, sweetgum, and loblolly, slash, and longleaf pines. Laurel oak usually occurs as a scattered tree and is not very abundant except in Florida. This species is widely used in the south as an ornamental tree but is shorter-lived than its associate, the willow oak. Though tolerant of shade, laurel oak (juvenile) grows rapidly in full sun.

In contrast with *Q. laurifolia,* this is a tree of woodlands in well-drained sandy soils (see the discussion of the next species). In contrast with *Q. phellos,* which it closely resembles, the leaves of *Q. phellos* are predominantly lanceolate, acute at both ends, sometimes more pubescent below, and never undulate or lobed. Ecologically, *Q. phellos* overlaps both *Q. hemisphaerica* and *Q. laurifolia.*

Quércus laurifòlia Michx.   Swamp laurel oak; diamond leaf oak

Distinguishing Characteristics.   This species is distinguished from laurel oak by its *leaves* which are more membranaceous and with conspicuous reticulate veins as seen with transmitted light, promptly or tardily deciduous or nearly overwintering in the south; spatulate-oblanceolate, or widest at or near the middle (rhombic), rarely lobed; apex acute to rounded and rarely aristate; base narrowly cuneate; upper surface dull, lower surface slightly puberulent to glabrate; *flowering* and with new leaf growth about 2 weeks before *Q. hemisphaerica* in the same general area; and ecology.

Range.   (Map 9-23) Swamp laurel oak is found in much wetter habitats (bottomlands, poorly drained silty soils, wet hammocks, and swamp margins) than laurel oak. The geographical ranges of the two are generally the same.

General Description.   The names of the laurel oaks have been confused for many years. Several authors have not distinguished the laurel oak and swamp laurel oak (Little, 1979). In the combined concept, the name is *Q. laurifolia* s. lat., but when separated, the laurel oak is *Q. hemisphaerica* and the swamp laurel oak is *Q. laurifolia.*

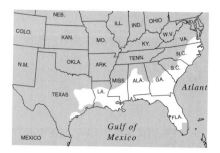

MAP 9-23   *Quercus hemisphaerica* and *Q. laurifolia.*

Quércus imbricària Michx.   Shingle oak

Distinguishing Characteristics (Fig. 9-66). *Leaves* deciduous, 3 to 6 in. (7.5 to 15 cm) long, ¾ to 2 in. (2 to 5 cm) wide, oblong to elliptical, margin entire to slightly repand, dark green and shiny above, pale to brown and pubescent below; fall color yellow or reddish. *Fruit* typically subglobose, ½ to ⅝ in. (12 to 15 mm) long, the nut enclosed one-third to one-half in a thin bowl-shaped cup with appressed red-brown scales. *Twigs* slender, dark-green to greenish brown, buds ovoid, pointed. *Bark* gray-brown, close, eventually with broad low ridges separated by shallow furrows.

Range. Pennsylvania south to western North Carolina, west to Arkansas, north to southern Iowa and southern Michigan; disjuncts in Louisiana and Alabama. Elevation: to 3500 ft in the southern Appalachians. Stream banks and mountain slopes and valleys.

General Description. The scientific name, given to this tree by the explorer-botanist Michaux indicates its use for the production of split shingles or shakes. Shingle oak, or, as it is sometimes called, "northern laurel oak," is a medium-size tree 50 to 60 ft high and 2 to 3 ft dbh (max. 80 by 5 ft). It is especially characteristic of the lower Ohio Valley, where it reaches its best development on moist soils along streams or on hillsides in mixture with such species as pin and overcup oaks, elms, and hickories.

A tree occasionally found in the Piedmont and Coastal Plain and frequently mistaken for *Q. imbricaria* is *Q. × rudkinii* Britt. (*Q. marilandica × phellos*). It has leaves the size and shape of shingle oak but lacks the tomentum on the abaxial surface.

Quércus incàna Bartr.   Bluejack oak

This is another of the entire-margined, unlobed, willow and laurel oak group which is a common, small tree in the sandhill scrub oak community in the Coastal Plain from southeastern Vir-

FIGURE 9-66   *Quercus imbricaria.* Shingle oak. (1) Twig × 1¼. (2) Leaf × ½. (3) Acorn × 1.

ginia to central Florida and west to Louisiana and eastern and central Texas, north to southwestern Arkansas and southeastern Oklahoma. Its frequent associates are *Q. laevis, Q. margarettiae, Q. marilandica,* and longleaf pine. It is recognized by its small leaves, 2 to 4 in. (5 to 10 cm) long, and ½ to 1 in. (1.2 to 2.5 cm) wide, which are grayish white pubescent beneath and pale blue- or gray-green above; fall color reddish.

Western Live Oaks

Evergreen; leaves unlobed; western species of the red oak subgenus.

Quércus wislizèni ADC.   Interior live oak

This tree is commonly shrubby but may reach some 50 to 70 ft in height and 12 to 24 in. dbh (Fig. 9-67). It has short 1 to 2 in. (2.5 to 5 cm) long, ½ to 1¼ in. (1.2 to 3 cm) wide, oblong-elliptical, glabrous, hollylike juvenile leaves; those on larger trees are entire, similar to those of canyon live oak. Interior live oak leaves persist for two seasons. The acorn is ¾ to 1½ in. (2 to 4 cm) long, ovoid, deeply encased in a deep, thin, bowl-like cup. The largest trees develop short, thick boles and irregular but wide-spreading crowns. It is most common on dry river bottoms, washes, and slopes where the soil is dry but rich. It is sometimes found in pure groves, but is much more commonly noted in association with digger pine. This tree occurs from Mt. Shasta south along the Sierra and Coast Ranges to Baja California at elevations of from sea level to 5000 ft.

Quércus agrifòlia Née   Coast live oak

Also designated as a holly-leaved oak, it closely resembles the previous species in both form and general appearance. Its leaves, however, are somewhat larger, ¾ to 3 in. (2 to 7.5 cm) long, ½ to 1½ in. (1.2 to 4 cm) wide, with axillary tufts of hairs below, and persist for only 1 year. Trees are found on dry loams and gravelly soils in open valleys and shallow canyons and on moist slopes in the coastal regions of southern California and Baja California from sea level to 4500 ft. Heights of 60 to 90 ft and dbh of 24 to 36 in. or more are fairly common. This species is quite gregarious and forms pure, open, but extensive stands. In mixed forests, California sycamore, white alder, numerous other oaks, and bigcone Douglas-fir are common associates. When fully exposed to the ocean, it seldom develops beyond shrubby proportions.

FIGURE 9-67   *Quercus wislizeni.* Interior live oak. Juvenile leaf × 1.

Quércus émoryi Torr.   Emory oak

It is probably the most common arborescent oak of southern Arizona and New Mexico. Its oblong-lanceolate, repand-sinuate, 1 to 2½ in. (2.5 to 6 cm) long leaves (Fig. 9-50), oblong-ovoid acorn, maturing in 1 year, and alligator-leatherlike bark are its principal identifying features. Under the most favorable conditions for growth, this species attains a height of from 40 to 60 ft and a dbh of as many inches. It is commonly encountered as a massive shrub, however, and as such is often browsed by both horses and cattle. Geographically, Emory oak is restricted to western Texas, southern Arizona, New Mexico, and northern Mexico.

Intermediate Oaks

Evergreen shrubs and small to medium-size trees; leaves entire or spiny toothed; western species combining characters of the other two sections.

Quércus chrysolèpis Liebm.   Canyon live oak

This is the second-largest oak in California, at least in terms of diameter and crown spread. At the time of its measurement some years ago, one famous old tree in the Hupa Valley was 95 ft tall, had a dbh of more than 6 ft, and featured a crown with a spread of more than 125 ft. The leaves of the canyon live oak, which persist for three or four years, are thick, and turn a dark blue-green in their second season. They are polymorphic, those on sprouts and young trees aculeate (hollylike), those on older trees entire (Fig. 9-68), 1 to 3 in. (2.5 to 7.5 cm) long. Large ovoid acorns, ¾ to 2 in. (2 to 5 cm) in length, with thick, shallow cups covered with golden tomentum, are most distinctive. This tree frequents cool, moist, canyon walls and dry, mountain slopes. Growth is never rapid, maturity being reached in about 300 years. Its principal forest associates include several other oaks, incense-cedar, and ponderosa pine. Canyon live oak extends from southwestern Oregon south through the Coast Ranges and Sierras to Baja California, east to central and southern Arizona and southwestern New Mexico. Elevation: 1000 to 6500 ft in the north; 5500 to 7500 ft in the south.

FIGURE 9-68   *Quercus chrysolepis.* Canyon live oak. Acorn and leaves × 1.

Canyon live oak hybridizes with the related Palmer or Dunn oak, **Q. pálmeri** Engelm. (*Q. dunnii* Kellogg), which is a small, often shrubby, southwestern oak of the open pinyon-juniper woodland or canyon flats at 3500 to 6000 ft of elevation in California and Arizona. It has evergreen, rounded leaves, ½ to 1½ in. (1.2 to 3.5 cm) long, coarsely dentate with bristle tips longer than in *Q. chrysolepis,* and with secondary veins 12 or fewer and not parallel (rather than more than 12 and parallel in *Q. chrysolepis*). See Tucker and Haskell (1960) for a thorough discussion of these species and the past confusion.

There are three other species in this section. See Manos (1993) for a distribution map and discussion of their characteristics, variation, and hybridization.

Betulaceae: The Birch Family

Although somewhat larger during previous geological periods, the Betulaceae now number only six genera and about 120 species of deciduous trees and shrubs which, with few exceptions, are restricted to the cooler regions of the northern hemisphere.

The introduced European hornbeam, *Carpinus betulus* L., is often used ornamentally in the United States. Another European species, *Corylus avellana* L., produces the filbert nuts of commerce, and in recent years most of the local supply has come from American-grown trees of this species.

Five genera with about 29 species are represented in North America (Table 9-17). The remaining genus *Ostryopsis* (monotypic) is restricted to eastern Asia.

Botanical Features of the Family

Leaves deciduous, alternate, simple, stipulate.

Flowers imperfect (plant monoecious), anemophilous, appearing before or with the leaves, or rarely autumnal; *staminate* aments preformed (except in *Carpinus*), pendulous, the individual flowers borne in clusters of 1 to 6 in the axils of bracts, each consisting of 2 to 20 stamens with or without a calyx and no corolla; *pistillate* flowers in short, spikelike or capitate aments, the individual flowers borne at the base of bracts,

TABLE 9-17   COMPARISON OF NATIVE GENERA IN THE BETULACEAE

Genus	Fruit
Betula birch	nutlets very small, laterally winged; borne in a compact ament with 3-lobed bracts
Alnus alder	nutlets similar to those of *Betula,* but ament woody and persistent at maturity
Carpinus hornbeam	nuts small, not winged; each subtended by a characteristic usually 3-lobed, leafy bract, borne in leafy spikelike clusters
Ostrya hophornbeam	nuts small, not winged; each enclosed in a bladderlike sac, borne in enlongated clusters
Corylus hazel	nuts large and not winged; in a leathery foliaceous or beaked husk

solitary or in clusters of two or three, comprising a 2-celled, superior ovary surmounted by a short style and a 2-lobed stigma, calyx present or absent, corolla absent. **Fruit** a small to medium-size, 1-celled, 1-seeded nut (or nutlet), winged or unwinged, subtended by a papery, leafy, or somewhat coriaceous bract, or in a semiwoody and persistent cone (ament).

BETULA L.   Birch

The genus *Betula* numbers about 50 species of trees and shrubs widely scattered through the northern hemisphere from the Arctic circle to southern Europe, the Himalaya, China, and Japan in the Old World, and in North America from the Arctic regions to the southeastern United States. Several species form vast forests in areas of the far north, while others, which are extremely dwarfed in habit, are found on the slopes of mountains at or near timberline. The dwarf or resin birch, *B. glandulosa* Michx., a small shrub common to the peat bogs and high mountains of the west and north, is a suitable browse plant for both sheep and cattle and in Alaska it is one of the important summer grazing plants for reindeer.

Because of their handsome foliage and showy bark, many of the birches are used for decorative purposes. Cultivars of the European white birch, *B. pendula* Roth (*B. alba* L. in part), and river birch, *B. nigra,* are exceedingly popular.

About 12 species of *Betula* are endemic to the temperate regions of North America (Table 9-18). Of the seven or eight arborescent species, three attain commercial size, abundance, and quality. Interspecific hybridization is common (Barnes and Sherik, 1974; DeHond and Campbell, 1989; Little, 1979).

Botanical Features of the Genus

Leaves deciduous, 2-ranked, mostly ovate, oval, or triangular; serrate (often doubly), dentate, or lobed.

TABLE 9-18   COMPARISON OF IMPORTANT BIRCHES

Species	Leaves	Fruiting aments	Twigs	Young bark
B. alleghaniensis yellow birch	doubly serrate, base rounded to remotely cordate	ovoid, erect; bracts pubescent	aromatic	bronze
B. lenta sweet birch	singly or doubly serrate, base cordate	oblong, erect; essentially glabrous	aromatic	black
B. papyrifera paper birch	doubly serrate, obtuse or rounded at the base, glandular below	cylindrical, pendent	nonaromatic	chalky white

Flowers: *staminate* aments preformed, borne in clusters of two or three, or solitary, the individual flowers consisting of 4 stamens adnate to a 4-parted calyx, each bract bearing 3 flowers; *pistillate* aments solitary, the individual flowers naked, borne in clusters of three and subtended by a 3-lobed bract.

Fruit a small, winged nutlet borne in an erect or pendent ament, the apically 3-lobed bracts usually deciduous from the persistent axis at maturity, releasing the nutlets; nutlets compressed, laterally winged. A key to the nutlets of northeastern birches has been published by Cunningham (1957).

Twigs slender, in certain species aromatic; usually greenish to reddish brown, glabrous or pubescent; spur shoots commonly present on old growth; *terminal buds* absent; *lateral buds* distichous, with several imbricated scales, only three of which are usually visible; *leaf scars* lunate to semioval, with 3 nearly equidistant bundle scars; *pith* small, homogeneous, terete, or remotely triangular; stipulate

Bétula alleghaniénsis Britton (*B. lutea* Michx. f.)   Yellow birch

Distinguishing Characteristics (Fig. 9-69)

Leaves 3 to 5 in. (7.5 to 13 cm) long, 1½ to 2 in. (4 to 5 cm) wide; *shape* ovate to oblong-ovate; *margin* sharply doubly serrate; *apex* acute to acuminate; *base* rounded or remotely cordate and inequilateral; *surfaces* dull, dark green, glabrous above, pale yellow-green and with tufts of hairs in the axils of the principal veins below; *petiole* slender, pubescent, ½ to ¾ in. (12 to 18 mm) long; *fall color* bright yellow.

Fruit in an ovoid, sessile, or short-stalked, erect ament, at maturity ¾ to 1¼ in. (2 to 3 cm) long; *bracts* pubescent on the back, longer than broad, often tardily deciduous; *nutlet* pubescent toward the apex, oval to ovate, about as wide as its lateral wings.

Twigs slender, yellowish brown to brown, aromatic, with a slight wintergreen taste; *terminal buds* absent; *lateral buds* ovate, acute, with chestnut-brown scales, ciliate on the margin.

Bark on young stems and branches yellowish, golden gray, or bronze-colored, separating at the surface and peeling horizontally into thin, curly, papery strips; eventually breaking up into reddish-brown fissures and plates on mature trunks.

Range

Northeastern and southern Appalachians (Map 9-24). Disjunct in southwestern Kentucky. Elevation: sea level to 2500 ft northward, 3000 to 6300 ft in the southern Appalachians. Northern swamps, lakes and stream banks; upland slopes and ridges in the mountains.

General Description

This species, the most important of the native birches, is a medium-size tree 60 to 70 ft high and 2 to 2½ ft dbh (max. 114 by 4½ ft). In the forest, the crown is irregularly rounded, and the long, usually well-formed bole terminates below in a shallow, wide-spreading root system.

Yellow birch is probably the most typical of northeastern hardwoods. In the mountainous sections it develops best on sandy loam soils in mixture with sugar maple and American beech (beech–birch–maple mixture) which grow under the light shade of such pioneer species as the aspens and pin cherry; the associated conifers include eastern hemlock, red spruce, balsam fir,

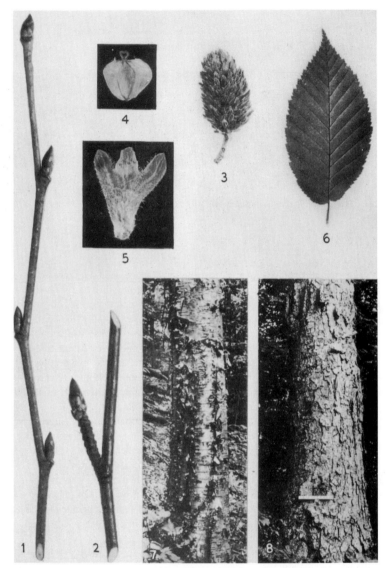

FIGURE 9-69   *Betula alleghaniensis.* Yellow birch. (1) Twig × 1¼. (2) Spur shoot × 1¼. (3) Fruiting ament × ¾. (4) Winged nutlet × 3. (5) Pistillate bract × 3. (6) Leaf × ½. (7) Bark of young tree. (8) Bark of old tree.

and eastern white pine. Farther south, yellow birch occurs on a variety of soils but always in moist, cool locations such as steep northerly slopes and the edges of sphagnum bogs. Temperature seems to be an important factor influencing distribution, and it may be more than coincidental that the southern limit for the species follows roughly the 70°F summer isotherm.

Yellow birch is a prolific seeder, usually producing large crops at 2- or 3-year intervals after about age 40. The winged nutlets are light and are carried a considerable distance by the wind; this probably accounts for the excellent reproduction which often takes place after fires. Seeds

MAP 9-24   **(Left)** *Betula alleghaniensis.* **(Right)** *Betula lenta.*

germinate on almost any dependably moist place, including moss-covered boulders and old par-tially rotted stumps. The young seedlings not only thrive in such situations but commonly per-sist for many years, and eventually may even send their roots downward over the surface of the boulder or stump until they reach the ground. Eventually, the stump may rot away completely and the tree may be left on "stilts." Among the conifers, hemlock is the chief competitor of yel-low birch in this respect, and it is common to find several small trees of each species competing for the supremacy of a single stump. Elsewhere, after a good seed year, there are countless thou-sands of small birch seedlings scattered over the forest floor. The roots have difficulty in grow-ing through the layer of leaves and other litter. Disturbance of this layer by logging or fire greatly improves subsequent seedling reproduction.

Yellow birch is moderately tolerant, less so than hemlock, sugar maple, and American beech, but more so than the aspens and pin cherry. Growth is not rapid, and trees 50 years old may be 50 ft tall and 6 in. in diameter. Maturity is reached in about 150 years, and old trees may reach the three-century mark.

The papery bark curls are highly flammable and burn even when wet, a useful feature to know when starting a campfire in rain-soaked woods. Oil of wintergreen may be obtained by distilling the young twigs or inner bark, but the amount is much less than in sweet birch. Yellow birch is harvested annually for furniture, paneling, cabinets, and veneer.

Bétula lénta L.   Sweet birch; black birch

Distinguishing Characteristics (Fig. 9-70)

Leaves 2½ to 5 in. (5 to 13 cm) long, 1½ to 3 in. (4 to 7.5 cm) wide; *shape* ovate to oblong-ovate; *margin* sharply and singly or irregularly doubly serrate; *apex* acute; *base* cordate, or unequally rounded; *surfaces* dull, dark green, glabrous above, pale yellow-green, with tufts of white hairs in the axils of the principal veins below; *petiole* stout, puberulent, ½ to ¾ in. (12 to 18 mm) long; *fall color* bright yellow.

Fruit in an oblong-ovoid, short-stalked or sessile, erect ament ¾ to 1½ in. (2 to 4 cm) long; *bracts* glabrous, or sparingly ciliate and slightly pubescent near the base, usually somewhat longer than broad, tardily deciduous; *nutlet* glabrous, obovoid, slightly broader than its lateral wings.

FIGURE 9-70   *Betula lenta.* Sweet birch. (1) Bark (*Photo by H.P. Brown*). (2) Pseudoterminal bud × 1¼. (3) Spur shoot × 1¼. (4) Leaf × ½. (5) Fruiting ament × ¾. (6) Winged nutlet × 3. (7) Pistillate bract × 3.

Twigs slender, reddish brown, lenticellate, with a strong wintergreen odor and taste; *terminal buds* absent; *lateral buds* lustrous, glabrous, sharply pointed, chestnut-brown, divergent.

Bark on young trees smooth, reddish brown to nearly black (Fig. 9-71), with prominent horizontal lenticels; on mature trees brownish black and breaking up into large thin irregular scaly plates.

Range
Northestern and southern Appalachians (Map 9-24). Local disjuncts in northcentral Alabama, southwestern Kentucky, and southern Quebec. Elevation: sea level northward, 1700 to 6000 ft in the southern Appalachians. Mesic uplands, coves, and slopes.

General Description
Sweet birch is a medium-size tree 50 to 60 ft high and 12 to 24 in. dbh (max. 80 by 5 ft), and in the forest it develops a long, clear bole which terminates below in a rather deep, wide-spreading root system. This species reaches its best development in Tennessee and Kentucky, but is often more abundant northward. Deep, rich, and moist but well-drained soils are preferred, yet this tree is also found on rocky sites where the roots often grow over and around boulders and rocky ledges, a habit much more typical, however, of the yellow birch. Never occurring in pure stands, sweet birch is found as a scattered tree with such species as white pine, hemlock, yellow birch, sugar maple, beech, black cherry, white ash, basswood, and yellow-poplar.

FIGURE 9-71   Young sweet birch, with yellow birch in the right background.

Sweet birch and yellow birch differ from most other native birches by erect fruiting aments and the presence of wintergreen oil in the twigs and inner bark of stems and roots. The twigs are a favorite for chewing. Although oil of wintergreen may be extracted from the twigs and bark of sweet birch, it is now mostly produced synthetically. The uses of the wood are the same as that of yellow birch.

The seeding habits and other silvical features of the sweet and yellow birches are similar, except that the former species is not so aggressive and is more exacting in its seedbed requirements.

Bétula papyrífera Marsh.   Paper birch; white birch

Distinguishing Characteristics (Fig. 9-72)

Leaves 2 to 4 in. (5 to 10 cm) long, 1½ to 2 in. (4 to 5 cm) wide; *shape* ovate to oval; *margin* coarsely doubly serrate; *apex* acute to acuminate; *base* rounded or obtuse; *surfaces* dull, dark green, glabrous above, pale yellowish green, glabrous or pubescent, minutely glandular below; *petiole* black-glandular, slender, ¾ to 1 in. (18 to 25 mm) long; *fall color* light yellow.

Fruit in a pendent, cylindrical, stalked ament, 1½ to 2 in. (4 to 5 cm) long; *bracts* puberulent on the back, about as long as broad, more or less deciduous at maturity; *nutlet* glabrous, elliptical to oval, narrower than its lateral wings.

Twigs slender, dull reddish brown to orange-brown, lenticellate; *terminal buds* absent; *lateral buds* ovoid, acute, gummy, covered with chestnut-brown scales.

FIGURE 9-72   *Betula papyrifera.* Paper birch. (1) Twig × 1¼. (2) Immature staminate aments × 1¼. (3) Flowering staminate aments × ½. (4) Portion of staminate ament × 5. (5) Staminate flower × 5. (6) Fruiting ament shedding bracts and fruits × ¾. (7) Winged nutlet × 3. (8) Pistillate bract × 3. (9) Leaf × ½. (10) Bark of young trees.

Bark at first dark brown, soon turning chalky to creamy white, separating into thin, papery strips; at the base of old trees, nearly black and deeply fissured.

Range

Northern (Map 9-25). Local disjuncts scattered south of the normal range. Elevation: sea level to 4000 ft. Margins of lakes, streams, and swamps; also uplands.

General Description

Paper birch, the most widely distributed of the native birches, is primarily a Canadian species and extends southward only through the northern United States where it is found in mountainous regions or in other localities where a cool, moist site is available.

This species is a medium-size tree 50 to 70 ft high and 12 to 24 in. dbh (max. 120 by 6 ft). The crown is pyramidal or later irregularly rounded, relatively open, and the long, cylindrical, often curved bole terminates below in a shallow root system.

Paper birch occurs as a scattered tree in the mixed conifer–hardwood forests of the north; here its associates include white, red, and jack pines, red, black, and white spruces, balsam fir, maples, aspens, American beech, yellow birch, and black ash. In some localities this birch, together with white spruce and balsam fir, comprises a large portion of the permanent forest. After fire, paper birch often seeds in over large areas where mineral soil has been exposed, and especially on moist sites it may form nearly pure stands; in this respect, paper birch is similar to the aspens and is commonly found in mixture with them on old burns. These species are all

MAP 9-25   *Betula papyrifera* and *B. cordifolia.*

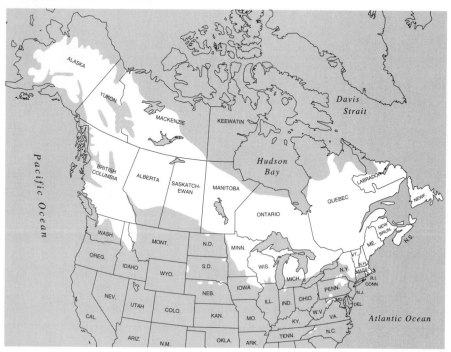

intolerant and often serve as a cover under which the slower-growing, more tolerant trees (especially spruce) become established. Paper birch is a fast-growing, short-lived tree and rarely attains an age of more than 80 years (max. 140).

The bark was used by Native Americans for utensils, canoes, and wigwam covers, and is now utilized for novelties of various sorts; it is also flammable and useful in starting a fire. Such uses by increasing numbers of campers have resulted in extremely unsightly peeled birches at northern campsites.

The wood has, in recent years, become more valued for veneer and pulp, and interest in the management of the species is increasing.

Although valued along with the European white birch as an ornamental, both trees may be damaged or killed by the bronze birch borer. Birch dieback, a poorly understood environmental disease, can cause heavy losses to both paper and yellow birch.

Bétula cordifòlia Regel   Mountain paper birch

This species, considered as *B. papyrifera* var. *cordifolia* (Regel) Fern. by Little (1979), is distinguished from paper birch by its usually cordate leaf base and other morphological differences, seedling growth habits, chromosome number (Grant and Thompson, 1975), and betulin content of the outer bark (O'Connell et al., 1988). Mountain paper birch occurs in eastern Canada south to northern Iowa, Wisconsin, Michigan, northern New York and New England, and local in the southern Appalachians of North Carolina and Tennessee (Map 9-25 in part).

Bétula populifòlia Marsh.   Gray birch

Distinguishing Characteristics (Fig. 9-73). *Leaves* triangular, with a narrow, pointed apex, doubly serrate; fall color pale yellow. *Staminate aments* usually solitary. *Fruit* in a spreading or ascending, cylindrical, glabrous or puberulent ament with deciduous bracts; bracts about the same in length as in width; nutlet somewhat narrower than its lateral wings. *Twigs* slender, lenticels warty-glandular, terminal bud lacking, laterals ovoid, gummy. *Bark* at first brownish, soon grayish white, exfoliating very little in comparison with that of paper birch; with black triangular patches, or inverted *V*'s, usually present on the trunk below the branch insertions.

Range.   Southern Ontario, east to Cape Breton, south to Pennsylvania and New Jersey; local disjuncts in northern Virginia, Ohio, and Indiana.

General Description.   Gray birch is the smallest of the northeastern tree birches and commonly attains a height of only 20 to 30 ft and a dbh of 15 in. or less (max. 60 by 2 ft). The root

FIGURE 9-73   *Betula populifolia.* Gray birch. (1) Leaf × ½. (2) Pistillate bract × 3. (3) Winged nutlet × 3. (4) Fruiting ament × ¾. (5) Twig with lateral bud × 1¼.

system is shallow, and the bole usually poorly shaped and limby, with an irregular, open, pyramidal crown. This birch is now very plentiful, especially through New England, and covers large areas on abandoned farms and burned-over land; it will grow on the poorest of sterile soils, and by prolific seeding has gained a foothold in advance of other species. In this respect, it is similar to both paper birch and the aspens. On sterile sites, gray birch is often associated with pitch pine and bear oak (*Q. ilicifolia* Wangenh.), these three species forming a very monotonous vegetation type covering wide areas. Farther south, or on better soils, other oaks occur with this species, and among the conifers white pine is most frequently seen. Gray birch serves at first as a cover crop for white pine but soon causes it considerable damage by excessive crowding. In its silvical features, gray birch is similar to paper birch. It is used as an ornamental, for fuel, and the wood is used for cabinetwork.

Bétula nìgra L.   River birch; red birch

Distinguishing Characteristics (Fig. 9-74). *Leaves* rhombic-ovate, conspicuously and often deeply doubly serrate, with a broadly wedge-shaped base; fall color yellow. *Fruit* in a cylindrical, erect, pubescent ament with deciduous bracts, maturing in late spring; bracts longer than broad; nutlet somewhat broader than its lateral wings. *Twigs* reddish brown, slender, usually puberulent, terminal bud lacking, lateral acute. *Bark* salmon-pink, papery, later becoming coarsely scaly.

Range.   Southern New Hampshire, south to northern Florida, west to eastern Texas, north to southeastern Minnesota; local disjuncts in New York, Vermont, and Massachusetts. Elevation:

FIGURE 9-74   *Betula nigra.* River birch. (1) Fruiting ament × ¾. (2) Pistillate bract × 3. (3) Winged nutlet × 3. (4) Leaf × ½. (5) Bark.

sea level to 1000 ft northward; to 3000 ft in the southern Appalachians. Alluvial banks of rivers and streams, floodplains.

General Description. River birch, the only species of *Betula* at low elevations in the south, is a medium-size tree 70 to 80 ft high and 2 to 3 ft dbh, usually much smaller (max. 100 by 5 ft), with a trunk which often divides 15 to 20 ft from the ground into several arching branches. It occurs as a scattered tree with such species as sycamore, elm, silver and red maples, willows, green ash, boxelder, and cottonwoods.

Besides the distinction of being the only typically southern birch, it is also the only one which matures its fruit in late spring. At this time high water is receding and silty shore lines are exposed which offer the best possible place for the windblown or waterborne seeds to germinate.

The silvical features are similar to those of the other birches. This species is seldom cut, except for pulpwood, because of its poor form and the high percentage of undesirable tension wood. Its use as an ornamental is increasing, particularly the cultivar 'Heritage', which is more hardy and has a more colorful bark. Even north of the natural range, river birch makes a desirable specimen tree for yards and parks where it often makes good growth even on dry soils. It is occasionally used as a street tree in the Pacific Northwest.

ALNUS Mill.   Alder

Alnus includes about 30 species of trees and large shrubs mostly distributed through the cooler regions of the northern hemisphere. The Eurasian species extend southward to northern Africa, Iran, the Himalaya, and Taiwan. In the new world, alders are found from Alaska and Canada to Guatemala, and on mountains to Argentina.

The European or black alder, *A. glutinosa* (L.) Gaertn., originally introduced for charcoal manufacture, is now used ornamentally, with several cultivars, in the eastern United States and Canada and has become naturalized in some areas. It is also widely planted on spoil banks and is being tested for intensive management for pulp. About 10 species of *Alnus,* seven of which attain tree size, are native to the United States and Canada. Only one western species, however, reaches commercial proportions and abundance. The common stream-bank alders of the eastern states and Canada are *A. rugosa* (DuRoi) Spreng., speckled alder, of the northeast, and *A. serrulata* (Ait.) Willd., hazel alder, of the southeast. The twigs and leaves of alders are important as deer and moose browse, and the buds and seeds are eaten by birds.

Alnus roots have nodules of nitrogen-fixing actinomycetes, and large quantities of nitrogen compounds are added to the soil from the roots and decaying leaves. See also under *Myrica.*

Botanical Features of the Genus

Leaves mostly ovate, oval, or obovate; usually irregularly serrate or dentate; 3-ranked.

Flowers: *staminate* aments preformed, in racemose clusters of 3 to 5, the individual flowers consisting of 1 to 4 stamens attached to a 4-parted calyx and subtended by 3 to 5 bractlets, with 3 to 6 flowers for each scale; *pistillate* aments often preformed, in clusters of 2 or 3, the individual flowers composed of a naked ovary surmounted by 2 stigmas and subtended by 2 to 4 bractlets, in clusters of 2 to 4 at the base of bracts.

Fruit a small nutlet borne in a persistent semiwoody ament; *nutlets* compressed, laterally winged, chestnut-brown.

Twigs slender to moderately stout, reddish or tinged with red; *terminal buds* absent; *lateral buds* stalked (in most species), covered by 2 or 3 valvate or imbricate scales; *leaf scars* raised, more or less triangular to semicircular, generally with 3 bundle scars; *pith* homogeneous, triangular in cross section.

Álnus rùbra Bong.   Red alder
Distinguishing Characteristics (Fig. 9-75)

Leaves 3 to 6 in. (7.5 to 15 cm) long, 1½ to 3 in. (4 to 7.5 cm) wide; *shape* ovate to elliptical; *margin* doubly serrate-dentate, the teeth glandular, slightly revolute; *apex* acute; *base* obtuse or rounded; *surfaces* dark green, glabrous or glabrate above, paler and rusty pubescent on the midrib and principal veins below; *petiole* grooved, ¼ to ½ in. (6 to 12 mm) long; *fall color* yellow-brown.

Fruit in an oblong to ovoid, long-stalked or rarely sessile ament, ½ to 1¼ in. (1.2 to 3 cm) long; *bracts* truncate, with greatly thickened, often rugose apices; *nutlets* orbicular to obovoid, with membranous lateral wings or a single encircling wing.

Twigs slender to moderately stout, bright red to reddish brown, terete or somewhat 3-angled on vigorous shoots; *pseudoterminal buds* ⅓ to ⅔ in. (8 to 17 mm) long, stalked, covered by 2 or 3 red, scurfy-pubescent scales; *lateral buds* slightly smaller, stalked, somewhat divergent; *leaf scars* raised, triangular to semicircular, with 3 bundle scars; *pith* remotely triangular in cross section, greenish white.

Bark grayish white, pale gray, or blue-gray at the surface, smooth or covered with small warty excrescences; on large trees breaking up into large flat plates of irregular contour; inner bark bright reddish brown.

Range

Northwestern (Map 9-26). Elevation: sea level to 2500 ft. Along streams and lower slopes.

General Description

Red alder is the most important hardwood in the Pacific Northwest, a region supporting few commercial broadleaved trees. Its wood is used for furniture, veneers, and wooden novelties. The mature tree commonly varies from 80 to 120 ft in height and 10 to 35 in. dbh (max. 130 by 6 ft). In dense stands it develops a clear, symmetrical, slightly tapered bole, rising from a shallow, spreading root system, and supporting a narrow, domelike crown. The crown of open-grown trees, however, is broadly conical and often extends nearly to the ground. Red alder is essentially a coastal species, and except in northern Washington and Idaho, where it occurs sporadically, it is rarely found more than 100 miles from the ocean. It makes its best growth on moist rich loamy bottomlands, slopes, and benches, although it also attains tree size on gravelly or rocky soils. This species occurs in pure stands or in mixture with Douglas-fir, Sitka spruce, western redcedar, western hemlock, Pacific yew, Oregon ash, black cottonwood, bigleaf and vine maples, and Pacific dogwood.

Red alder is one of the first trees to appear following wildfires and certain kinds of logging. Like aspen, it never forms a permanent forest but improves the soil for subsequent species, first by building up a mull humus layer on the forest floor, and, second, by increasing the nitrogen content of the soil through the agency of nitrogen-fixing nodules on its roots. The nitrogen con-

FIGURE 9-75   *Alnus rubra.* Red alder. (1) Twig × 1¼. (2) Young staminate (left) and pistillate (right) aments × ¾. (3) Fruiting aments × 1¼. (4) Winged nutlets × 2. (5) Leaf × ½. (6) Bark.

MAP 9-26   *Alnus rubra.*

tent of the leaves is also high. This tree is an annual seeder, with exceptional crops of light, widely dispersed seeds at about 4-year intervals. The seeds germinate well on either organic or mineral soils. Partial shade may be tolerated for the first 2 or 3 years, but after that, full light is needed. Growth is rapid, and 10-year-old trees may be 35 to 40 ft tall. Sawlogs are produced in 40 to 60 years. Red alder is rated as intolerant in comparison with its associates, except the poplars. Maturity is reached in 60 to 90 years. Sprouts from the stumps are often vigorous, but seldom reach large size. Whole stands may be defoliated by the tent caterpillar, but the attacks are cyclic, and little permanent damage results.

The common name "red" is for the color of the inner bark and heartwood.

Álnus rhombifòlia Nutt.   White alder; Sierra alder

Distinguishing Characteristics.   *Leaves* ovate, oval, to nearly orbicular, pale green, singly (rarely doubly) serrate or serrate-dentate, the teeth glandular; midrib often glandular above; fall color yellow. *Fruit* in an oblong ament, ⅜ to ¾ in. (1 to 2 cm) long; nutlet ovoid, remotely winged. *Twigs* slender, orange-red; pith triangular in cross section. *Bark* gray, divided into irregular plates covered by thin, appressed scales.

Range.   Washington and western Idaho, south through the Coast Ranges of California and on the west slopes of the Sierras to western Nevada and southern California. Elevation: near sea level to 8000 ft, but generally below 5000 ft. Foothill woodlands and stream banks.

General Description.   Under favorable conditions this tree attains a height of 50 to 80 ft and a dbh of 18 to 36 in. (max. 115 by 4 ft). Pure stands occur along the banks of streams and in canyon bottoms when moisture is plentiful, but white alder is seldom observed along water courses where the stream flow is intermittent. California sycamore, bigleaf maple, Pacific dogwood, and Oregon ash are the principal associates in mixed forests. Few species compare in altitudinal distribution with white alder. Along the north central California coast it often occurs only a few feet above sea level, while in the southern Sierra it ascends to elevations of 8000 ft.

Like most alders, this species is a prolific seeder. Young trees endure considerable competition and often form dense thickets when provided with plenty of moisture. Growth is fairly rapid, and maturity is reached in about 50 to 70 years.

White alder produces low-grade lumber, and it is doubtful if the wood will ever be of value except for fuel. It is also used as an ornamental.

CARPINUS L.   Hornbeam

About 30 species are included in this genus, which is restricted to the northern hemisphere. Unlike the other genera of the birch family, this one does not exhibit preformed staminate aments. One species, ***Carpìnus caroliniàna*** Walt., American hornbeam (bluebeech, ironwood, water beech), is found in the United States east of the Great Plains. It is a small, usually poorly formed, understory tree with elliptical, doubly serrate, distichous leaves and a twisted, fluted trunk, with dark bluish gray, smooth bark. The fruit is easily identified by the three-lobed, leafy bract which subtends the nutlet (Fig. 9-76). The species is very tolerant and commonly occurs as an understory in hardwood mixtures. The wood is extremely hard and tough, hence the common name "ironwood" often applied to this species. The twigs and leaves are browsed by deer and the nuts are eaten by birds and small mammals.

Carpinus betulus L., European hornbeam, with many different cultivars, is cultivated extensively in North America.

OSTRYA Scop.   Hophornbeam

Of some eight known species of this genus, three are native to North America. Eastern hophornbeam, *Ostrỳa virginiàna* (Mill.) K. Koch, has about the same range as American hornbeam but extends farther west in the plains region. The habits of both species are somewhat similar, but the American hornbeam is perhaps more common on moist sites. Eastern hophornbeam is easily

FIGURE 9-76   (Left) *Carpinus caroliniana.* American hornbeam. Nutlets and subtending leafy bracts × 2 (*Photo by Dr. T. L. Mellichamp*). (Right) *Ostrya virginiana.* Hophornbeam. Nutlets enclosed in papery saclike bracts × ¾ (*Courtesy of U.S. Forest Service*).

distinguished from other trees by its bark, which has a "shreddy" appearance, that is, broken into small, thin, narrow, vertical strips which curve away from the trunk; the leaves are similar to those of *Carpinus* but with some of the secondary veins with a prominent, submarginal, descending branch; the fruit, however, is very different and consists of nutlets enclosed in oval, flattened, papery sacs borne in hoplike clusters (Fig. 9-76).

Ostrỳa knowltònii Cov.   Knowlton hophornbeam

This tree is restricted to small isolated areas in Arizona, Utah, New Mexico, and western Texas. *Ostrỳa chisosénsis* Correll, Chisos hophornbeam, is found only in one small area of western Texas (Little, 1979).

The trees are often browsed by deer and the nutlets are eaten by various wildlife.

CORYLUS L.   Hazel; filbert

There are about 15 species of this genus scattered throughout the northern hemisphere, and two are native to the United States. The leaves are distichous, oval to broadly elliptical, doubly serrate, and more or less pubescent on both surfaces; the nuts are fairly large (as the European filbert of commerce) and enclosed by leafy bracts. A western one, *Còrylus cornùta* var. *califórnica* (A. DC.) Sharp, California hazel, is a shrub or small tree; the two eastern ones, *C. cornuta* Marsh. *var. cornuta*, and *C. americàna* Marsh, are both shrubs. *Corylus cornuta,* known as beaked hazel, is distinguished by the bracts which form a tubelike beak beyond the nut and lack stalked glands on the twig. The American hazel has broad, leafy bracts around the nut and long-stalked glands on the twig. Both have edible nuts, usually eaten quickly by squirrels. The twigs and leaves are also good deer browse.

Casuarinaceae: The Beefwood Family

The Beefwood family includes four genera and 70 species in Indomalaysia, Australia, and the western Pacific. They are very distinctive, monoecious or dioecious, evergreen trees and shrubs with drooping, green, slender, jointed twigs appearing as long needles from a distance. The leaves are minute, scalelike, in whorls and more or less connate, forming toothed sheaths at each node. Flowers are anemophilous and in spikes (staminate) or heads (pistillate) in spring. The small samaras are borne in woody, conelike multiples.

Casuarìna equisetifòlia L. ex J. R. & G. Forst.   Horsetail casuarina, Australian-pine, or beefwood tree

Scale leaves 6 or 7 per whorl; cone oblong, ¾ in. (19 mm) long and ½ in. (13 mm) in diameter. It reaches 130 ft tall and is important as a hedge or windbreak around citrus groves or cultivated fields, along seashores, inland as an ornamental, for erosion control, and for its nitrogen-fixing capabilities (see under *Myrica*). It has become naturalized and weedy in some areas of Florida, reproducing both by seed and numerous root sprouts.

Casuarìna cunninghamiàna Miq.   River-oak casuarina

Scale leaves 8 to 10 per whorl; cone subglobose, ½ in. (13 mm) long and ⅜ in. (10 mm) in diameter. It is commonly planted in Arizona and southern California, with some in Florida.

CARYOPHYLLIDAE

Cactaceae: The Cactus Family

Even though the Cactaceae are not important as trees, several attain treelike proportions, and their massive candelabra or organ-pipe appearance adds a unique aspect to landscapes of the southwestern United States and Florida Keys. They are an important source of shelter, water, and food for wildlife. Cacti are often the only woody plants in many parts of the arid west and form a characteristic vegetation including a tremendous variety of sizes and shapes.

The family includes 130 genera and about 1800 species of trees, shrubs, herbs, and vines. All are xerophytic stem succulents and indigenous to the western hemisphere. In terms of numbers, best development is reached in Central America and Mexico, although several are found in South America, and others occur in the United States. There are three genera of native cactus trees in North America, some reaching 50 to 60 ft tall and 2½ ft dbh.

The saguaro (pronounced *sa*-WAH-*ro*) is the best known and it forms one of the most striking features of the desert landscape. The largest individuals may be over 200 years old.

Botanical Features of the Family

Leaves of most cacti are reduced to spines, and even the spines may be lacking in some, so that photosynthesis takes place in the green, succulent stems; spines arise from swollen areas called *areoles,* and many cacti also have numerous, minute, barbed bristles (*glochids*) on the areoles.

Flowers usually perfect, insect/bird/or bat pollinated, actinomorphic, solitary, with many petaloid tepals which are white, yellow, or red; stamens many; ovary inferior.

Fruit a many-seeded berry, edible.

Carnègiea gigantèa (Engelm.) Britt. & Rose (*Cereus giganteus* Engelm.) Saguaro; giant cactus

The 2 to 10 erect branches are spiny, columnar, fluted with 12 to 30 vertical ribs, yellow-green, lacking glochids; 20 to 35(50) ft tall, 1 to 2½ ft dbh (Fig. 9-77). Flowers 2 to 3 in. (5 to 7.5 cm) across, the tepals white. Fruit 2 to 3½ in. (5 to 9 cm) long, a red or purple berry, edible, usually spineless. This occurs on rocky and gravelly soils of desert foothills, canyons, and outwashes in Arizona and southwestern California at 600 to 3600 ft of elevation.

DILLENIIDAE

Theaceae: The Tea Family

The tea family, including 40 genera and 600 species, is mainly tropical in distribution. In the southeastern United States, there are three genera and four species which are native trees and shrubs. The family is best known for the tea of commerce, *Camellia sinensis* (L.) Kuntze; the various highly ornamental cultivars of *Camellia japonica* L. and *C. sasanqua* Thunb. ex J. A. Murr.; and *Franklinia alatamaha* Bartr. ex Marsh.

FIGURE 9-77   *Carnegiea gigantea*. Saguaro cactus. (*Courtesy of U.S. Forest Service.*)

Franklinia is a tree of cultivation now, having last been seen in the wild in 1790 along the Altamaha River in coastal Georgia and now apparently extinct from its native habitat. The other natives are shrubs of *Stewartia,* silky camellia, and the loblolly-bay, described below.

Botanical Features of the Family

Leaves nonaromatic, simple, alternate, entire or serrulate, estipulate, deciduous or evergreen.

Flowers solitary, large, perfect, entomophilous; 5 sepals, 5 petals, many stamens, pistil single and superior.

Fruit a capsule or berrylike.

Gordònia lasiánthus (L.) Ellis   Loblolly-bay

Distinguishing Characteristics. *Leaves* persistent, elliptical to oblanceolate, 4 to 6 in. (10 to 15 cm) long, 1 to 2 in. (2.5 to 5 cm) wide, with small, blunt serrulations. *Flowers* solitary, 2 to 4 in. (5 to 10 cm) across, the 5 white petals fringed on the margin, the many golden-yellow, erect stamens conspicuous; appearing early to late summer. *Fruit* a capsule.

Range. Coastal Plain, eastern North Carolina to central Florida and west to southern Mississippi. Elevation: sea level to 500 ft. It is a common tree of wet habitats, pocosins, bays, swamp margins, and low flatwoods.

General Description. Trees to 60 ft tall with a narrow, compact crown. The leaf margins are frequently eaten by insects. See the discussion of "bay trees" under *Persea.*

Tiliaceae: The Linden Family

The Tiliaceae comprise about 50 genera and 450 species of trees, shrubs, and herbs, widely scattered throughout the world, but most abundant in the southern hemisphere. Jute, which consists of the bast fibers of several herbaceous species of the genus *Corchorus,* finds use in the production of papers, cordage, and coarse fabrics. *Elaeocarpus, Pentace, Grewia,* and *Tilia* are notable timber-producing genera. Although three genera of this family are found on the North American continent, only one, *Tilia,* is arborescent.

Botanical Features of the Family

Leaves deciduous, alternate, distichous, simple, stipulate.

Flowers perfect, actinomorphic, entomophilous, borne in cymes or corymbs; *sepals* 5; *petals* 5; *stamens* numerous, in multiples of 5; *pistils* 1, with a 2- to 10-celled, superior ovary.

Fruit a capsule, drupe, berry, or nutlike; seeds without endosperm.

TILIA L.   Basswood; linden; lime

Tilia includes perhaps 30 species widely distributed in eastern North America, Mexico, Europe, central China, and southern Japan. Several exotics are popular ornamentals in both eastern and western United States, particularly the European cut-leaf linden, *T.*

platyphyllos Scop. 'Laciniata'; the little-leaf linden, *T. cordata* Mill.; and the Japanese linden, *T. japonica* (Mig.) Simonkai. The American basswoods are also suitable for decorative use, while basswood honey is widely known in the eastern part of the country. The name basswood may have originated on account of the strong, tough bark or bast fibers which were used by primitive peoples for cordage of various sorts.

The classification of the North American basswoods has been problematical, with as many as 20 species in some earlier treatments to only one highly polymorphic species (Godfrey, 1988). Jones (1968) recognized three species; however, these intergrade, are highly variable, and with only a few distinguishing features, so it seems most realistic to recognize a single species, *T. americana,* with three varieties which have fairly distinct geographical ranges but with broad zones of secondary intergradation (Hardin, 1990).

Tília americàna L.   American basswood; American linden

Distinguishing Characteristics (Fig. 9-78)

Leaves 2½ to 7 in. (6 to 18 cm) long, 2 to 6¼ in. (5 to 16 cm) wide; *shape* broadly ovate to suborbicular; *venation* pinnipalmate; *margin* coarsely serrate; *apex* acuminate; *base* unequally cordate to almost truncate; *surfaces* nearly glabrous except for axillary tufts of hairs below to densely tomentose; *fall color* yellow to orange.

Flowers appearing in late spring when the leaves are nearly full grown, ½ to ⅝ in. (12 to 15 mm) wide, borne in few-flowered cymes, the peduncle long and slender, attached to a narrow, leaflike bract 4 to 5 in. (10 to 13 cm) long.

Fruit ¼ to ⅜ in. (6 to 10 mm) in diameter, short-ovoid or subglobose, nutlike, grayish tomentose; clustered at the end of a long peduncle attached to the persistent, leaflike bract; cotyledons palmately 5-lobed.

Twigs green to red; zigzag; *pith* homogeneous, terete; *terminal buds* lacking; *lateral buds* inequilateral, mucilaginous, usually with 2 to 3 visible scales; *leaf scars* half-elliptical; *bundle scars* numerous, scattered, not always distinct; *stipular scars* prominent.

Bark on young trees green or grayish green, later gray to brown, breaking up into narrow ridges, somewhat scaly on the surface.

General Description

Basswood is highly regarded as a timber tree. It varies from 70 to 80 ft in height and 2 to 3 ft dbh (max. 140 by 7 ft) with a long, clear, cylindrical, sometimes buttressed bole and deep, but wide-spreading, root system. Best development is reached on moist, deep, loamy soils. Because this tree is found in 16 forest types, the list of associates is lengthy. Some of the more common are eastern hemlock, northern red oak, red and sugar maples, white ash, yellow buckeye, American elm, and black cherry. American basswood is a very prolific sprouter and quickly regenerates by this means; in fact, the occurrence of a circle of sprouts around a stump or an old decadent tree is so characteristic that basswood can often be identified at some distance by this feature.

Seeds are borne almost yearly but require 2 years or longer for germination unless given special treatment. The young seedlings are easily recognized in the forest by their palmately 5-lobed cotyledons (Fig. 7-17), which look quite different from the mature basswood leaves. Subsequent growth is rather fast, and the tree matures in 90 to 140 years. Basswood is tolerant and

FIGURE 9-78 *Tilia americana.* Basswood. (1) Leaf × ½. (2) Bark of old tree and young sprout. (3) Inflorescence with bract × ½. (4) Fruits with persistent bract × ½. (5) Twig × 1¼.

will grow under a considerable cover, especially in youth. It is an important soil improver; in a study of the mineral content of the leaves of 24 hardwoods and softwoods, basswood was highest in calcium and magnesium and also yielded significant amounts of nitrogen, phosphorus, and potassium.

In addition to the valuable timber which it produces, basswood is highly prized in certain localities for its honey. The Iroquois and other Native Americans made rope from the bark by soaking it in water for several weeks or months to allow the nonfibrous portions to ret, after which it was twisted into the desired form. The leaves and twigs are browsed by deer and the fruits eaten by various birds and small mammals. There are a number of cultivars and they are popular street, park, and yard trees.

Tília americàna var. americàna   American basswood

Distinguishing Characteristics. *Leaves* nearly glabrous or puberulent with simple hairs except for tufts of hairs in the axils of the major veins below; green on both surfaces.

Range   Northeastern (Map 9-27). Elevation: sea level to 3200 ft. Moist bottomlands, rich coves, and slopes.

General Description.   This is the northern variety. It occurs as a codominant with sugar maple in the northwestern portion of the eastern deciduous forest (Braun, 1950).

Tília americàna var. heterophýlla (Vent.) Loud. (*T. heterophylla* Vent.)
White basswood; beetree

Distinguishing Characteristics. *Leaves* densely whitish or tan stellate-tomentose on the backs. The stellate hairs are closely matted and the surface is often glaucous. An occasional tree or shade leaves may become glabrate during the season.

Range.   Southwestern Pennsylvania, south to northwestern Florida, west to northeastern Mississippi, north to southern Illinois; disjuncts in western New York, Missouri, and northwestern Arkansas. Elevation: 200 to 5000 ft. Rich coves and slopes and mesic forests.

General Description.   This is the basswood of the southern Appalachians. It is a large tree and one of the frequent codominants, with yellow buckeye and sugar maple, in the cove hardwoods of the mountains (Braun, 1950). Populations north of North Carolina and west into Missouri are generally introgressants with var. *americana*.

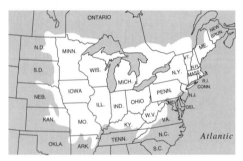

MAP 9-27   *Tilia americana* var. *americana;* distribution in southern Appalachians is var. *heterophylla*.

Tília americàna var. *caroliniàna* (Miller) Castigl. (*T. caroliniana* Miller and *T. floridana* Small)   Carolina basswood

Distinguishing Characteristics.   *Leaves* with the lower leaf surfaces tomentose with grayish or brownish, loose, easily detached, stellate and fasciculate hairs which either persist or are lost during the season; or, leaves puberulent from the beginning with a few fasciculate hairs along the main veins; pale or glaucous.

Range.   North Carolina, south to central Florida, west to central Texas, north to southeastern Oklahoma. Elevation: near sea level to 2000 ft. Mesic to drier flatwoods, edge of ponds, streams, and Florida sinks.

General Description.   This is a small tree of mixed hardwoods and pines of the southeastern Coastal Plain and outer Piedmont. Introgressants with var. *heterophylla* are common south into western Florida.

Tamaricaceae: The Tamarisk Family

This family of trees and shrubs includes four or five genera and 100 species and is native to Eurasia and Africa. Three species are naturalized.

Botanical Features of the Family

Plants halophytes and xerophytes with slender, upright, or spreading branches resembling those of a juniper.

Leaves small, simple, alternate, scalelike and appressed to the slender twig, estipulate, persistent or deciduous, with salt-excreting glands.

Flowers minute but showy, perfect with 4 or 5 sepals, petals, and stamens; ovary superior; white to pink, crowded in slender racemes, spikes, or panicles; appearing in the spring and summer; entomophilous.

Fruit a small capsule with hairy, windblown seeds.

Támarix chinénsis Lour.   Tamarisk; salt cedar

Referred to as *T. gallica* by earlier authors, tamarisk is not native and not an important forest tree, but it has been introduced as an attractive ornamental, a windbreak, and for erosion control. It is also an important honey tree. It is now naturalized in the southern United States and is a conspicuous and ecologically important tree of stream and river banks, lake shores, and marine shorelines. It is now weedy and of concern, particularly in the southwest, because of its deep roots and high water use. It grows to about 16 ft tall and 4 in. dbh and reproduces by seeds and root sprouts often forming dense thickets.

Salicaceae: The Willow or Poplar Family

The Salicaceae include two genera and about 350 species of trees and shrubs widely distributed throughout the world, but most abundant in the cooler regions of the northern hemisphere. The tropical species are restricted to mountainous regions, where they usually occur at or near timberline. The willow family, except for the genus *Populus,* is not currently a timber-contributing group of major importance, but many of its species are important in the natural regeneration of our forests, in conservation of soil and water, to wildlife, and popular as ornamentals.

The seeds of poplars and willows are short-lived and require abundant and continuous moisture for germination. Because of this they are, in nature, restricted to sites that are quite moist during the period of seed dispersal. In many species propagation by cuttings or root sprouts is exceptionally good, and this feature is of value in obtaining a network of fast-growing roots for erosion control, or rapid propagation of clones.

Certain species in this family are often difficult to separate from each other, and numerous natural hybrids have also been described. In contrast, some forms are very distinctive in appearance and are widely used as ornamentals. *Salix* and *Populus* are represented in North America by more than 120 species (Table 9-19).

Botanical Features of the Family

Leaves deciduous, alternate, simple, stipulate; the petioles often glandular.

Flowers imperfect (plants dioecious) or in some cases also androgynous; both sexes in aments, usually appearing before the leaves; individual flowers solitary, each subtended by a bract; *staminate* flowers with 1 to many stamens; *pistillate* flowers consisting of a 1-celled pistil with 2 to 4 parietal placentae bearing many ovules, the styles with 2 to 4, often 2-lobed stigmas; anemophilous and entomophilous.

Fruit a 1-celled, 2- to 4-valved capsule containing numerous small, comose seeds which are shed in late spring or early summer. These are extremely light in weight and are often carried considerable distances by wind. They rapidly lose their vitality, however, and unless a moist location is available soon after their release, they dry out and die. Given proper conditions, germination takes place rapidly, often within 24 to 48 hours.

SALIX L.   Willow

The genus *Salix* numbers about 300 species which are largely scattered through the cooler regions of the northern hemisphere. A few forms are tropical (Indonesia), and some are found in South Africa and southern South America. Others extend beyond the Arctic circle to the northern limits of tree growth, where they become greatly dwarfed and in some instances are actually reduced to a creeping or matlike habit. A

TABLE 9-19   COMPARISON OF GENERA IN THE SALICACEAE

Genus	Leaves	Flowers	Fruit	Buds
Salix willow	usually several times longer than broad; short-petioled	with nectar glands; bract margins entire	not inserted upon a disk	covered by a single caplike scale
Populus poplar	usually about as long as broad; long-petioled	without nectar glands; bract margins laciniate	inserted upon a disk	covered by several imbricated scales

number of shrubby forms serve as browse in the western cattle country, and the honey-bee obtains much of its pollen for rearing spring broods from the early flowering species. In the chemical history of aspirin, extract of willow bark was one of the precursors (Collier, 1963). Among the exotics commonly used for ornamental purposes are the graceful and stately weeping willow (*S. babylonica* L.) of eastern Asia; laurel willow (*S. pentandra* L.), white willow (*S. alba* L.), and crack willow (*S. fragilis* L.), all of European origin. The last two are common escapes and are found naturalized over a large portion of the eastern United States.

About 80 species of *Salix* are native to North America, but only about 30 of them attain tree size. Most of the commercial willow timber is produced by *S. nigra* Marsh. Hybridization and introgression occur among related, sympatric species.

Botanical Features of the Genus

Leaves alternate or rarely subopposite, distichous, mostly narrowly lanceolate to elliptical; margins entire or finely to coarsely toothed, usually short-petioled, or sessile; stipules often persisting for several weeks or longer.

Flowers (Fig. 9-79) entomophilous and also anemophilous, appearing before the leaves; aments ascending, the individual flowers (both sexes) with a basal nectar gland and a densely pubescent, entire-margined bract; *staminate* flowers with 1 to 12 (mostly 2) stamens; *pistillate* flowers with a single pistil composed of 2 carpels.

Fruit (Fig. 9-79) a 2-valved, 1-celled capsule containing a number of cottony or silky-haired seeds.

Twigs slender to stout, often brittle and easily broken at the base; glabrous, pubescent or hoary-tomentose; ranging through shades of red, orange, yellow, green, purple, or brown; lenticellate; *terminal buds* absent; *lateral buds* usually appressed, covered by a single caplike scale; *leaf scars* V-shaped, usually with 3 bundle scars; *stipular scars* often inconspicuous; *pith* homogeneous, terete.

FIGURE 9-79   *Salix.* Willow. (1) Pistillate ament × ¾. (2) Pistillate flower × 6. (3) Staminate ament × ¾. (4) Staminate flower × 6. (5) Capsule with stages of dehiscence and comose seeds × 5.

Sàlix nìgra Marsh.   Black willow

Distinguishing Characteristics (Fig. 9-80)

Leaves 3 to 6 in. (7.5 to 15 cm) long, ⅜ to ¾ in. (1 to 2 cm) wide; *shape* lanceolate, often falcate; *margin* finely serrate; *apex* acuminate, *base* obtuse or rounded; *surfaces* light green and somewhat lustrous above, glabrous (except on the veins) and green below; *petiole* short, terete; *fall color* yellowish.

Flowers terminal in aments, appearing on short leafy twigs; *staminate* flowers with 3 to 5 long, yellow stamens; *pistillate* with a solitary pistil and 2 nearly sessile stigmas.

Fruit a capsule ca. ¼ in. (6 mm) long, slender, ovoid-conic, short-stalked, glabrous.

Twigs slender, purplish green to pale orange-brown or yellow; *terminal buds* absent; *leaf scar* inconspicuous; *lateral buds* reddish brown or yellowish, ¹⁄₁₆ in. (1 to 2 mm) long.

Bark brown to nearly black, divided into deep fissures separating thick, interlacing, sometimes scaly ridges.

Range

Eastern (Map 9-28). Elevation: sea level to 5000 ft. River and stream banks, lake shores, wet depressions, ditches, and canals.

FIGURE 9-80   *Salix nigra.* Black willow. (1) Bark. (2) Leaf with stipules on twig × ½. (3) Fruiting ament × ¾. (4) Twigs with lateral buds × 1¼.

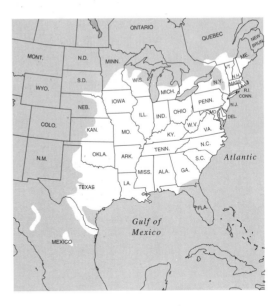

MAP 9-28   *Salix nigra.*

General Description

Black willow is a small to medium-size tree 30 to 60 ft high and about 14 in. dbh (max. 140 by 9 ft) with a broad, irregular crown and a superficial root system. Reproduction by seeds may be somewhat restricted for they must germinate on moist mineral soil soon after being shed; however, propagation by natural sprouts and root suckers is excellent.

Growth is rapid, and maturity is reached in 50 to 70 years. Like most willows, this species is very intolerant and is usually found as a dominant tree in hardwood mixtures or in pure stands. In the south, especially along the Mississippi River, pioneer well-stocked stands of black willow develop. On the best fine-textured alluvial soils, trees 40 years old may be 100 ft tall and nearly 20 in. dbh, with straight boles clear of limbs for as much as 40 ft.

Black willow is the largest and only commercially important of the willows and is used for furniture, cabinetwork, pulp, charcoal, and also as an ornamental.

POPULUS L.   Aspens, balsam poplars, and cottonwoods

The genus *Populus* consists of about 40 species widely distributed throughout the northern hemisphere, ranging from the forests of northern Africa, the Himalaya, China, and Japan northward beyond the Arctic circle. In the New World poplars are found from Alaska and Canada to northern Mexico.

Throughout much of the temperate world, races, ecotypes, clones, and hybrids are common. Within this rich variety, there are many whose form, foliage, and fast growth have attracted use as ornamental yard and street trees. Among the more important exotics in North America are the old world white poplar (*P. alba* L.) and the gray poplar [*P. ×canescens* (Ait.) Sm.] which have become naturalized and weedy in places; the Simon poplar (*P. simonii* Carr.), with its nearly rhombic leaves; the clones of Lombardy poplar (*P. nigra* L. 'Italica') with its fastigiate branches; and the widely cultivated Carolina poplar, *P. ×canadensis* Moench = *P. deltoides × P. nigra,* with only the staminate form known. The leaves of Carolina poplar may be distinguished from those of eastern cottonwood by their obtuse, usually eglandular bases and the finer serrations of the margin. The disadvantages of all these poplars as ornamentals include their early decline and breakup, insect pests and diseases, and aggressive root invasion which can clog sewers and drain pipes.

Another hybrid of interest is *P. ×gileadensis* Rouleau (*P. candicans* Ait.), called Balm-of-Gilead. The large, aromatic, resinous buds, known locally as "balm buds," are boiled and the steam inhaled or steeped in water and the liquid used as a folk medicine for pain, snakebite, broken bones, pulmonary problems, and many other ailments. The buds are rich in salicin, a glucoside that breaks down to salicylic acid. The effects of the buds may be similar to taking aspirin. Salicin is also readily hydrolyzed to saligenin which is of use as a pain reliever. "Balm-gilly" trees are still seen around old homesites in the northeastern United States and southern Appalachians.

Throughout the genus the high value of the wood as a source of pulp, veneer, and lumber coupled with some extremely rapid growth rates have prompted much activity by forest-tree geneticists. An enormous and highly successful project over the last half century has been the development of poplar hybrids. For historical perspective, see Schreiner (1949, 1950). Certain varieties (in the form of rooted cuttings) grow to be remarkable trees, even on spoil banks from coal mining. Average 10-year-old trees may be 30 ft tall and 5½ in. dbh. One 12-year-old tree was 56 ft by 10½ in. Pulpwood in 8 years, small logs in 15 years, and veneer stock in 20 years are entirely possible. To cover barren ground with a forest so quickly is a great environmental achievement.

About 10 species of *Populus* are native to North America, but only five or six of them occur in commercial size and quantity. Natural hybridization and introgression occur among related, sympatric species.

Botanical Features of the Genus

Leaves ovate to deltate (lanceolate or nearly so in *P. angustifolia* James and *P. ×acuminata* Rydb. of the Rocky Mountains); crenate-serrate, dentate, or lobed; usually with long, terete, or laterally compressed petioles.

Flowers anemophilous, in drooping aments appearing before the leaves, individual flowers (both sexes) solitary, inserted on a disk and subtended by a pubescent, fimbriate-margined bract; *staminate* flowers with either 6 to 12, or 12 to many stamens; *pistillate* flowers with a single pistil composed of 2 or 3 (rarely 4) carpels.

Fruit a 2- to 4-valved capsule containing a number of tufted seeds. The seeds are shed in large numbers and at the height of their dispersal, windblown masses of white "cotton" may accumulate to a depth of 6 in. or more in neighboring depressions.

Twigs stout to slender, mostly olive-brown to lustrous reddish brown, glabrous, pubescent, or hoary-pubescent; *terminal bud* present, resinous or nonresinous, covered by several imbricated scales; *lateral buds* of nearly the same size as the terminal bud, divergent or appressed, the first or lowest scale directly above the leaf scar; flower buds conspicuously larger; *leaf scars* nearly deltate to elliptical, with 3 bundle scars, either single or divided; *pith* homogeneous, stellate in cross section.

The genus includes three major groups of species, the aspens, balsam poplars, and cottonwoods (Table 9-20). In addition to the morphological differences indicated in the table, they also differ in range and habitat. Aspens are northern species and adapted to cold climates in either moist or dry soils. They are fire-adapted and readily sprout from roots when the trunks are burned or killed. The resulting clones can cover extensive areas. Balsam poplars are also northern in distribution and occur in swamps and along river banks. They also sprout from roots following fires and form clones. Cottonwoods are more southern in distribution and grow along river banks and in river bottomlands where they can withstand prolonged flooding.

Aspens

Pópulus tremuloìdes Michx.   Quaking aspen; trembling aspen; popple

Distinguishing Characteristics (Fig. 9-81)

Leaves with blades 1½ to 3 in. (4 to 7.5 cm) long and wide; *shape* suborbicular to broadly ovate; *margin* finely crenate-serrate; *apex* acute to acuminate; *base* cuneate, rounded, to subcordate; *surfaces* somewhat lustrous, green and glabrous above, duller and glabrous below; *petioles* laterally flattened, 1½ to 3 in. (3.8 to 7.5 cm) long; *fall color* bright yellow (Fig. 9-82).

Fruit ca. ¼ in. (6 mm) long, narrowly conical, curved, 2-valved.

Twigs slender, lustrous, reddish brown; *terminal buds* conical, sharp-pointed, sometimes very slightly resinous, covered by 6 to 7 visible, reddish-brown, imbricated scales; *lateral buds* incurved, similar to the terminal buds but smaller.

Bark smooth, greenish white to cream-colored, becoming furrowed with long, flat-topped ridges, dark brown or gray.

Range

Northern (Map 9-29). Elevation: sea level to 10,000 ft. Lowlands along streams and swamp margins, or upland slopes and valleys following fire.

General Description

Quaking aspen is the most widely distributed tree of North America. It is fast-growing, relatively short-lived, and commonly attains heights of 50 to 60 ft and dbh of 1 to 2 ft (max. 120 by 4½ ft). This tree is very intolerant and under competition develops a long, clear bole and small rounded crown. The root system is wide-spreading, and sometimes surface roots may extend

TABLE 9-20   COMPARISON OF ASPENS, BALSAM POPLARS, AND COTTONWOODS

Group	Flowers	Capsules	Buds
Aspens	with 6 to 12 stamens	thin-walled	essentially nonresinous
Cottonwoods and balsam poplars	with 12 to 60 stamens	thick-walled	resinous and aromatic

FIGURE 9-81 (1–3) *Populus tremuloides.* Quaking aspen. (1) Twig × 1¼. (2) Leaf × ½. (3) Bark. (4–6) *Populus grandidentata.* Bigtooth aspen. (4) Leaf × ½. (5) Bark of older tree. (6) Twig × 1¼.

nearly 80 ft from the base of the tree. Depending on soil depth and texture, other roots may go down 3 to 5 ft or more. Over its vast range, quaking aspen is found on many types of soil from moist loamy sands to shallow rocky soils and clay.

In old-growth forests this species occurred as a scattered dominant tree or along the edges of openings or water courses where there was sufficient light. Logging and subsequent fires usually destroyed the organic litter over wide areas and exposed mineral soil. Such sites are favorable to

FIGURE 9-82   Grove of quaking aspen in the fall. (*Courtesy of U.S. Forest Service.*)

aspen, an aggressive pioneer, and extensive pure stands of this species spring up and serve as a cover for the more tolerant northern conifers and hardwoods which develop slowly beneath this semiopen canopy. After 30 years or more, competition becomes excessive, much of the aspen dies, and the relatively few trees which are left maintain a position of dominance over the dense growth of other species below. In the lake states, these include the northern pines, spruces, and balsam fir, which in turn are finally replaced by hemlock and maples. Other aspen associates are many, including bigtooth aspen, paper birch, and balsam poplar, and in the west, Douglas-fir, lodgepole pine, and white fir.

Unless managed, a pioneer stand of aspen is transient, and although some individual trees may reach an age of 150 years (200 in the West), most lake states aspens over 60 years old are

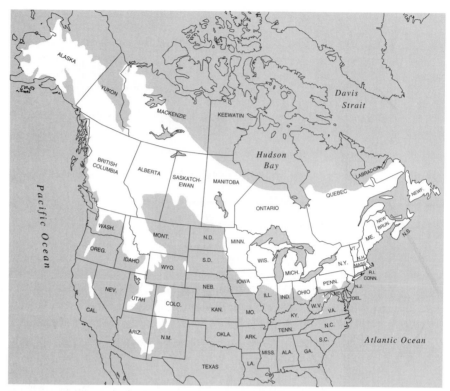

MAP 9-29 *Populus tremuloides.*

not worth harvesting because of their rapid deterioration. At least 500 organisms from deer and beaver to insects, fungi, and viruses feed on aspen (Graham et al., 1963). Trees are thin-barked, and until mature, they are easily killed by fire.

When aspen stands are cut or burned, innumerable root suckers grow quickly from those roots less than 3 or 4 in. deep and form a dense new forest. In Michigan, Minnesota, and Wisconsin, there are extensive areas of aspen forests which are valuable for pulpwood production and are easily regenerated by coppice systems.

Pópulus grandidentàta Michx.   Bigtooth aspen

Distinguishing Characteristics (Fig. 9-81).   *Leaves* with blades suborbicular to ovate, 2¾ to 5 in. (7 to 13 cm) long, usually larger than those of the preceding species, coarsely toothed, young leaves whitish tomentose; *petioles* 1½ to 2½ in. (3.8 to 6.3 cm) long, slender, flattened; *fall color* pale yellow to orange. *Fruit* similar to that of quaking aspen. *Twigs* often stouter than those of quaking aspen, dull, brownish gray; lateral buds gray, puberulous, divergent. *Bark* yellowish gray to tan and some with a green or orange cast, often not readily separated from that of the preceding species, later brown-gray and furrowed.

Range.   Southeastern Manitoba, east to Cape Breton, south to Virginia, west to northeastern Missouri; disjuncts in western North Carolina and central Tennessee. Elevation: sea level to 2000 ft northward, to 3000 ft in the southern mountains. Mesic to drier forests, floodplains, and uplands.

General Description.   Bigtooth aspen is a medium-size tree, 60 to 70 ft high and 2 ft dbh (max. 95 by 5 ft). It is similar in its silvical features to the preceding species. However, in the lake states, bigtooth aspen is less adaptable to site variation than quaking aspen and predominates on well-drained uplands of medium to good quality. With the cessation or control of forest fires, conditions are increasingly unfavorable for the development of new extensive stands of the highly intolerant aspens. Because under management these two species, especially bigtooth aspen, will produce in Michigan more wood per acre per year than any other tree native to the state (Graham et al., 1963), much effort has been made to develop effective silvicultural procedures.

Balsam Poplars and Cottonwoods

This group includes about six native species. Three are of primary importance (Table 9-21).

Pópulus balsamífera L.   Balsam poplar; Tacamahac poplar

Distinguishing Characteristics (Fig. 9-83)

   Leaves with blades 3 to 6 in. (7.5 to 15 cm) long and about half as wide; *shape* broadly ovate to ovate-lanceolate; *margin* finely crenate-serrate; *apex* abruptly acute to acuminate; *base* rounded or cordate; *surfaces* lustrous dark green, glabrous above, pale green or commonly with rusty brown blotches below; *petiole* terete, 2 to 3½ in. (5 to 9 cm) long; *fall color* yellow.

   Fruit ¼ to ⅓ in. (6 to 8 mm) long, ovoid, glabrous, 2-valved.

   Twigs moderately stout, reddish brown to dark brown, lustrous, lenticellate; *terminal buds* ovate to narrowly conical, covered by 5 imbricated scales sealed by a fragrant, amber-colored, sticky resin; *lateral buds* smaller, appressed, or divergent near the apex.

   Bark on young stems and limbs greenish brown to reddish brown, on older trunks eventually becoming gray to grayish black and dividing into flat, scaly or shaggy ridges separated by narrow, V-shaped fissures.

Range

Northern (Map 9-30). Elevation: sea level to 5500 ft in the Rockies. Lowland swamps, stream banks, floodplains, sandbars, and lower slopes.

TABLE 9-21   COMPARISON OF IMPORTANT POPLARS AND COTTONWOODS

Species	Leaves	Fruit
P. balsamifera balsam poplar	ovate-lanceolate; petiole terete	2-valved, glabrous
P. deltoides eastern cottonwood	deltoid; petiole compressed, glandular at the apex	3- or 4-valved, glabrous
P. trichocarpa black cottonwood	ovate-lanceolate; petiole terete	3-valved, pubescent

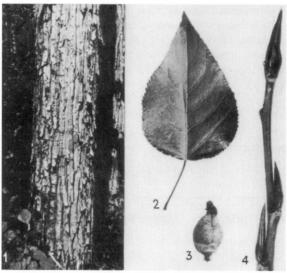

FIGURE 9-83 *Populus balsamifera.* Balsam poplar. (1) Bark. (2) Leaf × ½. (3) Capsule × 2. (4) Twig × 1¼.

MAP 9-30 *Populus balsamifera.*

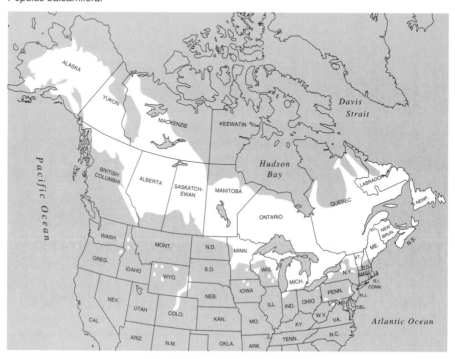

General Description

Balsam poplar is a fast-growing, medium-size tree 60 to 85 ft high and 12 to 24 in. dbh (max. 128 by 5 ft) with a long cylindrical bole, narrow, open, pyramidal crown, and shallow root system. It reaches its greatest size in the far northwest (Mackenzie River Valley of northwestern Canada). In this region, considered too cold for most trees, it is the largest, most characteristic species and occurs in open pure stands or mixed with other northern trees. Throughout its wide range, the associates of balsam poplar include balsam fir, white spruce, the aspens, and paper birch. Like other poplars, this species is intolerant. Besides the timber and pulpwood which it furnishes, balsam poplar serves as a cover crop for white spruce in certain sections of Canada.

Pópulus deltoìdes Bartr. ex Marsh.   Eastern cottonwood; eastern poplar

Distinguishing Characteristics (Fig. 9-84)

Leaves with blades 3 to 7 in. (7.5 to 18 cm) long, 3 to 5 in. (7.5 to 13 cm) wide; *shape* deltate to ovate-deltate; *margin* crenate-serrate, the teeth glandular; *apex* acuminate to acute; *base* truncate to cordate; *surfaces* lustrous green, glabrous above, somewhat paler and glabrous below; *petiole* flattened, 1½ to 3 in. (4 to 7.5 cm) long, glandular; *fall color* yellow to yellow-orange.

Fruit ca. ⅜ in. (10 mm) long, ovoid, 2- to 4-valved.

Twigs stout, angular, yellowish brown, glabrous; *terminal buds* ca. ¾ in. (18 mm) long, narrowly ellipsoidal to conical, lustrous brown, resinous, covered by 6 or 7 imbricated scales; *lateral buds* somewhat smaller, divergent.

Bark light greenish yellow or yellowish gray on young stems, eventually becoming ashy gray and dividing into thick, broad, flattened or rounded ridges separated by deep fissures.

Range

Eastern (Map 9-31). (This map includes the plains cottonwood, var. *occidentalis* Rydb. known also as *P. sargentii* Dode.) Elevation: sea level to 1000 ft eastward, and to 5000 ft westward. Floodplains, stream and river banks, valleys.

General Description

This species, the most important and largest of the eastern poplars or cottonwoods, is a medium-size to large tree 80 to 100 ft high and 3 to 4 ft dbh (max. 175 by 12 ft). Open-grown trees have a spreading crown supported by a massive trunk which is often divided near the ground and terminates below in an extensive superficial root system; in the forest, the bole is long, clear, and cylindrical, and the crown much smaller.

Not common in the northeast and Appalachian regions, eastern cottonwood, together with its varieties or closely related species, covers a wide range from the Rocky Mountains to the southern Atlantic Coast. It is especially common on moist alluvial soils through the plains and prairie states, where a winding belt of green cottonwood indicates the presence of a stream or water course. These "gallery forests" are a very characteristic aspect of the plains landscape and form the only natural shade and windbreak for hundreds of square miles. Although not found naturally on dry soils, this species was planted extensively around homesteads by the early settlers and when once established has proved to be relatively drought-resistant.

On the best alluvial soils in the Mississippi Valley growth is exceedingly fast, and young trees may grow 5 ft or more in height and 1 in. dbh yearly for the first 25 to 30 years. Cottonwood is very intolerant and occurs in pure strands or open mixtures with such species as black

FIGURE 9-84   *Populus deltoides.* Eastern cottonwood. (1) Twig × 1¼. (2) Leaf × ½. (3) Staminate aments × ½. (4) Staminate flowers, front and rear views × 3. (5) Pistillate flower and fimbriate-margined bract × 3. (6) Infructescences of capsules × ⅔. (7) Bark.

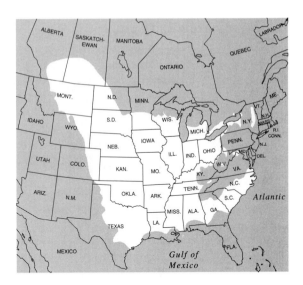

MAP 9-31 *Populus deltoides.*

willow, sycamore, American elm, and some of the bottomland oaks. In the South cottonwood may seed in heavily on old fields in mixture with sweetgum, by which it is eventually replaced.

Like other poplars, eastern cottonwood liberates large quantities of silky-haired seeds which may travel by air or on the surface of water for many miles. The small, tender seedlings initially grow very slowly and may be killed by high temperatures, brief moisture stress, or pelting rains. Propagation by unrooted cuttings is good, and young trees produced in this way make rapid growth. Cottonwood is a short-lived species, and growth peaks at about 45 years. Trees over 70 years old rapidly deteriorate, and the maximum life span is probably not greater than two centuries. Insects and diseases cause damage mainly in cultivated plantations. Fire is always a hazard. This tree is a favored browse plant of many animals. The wood is used for boxes, furniture, plywood, and pulp.

Pópulus trichocárpa Torr. & Gray   Black cottonwood; California poplar

Distinguishing Characteristics (Fig. 9-85)

Leaves with blades 3 to 6 in. (7.5 to 15 cm) long, 2 to 4 in. (5 to 10 cm) wide; *shape* ovate to ovate-lanceolate; *margin* finely crenate to crenate-serrate; *apex* acute to long-acuminate; *base* rounded or slightly cordate; *surfaces* dark green, glabrous above, rusty brown to silvery white, or occasionally pale green below; *petioles* 1½ to 3 in. (4 to 7.5 cm) long, terete in cross section; *fall color* yellow.

Fruit ⅓ to ¼ in. (8 to 13 mm) long, 3-valved, pubescent.

Twigs slender to moderately stout, orange-brown to light yellow-brown or greenish brown, slightly angular, lenticellate; *terminal buds* ¾ in. (18 mm) long, ovoid-conical, with 6 or 7 visible imbricated scales, resinous and giving a fragrant odor when crushed; *lateral buds* smaller, often divergent and falcate.

FIGURE 9-85   *Populus trichocarpa.* Black cottonwood. (1) Twig × 1¼. (2) Pistillate ament × ½. (3) Staminate ament × ½. (4) Staminate flower, bract removed × 3. (5) Pistillate flower, bract removed × 3. (6) Capsule × 2. (7) Dehiscing capsule with comose seeds × 2. (8) Leaf × ½. (9) Bark (*Photo by G.B. Sudworth, U.S. Forest Service*).

Bark tawny yellow to gray, and smooth on young stems; later, dark gray to grayish brown and separated by deep furrows into narrow, flat-topped ridges.

Range
Western (Map 9-32). Disjunct in southwestern North Dakota. Elevation: sea level to 2000 ft northward, to 9000 ft southward. Valleys, stream banks, floodplains, and upland slopes.

General Description
Black cottonwood, the largest of the American cottonwoods, is also the tallest broad-leaved tree of the Pacific Northwest. In the Puget Sound basin and vicinity, trees sometimes attain heights of 125 to 150 ft and dbh of 48 to 60 in. (max. 225 by 9 ft). Forest trees develop long, clear boles with narrow, cylindrical, round-topped crowns. This species occurs most frequently on moist, sandy, gravelly, or deep well-aerated alluvial soils. Dwarfed trees may be seen occasionally on poor, dry, sterile sites.

Black cottonwood forms limited pure stands and groves, especially on newly formed river bars. It also occurs with such species as Douglas-fir, western white pine, white spruce, western redcedar, western hemlock, paper birch, red alder, vine (*Acer circinatum* Pursh) and bigleaf maples, and numerous willows.

Large seed crops are released annually. The seed exhibits a high degree of viability, but its capacity to germinate is of very short duration. A moist sandy soil provides a suitable seedbed, and vigorous seedling development usually occurs on such sites. This species is very intolerant, and trees lacking vigor are soon suppressed by their more rapidly growing associates. Growth is quite rapid, particularly through the seedling and sapling stages. Trees on good sites grow fairly rapidly throughout their life span, with maturity being attained in about 150 to 200 years.

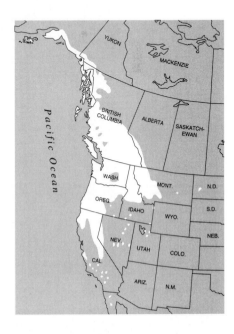

MAP 9-32   *Populus trichocarpa.*

Recently in the hardwood-deficient forests of the Pacific Northwest, much interest has developed in the cultivation of this species.

Pópulus angustifòlia James   Narrowleaf cottonwood

Distinguishing Characteristics.   *Leaves* with blades 2 to 5 in. (5 to 13 cm) long, ½ to 1 in. (1.2 to 2.5 cm) wide, lanceolate, apex acuminate, base rounded, margin serrulate, glabrous or nearly so, shiny green above, paler below; *petiole* short, laterally flattened at the base; *fall color* yellow. *Fruit* 2-valved.

Range.   In the west from southern Alberta and Saskatchewan south into northern Mexico and western Texas and from east central California east to western South Dakota and northwestern Nebraska; generally at 3000 to 9000 ft of elevation. Along stream banks and on moist, upland flats.

FIGURE 9-86   Narrowleaf cottonwood in Utah. (*Courtesy of U.S. Forest Service.*)

General Description.   Tree to 50 ft tall and $1\frac{1}{2}$ ft dbh with slender, upright branches (Fig. 9-86) and resinous buds. This is a common cottonwood in the northern Rocky Mountains and the southwestern United States. As the common name indicates, this has the narrowest leaf of all the poplars; willowlike. It is cultivated as a yard tree.

Pópulus fremóntii Wats.   Fremont cottonwood

Distinguishing Characteristics.   *Leaves* with blades 2 to 3 in. (5 to 7.5 cm) long and wide, broadly deltate, short-pointed at apex and nearly truncate at base, the margin coarsely crenate-serrate, glabrous; *petiole* $1\frac{1}{2}$ to 3 in. (3.7 to 5 cm) long, yellow, flattened; *fall color* bright yellow.

Range.   It is found from western Texas west to southern California, north to western Nevada, and east to southern Colorado. It is the common cottonwood at low elevations (to 6500 ft) in the southwest. This grows along stream and river bottoms with sycamore and willow and also in grasslands and woodlands.

General Description.   Tree 40 to 100 ft tall and 2 to 4 ft dbh with broad, flattened, open crown and light yellowish green leaves. It is a variable species with three recognized varieties (see Little, 1979).

Pópulus heterophýlla L.   Swamp cottonwood; swamp poplar

Distinguishing Characteristics.   *Leaves* with blades 4 to 7 in. (10 to 18 cm) long, 3 to 6 in. (7.5 to 15 cm) wide, ovate, crenate-serrate, cordate or rounded at the base; *petiole* $2\frac{1}{2}$ to $3\frac{1}{2}$ in. (6 to 8.5 cm) long, terete; *fall color* yellow. *Fruit* ovoid, 2- or 3-valved, long pedicelled. *Twigs* moderately slender, brownish gray, with an orange pith and slightly resinous, stout buds. *Bark* furrowed, somewhat scaly.

Range.   Along the Coastal Plain from southern Connecticut to northern Florida, west in the Gulf states to western Louisiana, and north in the Mississippi Valley to southern Illinois, Indiana, Ohio, and Michigan.

General Description.   Swamp cottonwood is a medium-size tree, 65 to 100 ft tall and 2 to 3 ft dbh, scattered through the bottomland forests of the southern Coastal Plain. It is similar in its habits to the other cottonwoods and, although utilized locally, is of secondary importance among the southern hardwoods.

Ericaceae: The Heath Family

The Heath family includes 125 genera and some 3500 species of trees, shrubs, rarely vines, and herbs widely scattered through the cooler regions of the world, but particularly abundant in southeastern Asia and South Africa. The family is of little consequence as a timber-contributing group, but several genera, *Rhododendron,* * *Kalmia, Enkianthus, Leucothoe, Pieris, Arctostaphylos,* and *Calluna,* include species which are highly prized for ornamental purposes.

The burls and root wood of briar, *Erica arborea* L., a small southern European tree, are used in making the bowls of tobacco pipes. Huckleberries (*Gaylussacia* spp.), as well as cranberries and blueberries (*Vaccinium* spp.), are important members of this family. The leaves of several shrubby genera, notably *Kalmia, Rhododendron, Leucothoe, Ledum,* and *Menziesia,* contain appreciable amounts of andromedotoxin, a substance which is

*This genus includes the "rhododendrons," which are mostly evergreen with campanulate flowers, and the "azaleas," which are deciduous with funnelform flowers. However, there is no constant distinction between the two groups.

very poisonous to livestock, particularly sheep. They are, however, browsed by deer in the winter without danger if eaten in small quantity along with other plants.

Certain of the above plants, as well as many others in this family, are of interest to the forester and ecologist on account of their widespread occurrence in acid bogs, where they often dominate the shrubby flora. When they are taken from their natural habitat, it is usually found necessary to keep the soil acid; otherwise these shrubs lose their vigor and often die. Of about 35 genera of the Ericaceae, two important genera in the United States are *Arbutus* and *Oxydendrum.*

Botanical Features of the Family

Leaves deciduous or persistent, alternate (rarely opposite or whorled), simple, estipulate.

Flowers perfect, mostly sympetalous and mainly 5-parted, actinomorphic or zygomorphic, entomophilous; ovary superior or inferior.

Fruit a capsule, berry, or drupe.

ARBUTUS L.   Madrone

This genus includes about 14 species scattered through the forests of the Mediterranean basin and North and Central America. The Pacific madrone is an evergreen tree native to western North America. Two other species are found in the Southwest.

Arbùtus menzièsii Pursh   Pacific madrone

Distinguishing Characteristics. *Leaves* persistent until the new leaves are fully grown, 2 to 5 in. (5 to 13 cm) long, oval to oblong, coriaceous, entire, or finely to coarsely serrate on vigorous growth; dark, shiny green above, pale to white below, shed in summer of second year, turning red before dehiscing. *Flowers* white, in drooping terminal panicles; appearing in early spring. *Fruit* an orange-red, berrylike drupe. *Twigs* slender, green, red, or brown; terminal buds ovoid, with numerous imbricated scales; lateral buds minute; leaf scars semicircular, with a single bundle scar. *Bark* very distinctive, dark reddish brown, dividing into thin, scaly plates which are deciduous during summer and fall.

Range. Coastal British Columbia south through western Washington and Oregon to southern California. Elevation: sea level to 5900 ft. Upland slopes and canyons, and low woods near coast.

General Description. Pacific madrone is a medium-size tree 80 to 125 ft tall and 2 to 4 ft dbh. In dense stands it forms a clear, symmetrical bole but is apt to produce a short, crooked trunk in rather open situations. The tree is found on a variety of soils but becomes shrubby on very poor sites. Best development is attained on well-drained soils near sea level. This species is quite gregarious and often forms nearly pure stands, although it occurs in much greater abundance as an understory species in Douglas-fir and redwood forests or in association with digger pine, ponderosa pine, California black oak, bigleaf maple, tanoak, red alder, and golden chinkapin.

The tree is a dependable annual seeder; the seeds exhibit a high percentage of viability, and germination is especially good in loose moist soils. Madrone appears able to endure dense shade throughout its life, although top light is conducive to more rapid growth.

The wood is used for furniture, interior trim, veneer, weaving shuttles, charcoal, and fuel. It is also a source of honey and used as an ornamental. Deer browse the leaves and branchlets, and the fruits are eaten by birds and small mammals.

OXYDENDRUM DC.   Sourwood

This is a monotypic genus and one of three trees of the Ericaceae in eastern United States.

Oxydéndrum arbòreum (L.) DC.   Sourwood

Distinguishing Characteristics.   *Leaves* deciduous, 3 to 8 in. (8 to 20 cm) long, 1 to 2¾ in. (2.5 to 7 cm) wide, sour-tasting, lanceolate or elliptic, narrowly serrulate at least toward the apex, essentially glabrous except strigose with stiff, straight hairs on the midrib below and petiole, apex acute, base rounded to cuneate; fall color dark red to scarlet or yellow. *Flowers* ca. ¼ in. (6 mm) long, white, pendent, and urn-shaped on elongated branches of a terminal, drooping panicle; appearing in midsummer. *Fruit* a gray capsule, about ⅜ in. (10 mm) long, held erect on the slightly drooping branches of the infructescence. *Twig* slender, yellow-green to red, buds partly embedded, leaf scars rounded with a single bundle scar, terminal bud lacking, stipular scars lacking, pith solid and homogeneous. *Bark* longitudinally furrowed and often blocky on large trees.

Range.   Southwestern Pennsylvania, central Virginia, and southeastern Maryland, south to northwestern Florida, west to Louisiana, north to southern Indiana. Elevation: near sea level to 5000 ft in the southern Appalachians. Mesic woods, bluffs, ravines, coves, slopes, and valleys.

General Description.   A small to medium tree, to 50 ft tall and 1 ft dbh, moderately intolerant and commonly found with mixed hardwoods or pine–hardwoods. The commercial importance is in the honey which brings a higher price than most other types. The foliage is browsed by deer.

RHODODENDRON L.   Rhododendron

This genus of rhododendrons and azaleas is one of the best known in horticulture and includes some 800 species found throughout the cooler and temperate portions of the northern hemisphere. About 21 species are native to North America, and many others have been introduced, especially from the Orient, for ornamental use. *Rhododendron macrophyllum* D. Don ex G. Don is the Pacific rhododendron of the Northwest and the state flower of Washington.

Rhododéndron máximum L.   Rosebay rhododendron; great
rhododendron

Distinguishing Characteristics (Fig. 9-87).   *Leaves* persistent, leathery, oblong, revolute. *Flowers* in large, showy terminal clusters, white to pink; appearing in late spring. *Fruit* an elongated sticky capsule with many extremely small seeds.

Range.   Mostly in the Appalachians and adjacent territory from southern New York to northern Georgia; also in Nova Scotia, Ontario, and Maine.

General Description.   This species is a very common and beautiful, large shrub or small tree and often forms extensive, almost impenetrable thickets, known locally as "rhododendron hells." It is the state flower of West Virginia. A very common associate is mountain-laurel, *Kalmia latifolia* L., with somewhat smaller leaves and abundant white to pink flowers. Together, these two species cover some 3 million acres of the southern Appalachians.

FIGURE 9-87   *Rhododendron maximum.* Rosebay rhododendron. (1) Flower bud × 1. (2) Infructescence × ½. (3) Inflorescence and leaves × ½. (*Photos by D. M. Brown.*)

Sapotaceae: The Sapodilla Family

This family of 70 genera and 800 species is pantropical in distribution with only a few temperate species. They are trees and shrubs with milky sap. Sapodilla [*Manilkara zapota* (L.) Royen], native of southern Mexico and Central America, has edible fruits and the latex, chicle, is used in chewing gum. It is widely cultivated in tropical regions. There are four species of *Bumelia* in the southern United States which reach tree size; only one is described here. *Bumelia* has recently been combined with the Old World genus *Sideroxylon.*

Botanical Features of the Family

Leaves alternate, simple, mostly estipulate, entire, coriaceous, often with dense *T*-shaped hairs, evergreen or deciduous.

Flowers small, perfect, white, in cymes; entomophilous; *sepals* and *petals* 4 to 12, each connate; *stamens* 3 to many, epipetalous; *ovary* superior, 2- to many-carpellate.

Fruit a berry with 1 to several large seeds.

Bumèlia lanuginòsa (Michx.) Pers.   Gum bumelia; woolly buckthorn

   Distinguishing Characteristics.   *Leaves* tardily deciduous, on spur branches, each 1 to 3 in. (2.5 to 7.5 cm) long, ⅜ to 1 in. (1 to 2.5 cm) wide, elliptical or obovate, apex round, base cuneate, margin entire, shiny dark green above, densely gray- or rusty-pubescent below. *Flowers* bell-shaped, 5-lobed, white, on clusters of long axillary pedicels; appearing in summer. *Fruit* ⅜ to ½ in. (10 to 12 mm) long, an elliptical black berry with one seed. *Twig* ending in a simple thorn to 19 mm long. *Bark* dark gray, furrowed with narrow, scaly ridges.

   Range.   Central Florida west to southern and western Texas, north to Kansas and central Missouri; disjunct in southwestern New Mexico and southeastern Arizona. Elevation: mainly to 2500 ft, but a southwestern variety to 5000 ft. Open, sandy woods of valleys and upland slopes.

General Description.   Tree to 50 ft tall and 1 ft dbh, with straight trunk and narrow crown of short, stiff branches, often thorny. The wood is used locally for cabinets and tool handles. The fruits are eaten by birds and small mammals.

Ebenaceae: The Ebony Family

The Ebenaceae include five genera and about 485 species of trees and shrubs widely scattered through the tropical and warmer forested regions of both hemispheres. However, previous to the Ice Age, ebenaceous plants flourished in Greenland and near the Arctic circle in both Asia and North America. The present floras of tropical Africa and those of the Indo-Malayan region are featured by many members of this family. While true ebony wood is produced by *Diospyros ebenum* J. König ex Retz., a number of other species also produce black or brownish black timbers which are marketed under the name of ebony.

Botanical Features of the Family

Leaves mostly deciduous, alternate, simple, entire, estipulate.

Flowers perfect and imperfect (plants usually dioecious or polygamous), small, actinomorphic, perianth 3- to 7-parted, each connate, stamens 3-many, ovary superior; entomophilous.

Fruit a berry with large seeds, edible, often with enlarged calyx attached.

DIOSPYROS L.   Persimmon; ebony

This is the largest genus of the Ebenaceae, with about 475 species, widely scattered through eastern and southwestern Asia, the Mediterranean region, Indo-Malaya, and North America. The very beautiful Macassar ebony (*Diospyros* spp.) comes from the Celebes Islands; *D. ebenum,* the true ebony, is largely produced in Ceylon; and *D. melanoxylon* Roxb. is a black Indian ebony.

Two species, common and Texas persimmon, *D. virginiana* and *D. texana* Scheele, respectively, are the only native members of this family found in the United States. Only the former is of any importance as a timber species. *Diospyros kaki* L.f., Japanese persimmon, is cultivated in the south for its very large, yellowish, edible fruits.

Botanical Features of the Genus

Leaves deciduous or persistent, entire.

Flowers regular (plant dioecious or polygamous).

Fruit globose, oblong, or pyriform, with 1 to 10 seeds, and subtended by the enlarged woody calyx, maturing after the leaves drop in the fall.

Dióspyros virginiàna L.   Common persimmon

Distinguishing Characteristics.   (Fig. 9-88). *Leaves* deciduous, 2½ to 6 in. (6 to 15 cm) long, 1½ to 3 in. (3.8 to 7.5 cm) wide, oblong-ovate to elliptical or oval, with a somewhat metallic luster, entire, venation slightly arcuate; fall color yellow to reddish. *Flowers* greenish yellow, somewhat urn-shaped or tubular, ⅜ to ⅝ in. (10 to 15 mm) long (plant dioecious), appearing in spring after the leaves. *Fruit* a subglobose berry, ¾ to 1½ in. (2 to 4 cm) in diameter, orange-

FIGURE 9-88 *Diospyros virginiana.* Common persimmon. (1) Bark. (2) Seed × ¾. (3) Berry × ¾. (4) Leaf × ½. (5) Tip of twig × 3.

colored, tinged with purple when ripe, with large seeds and subtended by the persistent woody calyx. *Twigs* moderately slender, grayish brown, glabrous or pubescent; terminal buds lacking, the laterals dark gray, covered by two overlapping scales; leaf scars lunate with a single bundle scar; pith intermittently homogeneous or chambered in the same twig. *Bark* blackish, broken up into small, conspicuous, square, scaly blocks.

Range. Southern Connecticut and Long Island, south to southern Florida, west to central Texas, north to southeastern Iowa. Elevation: sea level to 3500 ft. Dry flatwoods, upland woods, valleys, and bottomlands.

General Description. Common persimmon is ordinarily a small to medium-size tree, averaging 30 to 50 ft in height and 12 in. dbh (max. 130 by 4 ft). The bole is usually short with a shallow, or in youth moderately deep, root system and a characteristic round-topped crown. The tree is tolerant and is often found on moist bottomlands, where it occurs as scattered trees with other hardwoods; on old fields it may form thickets, and it is also very common along roadsides.

The fruit is exceedingly astringent when green, but edible when ripe, and is consumed locally. The distribution of persimmon depends largely on the widespread use of the fruit for food by a wide variety of animals, for the seeds are large and not readily disseminated by other means. Several varieties have been developed for fruit production. The wood is very hard and is used for furniture, veneer, weaving shuttles, and golfclub heads.

See under *Nyssa biflora* for ways of distinguishing sterile *Diospyros* from *Nyssa.*

Styracaceae: The Storax Family

This family has 10 genera and 150 species mainly in warm temperate and tropical areas of the Mediterranean region, Southeast Asia, and North and South America.

There are two genera native in the United States. They are trees and shrubs with resinous bark and usually stellate hairs on the leaves.

Botanical Features of the Family
Leaves alternate, simple, estipulate.
Flowers white, mainly perfect, regular; sepals and petals 4 to 8, distinct or connate; stamens 4 to many, usually epipetalous; carpels 3 to 5, connate, ovary superior or inferior; entomophilous.
Fruit a capsule, rarely samara, or dry or fleshy drupe.

Halèsia tetráptera Ellis (*H. carolina* and *H. monticola* of earlier authors)
Carolina silverbell

Distinguishing Characteristics.   *Leaves* 3 to 6 in. (7.5 to 15 cm) long, 1½ to 2½ in. (4 to 6 cm) wide, elliptical, acuminate at apex, margin serrulate, some stellate pubescence on the lower side; fall color yellow. *Flowers* white, drooping in clusters of 2 to 5, bell-shaped, ½ to 1 in. (1.2 to 2.5 cm) long, petals 4, connate; appearing before or with the developing leaves. *Fruit* oblong, 4-winged, 1¼ to 2 in. (3 to 5 cm) long, dry. *Twigs* brown, slender, stellate pubescent, bundle scar 1, stipular scars lacking, pith chambered, terminal bud lacking. *Bark* reddish brown, furrowed into loose, broad, scaly ridges.

Range.   West Virginia to southern Alabama and west to eastern Oklahoma. Elevation: ca. 1200 to 5500 ft. Moist, rich woods along streams, in coves, and on slopes of the mountains.

General Description.   Tree 30 to 80 ft tall. In flower in early to midspring, it is one of the very showy trees of the southern Appalachian slopes and coves.

The once commonly used name for this tree, *H. carolina,* should be applied instead to the little silverbell of the southeastern Coastal Plain (Duncan and Duncan, 1988; Godfrey, 1988; Reveal and Seldin, 1976).

Symplocaceae: The Sweetleaf Family
This is a small, monotypic family with about 350 species in moist tropics and subtropics of Asia and the Americas. There is a single species in the United States.

Symplòcos tinctòria (L.) L'Her.   Sweetleaf; horse-sugar

Distinguishing Characteristics.   *Leaves* alternate or appearing subopposite, simple, estipulate, deciduous or tardily so in the northern part of its range and evergreen further south, semicoriaceous, 3 to 5 in. (7.5 to 13 cm) long, 1 to 2 in. (2.5 to 5 cm) wide, elliptical or lanceolate, slightly serrulate or entire; fall color purplish green to bronze. *Flowers* small, 6 to 12 in dense, pale yellow clusters on the twigs before the new leaves appear, each perfect, actinomorphic, epigynous, with small, 5-parted calyx and corolla, but these nearly hidden by the many long stamens; entomophilous. *Fruit* an elliptical berry, ca. ⅜ to ½ in. (8 to 12 mm) long, greenish. *Twigs* glabrous to pubescent, light green, slender, pith chambered, bundle scar 1, estipulate. *Bark* gray, smooth or slightly furrowed.

Range.   Coastal Plain and Piedmont from southern Delaware to central Florida, west to eastern Texas, north into Oklahoma, Arkansas, and west Tennessee; in the southern Appalachians of western North Carolina and southeastern Tennessee southward. Elevation: below 1000 ft in the Coastal Plain and Piedmont; to 4000 ft in the Appalachians. Found on mountain slopes and ridges with mixed hardwoods and pine or in moist flatwoods and maritime forests.

General Description.   Shrub or small tree to 20 ft tall. The common names refer to the "sweetish" initial taste of the leaves which are eaten by livestock and wildlife. The "tinctoria" refers to the yellow dye once obtained from the leaves and bark.

ROSIDAE

Rosaceae: The Rose Family

The Rosaceae include about 100 genera and some 3100 species of trees, shrubs, vines, and subshrubs, widely scattered throughout the world but more numerous in temperate climates. From the standpoint of forestry, the family is relatively unimportant except for cherry wood, but it is extremely valuable, agriculturally, for apple, pear, plum, cherry, apricot, almond, peach, strawberry, loganberry, raspberry, blackberry, quince, and loquat. This family also includes a number of highly prized, ornamental genera such as *Spiraea, Crataegus, Physocarpus, Amelanchier, Sorbus, Rosa, Kerria, Rhodotypos, Pyracantha, Cydonia, Pyrus, Malus,* and *Prunus.*

Ten genera are represented by arborescent forms in the United States, but *Prunus* is the only timber-producing one of importance.

Botanical Features of the Family

Leaves deciduous or persistent; alternate (rarely opposite); simple, unifoliolate, or compound; mostly stipulate.

Flowers perfect, actinomorphic, 5- (rarely 4-) parted; stamens many; hypanthium present; ovaries inferior or superior; entomophilous.

Fruit a pome, drupe, follicle, or achene, rarely a capsule.

PRUNUS L.   Cherry; plum

This genus includes some 400 species of trees and shrubs which are widely distributed through the cooler regions of the northern hemisphere. Peach and nectarine, *P. persica* (L.) Batsch; garden plum, *P. domestica* L.; almond, *P. dulcis* (Mill.) D. A. Webb (*P. amygdalus* Batsch); apricot, *P. armeniaca* L.; sweet cherry (mazzard), *P. avium* (L.) L.; and the sour cherry, *P. cerasus* L., are all well-known members of this genus. There are also numerous cultivars of various species that are popular ornamentals for their flowers rather than fruits.

About 30 species of *Prunus* are included in the flora of the United States. Of the some 18 arborescent forms only *P. serotina* is important for timber.

Botanical Features of the Genus

Leaves deciduous or persistent, alternate, simple; usually with 2 glands on petiole just below the blade or on the base of the blade.

Flowers in terminal or axillary racemes, umbels, or corymbs, appearing before, with, or after the leaves; *perianth* perigynous; *calyx* 5-lobed; *petals* 5, separate, white or pink; *stamens* 15 to 20; *pistil* 1 (ovary 1-celled), superior but surrounded by the deciduous hypanthium.

Fruit a thin dry, or thick fleshy, 1-seeded drupe; pit bony, smooth, or rugose.

Twigs slender or stout, usually bitter to the taste, red to brown, often conspicuously lenticellate; *terminal buds* present, the scales imbricate; *lateral buds* of nearly the same size as the terminals; *leaf scars* semicircular for the most part, with scattered bundle scars; *stipular scars* present; spur growth is common in this genus.

Prùnus serótina Ehrh.   Black cherry

Distinguishing Characteristics (Fig. 9-89)

Leaves deciduous, 2 to 6 in. (5 to 15 cm) long, 1¼ to 2 in. (3 to 5 cm) wide; *shape* narrowly oval to oblong-lanceolate; *margin* finely serrate with callous incurved teeth; *base* cuneate; *apex* acuminate or abruptly pointed; *surfaces* dark green and very lustrous above, paler below, and at maturity usually with dense, pale or reddish-brown hairs along the midrib near the base of the leaf; *petiole* glandular just below the blade; *fall color* yellow to orange.

Flowers white, borne in racemes, appearing when the leaves are from half- to nearly full-grown.

Fruit ⅜ to ½ in. (8 to 12 mm) in diameter, depressed globose, almost black when ripe, ripening from June to October, flesh dark purple.

Twigs with a bitter almond taste, slender, reddish brown, or gray; usually with short spur shoots on older growth; *terminal buds* ca. ³⁄₁₆ in. (5 mm) long, ovoid, chestnut brown, with several visible scales; *lateral buds* similar but smaller; *leaf scars* small, semicircular; *bundle scars* 3, often not distinct; *stipular* scars minute.

Bark on young stems smooth, reddish brown to nearly black, with conspicuous, narrow, horizontal lenticels; on older trunks (Fig. 9-90) exfoliating in small, persistent, shiny, platy scales with upturned edges.

Range

Eastern (Map 9-33). Elevation: sea level to 5000 ft in the southern Appalachians; 4500 to 7500 ft in the southwest. Dry to mesic forests, fence rows, old fields, and edges of woods.

General Description

Black cherry is a medium-size tree 60 to 80 ft high and 2 to 3 ft dbh (max. 129 by 7 ft). In the forest it develops a long, straight, clear, cylindrical bole, a narrow oblong crown, and a relatively shallow root system. Best growth is made on rich, deep, moist soils where the tree may occur in pure stands of limited extent, or more commonly mixed with such species as northern red oak, white ash, sugar maple, basswood, white pine, and hemlock. In the northeast this species often reaches commercial proportions in virgin forests of the red spruce–white pine–northern hardwood association on sandy soils. In these and other dense stands, old-growth black cherry is usually a dominant tree because of its intolerance and early rapid growth. Open-grown cherry on good sites may grow 3 ft in height and ½ in. dbh a year for the first 20 years. In some studies, this tree at age 60 was 80 to 100 ft high and 20 to 24 in. dbh.

Some seed is produced yearly with large crops at 1- to 5-year intervals; they are spread by birds and under favorable conditions show a 90 percent germination rate. Regeneration by sprouts is also good. Black cherry attains an age of 150 to 200 years. Because of its thin scaly

FIGURE 9-89   *Prunus serotina.* Black cherry. (1) Twig × 1¼. (2) Inflorescence × ½. (3) Infructescence of drupes × ½. (4) Leaf × ½. (5) Bark of young tree. (6) Bark of old tree.

bark, it is severely damaged by surface fires. The defoliating eastern tent caterpillars and cherry scallop shell moth are the major insect pests. The black knot fungus and many other fungus pathogens often restrict the development and utility of cherry.

The wood is prized for furniture, paneling, and handles; the inner bark for medicine; and the twigs and leaves are a good deer browse and rabbits feed on seedlings. Partially wilted leaves can cause cyanide poisoning in livestock.

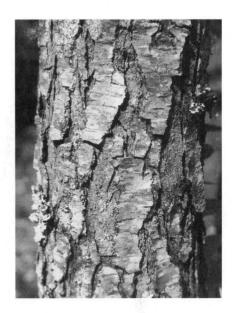

FIGURE 9-90   *Bark of black cherry.*

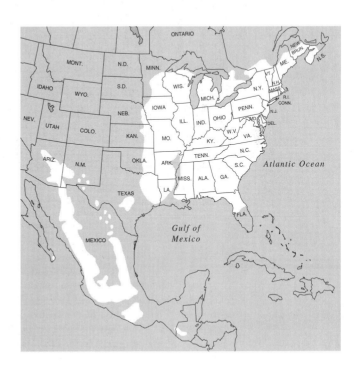

MAP 9.33   *Prunus serotina.*

Prùnus pensylvánica L.f   Pin cherry; fire cherry

Distinguishing Characteristics.   *Leaves* thin, yellow-green, usually narrower, more lance-olate, prolonged acuminate, and less shiny than those of black cherry; fall color bright yellow or red. *Flowers* borne in umbels. *Twig* with lens-shaped lenticels. *Bark* more reddish on young stems.

Range.   British Columbia to Newfoundland, south to northern Georgia, west to Colorado. Elevation: sea level to 6000 ft in the southern Appalachians. Clearings, often after a fire.

General Description.   Pin cherry is a common species occurring in and quickly invading disturbed or burned areas. It is a small tree of more ecological than commercial importance. The fruits are important for birds and small mammals, and the leaves and branchlets are important deer browse.

Prùnus virginiàna L.   Chokecherry

Distinguishing Characteristics.   Shrub or small tree with sharply serrate, obovate leaves and racemose flowers; fall color yellow; dark red or blackish drupes.

Range.   Together with its several varieties it covers nearly the entire northern continental United States and also a large area in Canada; sea level to 8000 ft of elevation. Found in moist soils of open sites.

General Description.   This species is very common along hedgerows where the seeds are left by birds. In sections where rabbit damage to other hardwoods and even conifers is extreme, it flourishes untouched, while in certain northern forest plantations it is practically the only species to survive in frost pockets where exceedingly low winter temperatures prevail. Chokecherry sprouts prolifically, and this, together with its general hardiness, seems to ensure its success even under the most extreme conditions. Although usually classed as a forest weed, this species may be useful in erosion control and is used in the plains states in shelterbelts. The fruits are an important food for many wildlife.

Prùnus subcordàta Benth.   Klamath plum

Originating from Oregon and California, it has nearly rounded leaves and produces a dark red or yellow, edible drupe.

Prùnus emarginàta Dougl. ex Eaton   Bitter cherry

It is a tree of widespread occurrence in both the northern Rocky Mountains and Pacific regions from British Columbia to southern California, and eastward in Arizona and western New Mexico. It has oblong-obovate leaves and bright red drupes turning black at maturity.

MALUS Mill.   Apple

This genus numbers about 30 species of trees and shrubs scattered throughout the forests of the northern hemisphere. The most important species is ***Màlus sylvéstris*** (L.) Mill. (*M. pumila* Mill.), the common apple. This tree was introduced in colonial times and is now naturalized over a large portion of the United States. The leaves are elliptical to ovate, whitish pubescent below and along the petiole; the young twigs and buds are somewhat white tomentose, and the former have a characteristic semisweet taste. There are a number of native species of little or no importance as timber producers. It is the state flower of Arkansas and Michigan.

PYRUS L.   Pear

This genus includes about 20 species distributed through Europe, Asia, and northern Africa. The introduced common pear, *Pỳrus commùnis* L., escapes cultivation and the tree bears a superficial resemblance to the apple. The leaves of the pear, however, are thinner, more lustrous, and nearly glabrous; the twigs are less pubescent and often have a thorn terminating a spur branch.

SORBUS L.   Mountain-ash

Of about 80 species, four are found in the United States, two in the east, and two in the west. The common eastern species is *Sórbus americàna* Marsh., American mountain-ash. It is a small tree or shrub common to rocky hillsides and spruce-fir forests in the Appalachians and is easily recognized by its alternate, glabrous, odd-pinnately compound leaves with 13 to 17 lanceolate, acuminate, sharply serrate leaflets, fall color red; clusters of bright red fruits; twig with resinous buds and an odor of almond when broken.

The European mountain-ash or rowan tree, *Sorbus aucuparia* L., with numerous cultivars, has been introduced for ornamental purposes. It differs from the native species in its white pubescent twigs and leaflets, nonresinous buds, and acute to obtuse leaflets. It has escaped from cultivation in certain sections and is often found growing wild in Alaska and across southern Canada and the northern United States.

AMELANCHIER Medic.   Serviceberry; shadbush; juneberry

This genus comprises about 16 species, and one or more of them is found in every state and province of the United States and Canada. They are important deer browse, and the fruits are eaten by humans and wildlife. Of some 10 species native to the United States, seven reach small tree size. The name "shadbush" often used for these trees, is based on the flowering time which is the same as when the shad "run the rivers" to spawn.

Amelánchier arbòrea (Michx. f.) Fern.   Downy serviceberry

Leaves singly serrate, oblong to elliptical, white tomentose at flowering but becoming smooth, the petioles pubescent; fall color yellow to red. *Flowers* white in small racemes, appearing just before or with the developing leaves; petals long and strap-like. *Fruits* like very small, reddish to purple apples and quite edible. *Bark* gray, often streaked with darker lines. *Twigs* with a faint bitter-almond taste, the terminal buds are slender, ¼ to ½ in. (6 to 12 cm) long. This small tree occurs in moist woods from New Brunswick south to northern Florida, west to eastern Texas, and north to eastern Minnesota. It is most common at low elevations. There are also many cultivars planted as ornamentals.

Amelánchier laèvis Wieg. [A. arborea var. laevis (Wieg.) Ahles]   Allegheny serviceberry

It differs from *A. arborea* by having bronze-colored young leaves, leaves glabrous or puberulent and at least half-grown at flowering, petioles and pedicels glabrous, and pomes purple-black and sweet. It is found from Minnesota to Newfoundland, south to eastern Kansas, Missouri, Indiana, Ohio, Delaware, and in the Appalachians to Georgia and Alabama, generally at 3000 to 6000 ft of elevation. It is very showy with its white flowers in the spring.

Amelánchier alnifòlia (Nutt.) Nutt.   Western serviceberry or shadbush

This shrub or small tree, 20 to 40 ft tall, extends along the coast from southeastern Alaska to northern California, and eastward to southwestern Ontario and Wisconsin. It has purple to blue-black pomes; smooth, gray, and often muscular-appearing stems; and leaves which are usually entire below the middle.

CRATAEGUS L.   Hawthorn; thornapple

Crataègus is a very complex genus because of interspecific hybridization and apomixis (Dickinson, 1985). Approximately 35 aborescent species may be recognized in the United States (Little, 1979, 1980a and b). The group is of considerable interest to the plant taxonomist, but the identification of closely related forms is not usually attempted. All are shrubs or small trees with simple serrate or lobed leaves and branches which are armed with thorny modified branchlets and fruits like small apples (Fig. 9-91). The hawthorns are typical of open pastures, where they are often aggressive and difficult to eradicate. Certain species are used as ornamentals. These are important for deer and cattle browse and Figure 9-91, part 1, shows the typical effects of overgrazing on pasture trees.

The Legumes

The legumes consist of about 630 genera and nearly 15,500 species of trees, shrubs, lianas, and herbs widely scattered throughout the world. They are second only to the grasses in their economic importance. Among the herbaceous species are such important forage and food plants as clover, vetch, alfalfa, bean, soybean, peanut, and pea.

FIGURE 9-91   *Crataegus.* Hawthorn. (1) Pasture trees after grazing. (2) Inflorescence × ¾. (3) Pomes and seed × ¾. (4) Thorn × 1. (5) Twig × 1½

They are also important for forest products such as lumber, tannins, gums, resins, dyes, and drugs. Several are important as crop weeds or poisonous to livestock. Legumes often have root nodules containing nitrogen-fixing bacteria of great value in enriching the soil.

Legumes have long been classified in one family, Leguminosae or Fabaceae s. lat., on the basis of the entomophilous flower, single superior carpel, generally compound (rarely simple) leaves, and the unique fruit type (the *legume*) which normally splits along two sutures, or it may remain indehiscent. As a single family it was then divided into three subfamilies based mainly on floral morphology. It is felt now that these three groups are more consistent with the customary concepts of *families* of flowering plants and they are treated that way here (Table 9-22). However, the phylogenetic relationships are still not well resolved, and with additional investigation, it may be appropriate to again combine the three groups into one family (Judd et al., 1994).

Mimosaceae: The Mimosa Family

This is a family of 40 genera and 2000 species. One of the common native genera is *Prosopis* which includes the mesquites of the Southwest. These are spiny trees and shrubs characteristic of desert and dry prairie landscapes. The leaves and pods are edible and are most important to the existence of many species of wildlife. The wood is hard and durable and is also used in outdoor cooking for its aromatic smoke. *Acacia* is another tree of the southern United States. This is a very large genus with 1200 species widely distributed in the tropics and subtropics. Many species are used extensively for such products as gums, tannings, wood, fuel, food, forage, dyes, perfumes, and as cultivated ornamentals.

TABLE 9-22   COMPARISON OF THE THREE LEGUME FAMILIES

Family	Symmetry	Stamens	Petals	Leaves
Mimosaceae	Actinomorphic	much larger than petals; 4–10 to many	usually valvate, fused	mostly bipinnate
Caesalpiniaceae	slighly to strongly zygomorphic	usually 10 and same length or shorter than petals; 10 usually separate	imbricate, upper petal inside lateral petals; 2 lower petals separate	bipinnate, pinnate, or 1-foliolate
Fabaceae	strongly zgomorphic	usually 10 and same length or shorter than petals; 10 either separate or fused into a filament tube, or 9 fused and 1 separate	imbricate, upper petal outside lateral petals (wings); 2 lower petals usually fused (keel)	pinnate, or 1-foliolate; pinnate, or palmately compound

Albízia julibríssin Durazzini   Silktree; mimosa

Distinguishing Characteristics. *Leaves* bipinnate, 6 to 15 in. (15 to 38 cm) long, leaflets ⅜ to ⅝ in. (10 to 15 mm) long, with the major vein near the leading margin, the margins entire. *Flowers* many in a round head, each flower small but with long stamens whitish at base and pink to red toward the ends; appearing after the leaves. *Fruit* a flat legume, 5 to 8 in. (13 to 20 cm) long. *Twig* with 3-lobed leaf scars and 3 bundle scars, stipular scars present, pseudoterminal bud; pith solid.

Range. Mimosa is a native of Asia from Iran to China and Japan, and it is widely planted as an ornamental. It has escaped and become naturalized in the midwestern and southeastern United States mainly along roadsides, disturbed areas, and edges of woods.

General Description. This is a tree with a short trunk and broad, flattened crown to 20 ft tall. It is a showy tree, flowering over a long period during the summer. The leaflets fold up at night.

Caesalpiniaceae: The Caesalpinia Family

This family has about 150 genera and 2200 species of trees, shrubs, lianas, and herbs. Seven aborescent genera are represented in North America, with *Gleditsia* being the most important timber tree.

GLEDITSIA L.   Honeylocust

This genus includes about 14 species of trees scattered through the forests of North and South America, eastern and central Asia, and tropical Africa. They produce little timber, although several species are highly prized for ornamental purposes.

The genus is represented in the United States by two species. *Gleditsia aquatica* Marsh., waterlocust, is an unimportant bottomland species of the south, while *G. triacanthos,* the honeylocust, is a tree of secondary commercial importance. *Gleditsia ×texana* Sarg. is a commonly occurring hybrid between these two.

Botanical Features of the Genus

Leaves deciduous, alternate, 1- to 2-pinnately compound, often clustered on 2-year-old twigs, stipules inconspicuous.

Flowers perfect and imperfect (polygamous and often functionally dioecious), regular, greenish yellow, borne in axillary spikelike racemes; *calyx* 3- to 5-lobed; *petals* 3 to 5; *stamens* 6 to 8, distinct; *pistils* with 2 to many ovules.

Fruit either an elongated, compressed, many-seeded, usually indehiscent legume, or a short, few seeded, tardily dehiscent legume; seeds suborbicular, with endosperm.

Twigs stout, conspicuously zigzagged, armed with heavy, 3-branched (rarely 2- to many-branched) thorns; *pith* homogeneous; *terminal buds* lacking; *lateral buds* partly submerged, superposed, scaly; *leaf scars* U-shaped; *bundle scars* 3; *stipular scars* lacking.

Gledítsia triacánthos L.   Honeylocust

Distinguishing Characteristics (Figs. 9-92 and 9-93)

Leaves both pinnate and bipinnately compound, the pinnate with 15 to 30 nearly sessile leaflets, the bipinnate leaves with 4 to 7 pairs of pinnae, 4 to 8 in. (10 to 20 cm)

FIGURE 9-92 *Gleditsia triacanthos.* Honeylocust. (1) Twig × 1¼. (2) Branched thorn × 1¼. (3) Bipinnate leaf × ½. (4) Once-pinnate leaf × ½. (5) Bark.

FIGURE 9-93   Legume and seed of honeylocust × ½.

long; *leaflets* ⅜ to 1¼ in. (1 to 3 cm) long, ½ to ⅞ in. (1.3 to 2.2 cm) wide on pinnate leaves, smaller on bipinnate ones; *shape* of leaflets ovate, ovate-lanceolate, or elliptical; *margin* crenulate; *apex* acute or rounded; *base* acute or inequilateral; *surfaces* glabrous, dark green, lustrous above; dull yellow-green, glabrous or nearly so below; *rachis* grooved above, pubescent, swollen at base; *fall color* yellow.

Flowers small, perfect and imperfect, appearing before the leaves; *petals* greenish white; *pistil* with many ovules.

Fruit a reddish-brown to purplish-brown, strap-shaped, usually twisted legume, 6 to 18 in. (15 to 45 cm) long and about 1 in. (25 mm) wide; *seeds* oval, dark brown, ⅓ in. (8 mm) long, surrounded by sweet-tasting, yellow-green pulp.

Twigs greenish brown to reddish brown, lustrous, with 3-branched (rarely simple or 1-branched) thorns, 2 to 3 in. (5 to 8 cm) long; *lateral buds* minute, superposed.

Bark on mature trees grayish brown to nearly black, often conspicuously lenticellate, broken up into long, narrow, longitudinal, and superficially scaly ridges which are separated by deep fissures; often with clusters of large, many-branched thorns.

Range

Eastern (Map 9-34). The map shows its original range, much extended now through the eastern United States, from New England to South Carolina, by cultivation and naturalization. Elevation: sea level to 2000 ft. Floodplains of streams and rivers, lake shores, hammocks, old fields, fence rows, and limestone upland woods.

General Description

Honeylocust is a medium-size tree 70 to 80 ft high and 2 to 3 ft dbh (max. 140 by 6 ft), with a rather short bole and open, narrow or spreading crown; the root system is wide and deep. Root sprouts are frequent. Although commonly found on rich, moist bottomlands or on soils of a limestone origin, this species is very hardy and drought-resistant when planted elsewhere, especially in the plains and prairie states, where it has been widely used as windbreaks. When trimmed, honeylocust makes a desirable tall hedge, which soon becomes impassable because of the many forbidding thorns.

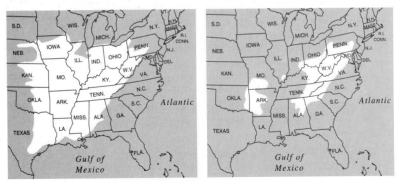

MAP 9-34   **(Left)** *Gleditisia triacanthos* (original range; now naturalized east to the coast and planted in the western states). **(Right)** *Robinia pseudoacacia* (original range; now naturalized from Maine to California and southern Canada).

Good seed crops occur nearly every year. Growth is rapid, and maturity is reached in about 120 years, although older trees are sometimes found. Honeylocust is intolerant, and hence it occurs in the open or as a dominant tree in the forest, in mixture with other bottomland hardwoods including Nuttall and willow oaks, sweetgum, green ash, American elm, red maple, and black tupelo. Honeylocust, though a legume, does not appear to have root nodules.

This species undoubtedly owes its name to the legumes with the sweetish pulp between the seeds. When green, these pods are eagerly eaten by cattle and wildlife, and the propagation of thornless honeylocust to be planted as a pasture tree has been recommended. Seed dispersal is by stream waters, wind, deer, cattle, and rodents.

The thornless *G. triacanthos* f. *inermis* (Pursh) Schneid. is sometimes found growing wild, and in recent years clones of it have been planted by the thousands as street or yard trees in cities. Certain of the cultivars bear no fruit. Many American elm shade trees killed by the Dutch elm disease are being replaced by the thornless, podless honeylocust; thus a tree previously rare in cities has become exceedingly common. It is probably overused for it is attacked by several insects and fungous diseases.

Strong, durable, honeylocust wood has been used for bows, construction lumber, and fence posts; the thorns and pods have been used for various items by local people.

Cércis canadénsis L.   Eastern redbud

Distinguishing Characteristics. *Leaves* alternate, unifoliolate (appearing simple), blade nearly orbicular or reniform, 2½ to 5 in. (6 to 12.5 cm) long and wide, entire margined, membranaceous, and glabrous; *petioles* 1½ to 4 in. (4 to 10 cm) long; with upper and lower pulvini; fall color yellow. *Flowers* bright pink, clustered and appearing before the leaves in early spring. *Fruit* a flat legume, 2½ to 3¼ in. (6 to 8 cm) long, turning black. *Twig* slender, brown to black with small, black, rounded buds often superposed, leaf scar with a fringe at the top, 2 or 3 bundle scars, stipular scars lacking, and pseudoterminal bud. *Bark* smooth, dark gray to black.

Range.   New Jersey south to central Florida, west to southern Texas, north to southeastern Nebraska. Elevation: sea level to 2200 ft. Rich, moist, mixed deciduous or pine woods.

General Description.   This is a small tree to about 45 ft tall and commonly used as an ornamental. The pink flowers are very showy in the spring, often contrasting with the white of flowering dogwood.

California redbud, *C. occidentàlis* Torr. ex Gray, is similar except for a more leathery leaf and shorter petioles and occurs along mountain streams, dry hillsides, or in canyons in California, southern Nevada, southern Utah, and Arizona.

Chinese redbud, *C. chinensis* Bunge, is becoming popular as an ornamental.

Gymnócladus dioìcus (L.) K. Koch   Kentucky coffeetree

Distinguishing Characteristics.   *Leaves* alternate, deciduous, bipinnate, 12 to 32 in. (30 to 80 cm) long; leaflets 2 to 2½ in. (5 to 6 cm) long, ¾ to 1½ in. (2 to 4 cm) wide, with acute apex; fall color yellow. *Flowers* imperfect (trees dioecious), white to purplish in large panicles, appearing in spring after the leaves. *Fruit* (Fig. 9-94) a hard, thick pod, 4 to 7 in. (10 to 18 cm) long, 1½ to 2 in. (4 to 5 cm) wide, dark reddish brown, with a thick, inedible pulp surrounding the large seeds. *Twig* stout, brown, with large leaf scars and thick salmon colored to brown pith, bundle scars 3 to 5, terminal bud lacking, lateral buds partly concealed, stipular scars present. *Bark* gray, deeply furrowed into narrow scaly ridges.

Range.   Southern Ontario, east to central New York, southwestward to Oklahoma, north to southern Minnesota; cultivated and naturalized eastward. Elevation: 300 to 2000 ft. Valleys and mixed forests, never common.

General Description.   This is a medium to large (100 ft) tree. The roasted seeds were once used as a substitute for coffee; however, raw seeds and the pulp between them are poisonous.

Fabaceae s. str. (Papilionaceae): The Bean or Pea Family

This family, with about 440 genera and 11,300 species, is the largest, most advanced, and economically the most important of the three legume families. There are eight genera and 11 species reaching tree size in the United States.

FIGURE 9-94   *Gymnocladus diocious.* Kentucky coffeetree. (1) Twig × 1¼. (2) Legume and seed × ½.

ROBINIA L.   Locust

Robinia includes about 10 species of trees and shrubs, all of which are found in the United States and Mexico. Several of these have ornamental value, and *R. pseudoacacia* is a timber tree of some importance. Four species reach tree size in the United States.

Botanical Features of the Genus

Leaves deciduous, alternate, pinnately compound, mostly spinose-stipulate.

Flowers perfect, papilionate, borne in racemes which appear just after the leaves; *calyx* 5-lobed; *corolla* consisting of a large obcordate standard, 2 obtuse wings, and an incurved keel; *stamens* 10, diadelphous; *pistil* with many ovules.

Fruit a many-seeded, nearly sessile legume; *seeds* reniform, without endosperm.

Twigs moderately stout, angular, somewhat zigzag, reddish brown, usually with stipular spines at least on vigorous branches; *pith* homogeneous; *terminal buds* lacking; *lateral buds* naked, submerged beneath the leaf scar, often superposed; *leaf scars* broadly ovate to somewhat reniform; *bundle scars* 3.

Robínia pseudoacàcia L.   Black locust

Distinguishing Characteristics (Fig. 9-95)

Leaves 6 to 14 in. (15 to 35 cm) long, pinnately compound with 7 to 19 subopposite or alternate leaflets; *leaflets* 1½ to 2 in. (4 to 5 cm) long, ½ to ¾ in. (12 to 18 mm) wide; *shape* elliptical, ovate-oblong, or ovate; *margin* entire; *apex* mucronate or notched; *base* rounded; *surfaces* dull, dark blue-green, glabrous above, paler and glabrous, except for slight pubescence on the midrib, below; *fall color* yellow.

Flowers ca. ¾ in. (18 mm) long, white, fragrant, in a drooping raceme.

Fruit a flat, brown, oblong-linear, glabrous legume, 2 to 4 in. (5 to 10 cm) long and ca. ½ in. (12 mm) wide; *seeds* 4 to 8, ca. ³⁄₁₆ in. (5 mm) long, reniform.

Twigs (see generic description).

Bark on mature trees reddish brown to nearly black, deeply furrowed into rounded, interlacing, fibrous, superficially scaly ridges. The inner bark contains a poisonous principle; stock have died from browsing the bark or young shoots, and children have been made ill by chewing them.

Range

East central (Map 9-34). Elevation: 500 to 5000 ft. Now naturalized throughout southern Canada, the United States, and parts of Europe and Asia. Cove forests and open, upland slopes, fence rows, disturbed ground, and also limestone soils.

General Description

Black locust is a medium-size tree 40 to 60 ft high and 1 to 2 ft dbh (max. 100 by 7 ft), and on good sites it may develop a clear straight bole. However, there are several growth forms of this species, and certain trees are spreading in habit with poorly developed trunks. The root system, although often shallow and wide-spreading, may develop several very deep roots, and in the arid Southwest, such vertical roots may be from 20 to 25 ft long. The crown is open and irregular. This tree does best on moist, rich, loamy soils or those of limestone origin, but is

FIGURE 9-95 *Robinia pseudoacacia.* Black locust. (1) Twig with stipular spines and buried buds × 1¼. (2) Leaf × ½. (3) Inflorescence × ½. (4) Legume × ¾. (5) Dehisced legume with seeds × ¾. (6) Bark.

very cosmopolitan and is found on a wide variety of sites, especially old fields and similar cleared areas.

Abundant seed is produced almost every year. Black locust is a fast-growing species, especially in youth, when on the best soils it will average 2 to 4 ft in height a year. It is intolerant and is not found in dense woods except as a dominant tree. Some associates are dry-soil oaks, hickories, yellow-poplar, white ash, black walnut, eastern redcedar, and shortleaf and Virginia pines. When cut, this locust sprouts vigorously from stump and roots; in this way it spreads across abandoned fields.

Black locust was once planted extensively for railroad ties and fence posts, but on certain sites the locust borer has severely damaged—even destroyed—whole plantations. Tree vigor is the important factor, and fast-growing trees on the best soils exhibit the greatest resistance. Black locust is used for erosion control and spoil-bank stabilization. It is naturally restocking large areas in the southern mountains. Like most legumes, this species improves the soil through the nitrogen-fixing bacteria in root nodules; the leaf litter decomposes very rapidly, releasing much nitrogen, calcium, and potassium.

The wood swells or contracts very little with changes in moisture content and therefore finds a special use for such items as insulator pins and "tree nails," the latter once used in wooden-ship construction. Deer browse the foliage and birds and small mammals eat the seeds.

There are several forms of this species; one of these (a clone or mixture of clones), shipmast locust, *R. pseudoacacia* var. *rectissima* Raber, is especially valuable because of its tall, straight bole, and fewer branches.

Black locust was introduced into Germany very early (about 1601) and has now become in Europe one of the most widely distributed of exotic North American trees.

Robínia neomexicàna Gray   New Mexico locust

Distinguishing Characteristics. *Leaves* pinnate, 4 to 10 in. (10 to 25 cm) long, with 13 to 21 leaflets, each ½ to 1½ in. (1.2 to 4 cm) long, ¼ to 1 in. (6 to 25 mm) wide, elliptical, with bristle tip, entire; fall color yellow. *Flowers* purplish pink, in drooping racemes, appearing in late spring and early summer after the leaves. *Fruit* a flat legume, 2½ to 4½ in. (6 to 11 cm) long. *Bark* light gray, furrowed into scaly ridges.

Range. Southeastern Nevada, east to southern and central Colorado, south to western Texas, west to southeastern Arizona. Elevation: 400 to 8500 ft. Canyons and moist slopes.

General Description. Spiny tree to 25 ft tall and 8 in. dbh. It is planted as an ornamental and for erosion control. Foliage and flowers are browsed by livestock and wildlife; Native Americans ate the flowers and pods.

Cladrástis kentúkea (Dum.-Cours.) Rudd [*Cladrastis lutea* (Michx. f.) K. Koch]   Yellowwood

Distinguishing Characteristics. *Leaves* 8 to 12 in. (20 to 30 cm) long, pinnate with (5)7 to 9(11) leaflets, alternate or subopposite on the rachis, each 2½ to 8 in. (6 to 20.5 cm) long, 1¼ to 5 in. (3 to 12.5 cm) wide, broadly elliptical, abruptly acuminate. *Flowers* appearing with the leaves, white, fragrant, in drooping panicles ca. 1 ft (30 cm) long; the lower keel petals separate. *Legume* thin, flat, indehiscent, pendent, 1 to 3 in. (3 to 8 cm) long, ⅜ to ½ in. (8 to 11 mm). *Bark* smooth and gray. *Twig* with leaf scars nearly encircling the bud, which is short, naked, and golden pubescent; bundle scars 3 to 9; terminal bud absent; stipular scars lacking; pith solid.

Range. This is a rare tree; Kentucky, southwestern Virginia, and western North Carolina, south to Alabama, west to eastern Oklahoma; disjunct in southern Indiana. Elevation: 300 to 3500 ft. Stream banks, moist mountain coves and slopes, and limestone cliffs.

General Description.   Yellowwood is a tree to 50 ft tall and 1½ ft dbh and very showy in flower. It is cultivated as an ornamental tree, and the yellow heartwood is used for paneling, gunstocks, or turning into platters or bowls. The nomenclature is somewhat debatable, and both names are found in the current literature.

Elaeagnaceae: The Oleaster Family

This is a small family of three genera and 50 species in warm temperate to subtropical regions. They are deciduous or evergreen trees and shrubs with silvery or brown stellate hairs or scales (lepidote) on the twigs and leaves. The roots have nodules with nitrogen-fixing bacteria; see under *Myrica*. The genus *Elaeagnus* has one shrubby species, silverberry, native to Alaska, western Canada, and the northern Great Plains. Two Asiatic shrubs, autumn elaeagnus and thorny elaeagnus, have become naturalized and weedy in many areas. Russian olive deserves more description below.

Botanical Features of the Family
Leaves deciduous or persistent, alternate (rarely opposite or whorled), simple, entire, estipulate.
Flowers in late spring and early summer, solitary or in small umbels, perfect or imperfect (plant dioecious), regular, with 2 to 4 connate sepals, no petals, stamens 2, 4, or 8, carpel 1 superior to appearing inferior, entomophilous.
Fruit an achene surrounded by a fleshy calyx tube and drupelike in appearance.

Elaeágnus angustifòlia L.   Russian-olive

This is a deciduous shrub or small tree to 25 ft tall, sometimes with spiny twigs, and covered with silvery or brownish scalelike, stellate trichomes on twigs, leaves, flowers, and fruits. *Leaves* alternate, 1½ to 3¼ in. (4 to 8 cm) long, ⅜ to ¾ in. (1 to 2 cm) wide, lanceolate or oblong, entire, gray-green. *Flowers* bell-shaped, ca. ⅜ in. (1 cm) long, fragrant, axillary. *Fruit* drupelike, ⅜ to ½ in. (1 to 1.2 cm) long, elliptical, yellow to pinkish, sweet. It is a native of Europe and Asia and has been planted as an ornamental, for erosion along rivers, and as windbreaks in the plains. It has become naturalized and locally weedy in moist woods, along streams and rivers, and on slopes throughout the United States and southern Canada. The silvery lepidote leaves and twigs make this particularly attractive as a yard, park, or street tree, and the fruits are eaten by birds and small mammals.

Myrtaceae: The Myrtle Family

A tropical and subtropical family with 140 genera and over 3000 species, it is found mainly in the southern hemisphere, particularly South America and Australia. None are native in North America, but several trees are widely cultivated in the southern United States and California and some have become naturalized, weedy, and conspicuous components of many areas.

They are evergreen trees or shrubs with alternate (*Eucalyptus*), opposite or whorled, simple leaves, which are entire, punctate-leathery, and aromatic when crushed; the flowers are showy, with a thick hypanthium and 4 or 5 petals and many stamens; the fruit is a berry or capsule; pollination is done by insects, birds, or bats.

Some trees are extensively cultivated for the fruit (guava, surinam cherry), spices (cloves, allspice), eucalyptus oil used in medicines, or as ornamentals (bottlebrush, eucalyptus). Two genera have become important in the United States. *Eucalýptus* spp. from Australia have been introduced and widely planted as ornamentals in the southern United States, mainly California and Florida. Some have become naturalized in California and form extensive forests. They have been planted for their attractive leaves and bark, rapid growth, and for windbreaks, soil stabilization, and fuel. The highly flammable leaves and twigs, however, are a dangerous and unwanted fuel during wildfires in California. These are tall trees to 120 ft tall and 3 ft dbh, evergreen, with narrow, leathery leaves on drooping branches and with an odor of camphor when crushed, and mottled green and brown bark. Some species are grown in plantations in various parts of the world for pulpwood, fuel, and lumber (Zobel et al., 1987), and form possibly the world's most productive industrial forests (Laarman and Sedjo, 1992).

Melaleùca quinquenérvia (Cav.) S. T. Blake   Cajeput-tree; Punktree

This tree is a native of Australia but has become naturalized in southern Florida, particularly in the Everglades. It is so prolific and widespread by small, windblown seeds, that it is now detrimental and of great environmental concern.

Cornaceae: The Dogwood Family

The Cornaceae s. l., including the Nyssaceae, has about 15 genera and 120 species of trees, shrubs, and few herbs scattered through the forests of the northern hemisphere (Table 9-23). See Eyde (1988) for the reasons for maintaining one family.

Botanical Features of the Family

Leaves deciduous, alternate or opposite, simple, usually entire, estipulate.
Flowers perfect or imperfect, 4- or 5-parted, ovary inferior, entomophilous.
Fruit a drupe or berry.

CORNUS L.   Dogwood or cornel

Cornus is a genus of small trees and shrubs (rarely herbs) numbering about 40 species. Except for a single Peruvian form, the dogwoods are restricted to the northern hemisphere. Probably the best known of the exotic ornamentals in North America are the cornelian cherry, *Cornus mas* L., and kousa dogwood, *C. kousa* Hance.

TABLE 9-23   COMPARISON OF THE NATIVE GENERA OF THE CORNACEAE S. LAT.

Genus	Leaves	Twigs	Fruit
Cornus dogwood	usually opposite; veins arcuate	pith homogeneous; bud scales 2, valvate	blue, white, or red drupe; 1–2 seeds; pit barely grooved
Nyssa tupelo	alternate; veins not arcuate	pith diaphragmed; bud scales 3–5, imbricate	blue or purple drupe; pit winged or ridged; 1-seeded

Sixteen species of *Cornus* are native to the United States, and 11 attain tree size. These are of but minor importance and only two of them will be considered in detail.

Cornus alternifolia L., alternate-leaf dogwood or pagoda dogwood, with alternate leaves, greenish-brown twigs, and blue fruit, is a small tree of the east; *Cornus drummondii* C. A. Meyer, rough-leaf dogwood, is a shrub or small tree of the central United States with leaves having scattered, bristly hairs on the upper surface; *Cornus occidentalis* (Torr. & Gray) Cov., western dogwood, is a large shrub or small tree native to the Pacific northwest with hairy inflorescence branches.

Botanical Features of the Genus

Leaves opposite, or rarely alternate, with entire or finely toothed margins, and arcuate venation.

Flowers perfect, usually small, in terminal cymes, panicles, or large-bracted heads; flower parts in 4s, calyx and corolla present.

Fruit a red, white, blue, or green 2-celled, 2-seeded drupe.

Córnus flórida L.   Flowering dogwood

Distinguishing Characteristics (Fig. 9-96).   *Leaves* opposite, oval, arcuately veined, fall color dark red. *Flowers* in heads, with four very conspicuous white or pink, notched bracts; appearing before the leaves. *Fruit* a bright red drupe. *Twigs* slender, somewhat angled, purplish or greenish with a glaucous bloom; *terminal flower* buds subglobose and stalked, *leaf buds* acute, and covered with two valvate scales. *Bark* broken up into small blocks.

Range.   Southern Michigan, southern Ontario, and southern Maine, south to central Florida, west to eastern Texas, and north to central Missouri. Elevation: sea level to 5000 ft in the southern Appalachians. Hardwood and mixed conifer forests, mountain slopes, and coves.

General Description.   Flowering dogwood is a small, bushy, tolerant tree which rarely attains a height of more than 40 ft and dbh of 12 to 18 in. The trunk is short with little taper; from 6 to 10 ft above the ground it usually breaks up into several large, wide-spreading limbs resulting in a low, dense crown. Best development is reached as an understory species in association with other hardwoods. This tree is usually found on well-drained friable soils. Its leaves are exceptionally rich in calcium and fluorides. Shallow-rooted, dogwood is very drought-sensitive. Flowering dogwood is a widely used ornamental with numerous cultivars and makes a striking display when it is in full bloom in the early spring, and then with the red fruit and red autumn leaves. It is the state flower of North Carolina and Virginia. All parts are important deer browse, particularly in the spring. The wood is white and hard and used for spools and small pulleys; they were once used for shuttles for weaving, but these have now been replaced by plastic.

Dogwood anthracnose, a damaging fungous disease, has spread through the Northeast, south to South Carolina on flowering dogwood and in the West on Pacific dogwood. It has the potential to cause major destruction to the native stands.

Córnus nuttállii Audubon   Pacific dogwood

Distinguishing Characteristics (Figs. 9-97, 9-98).   *Leaves* opposite, ovate to obovate. *Flowers* in heads, with 4 to 7 white, acute or truncate bracts, appearing in spring and early summer or sporadically until fall. *Fruit* a bright red to orange-red drupe. *Twigs* similar to those of the preceding species. *Bark* smooth or with thin scaly plates near the base of the tree.

FIGURE 9-96 *Cornus florida.* Flowering dogwood. (1) Twig × 1¼. (2) Flower bud × 1¼. (3) Head with 4 white bracts and small central flowers × ½. (4) Flower × 3. (5) Cluster of drupes × 1. (6) Leaf × ½. (7) Branch in flower (*Photo by C. A. Brown*). (8) Bark.

Range. Southwestern British Columbia, south to western Oregon, and in mountains to southern California. Elevation: sea level to 6000 ft. Moist slopes and valleys as an understory of conifers.

General Description. This species is a small tree, rarely ever attaining a height of more than 60 ft or a dbh of 12 to 20 in. Best development is reached in the Puget Sound Basin and in the redwood belt of California. Under forest conditions it develops a slightly tapered stem which extends through the crown, but in more open situations the bole is commonly short and supports a number of spreading limbs forming an ovoid to rounded-conical crown, or it may break up at

FIGURE 9-97 *Cornus nuttallii.* Pacific dogwood. (1) Leaf × ½. (2) Head of flowers with 5 bracts × ¾.

FIGURE 9-98 Bark of Pacific dogwood.

the ground into several nearly erect stems resulting in a bushy habit. Pacific dogwood is one of North America's finest ornamental trees. The tree is peculiar in that it frequently flowers a second time during the late summer while the fruits of the first flowering are turning red. The snowy-white bracts and the brilliant red fruits against a background of lustrous green foliage produce an extremely beautiful effect.

NYSSA L.   Tupelo

The genus consists of five arborescent or shrubby species. One of these occurs in central and western China, another from the Himalaya to Java, and the remaining species are in the eastern United States (Table 9-24). Fossil leaves, pollen, fruit, and wood of many Tertiary *Nyssa* species are widely distributed across Europe, Asia, and North America. Large numbers of fruits are found in the brown coal of Brandon, Vermont (Eyde, 1963).

Botanical Features of the Genus

Leaves deciduous, alternate, simple, petiolate, often crowded toward the tips of the twigs, especially on side branchlets.
Flowers perfect or imperfect (plant polygamo-dioecious), appearing with or before the leaves, small, greenish white, borne in capitate clusters, racemes, or solitary.
Fruit an ovoid or oblong drupe, with a 1-celled, 1-seeded, winged or ridged pit.
Twigs slender to stout, glabrous, greenish brown, olive-brown, tan, or reddish brown; *pith* mostly diaphragmed; *terminal buds* present, with several imbricated scales; *lateral buds* similar but smaller; spur growth often abundant; *leaf scars* reniform to semicircular; *bundle scars* 3.

Nýssa aquática L.   Water tupelo

Distinguishing Characteristics (Figs. 9-99, 9-100, 9-101, and 9-102)
    Leaves 5 to 8 in. (13 to 20 cm) long, 2 to 4 in. (5 to 10 cm) wide; *shape* oblong-obovate; *margin* entire to repand-toothed near apex; *apex* acute to acuminate; *base* cuneate to rounded; *surfaces* dark green and lustrous above, paler and more or less downy below; *fall color* red.

TABLE 9-24   COMPARISON OF IMPORTANT SPECIES

Species	Leaves	Fruit	Twigs
N. aquatica water tupelo	5–8 in. (13–20 cm) long, oblong-obovate, sometimes irregularly toothed	ca. 1 in. (2.5 cm) long, reddish purple; the pit prominently ribbed	stout, buds globose, ⅛ in. (3 mm) or less in diameter
N. sylvatica black tupelo	2–5 in. (5–13 cm) long, obovate, rarely toothed	⅜–½ in. (9–12 mm) long, blue-black; the pit indistinctly ribbed	slender; buds ovoid, ¼ in. (6 mm) long, commonly divergent

FIGURE 9-99   *Nyssa aquatica.* Water tupelo. (1) Twig × 1¼. (2) Staminate inflorescence × ¾. (3) Leaf × ½. (4) Drupes × ¾. (5) Pit showing ridges × 1½.

FIGURE 9-100   Fruit pits of *Nyssa* × 1. (1) N. *aquatica.* (2) *N. sylvatica.* (3) *N. biflora.* (4) *N. ogeche.*

FIGURE 9-101   Water tupelo swamp. Note buttresses and high water marks. (*Courtesy of U.S. Forest Service.*)

FIGURE 9-102   Bark of water tupelo. (*Photo by J. C. Th. Uphof.*)

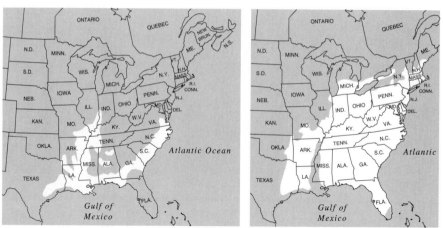

MAP 9-35   **(Left)** *Nyssa aquatica.* **(Right)** *Nyssa sylvatica* and *N. biflora.*

Flowers appearing in March and April; *staminate* in dense clusters; *pistillate* solitary on long slender peduncles; stamens present, often functioning.

Fruit pendent on slender stalks; ca. 1 in. (3 cm) long, oblong, dark reddish purple; *pit* light brown to whitish and conspicuously ribbed with about 10 thin ridges.

Twigs rather stout, reddish brown; *pith* diaphragmed; *terminal buds* yellowish, usually small and somewhat globose or rounded, $\frac{1}{16}$ to $\frac{1}{8}$ in. (1.5 to 3 mm) in diameter; *lateral buds* small and inconspicuous; *leaf scars* rounded; *bundle scars* 3, conspicuous.

Bark thin, brownish gray with scaly ridges.

Range

Southeastern (Map 9-35). Elevation: sea level to 500 ft. Floodplain forests, swamps, pond and lake margins.

General Description

Water tupelo is a medium-size to large tree 80 to 90 ft high and 3 to 4 ft dbh (max. 110 by 8 ft). The trunk is buttressed at its base but tapers rapidly to a long, clear bole; the crown is rather narrow and usually open. Water tupelo is one of the most characteristic of southern swamp trees and is found on sites which are periodically under water. For a short time during the summer, this tree may be found on dry ground, while in the fall, winter, and spring the water is often 3 to 6 ft deep over the same area (Fig. 9-101). Water tupelo occurs in almost pure and very dense stands or mixed with baldcypress, which is its almost constant associate. Others include overcup and water oaks, black willow, swamp cottonwood, red maple, sweetgum, and slash pine.

This tupelo is a prolific annual seeder, and the heavy seeds are distributed by water, birds, and rodents. Following the recession of high water, they become lodged in the mud and may germinate even after more than a year of submergence. The growth of trees on moist but well-drained bottomlands is rapid, while that of trees standing on extremely wet sites is much slower. Water tupelo is intolerant, and on the better sites is suppressed by other species.

The timber is commercially important for lumber, veneer, and pulp, and the root wood, which is especially light and spongy, is used locally for bottle corks and fishnet floats. Tupelo

honey is an important item in a number of localities where the trees are abundant; l.
famous gourmet tupelo honey is from the ogeechee tupelo mentioned later.

Nýssa sylvática Marsh.   Black tupelo; blackgum; sourgum

Distinguishing Characteristics (Figs. 9-100, 9-103).   Black tupelo differs from the pr.
ing species as follows: *leaves* smaller, 2 to 5 in. (5 to 13 cm) long, 1 to 3 in. (2.5 to 7.5 .
wide, obovate and usually entire or with 1 or 2 large teeth on the upper third of the blade; f.
color orange-yellow to brilliant red to dark red; *fruit* in clusters of 4 or 5, smaller, ⅜ to ½ in. (.
to 12 mm) long, with an indistinctly ribbed pit; *twigs* more slender, and the ovoid terminal buds
are ca. ¼ in. (6 mm) long; *bark* "blocky," or with the appearance of alligator hide; and the base
of the trunk is less swollen.

Range   Eastern (Map 9-35). Elevation: sea level to 4000 ft. Mesic forests, swamp borders,
also dry slopes.

General Description.   Black tupelo is usually a medium-size tree, 50 to 60 ft high and 2 to
3 ft dbh (max. 139 by 5 ft). Best growth is made on moist alluvial soils with some drainage, but
the tree is very cosmopolitan and also grows on relatively dry upland sites. It is found in 29 forest-cover types, and its associates include both wet-soil and dry-soil hardwoods and softwoods.

Large trees are often hollow all the way to the ground, because of various decay-producing
fungi and many wood-boring insects. However, the tree may continue to grow for many
decades, adding new wood and increasing its girth each year while the hollow cavern in its
trunk gets larger as well. Such trees are of no value for lumber but are a boon to wildlife, for the
hollow center can provide shelter for several generations of wildlife species from insects and
nesting birds to rabbits, squirrels, 'possums, and even hibernating bears. The tree can still bear
leaves, be browsed by deer, and berries eaten by birds and various mammals. In earlier days,

FIGURE 9-103   *Nyssa sylvatica*. Black tupelo. (1) Twig × 1¼. (2) Leaf × ½. (3) Drupes × ¾. (4) Bark.

hollow gum logs were often cut and used for "bee gums," "rabbit gums," or storage containers for various other items (Elliott, 1994).

The wood is soft and light, but the fibers interlock, so it is very tough. It is used for crates and boxes, and if the trunk is not hollow, the logs can be used for railroad ties and wharf pilings, gun stocks, chopping bowls, ox yokes, and mauls.

Nýssa biflòra Walter *[N. sylvatica* var. *biflora* (Walt.) Sarg.]   Swamp tupelo

Much of the tupelo harvested from southern coastal plain swamps is from swamp tupelo. This may be distinguished from black tupelo by its narrower [⅝ to 1½ in. (1.5 to 4 cm) wide], often oblanceolate leaves, and fruit pit which has ridges slightly more prominent than those of *N. sylvatica* (Fig. 9-100). Swamp tupelo, as its name indicates, is typical of very wet sites, while the more upland and northern *N. sylvatica* commonly inhabits higher ground and moist sites. Swamp tupelo is considered to be a distinct species according to a study by Burckhalter (1992).

This and other species of *Nyssa* may produce root sprouts which grow vigorously and form thickets around the base of the tree (Eyde, 1963). They are important deer browse.

Black and swamp tupelo are easily confused with persimmon (*Diospyros virginiana*) without flowers or fruits. *Diospyros* is recognized by having leaves gray-green below with darker venation, with even the ultimate veins being obvious without magnification, rather than green below with obscure ultimate veins; twig with a pseudoterminal rather than true terminal bud; one bundle scar rather than three; year-old twigs with chambered rather than diaphragmed pith; and the adaxial petiole and proximal midrib surfaces with minute glandular hairs rather than eglandular.

The remaining tree species, **N. ogèche** Bartr. ex Marsh, Ogeechee tupelo, with tomentose flowers and more or less hairy leaves, is found in coastal Georgia, adjacent South Carolina, and northern Florida. Thousands of seedlings have been planted in western Florida for honey production. It is related to *N. aquatica* and has the largest fruits (Fig. 9-100).

Aquifoliaceae: The Holly family

The Aquifoliaceae include four genera and about 420 species of trees and shrubs of wide distribution through the temperate and tropical forests of both hemispheres.

Two genera and about 15 species are found in the United States and Canada. *Nemopanthus mucronatus* (L.) Trel., the mountain holly, is a large shrub or small tree of southern Canada and eastern United States. *Ilex* is the important tree.

Botanical Features of the Family
Leaves often evergreen, but in some species deciduous, alternate, simple, stipulate.
Flowers usually imperfect (most species dioecious), superior ovary, small, 5-parted; entomophilous.
Fruit a drupe, with several stones (pyrenes).

ILEX L.   Holly

The genus *Ilex* consists of 300 to 350 species of evergreen or deciduous trees and shrubs, widely scattered throughout the world and appearing in the floras of every continent with the exception of Australia. *Ilex aquifolium* L., English holly, was successfully introduced into North America many years ago and bears fruit more plentifully than the American species, *I. opaca.* The leafy sprays of both species are used for Christmas decoration. In the west, the climate of the Puget Sound region is favorable to holly culture, and holly farms have paid good dividends. The English holly and many of its cultivars are those chiefly favored, although other species and hybrids are very popular ornamentals. Holly culture is also practiced to a certain extent in the Southeast, where the native species is used almost exclusively.

The flora of eastern United States includes about 16 species of *Ilex,* 14 of which are usually arborescent. One of these, *Ilex opaca,* is a timber tree of secondary importance.

Botanical Features of the Genus

Leaves deciduous or persistent; entire, serrate, or aculeate (spiny-toothed); stipulate with very small, nearly black, triangular, persistent stipules.

Flowers perfect and imperfect (dioecious or polygamous), corolla white, axillary, small.

Fruit a red or black (or rarely yellow) drupe.

Ìlex opàca Ait.   American holly

Distinguishing Characteristics (Fig. 9-104).   *Leaves* persistent, leathery, 2 to 4 in. (5 to 10 cm) long, elliptical, entire or spiny-toothed. *Flowers* imperfect (plant dioecious), solitary or cymose, small, greenish white. *Fruit* red (reputedly poisonous if eaten), containing a few ribbed stones. *Bark* light gray or sometimes rough and warty and usually with variously colored crustose lichens.

Range.   Eastern Massachusetts, south to central Florida, west to southcentral Texas, north to southeastern Missouri. Elevation: sea level to 5000 ft in the southern Appalachians. Floodplains and mixed hardwood forests.

FIGURE 9-104   *Ilex opaca.* American holly. Branch with leaves and drupes × ½.

General Description.   This species is the largest of the native hollies and varies from 40 to 50 ft in height and 1 to 2 ft dbh (max. 100 by 4 ft). The bole is straight and regular but usually short. The tree does best on deep, moist bottomlands but will persist, especially in the north, on dry, gravelly soil. American holly is very tolerant of forest competition and is also quite resistant to salt-water spray; it is used along the coast in exposed places as an ornamental.

Fruit dispersal is facilitated by birds. Growth is slow, and the tree matures in 100 to 150 years. It may be propagated by cuttings and is now raised in this way for decorative purposes. In this connection, the production of fruit can be assured by taking cuttings from pistillate trees only. The branches and leaves are in demand during the Christmas season, and in certain sections the natural stands of this tree have been nearly exterminated. Holly seems to have been a typically southern tree, but during the last few centuries it has moved steadily northward (seeds carried by birds and landscapers) until it has now reached New England. It is also cultivated, and many cultivars have been described.

Since the days of the Greeks, Romans, and Druids, and presumably much earlier, hollies with their evergreen leaves and bright red fruits attracted attention and played an important part in primitive magic, medicine, and folklore (see Dengler, 1966).

The wood is hard and white and used for veneer, cabinetwork, handles, carvings, and various specialty items. The fruit is an important food for birds.

Rhamnaceae: The Buckthorn Family

The Rhamnaceae include 53 genera and about 900 species of trees and shrubs (sometimes lianas, rarely herbs) widely scattered through the tropics and warmer regions of the world. *Ceanothus* L., an American genus, consists of about 80 shrubby species, many of which are found in the semiarid west. Here they may serve as browse for both sheep and cattle. *Ceanothus* roots contain nitrogen-fixing actinomycetes (see under *Myrica*). The seeds of several *Ceanothus* species are eaten by Native Americans and to a limited extent by livestock. The roots, bark, stems, and even leaves of many rhamnaceous plants contain compounds used for pharmaceutical purposes. The fruits of the common jujube, *Ziziphus jujuba* Mill., are edible, and this species is now widely cultivated in many sections of Asia. While there are a few species which produce timbers of commercial rank, the family is not important for timber.

Ten genera and about 100 species of the Rhamnaceae are found in the United States. *Rhamnus,* however, is the only genus with species of special economic interest. Probably the heaviest (specific gravity 1.3) wood grown in the United States is from leadwood, *Krugiodendron ferreum* (Vahl) Urban, found in southern Florida.

Botanical Features of the Family
Leaves deciduous or persistent, alternate or subopposite, simple, stipulate.
Flowers perfect or polygamous, small, actinomorphic, mostly 5-parted, ovary 2- or 3-carpellate, superior, entomophilous.
Fruit drupe or capsule, sometimes winged.

RHAMNUS L.   Buckthorn; cascara

This genus has 100 or more species of trees and shrubs widely scattered through the temperate and tropical forests of both hemispheres. *Rhamnus cathartica* L., the European buckthorn, was introduced into the United States for decorative purposes and has become naturalized in many sections of the East.

Twelve species of *Rhamnus* are native to the United States, and five of these are arborescent. *Rhamnus purshiana* is an important tree of the Pacific Coast.

Botanical Features of the Genus
Leaves deciduous or persistent, alternate or subopposite, simple, stipulate.
Flowers perfect or polygamous, axillary.
Fruit a drupe, fleshy, several-seeded or sometimes 1-seeded.

Rhámnus purshiàna DC.   Cascara buckthorn; bearberry; bitter-bark; chittimwood

Distinguishing Characteristics (Fig. 9-105).   *Leaves* deciduous, simple, alternate or subopposite, 2 to 6 in. (5 to 15 cm) long, elliptical to oblong-ovate, finely serrate or entire, and often remotely revolute; fall color yellow. *Flowers* axillary in cymes, yellowish green, 5-parted, appearing in spring and early summer. *Fruit* globose, bluish black, with 2 or 3 obovoid stones. *Twigs* slender, with naked, hoary tomentose buds; leaf scars elevated, narrow lunate, with a few scattered bundle scars; stipular scars conspicuous; pith homogeneous. *Bark* smooth, or superficially scaly.

Range.   Southwestern British Columbia, south to northern California; also in the Rockies of northern Idaho to western Montana. Elevation: sea level to 5000 ft. Disturbed areas, roadsides, and understory of mixed forests.

General Description.   Cascara buckthorn is a small tree usually not more than 30 to 40 ft high and 10 to 15 in. dbh (max. 60 by 3 ft). It is moderately gregarious and often forms small groves on moist bottomlands and burns. It is by no means restricted to such sites, however, and

FIGURE 9-105   *Rhamnus purshiana.* Cascara buckthorn. (1) Twig × 1. (2) Leaf × ⅗.

may also be found on gravelly or sandy soils, near sea level or at moderately high elevations. It occurs as an understory species in Douglas-fir forests and is commonly mixed with grand fir, western hemlock, bigleaf and vine maples, and red alder in many sections of the Pacific Northwest.

The cascara buckthorn is a prolific annual seeder. Moist forest litter and mucky soils make the best seedbeds. Growth is extremely rapid on such sites, and maturity is reached in about 50 years.

When the early Spanish missionaries explored northern California, they found that the Native Americans near the Oregon border were using the intensely bitter bark of this tree as a cathartic, and it was christened "cascara sagrada," or the sacred bark. In modern times Portland, Oregon, has become the center for collectors to bring in their annual "peel." The peeled tree dies, but vigorous sprouts seem to ensure a continuing supply of the bark.

Sapindaceae: The Soapberry Family

This family of 140 genera and 1500 species is found mostly in tropical and subtropical climates with only a few representatives in the north temperate zone. They are trees, shrubs, and vines. Some are favorite ornamentals in North America, for example, Goldenrain tree, *Koelreuteria paniculata* Laxm. Some others are important for timbers or for tropical edible fruits, such as lychee (*Litchi*) and akee (*Blighia*).

The Sapindaceae, Hippocastanaceae, and Aceraceae are very closely related, and there is recent evidence indicating that all three should be included in the Sapindaceae s. l. (Judd et al., 1994).

Botanical Features of the Family

Leaves persistent or deciduous, alternate (rarely opposite), pinnate or bipinnate, or simple, mostly estipulate, often with toxic saponins.

Flowers small, imperfect (tree monoecious or dioecious), 4 or 5 parted, ovary 3-carpellate, superior, actinomorphic or zygomorphic, entomophilous.

Fruit a berry, drupe, capsule, nut, samara, or schizocarp.

Sapíndus drummóndii Hook. & Arn.   Western soapberry

Distinguishing Characteristics.   *Leaves* tardily deciduous, alternate, pinnately compound, 5 to 8 in. (13 to 20 cm) long with 11 to 19 leaflets, alternate or subopposite on the rachis, each 1½ to 3 in. (4 to 7.5 cm) long, ⅜ to ¾ in. (1 to 2 cm) wide, lanceolate and falcate, acuminate, entire; fall color yellow. *Flowers* small, yellow-white, in erect panicles, in late spring or summer. *Fruit* berrylike, ⅜ to ½ in. (10 to 12 mm) in diameter, yellow to orange turning black, poisonous. *Twig* yellow-green, puberulent, with triangular to 3-lobed leaf scar and 3 bundle scars, buds with 2 scales, terminal bud lacking, stipular scar lacking, pith solid and homogeneous. *Bark* light gray, becoming rough and furrowed.

Range.   Southwestern Missouri, south to Louisiana, west to southern Arizona, northeast to southeastern Colorado. Elevation: 2400 to 6200 ft. Along streams, limestone uplands, in open grasslands in western plains, upper desert, and on mountain slopes in hardwood forests.

General Description.   This is a medium-size tree 20 to 40 ft tall and to 1 ft dbh. The fruits have been used as a substitute for soap for washing clothes; however, these fruits are poisonous if eaten and may cause a skin rash. The wood splits easily and is used for making baskets.

Hippocastanaceae: The Buckeye Family

The Hippocastanaceae include two genera and about 15 species of trees and shrubs scattered in the forests of northern South America, Central America, Mexico, eastern and western United States, southeastern Europe, eastern Asia, and India. As a group they are of little value for the timber which they produce; but many of them, either because of their showy flowers or handsome foliage, are highly prized for ornamental purposes. One genus, *Aesculus,* is represented in North America. The twigs, leaves, and seeds are poisonous if eaten.

Botanical Features of the Family and Genus

Leaves deciduous, opposite, palmately compound, with 5 to 9 (or rarely 11) leaflets, each short-stalked, serrate, petiole long, estipulate.

Flowers perfect or often imperfect in the same panicle; calyx connate and 5-lobed; corolla 4 or 5 parted, zygomorphic; ovary superior; entomophilous; appearing with the leaves in erect, terminal, many-flowered panicles.

Fruit a leathery capsule with 1 to 6 large brown seeds each with a large, light colored hilum.

AESCULUS L.   Buckeye; horsechestnut

The genus *Aesculus* consists of about 13 species of trees or large shrubs widely distributed throughout the forests of the northern hemisphere. Only two species are important forest trees.

Aèsculus flàva Soland. *(A. octandra Marsh.)*   Yellow buckeye

Distinguishing Characteristics (Figs. 9-106, 9-107, and 9-108).   *Leaves* palmately 5-foliolate, with nearly elliptical, serrate leaflets, fall color yellow. *Flowers* yellowish, petals 4, with the stamens usually shorter than the 2 lateral petals; pedicels with glandular hairs. *Fruit* smooth. *Twigs* stout, with large nonresinous terminal buds; leaf scars large, obdeltate with several bundle scars arranged in a *V*-shaped pattern. *Bark* breaking up into large scaly plates.

Range.   Extreme southwestern Pennsylvania, south along the Appalachians to northern Georgia and Alabama, west through southern Ohio to southern Illinois. Elevation: 5000 to 6300 ft. Mesic slopes and coves, and along rivers and streams.

General Description.   The yellow buckeye is a medium-size to large tree 60 to 90 ft high and 2 to 3 ft dbh (max. 140 by 5 ft). Best development is made on deep fertile soils in the mountains of North Carolina and Tennessee, where it occurs in mixture with other hardwoods. It is often a bottomland species, but in the southern Appalachians it is found in rich, high mountain slopes and coves, where it is sometimes one of the co-dominants with basswood and sugar maple. Growth is fairly rapid, and maturity is reached in 60 to 80 years. It is tolerant and maintains itself well in the climax forests of its range. The wood is used for furniture and for turning and carving.

Aèsculus glàbra Willd.   Ohio buckeye; fetid buckeye

Distinguishing Characteristics.   This species differs from *A. flava* in the following features: (1) leaves slightly smaller, the 5 leaflets more nearly lanceolate; (2) bruised foliage and twigs give

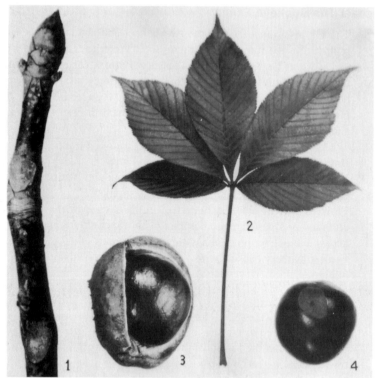

FIGURE 9-106   *Aesculus flava.* Yellow buckeye. (1) Twig × 1¼. (2) Leaf × ½. (3) Capsula × ¾; the atypical short prickles seen on the left side are due to introgression from *A. glabra*. (4) Seed × ¾.

FIGURE 9-107   Flowering branch of yellow buckeye.

FIGURE 9-108   Bark of yellow buckeye. (*Courtesy of U.S. Forest Service.*)

off a disagreeable odor; (3) stamens longer than the 4 light yellow petals (Fig. 9-109); (4) pedicels without glandular hairs; (5) fruit somewhat prickly; and (6) bud scales prominently keeled.

Range.   Southern Michigan, east to western Pennsylvania, south to central Alabama, west to Texas, and north to central Iowa. Elevation: 500 to 2000 ft. Valleys and mountain slopes, along stream and river banks, flatwoods, and often isolated in open fields. The western populations, with 7 to 11 narrower leaflets, are considered as *A. glabra* var. *argùta* (Buckl.) Robinson (*A. arguta* Buckl.).

General Description.   This is a medium-size tree, 30 to 70 ft tall and with an irregular, rounded crown 1 to 2 ft dbh. It is the state tree of Ohio, and it is used extensively as an ornamental. The wood is used for furniture, boxes, and locally for fuel.

Several other species, briefly mentioned here, are very showy in their native habitats or cultivated as ornamentals.

Aèsculus parviflòra Walt.   Bottlebrush buckeye

This is shrubby with small, white flowers in a long, slender, erect inflorescence. A native mainly of Alabama, it is widely cultivated northward and eastward.

Aèsculus califórnica (Spach) Nutt.   California buckeye

A small tree in the mountains of California, it has whitish flowers in very showy, long, slender inflorescences.

Aèsculus sylvática Bartr.   Painted buckeye

This is a yellow-flowered shrub or small tree in the Piedmont of the southeastern United States.

FIGURE 9-109   *Aesculus glabra.* Ohio buckeye. Flowering branch. (*Courtesy of U.S. Forest Service.*)

Aèsculus pàvia L.,   Red buckeye

It is a red-flowered shrub or small tree of the Coastal Plain of the Southeast. A yellow-flowered variety occurs in southwestern Texas.

Aèsculus hippocástanum L.   Horsechestnut

Originally a native of the Balkan peninsula, this is now widely planted throughout the world as a street and shade tree. It was introduced into the United States many years ago. It is characterized by seven obovate leaflets, white flowers in a compact panicle, prickly fruit, and dark brown to nearly black, sticky buds. Red horsechestnut, *A. ×carnea* Hayne, readily recognized by its pinkish to scarlet flowers, is a widespread ornamental and of hybrid origin between the horse-chestnut and red buckeye.

Interspecific hybridization and introgression between sympatric species have been the topic of considerable interest. *Aesculus glabra × flava, A. flava × sylvatica,* and *A. pavia × sylvatica* are good examples of both local and dispersed introgression (Hardin, 1957b). See DePamphilis and Wyatt (1989, 1990) for a more recent study.

Aceraceae: The Maple Family

The Maple family includes two genera with some 112 species of trees and shrubs. One genus, *Dipteronia* Oliv., includes two small trees, both of central China; the remaining species are in the genus *Acer.*

Botanical Features of the Family

Leaves deciduous (rarely persistent), opposite, simple or compound, mostly estipulate; the simple leaves usually palmately veined and lobed and long-petioled; the compound leaves pinnate.

Flowers regular; imperfect and perfect (most species polygamous or dioecious); borne in (1) racemes, panicles, corymbs, or fascicles, which appear before or with the leaves, or (2) in lateral fascicles from separate flower buds, which appear before the leaves unfold; *calyx* normally 5-parted; *petals* 5 or 0; *stamens* 4 to 12 (mostly 7 or 8); *pistils* 2-lobed, 2-celled, compressed, each lobe winged.

Fruit a double (rarely triple) samara, united at the base, each half long-winged and 1-seeded; *seeds* compressed, lacking endosperm. (In *Dipteronia* the wing completely surrounds the seed cavity.)

Twigs moderately stout to slender; *pith* homogeneous, terete; *terminal buds* with either imbricate or valvate scales; *lateral buds* similar but smaller and sometimes collateral; *leaf scars* more or less U-shaped; *bundle scars* 3, rarely 5 to 7 or more; stipular scars rarely present.

ACER L.　　Maple

The genus *Acer* consists of about 110 species of trees and shrubs widely scattered through the northern hemisphere but most abundant in the eastern Himalayan Mountains and in central China. Old World maples range southward to the mountains of Java and northern Africa; in the New World they are found from Alaska and Canada to the mountains of Guatemala. Many species and cultivars, both Asiatic and European, are used in this country as popular ornamentals. These include the Norway maple, *A. platanoides* L., with broad 7-lobed leaves and milky sap; sycamore maple, *A. pseudoplatanus* L.; plane-tree maple (Shantung maple), *A. truncatum* Bunge; paperbark maple, *A. griseum* (Franch.) Pax; Amur maple, *A. ginnala* Maxim.; Japanese maple, *A. palmatum* Thunb. ex J. A. Murr.; and fullmoon maple, *A. japonicum* Thunb. ex J. A. Murr. These have many cultivars selected for their attractive foliage and bark.

TABLE 9-25 COMPARISON OF IMPORTANT MAPLES

Species	Leaves	Flowers	Fruit
A. saccharum sugar maple	3½–5½ in. (9–14 cm) in diameter, 5-lobed; glabrous below; margin entire	appearing with the leaves; bright yellow, long-pedicelled, apetalous; species polygamous	autumnal; *U*-shaped; wings ca. 1 in. (2.5 cm) long, slightly divergent
A. barbatum southern sugar maple	1½–3 in. (4–7.5 cm) in diameter, 5-lobed; pubescent below; margin entire	same	same
A. nigrum black maple	4–5½ in. (10–14 cm) in diameter, mostly 3-lobed; pubescent below; margin entire	same	same
A. macrophyllum bigleaf maple	6–10 in. (15–25 cm) in diameter, deeply 5-lobed; glabrous below; margin entire	same, but species polygamous	autumnal; wing 1–1½ in. (2.5–4 cm) long, slightly divergent; outside of seed cavity covered with stout, pale brown hairs
A. rubrum red maple	2½–4 in. (6–10 cm) in diameter, usually 3-lobed, the sides of the middle lobe mostly converging toward the apex; silvery below; margin serrate	appearing before the leaves, short pedicelled; species polygamous, corolla reddish	vernal; wings ca. ¾ in. (2 cm) long, slightly divergent
A. saccharinum silver maple	4–6 in. (10–15 cm) in diameter, 5-lobed, margins of the middle lobe usually divergent; silvery below; margin serrate	same but apetalous	vernal; wings ca. 2 in. (5 cm) long, extremely divergent
A. negundo boxelder	pinnately compound with 3–7 leaflets	usually appearing with the leaves; species dioecious	autumnal; *V*-shaped; wings ca. 1½ in. (4 cm) long, slightly convergent at tips

Of the 14 maples indigenous to the United States, seven are important as forest trees and also as deer browse throughout the year (Table 9-25). Some hybridization and possibly introgression occur among related, sympatric species.

Àcer sáccharum Marsh.   Sugar maple

Distinguishing Characteristics (Figs. 9-110, 9-111)

Leaves 3½ to 5½ in. (9 to 14 cm) in diameter; *shape* orbicular, usually palmately 5-lobed (rarely 3-lobed); *margin* of lobes entire or sparingly sinuate-toothed; *apex*

FIGURE 9-110   *Acer saccharum.* Sugar maple. (1) Twig × 1¼. (2) Inflorescence × ½. (3) Staminate flower × 2. (4) Perfect flower × 2. (5) Double samara × ¾. (6) Leaf × ½. (7) Bark.

acuminate; *base* cordate; *surfaces* glabrous, bright green above, paler below; *fall color* yellow, orange, or red.

    Flowers perfect and staminate (pistil abortive); bright yellow, long-pedicelled, appearing with the leaves in crowded, umbel-like corymbs, apetalous.

    Fruit autumnal, borne on slender stems, somewhat horseshoe-shaped with nearly parallel or slightly divergent wings, about 1 to 1¼ in. (2.5 to 3 cm) long.

FIGURE 9-111   Open-grown sugar maple.
(*Courtesy of U.S. Forest Service.*)

Twigs slender, shiny, and brownish with light-colored lenticels; *pith* white; *terminal buds* ¼ to ⅜ in. (6 to 9 mm) long, acute, sharply pointed, with 4 to 8 pairs of visible scales; *lateral buds* smaller; leaf scars *V*-shaped; *bundle scars* 3.

Bark gray, on older trees deeply furrowed, with long, irregular, thick plates or ridges, sometimes scaly, very variable.

Range

Northeastern (Map 9-36). Local disjuncts in central North Carolina, northwestern South Carolina, and northeastern North Dakota. Elevation: sea level to 2500 ft northward, 3000 to 5500 ft in the southern Appalachians. Mesic forests and rich mountain coves and slopes.

General Description

Sugar maple commonly attains a height of 60 to 80 ft and a dbh of 2 ft (max. 135 by 7 ft), and under forest conditions develops a clear, straight, full bole; in the open the trunk often branches

MAP 9-36   **(Left)** *Acer saccharum.* **(Right)** *Acer nigrum.*

near the ground, and a large dense, rounded, or ovoid crown is produced; the root system is shallow and wide-spreading to deep, depending on the soil.

Best growth is made on moist, rich, well-drained soils, but the species will persist on more sterile sites. In the Adirondack virgin forest, the common associates are American beech and yellow birch, red spruce, eastern white pine, eastern hemlock, and an occasional black cherry; farther south, sugar maple is found in mixture with various hardwoods, including basswood, buckeye, white ash, yellow-poplar, hickories, and oaks. Sugar maple is found in many forest-cover types and is a major component in six of them (Braun, 1950; Burns and Honkala, 1990).

In good seed years (2- to 5-year intervals), just before the leaves expand, nearly every tree is so covered with flowers that at a distance it appears to be enveloped in a yellow haze. By autumn, enormous quantities of the winged fruits have developed and are released. Seed traps indicate a fall of 8 million per acre under some old-growth stands. The following spring countless numbers of seedlings unfold their straplike cotyledons as they emerge from their winter covering of leaves. They prosper even under a heavy forest cover and are extremely tolerant. One of the most tolerant of major species, sugar maple responds to release from extreme and prolonged suppression. It also regenerates by stump sprouts and sometimes root suckers. It may attain an age of 300 to 400 years.

Besides its primary importance as a timber producer, sugar maple is used as an ornamental tree, is an important source of browse, and also is tapped for valuable syrup and sugar. Thirty-two gallons of the spring sap may be boiled down to a gallon of syrup or 8 pounds of sugar, but the sugar content of the sap varies widely from tree to tree (Leaf and Watterston, 1964). Individuals are being sought with the highest possible sugar content, to use in tree-breeding programs for the production of high-yielding sugar orchards.

A variant with light gray, almost chalky bark is known as Chalk maple, *A. leucoderme* Small or *A. saccharum* var. *leucoderme* (Small) Sarg. It is rare and local from North Carolina and eastern Tennessee west to Texas and Oklahoma.

Àcer barbàtum Michx.   Southern sugar maple; Florida maple

Distinguishing Characteristics.   *Leaves* 1½ to 3 in. (4 to 7.5 cm) long and wide, with 3 to 5 lobes and entire margin, pubescent beneath; fall color yellow to red. *Flowers* yellow to red. *Twigs* tan and slender. *Bark* light gray, smooth, becoming furrowed.

Range.   Piedmont and Coastal Plain from Virginia to central Florida and west to eastern Texas and Oklahoma. Elevation: sea level to 2000 ft. Valleys, bottomlands, and upland slopes.

General Description.   This is a tree to 60 ft tall and 2 ft dbh. This southern sugar maple differs from the typical sugar maple in having leaves pubescent and often glaucous beneath, usually smaller, and the lobes round to acute at the apex. The treatment of this species has sometimes been as *A. saccharum* var. *floridanum* (Chapm.) Small & Heller or *A. saccharum* subsp. *floridanum* (Chapm.) Desmarais [see Desmarais (1952) and Kreibel (1957)]. It is not tapped for syrup.

Àcer nìgrum Michx. f.   Black maple

Distinguishing Characteristics.   *Leaves* somewhat like those of sugar maple but usually 3-lobed (Fig. 9-112), pubescent in varying degrees, and with a drooping habit; base of petiole with 2, often foliaceous stipules; fall color yellow. *Fruit* often with a slightly larger seed cavity than that of sugar maple. *Twigs* commonly stouter, with conspicuous warty lenticels and larger, more hairy buds. *Bark* more corrugated than that of sugar maple.

Range   Northeastern (Map 9-36). Local disjuncts in western Virginia, western North Carolina, northwestern Tennessee, and northwestern Arkansas. Elevation: sea level to 2500 ft. Moist valleys and upland mixed forests.

General Description.   The silvical features of this species are similar to those of sugar maple, except that black maple will grow on the moister soils of river bottoms. Where the ranges of sugar and black maple overlap, frequent hybridization occurs. There has been considerable debate regarding whether to recognize black maple as a distinct species or as a variety or subspecies of the sugar maple. See Desmarais (1952) and Kreibel (1957) for additional discussions.

FIGURE 9-112   *Acer nigrum.* Black maple. (1) Twig × 1¼. (2) Leaf × ½. (3) Bark.

Àcer macrophÿllum Pursh   Bigleaf maple

Distinguishing Characteristics (Fig. 9-113)

Leaves 6 to 10 in. (15 to 25 cm) in diameter; *shape* orbicular or nearly so, usually palmately 5-lobed; *margin* of lobes entire to sinuate or sparingly toothed; *apex* acute; *base* cordate; *surfaces* glabrous, bright green above, pale below; *petioles* with milky cell sap; *fall color* yellow or orange.

Flowers perfect and staminate; yellow, scented; in slightly puberulent racemes appearing with the leaves.

Fruit 1 to 1½ in. (2.5 to 4 cm) long with slightly divergent wings; the portion covering the seed densely pubescent.

Twigs stout, dark red, or reddish brown to greenish brown, often dotted with rather conspicuous lenticels; *pith* white; *terminal buds* stout, blunt, with 3 or 4 pairs of green- to reddish-colored scales; *lateral buds* small, slightly appressed; *leaf scars* V-shaped to U-shaped, with 5 to 9 bundle scars.

Bark light gray-brown and smooth on young stems, but becoming darker and deeply furrowed on old trunks.

Range

Western (Map 9-37). Elevation: sea level to 1000 ft northward, 3000 to 5500 ft southward. Stream banks, rain forests, and moist canyons.

General Description

Bigleaf maple is one of the few commercial hardwoods on the Pacific Coast. It grows on a variety of soils throughout its range and is usually a small to medium-size tree some 50 ft tall and 1½ ft dbh. Best development is made on rich bottomlands, where it attains a height of more than 80 ft and a dbh of 3 to 4 ft (max. 100 by 9 ft). The trees are usually scattered or in small groves in association with both coniferous and other broad-leaved species, including Douglas-fir, western redcedar, western hemlock, red alder, northern black cottonwood, Oregon white oak, and Pacific madrone. In some sections of southwestern Oregon, however, this maple is the principal forest species, particularly where it invades logged and burned lands.

A rather narrow crown is developed under forest conditions, and the bole is often free of limbs for one-half to two-thirds of its length. In more or less open situations the trunk usually divides a short distance above the ground into several stout, ascending branches, forming a rather compact ovate to subglobose crown. Regardless of habitat, however, the root system is generally shallow and wide-spreading.

An abundance of seed is produced annually, and natural regeneration by this means is excellent; stump sprouts are also quite vigorous. Growth is rapid during the first 40 to 60 years, but decreases considerably later, and maturity is eventually reached between 200 and 300 years. Old trees are commonly defective; large burls occasionally develop along the boles. The demand for western maple burls and fancy grained logs has had much to do with increasing the commercial importance of this species. The wood is used for veneer, furniture, woodenware, and locally for fuel.

Àcer rùbrum L.   Red maple

Distinguishing Characteristics (Fig. 9-114)

Leaves 2½ to 4 in. (6 to 10 cm) in diameter; *shape* orbicular, palmately 3- or 5-lobed (usually 3) with acute sinuses, sides of the terminal lobe usually convergent;

FIGURE 9-113   *Acer macrophyllum.* Bigleaf maple. (1) Twig × 1¼. (2) Raceme of staminate flowers × ¾. (3) Raceme of perfect and staminate flowers × ¾. (4) Staminate, pistillate, and perfect flowers × 2. (5) Double samara × ¾. (6) Bark.

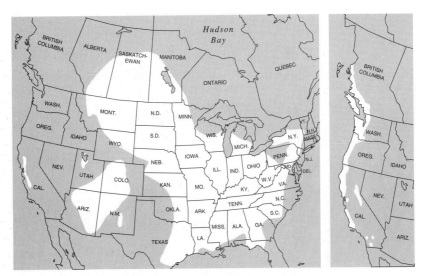

MAP 9-37   (Left) *Acer negundo.* **(Right)** *Acer macrophyllum.*

margin of lobes serrate; *surfaces* light green above, at maturity paler and glaucous below; *fall color* red or sometimes yellow.

Flowers perfect and staminate; appearing in early spring before the leaves, yellow or bright red; short- to long-pedicelled, fascicled; *corolla* present.

Fruit borne in clusters on long slender stems; wings slightly divergent, ca. ¾ in. (2 cm) long, maturing in late spring.

Twigs slender, dark red, lustrous, odorless or nearly so, dotted with minute lenticels; *terminal buds* obtuse with 2 to 4 pairs of visible, red scales; *lateral* and *collateral* buds smaller than the terminal, slightly stalked; *leaf scars* V-shaped; *bundle scars* 3.

Bark on young trees smooth and light gray, eventually on the older trunks breaking up into long, narrow, scaly plates separated by shallow fissures.

Range
Eastern (Map 9-38). Elevation: sea level to 6000 ft. This has a very broad ecological range from drier upland slopes to floodplains and swamps.

General Description
Red maple is a medium-size tree 50 to 70 ft high and 12 to 24 in. dbh (max. 116 by 6 ft) with a long, fairly clear bole, an irregular or rounded crown, and a shallow root system. It is characteristic of swampy sites and is associated with such species as black ash, black tupelo, cottonwood, American elm, and the bottomland oaks; however, red maple is often found in drier locations, and in the Northeast it is commonly mixed with white pine and the northern hardwoods on moderately moist, sandy loam soils, or even on rocky uplands. Over its extensive range, it is a most cosmopolitan species, occurring in 54 forest-cover types, and with many associates, including both hardwoods and softwoods. In the pocosins and swamps of the Southeast, the smaller, shallowly 3-lobed leaves have been recognized as var. *trilobum* T. & G. ex K. Koch.

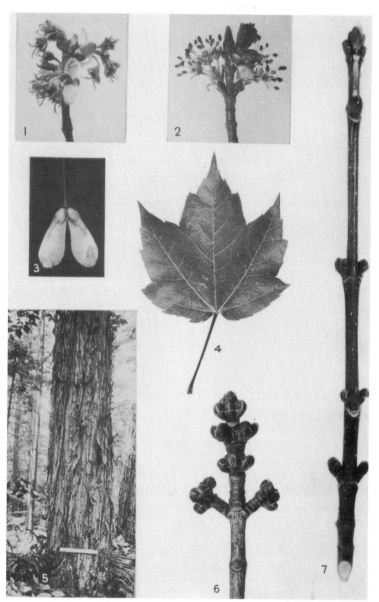

FIGURE 9-114 *Acer rubrum.* Red maple. (1) Perfect flower × ¾. (2) Staminate flowers × 1. (3) Double samara × ¾. (4) Leaf × ½. (5) Bark of old tree. (6) Flower buds × 1¼. (7) Twig × 1¼.

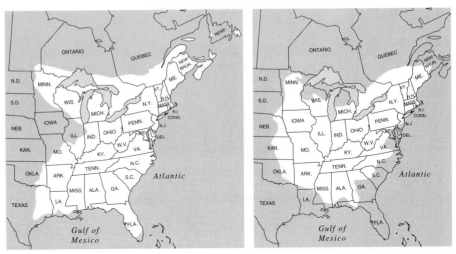

MAP 9-38   (Left) *Acer rubrum.* **(Right)** *Acer saccharinum.*

Red maple is one of the first trees to flower in the spring, long before the leaves appear. The fruit matures quickly and is shed in early summer. It germinates immediately or may hold over until the following spring. Growth is rapid, and maturity is reached in 70 to 80 years, although certain individuals may attain an age of 150 years. Many second-growth stands are of sprout origin, but quality is often poor because of butt rot. On a tolerance scale, this tree is intermediate; it often pioneers effectively on disturbed sites. This species is said to be the most abundant and widespread tree of eastern North America. Easily top-killed by fire, it responds with vigorous sprouts.

Red maple is used widely as an ornamental and shade tree, provides a spectacular display in early spring with red flowers and fruits, then after the first fall frosts, its leaves often turn a brilliant scarlet. Twigs and leaves are excellent deer browse, and the fruits are eaten by small mammals. Partially wilted leaves, however, are poisonous to livestock, particularly horses and ponies.

Àcer saccharìnum L.   Silver maple

Distinguishing Characteristics (Fig. 9-115)

Leaves 4 to 6 in. (10 to 15 cm) in diameter; *shape* orbicular, deeply palmately 5-lobed, the sides of the terminal lobe divergent, the lobes often again lobed, sinuses acute or often rounded; *margin* of lobes serrate; *surfaces* pale green above, silvery below at maturity; *fall color* pale yellow to orange.

Flowers perfect and staminate; among the first to appear in the spring and long before the leaves unfold; *corolla* lacking, otherwise similar to those of red maple.

Fruit the largest of the eastern maples, with widely divergent wings 1½ to 2½ in. (4 to 6 cm) long; often aborted on one side; maturing in late spring, germinating as soon as released.

Twigs and buds very similar to those of red maple, but often more reddish brown, and with a decidedly fetid odor when bruised.

FIGURE 9-115   *Acer saccharinum.* Silver maple. (1) Staminate and perfect flowers × 1. (2) Double samara × ¾. (3) Leaf × ½. (4) Twig × 1¼. (5) Bark.

Bark on young trees silvery gray, later breaking up into long, thin, scaly plates which are unattached at the ends.

Range

Eastern (Map 9-38). Disjuncts in eastern Louisiana and upper Michigan. Elevation: sea level to 2000 ft, and to ca. 4500 ft in the southern Appalachians. Floodplains, swamps, and moist mountain coves and slopes.

General Description

Silver maple is a medium-size tree 60 to 80 ft high and 2 to 3 ft dbh (max. 125 by 7 ft) and usually has a short bole which divides near the ground into several upright branches; the crown is wide-spreading, and the root system shallow. This maple is a characteristic bottomland species and is not found on dry soils. Young trees recover well even from several weeks of inundation (Hosner, 1960). Associates are fewer than in red maple and include American elm, cottonwood, red maple, sycamore, sweetgum, black willow, and river birch.

Silver maple is a very fast-growing tree, moderately intolerant, reaching maturity in about 125 years. The branches are brittle and often break off during high winds or when loaded with snow or ice; this contributes to early disintegration, for wood-destroying fungi readily enter the exposed wood. Several horticultural varieties are used for ornamental planting, including a cut-leaf form. Planted trees seem to do well even on dry clay soils.

Àcer pensylvánicum L.   Striped maple; moosewood

A shrub or small tree to 35 ft tall, it is distinguished by its green bark with conspicuous white, vertical stripes; leaves with 3 shallow and broad terminal lobes and serrulate or doubly serrate margins; and pendulous terminal racemes of yellow-green flowers (Fig. 9-116). It is mainly a tree of southeastern Canada, west to Michigan and northern Wisconsin, and south along the higher elevations (5500 ft) of the Appalachians to northern Georgia.

FIGURE 9-116   *Acer pensylvanicum.* Striped maple. Flowering branch with leaf. (*Courtesy of U.S. Forest Service.*)

Àcer spicàtum Lam.   Mountain maple

A shrub or small tree to 25 ft tall, it is distinguished by its brown, nonstriped bark; leaves with 3 shallow and broad terminal lobes and coarsely serrate margins; and erect terminal panicle of pale yellow flowers (Fig. 9-117). It is primarily a northern tree of southeastern Canada, south to Wisconsin, and also in the higher elevations (6000 ft) of the Appalachians to northern Georgia.

Àcer negúndo L.   Boxelder, Ash-leafed maple

Distinguishing Characteristics (Fig. 9-118)

Leaves pinnately compound with 3 to 7 (rarely 9) leaflets, ca. 6 in. (15 cm) long, 3½ in. (9 cm) wide; *leaflets* short-stalked; *terminal leaflet* often 3-lobed; *shape* very

FIGURE 9-117   *Acer spicatum.* Mountain maple. Flowering branch with leaves. (*Courtesy of U.S. Forest Service.*)

FIGURE 9-118   *Acer negundo.* Boxelder. (1) Twig × 1¼. (2) Leaf × ½. (3) Double samara × ¾. (4) Bark (*Photo by R. A. Cockrell.*)

variable, mostly ovate, oval, obovate, or ovate-lanceolate; *apex* acuminate; *base* cuneate, rounded, or cordate; *margin* coarsely serrate or lobed; *surfaces* light green, glabrous, or slightly pubescent above, pale green, pubescent along the veins below; *rachis* stout, enlarged at the base; *fall color* pale yellow.

   Flowers imperfect (plant dioecious), apetalous, yellow-green, the *staminate* fascicled, the *pistillate* in drooping racemes, appearing with or before the leaves.

   Fruit borne on slender stems, *V*-shaped, with slightly convergent wings 1 to 1½ in. (2.5 to 4 cm) long.

Twigs stout, green to purplish green, lustrous or covered with a glaucous bloom, lenticellate; *pith* terete, white; *terminal buds* ovoid, with about 4 visible, usually bluish white, tomentose scales; *lateral buds* short-stalked, appressed; *leaf scars* V-shaped, *bundle scars* 3 (rarely 5).

Bark thin, light brown, with narrow, rounded, anastomosing ridges separated by shallow fissures; on old trees more deeply furrowed.

Range

Eastern and central (Map 9-37). Disjunct areas in Colorado, New Mexico, Arizona, Utah, and California; naturalized in southeastern Canada, the northeastern United States, and the northwestern United States. Elevation: sea level to 8000 ft. Stream and river banks, floodplains, swamp margins, and moist upland slopes.

General Description

Boxelder has little, if any, commercial importance, but it is one of the most common and best known of the maples. It is usually a small or medium-size tree, 30 to 60 ft tall and to 2½ ft dbh (max. 95 to 6 ft), with an irregular bole, shallow root system, and bushy, spreading crown. Most common on deep, moist soils of bottomlands, it is also found on poorer sites and is perhaps the most aggressive of the maples in unfavorable locations. The early settlers in the Middle West were acquainted with its hardiness, especially in extremes of climate, and planted it widely as a street tree and around their homesteads. Boxelder, however, is not a decorative tree, and although it makes rapid growth, it is short-lived and usually of poor form. Sprouts usually emerge along the trunk, and when these are removed, others appear in increasing numbers.

Anacardiaceae: The Cashew Family

This family includes about 70 genera and about 600 species of trees and shrubs found mostly in the warmer regions of the world. Various drugs, dyes, waxes, and tannins are obtained from the juice, which is either milky or clear and acrid, turning black upon drying; this feature is utilized in the production of Chinese lacquer, which is obtained from the sap of *Toxicodendron vernicifluum* (Stokes) Barkley. Some species have highly colored woods and are valuable as timber producers, while others, such as quebracho wood of South America, one of the heaviest and hardest woods in the world, yield large amounts of tannin. Pistachio nuts of commerce come from *Pistacia vera* L., and *P. chinensis* Bunge is becoming very popular as an ornamental lawn, street, or park tree in the southern states. The popular, edible cashew nut comes from the tropical American species, *Anacardium occidentale* L. The shell of the cashew nut contains a poison which causes severe burns and is used by certain tribes of natives to produce scarred designs on the skin similar in appearance to tattoos. Another well-known tropical species (*Mangifera indica* L.) produces the mango fruit which is sold in most markets.

Botanical Features of the Family

Leaves deciduous or persistent, usually alternate, simple or compound, estipulate.
Flowers imperfect (plants dioecious or polygamo-dioecious), actinomorphic, mostly 5-parted, ovary superior and 3-carpellate, entomophilous.
Fruit a drupe or nutlike.

RHUS L.   Sumac

Autumn foliage colors of many of the sumacs are brilliant red and outstanding. None of these are poisonous and many are important browse for wildlife throughout the year.

Rhùs týphina L.   Staghorn sumac (Fig. 9-119)

This is a small tree or large shrub with stout pubescent branches which bear a resemblance to a stag's horns "in the velvet." The leaves are large and pinnately compound with 11 to 31 leaflets, coarsely serrate on the margins; fall color orange-red or yellowish. Flowers small, in compact terminal panicles, appearing in spring after the leaves. The fruit is in upright, compact, red, cone-shaped panicles. It is found in southeastern Canada and northeastern quarter of the U.S. and southward in the Appalachians. This well-known name should now be changed to *R. hirta* (L.) Sudworth.

FIGURE 9-119   *Rhus typhina.* Staghorn sumac. (1) Twig × 1¼. (2) Infructescence × ½. (3) Leaf × ½.

Rhùs glàbra L.   Smooth sumac

This is a shrub similar to the above, except that the branches are glabrous and the fruit is borne in more open clusters. It is common in the East and also in the western mountains.

Rhùs copallìna L.   Shining sumac (flameleaf sumac)

This is a small shrub to small tree (to 26 ft) of the East; the rachis of the pinnate leaves is conspicuously winged.

Rhùs aromática Ait.   Fragrant sumac

This has trifoliolate leaves similar in appearance to those of poison-oak; they are, however, hairy and have an aromatic odor; the fruit is red and borne in open clusters. This shrub is often found on dry, sterile hillsides, mainly northward.

Rhùs trilobàta Nutt.   Skunkbush or squawbush

This is a shrub similar to the above, but western and very common in the inland empire and the Rocky Mountains. The bruised, deeply lobed or compound leaves give off a fetid odor; the fruits are a bright orange-red.

Rhùs integrifòlia (Nutt.) Brewer & Wats.   Lemonade sumac

This is an evergreen, aromatic shrub or small tree. The sour, sticky, dark red, hairy fruits can be used to make a refreshing drink. It is found in coastal southern California.

TOXICODENDRON Mill.   Poison sumacs

Some authors continue to treat these species in the genus *Rhus*. Although not forest trees, these species are so *poisonous* to the touch, that they should be recognized by all field biologists, hunters, fishermen, and campers in general, and taught to all children at an early age. Contact dermatitis is an allergic reaction to an oil in the cell sap, and although some people are not sensitive to this, sensitivity may be acquired, and it is foolish to handle the plants without some fear and extreme care. Direct or indirect contact with the bruised leaves or other portions of the plant is necessary to produce the irritation, which does not, however, begin until several hours or even a few days after the contact. It is also dangerous to walk through smoke from burning leaves or to handle clothing, tools, or other articles that have bruised the leaves, twigs, or roots.

Toxicodéndron vérnix (L.) Kuntze   Poison-sumac (Fig. 9-120)

This is a large shrub or small tree of the East with pinnate leaves of 7 to 13 entire leaflets, the petiole, rachis, and petiolules usually reddish; fall color orange to scarlet; fruit ivory-white in color and borne in open, pendent panicles; twigs stout, yellowish brown, and usually mottled; leaf scars shield-shaped with numerous bundle scars. It is found in northern bogs, along creeks, and in southern swamps and pocosins.

Toxicodéndron rádicans (L.) Kuntze   Poison-ivy (Fig. 9-121)

This is a vine or small shrub with characteristic trifoliolate leaves, which turn red in the fall; fruit yellowish-white; twigs and naked buds brownish, the leaf scars *V*- or *U*-shaped, with sev-

FIGURE 9-120   *Toxicodendron vernix.* Poison-sumac. (1) Twig × 1¼. (2) Leaf × ½. (3) Infructescence × ½.

eral bundle scars, the lenticels usually conspicuous. This is a ubiquitous weed in all areas of the east.

Toxicodéndron pubéscens Mill.   Eastern poison-oak

This is a species of the South. It is shrublike, and the leaflets are more conspicuously 3- to 7-lobed and pubescent than in the preceding species. It is relatively uncommon and occurs in dry woodlands, thickets, old fields, and sandy habitats of the southeast.

Toxicodéndron diversilòbum (Torr. & Gray) Greene   Western poison-oak (Fig. 9-122)

This is a common shrub, vine, or small tree of canyons, slopes, and oak woodlands along the Pacific Coast. It is a diffusely branched, leafy shrub of dry habitats.

FIGURE 9-121   *Toxicodendron radicans.* Poison ivy. (1) Twig × 1¼. (2) Trifoliolate leaf × ½. (3) Infructescence × ½. (*Courtesy of U.S. Department of Agriculture.*)

Simaroubaceae: The Quassia Family

The Quassia or Bitterwood family with about 25 genera and 150 species is chiefly tropical and subtropical and is represented in North America by only five native and one naturalized tree species. One of the best-known tropical species is *Quassia amara* L., bitterwood, of northern South America. The wood contains a water-soluble bitter principle which is used commercially in the manufacture of insecticides and in medicines. The family is one of trees and shrubs often with very bitter bark and other parts. One introduced, ornamental tree, tree-of-heaven, has become naturalized and increasingly common.

FIGURE 9-122   *Toxicodendron diversilobum.* Western poison-oak. Leafy branch with fruits. (*Courtesy of U.S. Forest Service.*)

Botanical Features of the Family
Leaves alternate; pinnately compound, unifoliolate, or simple; stipulate or estipulate.
Flowers small, in large panicles, regular, 3- to 8-parted; pistils 2 to 5 separate, ovaries superior; plants dioecious or polygamous; entomophilous or ornithophilous.
Fruit a capsule, drupe, berry, or samara.

Ailánthus altíssima (Mill.) Swingle   Tree-of-heaven

Distinguishing Characteristics (Fig. 9-123).   *Leaves* alternate, pinnately compound, 1 to 2 ft (3 to 6 dm) long with mostly 13 to 25, or more, ovate-lanceolate leaflets, each 3 to 5 in. (7.5 to 13 cm) long, 1 or 2 in. (2.5 to 5 cm) wide; apex acuminate; base unequally rounded or subcordate; margin entire except for 1 to 5 rounded, basal teeth, each with a prominent dark green gland beneath near the tooth apex; surfaces puberulent and glabrate; fall color yellow. *Flowers* small, yellowish, in large, terminal panicles, appearing in late spring and early summer, the trees

FIGURE 9-123   *Ailanthus altissima.* Tree-of-heaven. (1) Twig × 1¼. (2) Samara × 1. (3) One leaflet attached to part of rachis × ½.

usually dioecious. *Fruit* an oblong, twisted samara, 1¼ to 1½ in. (3 to 4 cm) long, with the seed cavity in the center, cream or reddish-brown, 1 to 5 per flower; borne in large clusters and many remaining on the tree during the winter. Twig light brown, very stout, pith homogeneous, light brown; leaf scars heart shaped with many bundle scars; stipular scars lacking; terminal bud lacking. *Bark* light brown-gray, smooth and becoming rough and fissured.

Range.   Naturalized throughout temperate North America in disturbed areas, waste places, roadsides, and around buildings.

General Description.   This tree was introduced from eastern Asia and has been used considerably for ornamental purposes. The name "tree-of-heaven" is rather dubious for the staminate flowers, bruised leaves, and broken twigs have an exceedingly disagreeable odor. The species grows rapidly, and is very hardy, especially in its ability to flourish on poor hard-packed soils in the smoky atmosphere of industrial cities. The height is 50 to 80 ft and dbh of 1 to 2 ft, with a spreading, rounded, open crown. Seedlings and root suckers are plentiful and aggressive, and when once established, the tree is difficult to eradicate. Stump sprouts are also numerous and sometimes grow in length at the rate of an inch a day. This species is very weedy and a real pest on good sites in prime hardwood forests.

Meliaceae: The Mahogany Family

The Mahogany family, which includes some of the finest known cabinet woods, consists of about 50 genera and 550 species of trees and shrubs, mostly tropical. An extremely important member of this family is neem (*Azedirachta indica* A. Juss.), of India, where it is revered for its many uses. In fact, it is used for so many things that it has been called "the village pharmacy." Neem is now widely cultivated in the tropics and subtropics and used for fuel, fodder, food, timber, soaps, toothpaste, lotions, oils, insecticides, and medicines. Having stood the test of modern research, neem stands true to its Sanskrit name, "arishta," meaning "reliever of sickness." In the United States, the evergreen neem trees can be found cultivated in southern Florida, southern California, Arizona, and Washington, D.C.

The family is represented in the United States by the naturalized Chinaberry and a single native species, the West Indies mahogany, *Swietenia mahagoni* (L.) Jacq., which reaches its northern limit in extreme southern Florida.

Botanical Features of the Family

Leaves deciduous or persistent; alternate; simple, unifoliolate, pinnately or bipinnately compound, the leaflets often oblique; estipulate.

Flowers perfect or imperfect, regular, 4 to 5 parted, stamens 8 to 10 monadelphous; pistil 1, superior; entomophilous.

Fruit a capsule or drupe.

Mèlia azédarach L.   Chinaberry

Distinguishing Characteristics (Fig. 9-124).   *Leaves* bipinnate, 8 to 18 in. (20 to 46 cm) long, leaflets 1 to 2 in. (2.5 to 5 cm) long and ⅜ to ¾ in. (1 to 1.9 cm) wide, lanceolate or ovate, serrate or lobed. *Flowers* pale purple, fragrant, and showy in large terminal panicles, appearing in spring after the leaves. *Fruit* a yellow drupe, ca. ⅝ in. (15 mm) in diameter, wrinkled, remaining attached through the winter; poisonous if eaten. *Twig* stout, leaf scars 3-lobed, bundle scars 9 in 3 *C*-shaped groups, terminal bud lacking, buds appearing naked, pith homogeneous and white.

Range.   Chinaberry has become naturalized and occurs in dry soils or disturbed areas, pastures, barnlots, and roadside fencerows, usually below 1000 ft of elevation, in the southeastern states and also California.

General Description.   This tree, originally a native of the Orient, has been extensively cultivated in the south as an ornamental and shade tree. It is deciduous or evergreen southward and reaches 40 ft tall and 1 ft dbh. The fruits are disseminated by birds but are poisonous to livestock.

Rutaceae: The Rue Family

This is a large family of about 150 genera and 1500 species of trees and shrubs distributed over the warmer and temperate regions of the world. All are characterized by a bitter-tasting, aromatic, volatile oil.

The family is of importance in horticulture, and the most noteworthy introduced genus is *Citrus* (orange, tangerine, lemon, lime, grapefruit) with a num-

FIGURE 9-124   *Melia azedarach.* Chinaberry. Branch with drupes persisting in the winter. (*Courtesy of Florida Experiment Station.*)

ber of species and varieties. Several other tropical genera produce excellent cabinet woods and structural timbers.

There are four native genera in North America. The more common species are Hercules-club (also called toothache tree), *Zanthoxylum clava-herculis* L., a small tree of the south; common prickly-ash, *Z. americanum* Mill.; baretta, *Helietta parvifolia* (Gray) Benth., found in southern Texas and northeastern Mexico; torchwood (sea amyris), *Amyris elemifera* L., of southern Florida and the West Indies; and *Ptelea,* described here.

Botanical Features of the Family

Leaves deciduous or persistent, alternate or some opposite, mostly compound or unifoliolate, with glandular-punctate dots, estipulate, aromatic.

Flowers usually regular, white or greenish, bisexual or unisexual, 4 to 5 parted, stamens 8 to 10, pistil 1, superior; entomophilous.

Fruit a drupe, follicle, samara, or hesperidium (the pulp in citrus fruits is derived from enlarged hairs).

Stem with or without thorns.

Ptèlea trifoliàta L.   Common hoptree

Distinguishing Characteristics. *Leaves* palmately trifoliolate, 4 to 7 in. (10 to 18 cm) long, leaflets each 2 to 4 in. (5 to 10 cm) long, ¾ to 2 in. (2 to 5 cm) wide, ovate or elliptical, acuminate, entire or serrulate, with small punctate dots; fall color yellow. *Flowers* greenish white, ca. ⅜ in. (10 mm) wide, in terminal panicles, appearing with the leaves. *Fruit* a round, waferlike samara, ca. ⅞ in. (22 mm) in diameter, yellow-brown, in drooping clusters. *Twigs* slender, brown, pubescent, with a rank odor, leaf scar horseshoe shaped with 3 bundle scars, stipular scars lacking, terminal bud lacking, lateral buds naked, pith homogeneous, lenticels large and brown. *Bark* gray-brown, thin, smooth or scaly.

Range. Southern Ontario, east to western New York and New Jersey, south to southern Florida, west to Texas, north to southern Wisconsin; also local west to Arizona and southern Utah. Elevation: near sea level to 8500 ft in the southwestern mountains. Rocky slopes and edges of woods.

General Description. Small aromatic tree to 20 ft tall and 6 in. dbh. This widespread and variable species has been divided into several subspecies and varieties (Bailey, 1962).

Araliaceae: The Ginseng Family

This is a family of about 55 genera and 700 species widely distributed in temperate and tropical regions. They are herbs, shrubs, trees, and woody vines. It is best known for the commonly cultivated English ivy (*Hedera helix* L.); the very popular indoor/outdoor ornamental, *Schefflera;* and the commercially important herbal, ginseng (*Panax quinquefolius* L.), with root extracts now in cosmetics and medicinal or quasi-medicinal preparations.

Some recent evidence indicates that this family should be included within the Apiaceae s. l. (Judd et al., 1994).

Botanical Features of the Family

Leaves alternate (rarely opposite or wholed), simple or pinnately or palmately compound and often very large; with or without stipules.

Flowers perfect or imperfect; in a head, umbel, or panicle; 5-parted, ovary inferior; entomophilous.

Fruit a berry, drupe, or schizocarp.

Aràlia spinòsa L.   Devils-walkingstick; prickly ash

Distinguishing Characteristics. *Leaves* large, alternate, mostly bipinnate, 15 to 30 in. (38 to 76 cm) long and wide, often clustered at the top of an unbranched trunk (or with a few branches); the leaflets many, 2 to 3½ in. (5 to 9 cm) long, ovate or elliptical, serrulate, often with prickles on midrib beneath; fall color yellow. *Flowers* small, white, in large terminal panicles to 16 in. (40 cm) long, in late summer. *Fruit* a purplish black berry, ¼ in. (6 mm) in diameter on red pedicels and infructescence branches, persisting into the winter. *Twig* stout, with a circle of prickles at the nodes or scattered; leaf scar nearly encircling twig with one row of many bundle scars; stipular scar lacking; pith solid, large.

Range. New York and New Jersey, south to central Florida, west to eastern Texas, north to southeastern Missouri; naturalized northward into New England, southern Ontario, and Wisconsin. Elevation: near sea level to 3500 ft northward, to 5000 ft in the southern Appalachians. Moist soils along streams in hardwood forests, edge of woods, and roadsides.

General Description. Shrub or tree to 30 ft tall and 8 in. dbh, the trunk and branches prickly, the prickles straight, slender, and sharp pointed. The trunk is unbranched or with few branches and the large, compound leaves are clustered near the top, forming a unique and characteristic appearance. The fruits are eaten by birds and small mammals.

ASTERIDAE

Oleaceae: The Olive Family

The Olive family includes about 30 genera and some 600 species of trees and shrubs distributed mostly through the temperate and tropical forests of the northern hemisphere. The genera *Fraxinus* and *Olea* are noted for the many fine timbers which they produce, and *Olea europaea* L. furnishes the olives and olive oil of commerce. While originally a native of the Mediterranean basin, the olive is now widely cultivated throughout the warmer regions of the world, and several varieties are grown in California. Among the shrubby members of this family commonly used for ornamental purposes, are *Syringa* (lilac), *Osmanthus* (tea olive), *Forsythia* (goldenbell), *Jasminum* (jasmine), and *Ligustrum* (privet). Some *Ligustrum* species have become naturalized, and particularly *L. sinense* Lour. is weedy and forms dense thickets in wet areas of the Southeast. *Chionanthus virginicus* L., the native fringetree, and several ashes, *Fraxinus,* are also used for ornamental purposes.

Four genera are represented by native arborescent species in the United States, but only one, *Fraxinus,* is an important timber producer (Wilson and Wood, 1959).

Botanical Features of the Family
Leaves deciduous or persistent, opposite or rarely alternate, simple or pinnately compound, estipulate.
Flowers perfect and/or imperfect, actinomorphic; *calyx* 4-lobed or lacking; *corolla* 4- or rarely 5- to 16-lobed, or lacking; *stamens* 2 (rarely 3 to 5), adnate to the corolla and alternating with its lobes, rudimentary or lacking in the pistillate flowers; *pistils* 1, superior, the ovary 2- (rarely 3-) celled, with 2 ovules in each cell, with a single style and a 2-lobed stigma, rudimentary or lacking in the staminate flowers; entomophilous or anemophilous.
Fruit a samara, capsule, berry, or drupe.

FRAXINUS L.   Ash

The genus *Fraxinus* includes about 70 species of trees, rarely shrubs, largely restricted to temperate regions of the northern hemisphere, but extending into the tropical forests of Java and also Cuba. *Fraxinus excelsior* L., European ash, is often planted in North America as a street and shade tree. Flowering ash, *F. ornus* L., also a native of both Europe and Asia, is commonly used ornamentally in the Pacific Northwest; this species produces the "manna" of commerce, a medicinal substance used in the preparation of laxatives. A white wax is obtained from scale insects which feed on *F. chinensis* Roxb.

Numerous other species produce timbers of intrinsic value. A beautiful veneer stock, which is sold in this country under the name of Tamo, is from *F. mandshurica* Rupr. and *F. sieboldiana* Blume, the Manchurian and Japanese Siebold ashes, respectively.

The arborescent flora of the United States contains 16 to 17 species of ash. Two are considered of primary importance (Table 9-26), and seven others are briefly described, four in the East and three in the West. Most are important as deer browse and the fruits as food for birds and small mammals.

Interspecific hybridization does occur, and although hybridization between *F. americana* and *F. pennsylvanica* has been suggested as an origin for the biltmore ash (Miller, 1955; Santamour, 1962), there is no micromorphological evidence to support this hypothesis (Hardin and Beckmann, 1982).

Botanical Features of the Genus

Leaves deciduous, opposite, odd-pinnately compound (rarely reduced to a single leaflet), the leaflets serrate or entire.

Flowers perfect, and/or imperfect, appearing in the early spring before or with the unfolding of the leaves; *calyx* 4-lobed or lacking; *corolla* with 2 to 6 petals, or absent (the latter in all North American species except *F. cuspidata*); *stamens* 2 to 4; *pistils* 1, with a 2-celled ovary; anemophilous.

Fruit a 1-seeded samara with an elongated terminal wing; seed narrow and elongated, with endosperm.

Twigs slender to stout, glabrous or pubescent; *pith* homogeneous, terete between the nodes; *terminal buds* present, with 1 to 3 pairs of scales; *lateral buds* similar to the terminals but smaller; *leaf scars* suborbicular to semicircular, sometimes notched on the upper edge; *bundle scars* numerous, arranged in an open *U*- or *V*-shaped line, or sometimes an ellipse.

TABLE 9-26   COMPARISON OF IMPORTANT ASHES

Species	Leaves	Flowers	Fruit	Twigs
F. americana white ash	with about 7 serrate to entire, petioluled leaflets glabrous or pubescent and "papillose" below	imperfect; species dioecious	lanceolate to oblanceolate; wing narrowed or lacking along the outside of the seed cavity	terete, glabrous or pubescent; leaf scars notched
F. pennsylvanica green ash	with about 7 sharply serrate, petioluled leaflets, glabrous to pubescent below and on rachis; leaflets not "papillose" below	same	narrowly oblanceolate; wing often extending along the seed cavity	terete, glabrous to velvety-pubescent, leaf scar truncate to shallowly notched

Fráxinus americàna L.   White ash

Distinguishing Characteristics (Fig. 9-125)

Leaves 8 to 12 in. (20 to 30 cm) long, with 5 to 9 (mostly 7, and rarely 11 or 13) leaflets; *leaflets* 2½ to 5 in. (6 to 13 cm) long, 1¼ to 2¾ in. (3 to 7 cm) wide; *shape* ovate to oblong-lanceolate, elliptical, or oval; *apex* acute to acuminate; *base* rounded to acute, the stalks stout and narrowly winged; *margin* serrate, remotely crenate-serrate, or entire; *surfaces* dark green, glabrous above; whitish or pale green, glabrous or pubescent below, "papillose" because of raised cuticle; *rachis* slightly grooved, glabrous; *fall color* yellow, bronze, or purplish.

Flowers imperfect (plant dioecious), apetalous, both sexes appearing in glabrous panicles before or with leaves; *calyx* 4-parted, minute.

Fruit a lanceolate to oblanceolate samara, 1 to 2 in. (2.5 to 5 cm) long, and ca. ¼ in. (6 mm) wide; *wing* usually rounded or slightly emarginate (rarely pointed) at the apex, not greatly narrowed at the seed cavity and not extending along side of seed.

Twigs stout, glabrous or pubescent, dark green to gray-green, occasionally purplish, lustrous, lenticellate; *terminal buds* broadly ovoid, obtuse, covered with 4 to 6 brownish scales; *lateral buds* somewhat triangular, the first pair at the same level as the terminal bud; *superposed buds* occasionally present on vigorous shoots; *leaf scars* semiorbicular, usually notched at the top; *bundle scars* numerous and arranged in a broadly *U*-shaped line, sometimes nearly closed at the top.

Bark ashy gray, or on young stems sometimes with an orange tinge, later finely furrowed into close diamond-shaped areas separated by narrow interlacing ridges; on very old trees slightly scaly along the ridges.

Range

Eastern (Map 9-39). Disjuncts in eastern South Carolina and upper Michigan. Elevation: sea level to 2000 ft northward, to 5000 ft in the southern Appalachians. Moist upland slopes, valleys, coves, and bottomlands.

General Description

White ash, the most abundant and important of American ashes, is a tree 70 to 80 ft high and 2 to 3 ft dbh (max. 125 by 7 ft). The bole is long, straight, clear, and cylindrical and terminates below in a root system which is deep in porous soils but shallow and spreading on rocky sites; the crown is somewhat open. This tree is intermediate in tolerance except in the seedling stage, when it is often found in considerable numbers under forest cover. White ash commonly occurs on deep, moist, fertile upland soils in association with such species as basswood, yellow-poplar, black cherry, American beech, oaks, hickories, and red maple; in the South it may be found on loamy ridges in the bottoms accompanied by the hickories, swamp chestnut, willow, and cherrybark oaks, loblolly pine, and sweetgum, or elsewhere on well-drained slopes and coves; toward the northern limits of its range, white ash occurs with white pine and the beech–birch–maple–hemlock mixture, mostly as a scattered tree. This ash is a component of some 24 forest-cover types, but in all these it develops well only on the most fertile soils.

Although some seed may be produced each year, good crops develop only at 3- to 5-year intervals. On good sites, growth at first is rapid, and a height of 6 ft may be attained by the end of the third season. Sprouts from young trees are vigorous, often growing 5 ft or more in height the first year.

FIGURE 9-125 *Fraxinus americana.* White ash. (1) Twig × 1¼. (2) Staminate inflorescence × ½. (3) Staminate flower × 4. (4) Pistillate inflorescence × ½. (5) Pistillate flower × 4. (6) Samara × 1. (7) Leaf × ⅓. (8) Bark.

The Biltmore ash, recognized by some authors, is a form of white ash with twigs, petioles, rachises, and backs of the leaflets densely pubescent. Typical white ash is glabrous.

White ash is used for baseball bats, tennis racquets, hockey sticks, oars, and other playground and sports equipment.

Fráxinus pennsylvánica Marsh.   Green ash

Distinguishing Characteristics (Fig. 9-126)

Leaves 6 to 10 in. (15 to 25 cm) long, with 7 to 9 leaflets; *leaflets* 2 to 5 in. (5 to 13 cm) long, 1 to 1½ in. (2.5 to 4 cm) wide; *shape* lanceolate to ovate-lanceolate, or elliptical; *margin* serrate, sometimes entire below the middle; *apex* acute to acuminate; *base* gradually cuneate to unequally obtuse, the stalks slender; *surfaces* yellow-green above; pale and glabrous to silky pubescent below, not "papillose"; *rachis* moderately stout, grooved, glabrous to pubescent; *fall color* yellow.

Flowers imperfect (species dioecious), apetalous, both sexes borne in glabrous to tomentose panicles which appear after the leaves have begun to unfold; *calyx* remotely lobed or cup-shaped.

Fruit a narrowly oblanceolate samara, 1¼ to 2¼ in. (3 to 6 cm) long, ¼ in. (6 mm) or less wide; *wing* pointed or slightly emarginate at the apex, abruptly narrowed and extending along the slender seed cavity.

FIGURE 9-126   *Fraxinus pennsylvanica.* Green ash. (1) Twig × ¼. (2) Leaf × ⅓. (3) Samara × 1. (4) Bark.

Twigs stout to moderately slender, flattened at the nodes, gray to greenish brown, glabrous to velvety pubescent; *terminal buds* conical to ovate, rusty brown, pubescent; *lateral buds* reniform to triangular; *leaf scars* semicircular, shallowly notched to straight along the upper edge; *bundle scars* forming a *U*- or *V*-shaped line.

Bark similar to that of white ash but not as deeply furrowed.

Range

Eastern (Map 9-39). Elevation: sea level to 3000 ft in the southern Appalachians. Poorly drained bottomlands, stream and lake borders, swamps, and wet woodlands.

General Description

Green ash is the most widely distributed of American ashes. It is a small to medium-size tree 30 to 50 ft high and 20 in. dbh (max. 145 by 6 ft) with a broad irregular crown, a short, usually poorly formed trunk, and a superficial fibrous root system. It is common, especially through the Middle West, as a scattered tree along stream banks and the borders of swamps. Best development appears to be reached east of the Appalachians. Green ash has been widely planted throughout the plains states and adjacent Canada. It is exceedingly hardy to climatic extremes; although naturally a moist bottomland or stream-bank tree, it will, when once established, persist on dry sterile soils, and has been used successfully in shelterbelts. Under forest competition, green ash is intolerant to moderately tolerant. Its associates include boxelder, the bottomland oaks and hickories, sweetgum, cottonwood, willows, red maple, and, farther north, quaking aspen.

As in white ash, green ash also has both glabrous and densely pubescent forms. The pubescent form has been called red ash; the wood, however, is sold as white ash.

Fráxinus caroliniàna Mill.   Carolina ash

Distinguishing Characteristics. *Leaves* of 5 to 7 leaflets, each 2 to 4½ in. (5 to 11 cm) long, 1 to 2 in. (2.5 to 5 cm) wide, elliptical to ovate, lanceolate, pale below, with slender stalks, serrate; fall color yellow to bronze. *Fruit* 1¼ to 2 in. (3 to 5 cm) long, yellow-brown, broadly elliptical, wing extending to base of seed, and sometimes 3-winged. *Twigs* slender, glabrous, green to brown. *Bark* light gray, thin, and scaly, becoming rough and furrowed.

MAP 9-39   (Left) *Fraxinus americana.* **(Right)** *Fraxinus pennsylvanica.*

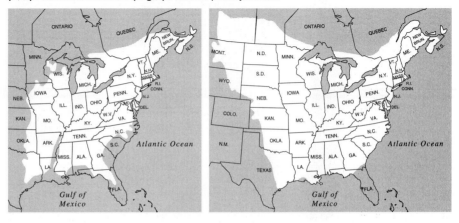

Range. Coastal Plain from northeastern Virginia to southern Florida and west to southeastern Texas and southern Arkansas. Elevation: sea level to 500 ft. Swamps, stream and river banks, flatwoods depressions, and pond margins.

General Description. Tree to 50 ft tall. This is one of the most variable of the ashes, and several varieties have been described. The variation is in the pubescence of twigs and leaves and shape and size of the samaras.

Fráxinus nìgra Marsh.   Black ash

Distinguishing Characteristics (Fig. 9-127). *Leaves* with 7 to 13 oblong to oblong-lanceolate, serrate, sessile leaflets, each 4 to 5½ in. (10 to 14 cm) long, 1 to 1½ in. (2.5 to 4 cm) wide; fall color yellow-brown. *Flowers* perfect and imperfect (polygamous or dioecious), soon naked as the minute calyx falls away, borne in panicles before the leaves. *Fruit* an oblong-elliptical samara with a wide wing extending along the flattened and indistinct seed. *Twigs* stout, grayish; terminal buds ovate-conical, dark brown to nearly black, laterals rounded, the first pair borne some distance below the terminal. *Bark* grayish, relatively smooth, later shallowly furrowed or scaly.

Range. Southeastern Manitoba, east to Newfoundland, south to West Virginia, west to Iowa; disjuncts in northeastern North Dakota and northern Virginia. Swamps, peat bogs, stream and river banks.

FIGURE 9-127   *Fraxinus nigra. Black ash.* (1) Twig × 1¼. (2) Leaf × ⅓. (3) Samara × 1. (4) Bark.

General Description.   Black ash, a typically northern tree, varies from 40 to 50 ft in height and 18 in. dbh (max. 108 by 5 ft). The bole is often poorly shaped, supports a small open crown, and terminates below in a very shallow, fibrous root system. This species occurs as a scattered tree associated with northern white-cedar, balsam fir, black spruce, red maple, and sometimes yellow and paper birch; farther south, American elm, black tupelo, and other swamp hardwoods are included. Black ash is intolerant and is not found under heavy forest cover. In a few localities it is abundant and of some importance, although the wood is of a much poorer quality than that of the other northern ashes. From early times black ash has furnished material for pack baskets fabricated by the Native Americans of the Northeast.

Fráxinus profúnda (Bush) Bush (*F. tomentosa* Michx. f.)   Pumpkin ash

Distinguishing Characteristics.   *Leaves* of 7 to 9 leaflets, each 3 to 7 in. (7.5 to 18 cm) long, 2 to 3 in. (5 to 7.5 cm) wide, elliptical or lanceolate, entire to slightly serrulate, pubescent below particularly along midrib, and with a slender stalk. *Fruit* 2 to 3 in. (5 to 7.5 cm) long, broadly elliptical, oblanceolate, or spatulate, with wing extending to base. *Twigs* stout, light gray, densely pubescent when young, leaf scar deeply notched at top. *Bark* gray, furrowed into diamond patterns.

Range.   Coastal Plain of New Jersey and southeastern Virginia, south to northern Florida, west to northwestern Louisiana, north to southeastern Missouri, southern Illinois, southern Michigan, Ohio, and northwestern Pennsylvania. Elevation: near sea level to 500 ft. Swamps and bottomlands.

General Description.   Tree to ca. 100 ft tall and 2 ft dbh. This is an uncommon tree similar to green ash but with larger leaves and larger samaras. It often occurs with baldcypress, water tupelo, and swamp cottonwood.

Fráxinus quadrangulàta Michx.   Blue ash

Distinguishing Characteristics (Fig. 9-128).   *Leaves* with 7 to 11 leaflets, each lanceolate to oblong-ovate, $3\frac{1}{4}$ to 5 in. (8 to 13 cm) long, 1 to $1\frac{1}{2}$ in. (2.5 to 4 cm) wide, serrate, with slender stalk; fall color yellow. *Flowers* perfect, soon naked as the calyx falls away, borne in panicles as the leaves unfold. *Fruit* oblong to spatulate, with wing surrounding the flattened seed. *Twigs* stout, 4-angled and 4-winged between the nodes; terminal buds broadly ovoid, reddish brown. *Bark* on mature trees, with long, loose, scaly plates, giving a shaggy appearance to the trunk.

Range.   Southern Wisconsin, southern Michigan, and western Ohio, south to northwestern Georgia, west to eastern Oklahoma; disjuncts in southwestern Ontario, eastern Kansas, and northwestern Missouri. Elevation: 400 to 2000 ft. Dry, rocky, limestone slopes and moist river valleys.

General Description.   Blue ash is a medium-size tree to 80 ft tall and 2 ft dbh (max. 120 by 4 ft) which occurs especially on dry limestone uplands through the Ohio and Upper Mississippi valleys. Here its associates include chinkapin and other oaks, hickories, and redbud. This ash occurs as a scattered tree and is relatively rare in comparison with white ash, which often accompanies it on the better soils. The inner bark contains a mucilaginous substance which turns blue upon exposure to the air. A blue dye prepared by macerating the bark in water was used by the pioneers for dyeing cloth. Blue ash has been planted to some extent in the prairie region. Its silvical features are similar to those of the other upland ashes.

Fráxinus anómala Torr. ex Wats.   Singleleaf ash

Distinguishing Characteristics.   *Leaves* appearing simple (actually unifoliolate) or occasionally pinnate with 2 to 3 leaflets, $1\frac{1}{2}$ to 2 in. (4 to 5 cm) long, 1 to 2 in. (2.5 to 5 cm) wide,

FIGURE 9-128   *Fraxinus quadragulata.* Blue ash. (1) Twig × 1¼. (2) Samara × 1.

ovate and entire. *Fruit* ca. ¾ in. (19 mm) long, ⅜ in. (9 mm) wide, elliptical, with wing extending to base. *Twigs* slender, brown, glabrous, 4-angled or slightly winged. *Bark* brown and furrowed.

Range.   Northeastern Utah and western Colorado, south to northwestern New Mexico, west to eastern California. Elevation: usually 2000 to 6500 ft and to 11,000 ft in California. Dry canyons, hillsides, and ponderosa pine forests.

General Description.   Shrub or small tree to 25 ft tall and 6 in. dbh. This species is unique because of its unifoliolate leaf.

Fráxinus latifòlia Benth.   Oregon ash

Distinguishing Characteristics (Fig. 9-129).   *Leaves* 5 to 12 in. (13 to 30 cm) long, with 5 to 9 leaflets, each 1½ to 4 in. (4 to 10 cm) long, 1 to 1½ in. (2.5 to 4 cm) wide, ovate, obovate, or elliptical, sessile or slender-stalked, serrulate or entire, usually tomentose below; fall color yellow. *Flowers* paniculate, appearing with the leaves (plants dioecious). *Fruit* oblong, elliptical, oblanceolate, or spatulate, 1¼ to 2 in. (3 to 5 cm) long, the wing extending nearly to the base of the slightly flattened seed. *Twigs* stout, densely tomentose, with conical terminal buds and small, ovoid lateral buds; leaf scars suborbicular, the bundle scars arranged in a *U*-shaped line. *Bark* dark gray to gray-brown, with an interwoven pattern similar to that of white ash.

Range.   Western Washington, south along the coast to San Francisco Bay and south along the lower western slopes of the Sierras to southern California. Elevation: sea level to 5500 ft. Stream and river banks and bottomlands or in drier canyons.

FIGURE 9-129   *Fraxinus latifolia.* Oregon ash. (1) Twig × 1¼. (2) Leaf × ½. (3) Staminate inflorescence × 1. (4) Samara × 1. (5) Bark.

General Description. Oregon ash is a timber tree of secondary importance. Ordinarily it attains a height of 60 to 80 ft and a dbh of 2 to 4 ft (max. 80 by 6 ft). A clear, symmetrical bole supporting a narrow, compact crown is found in forest-grown trees. The root system is moderately shallow but wide-spreading, and the trees are unusually windfirm. Nearly pure fringes or strips of this ash occur along the banks of water courses and margins of swamps, but it occurs more abundantly in mixture with other species. In the northern part of its range it is chiefly associated with bigleaf maple, red alders, willows, Oregon white oak, grand fir, black cottonwood, and Douglas-fir. To the south, however, these species are largely replaced by digger and ponderosa pines, white alder, California-laurel, California sycamore, and California black oak.

Seed is produced after the thirtieth year, and heavy crops are released every 3 to 5 years thereafter. Seedling trees can endure moderate shading when there is an abundance of soil moisture, although they require considerably more light after passing the sapling stage. However, trees which have been suppressed for protracted lengths of time are able to resume a normal rate of growth soon after being released. The growth rate is moderately rapid for the first 60 to 100 years, after which it decreases gradually, and maturity is ultimately reached in about 200 to 250 years. Natural regeneration is also accomplished by sprouts from the root collar.

Fráxinus velùtina Torr.   Velvet ash

Distinguishing Characteristics. *Leaves* of 5 to 9 leaflets, each 1 to 3 in. (2.5 to 7.5 cm) long, ⅜ to 1¼ in. (1 to 3 cm) wide, lanceolate to elliptical, with slender stalk, pubescent below; fall color yellow. *Fruit* ¾ to 1¼ in. (2 to 3 cm) long, narrow, oblanceolate, wing extending to midway of seed. *Twigs* gray or brown, pubescent when young. *Bark* gray, furrowed with broad, scaly ridges.

Range. Western Texas, southern New Mexico, Arizona, southwestern Utah, southern Nevada, and southern California. Elevation: 2500 to 7000 ft. Stream banks, canyons, mountain slopes, and desert grasslands.

General Description. Tree to 40 ft tall and 1 ft dbh. This is the common ash of the southwest and frequently planted for shade.

OSMANTHUS Lour.   Osmanthus

There are ca. 15 species, mostly Asiatic. Several are cultivated as attractive, evergreen ornamentals with very aromatic flowers appearing in the fall. Two popular species are *O. heterophyllus* (G. Don) P. S. Green, holly tea olive, with many cultivars, and *O. fragrans* Lour., fragrant tea olive. There is only one native species in North America.

Osmánthus americànus (L.) Benth. & Hook. f. ex Gray   Devilwood; wild-olive

Distinguishing Characteristics. *Leaves* opposite, persistent, 3½ to 5 in. (9 to 13 cm) long, ¾ to 1½ in. (2 to 4 cm) wide, lanceolate to elliptical, thick and coriaceous, entire, and sometimes revolute. *Flowers* small, fragrant, white or yellowish, bell-shaped with 4 petal lobes, in axillary clusters; appearing in spring. *Fruit* berrylike, ⅜ to ¾ in. (10 to 19 mm) long, elliptical, dark blue. *Bark* gray, scaly.

Range. Coastal Plain from southeastern Virginia to central Florida, west to southeastern Louisiana. Elevation: sea level to 500 ft. It occurs in moist bay forests, maritime forests, edge of swamps, in river valleys, and on dry sandy ridges and dunes.

General Description. This is a small, evergreen tree to 30 ft tall and 1 ft dbh. It is easily distinguished from the other bay or maritime trees by its opposite leaves. The fruits are eaten by birds and small mammals.

Scrophulariaceae: The Figwort Family

This family of mostly herbs, some shrubs, and few trees has about 220 genera and 4000 species with a cosmopolitan distribution but mainly in the temperate zone. Of economic importance are foxglove, *Digitalis purpurea* L. (source of digitalis glycosides used in medicine), and ornamental herbs such as the common snapdragon (*Antirrhinum majus* L.). *Paulownia* is the only tree of this family in the United States.

Botanical Features of the Family

Leaves alternate, opposite or whorled, simple or compound, estipulate, deciduous.
Flowers perfect, irregular, 5-parted with connate calyx and connate and tubular corolla, stamens 2 or 4(5), epipetalous, carpels 2, fused, ovary superior; entomophilous.
Fruit a capsule with seeds winged or angled.

Paulòwnia tomentòsa (Thunb.) Sieb. & Zucc. ex Steud.   Royal paulownia, Empress-tree

Distinguishing Characteristics.   *Leaves* opposite, 6 to 16 in. (15 to 40 cm) long and wide, broadly ovate, apex acuminate, base cordate, the lower surface pubescent with erect, branched hairs (seen if scraped off and examined under a microscope); petiole 4 to 8 in. (10 to 20 cm) long. *Flowers* about 2 in. (5 cm) long, broadly tubular with 5 unequal lobes, pale violet and fragrant, in erect panicles to 1 ft (30 cm) long, appearing in early spring before the leaves, and from conspicuous, tan buds formed the previous summer. *Fruit* an ovoid capsule, 1 to 1½ in. (2.5 to 4 cm) long, pointed at apex, splitting into 2 valves, with small winged seeds, persisting through the winter. *Twigs* stout, light brown, pubescent, leaf scar nearly elliptical, bundle scars many in a nearly closed ellipse, stipular scars lacking, terminal bud lacking, bud scales ca. 4 and blunt, the pith hollow in the second-year branch. *Bark* gray-brown, with furrows.

Range.   This native of China was introduced into the United States in 1834 as a very attractive ornamental, particularly when in flower. It has now become naturalized in the eastern United States and is seen along roadsides, edges of woods, along river banks, in waste places, and in pastures.

General Description.   This is a deciduous tree to 50 ft tall and 2 ft dbh. It has a very rapid growth on good sites, with first-year saplings exceeding 7 ft tall and leaves up to 2 ft (60 cm) long the first year.

Paulownia somewhat resembles Catalpa vegetatively; however, Catalpa differs in its often whorled leaves, lacking the stalked glands and branched hairs on the lower leaf surface, and with continuous pith in the second-year branch. The flowers and fruits are very different. *Paulownia* is still placed in the Bignoniaceae with *Catalpa* by some authors (Duncan and Duncan, 1988). However, it has been shown conclusively that it belongs in the Scrophulariaceae and only superficially resembles *Catalpa.*

Bignoniaceae: The Trumpet-creeper Family

The Bignoniaceae include about 112 genera and 750 species of trees, shrubs, vines, and herbs, the majority of which are tropical. *Cybistax donnell-smithii* (Rose) Siebert, a native of Mexico and Central America, has a beautiful wood which enters the American markets under the names of "prima vera" or "white mahogany." A number of other very fine timbers come from the Indo-Malayan species of the genus *Stereospermum.*

The sausage-tree, *Kigelia africana* (Lam.) Benth., a tropical species, so named because of its peculiar sausage-shaped fruits suspended on long slender stems, is cultivated in southern Florida and southern California.

Four genera with arborescent forms are native to this country, but only one (*Catalpa*) is of sufficient importance to be described.

Botanical Features of the Family

Leaves mostly deciduous, opposite or whorled (rarely alternate), simple or compound, estipulate.

Flowers perfect, usually large and showy, tubular, zygomorphic, 5-parted, ovary superior; entomophilous and ornithophilous.

Fruit a capsule or rarely berrylike, seeds usually winged.

CATALPA Scop.   Catalpa

Catalpa consists of 12 species distributed through the forests of eastern Asia, eastern North America, and the West Indies. Two species are included in the arborescent flora of the United States. They are native to the southeastern states but have become widely naturalized in the East and are cultivated in the West. They are very similar and often difficult to distinguish. The trees are used ornamentally for their large, showy panicles of white flowers and long, slender, cigar-shaped fruits. They are also well-known for the "catalpa worms" (caterpillars) used for fishbait, and the wood which is resistant to decay and used for fence posts.

Botanical Features of the Genus

Leaves deciduous, opposite or whorled in 3s, simple, long-petioled, the blade heart-shaped, sometimes palmately lobed, pubescent below with unbranched hairs; fall color yellowish green or brownish yellow.

Flowers large and showy in many-flowered panicles or corymbs; corolla tubular, 2-lipped; appearing in late spring after the leaves.

Fruit a long, pendant, semipersistent, slender, terete capsule with many flat, 2-winged seeds, fringed or tufted at the ends of the opposing wings.

Twig stout; terminal bud lacking, lateral buds small, hemispherical, with ca. 6 pointed bud scales; leaf scars nearly circular, raised with a depressed center, the bundle scars many in a closed ellipse; estipulate; pith solid and homogeneous, white.

Catálpa speciòsa Warder ex Engelm.   Northern catalpa; western catalpa

Distinguishing Characteristics (Fig. 9-130). *Leaves* 6 to 12 in. (15 to 30 cm) long, ovate or oval, entire, gradually acuminate at apex, cordate at base, generally inodorous; petiole 4 to 6 in. (10 to 15 cm) long. *Flowers* in few-flowered panicles, each white with 2 yellow-orange lines and thin purplish brown spots and stripes in the throat and on the lower lobe, corolla 2 to 2½ in. (5 to 6.5 cm) across. *Fruit* 8 to 18 in. (20 to 46 cm) long, ½ to ⅝ in. (12 to 15 mm) in diameter, with a thick wall; seed wings rounded and fringed at the ends. *Bark* reddish brown, thick with thick scales.

FIGURE 9-130 *Catalpa speciosa.* Northern catalpa. (1) Capsule × ⅓. (2) Inflorescence × ¼. (3) Seed × ¾. (4) Twig × 1.

Range.   Native in southwestern Indiana and southern Illinois, western Kentucky and western Tennessee, southeastern Missouri, and northeastern Arkansas. Elevation: 200 to 500 ft. Alluvial forests, base of bluffs, river banks.

General Description.   Northern catalpa normally attains a height of 60 ft and dbh to 2 ft, with a maximum of 120 ft and a dbh of 6 ft. The bole is well formed if grown under proper conditions of soil, moisture, and side shading, but otherwise may be crooked. The species occurs as scattered trees, and is exceedingly reactive to soil conditions. On rich moist soils a growth of 2 ½ ft in height and a dbh increase of ½ in. per year may be attained, but on poorer locations the growth is much less. Catalpa is intolerant, but natural pruning does not take place readily, and best results are obtained in rather dense, pure stands. The seasoned timber is very durable when used for posts or ties, although the living trees are subject to heart rot. This species has been widely planted through the Middle West, and it is said that on the proper soil this catalpa will produce more good fence posts in a short time than any other native tree. It is also commonly planted as an ornamental.

Catálpa bignonioìdes Walt.   Southern catalpa, Common catalpa

Distinguishing Characteristics. *Leaves* 5 to 10 in. (13 to 25 cm) long with an abruptly acuminate apex, sometimes shallowly 3-lobed, and with an unpleasant odor if crushed. *Flowers* in many-flowered panicles, each white with 2 yellow-orange lines and prominent purple spots and stripes in the throat and on the lower lobe, corolla $1\frac{1}{4}$ to 2 in. (4 to 5 cm) across. *Capsule* 6 to 12 in. (15 to 30 cm) long, $\frac{5}{16}$ to $\frac{3}{8}$ in. (8 to 10 mm) in diameter, with a thin wall; seed wings narrowed and tufted at the ends. *Bark* gray-brown, thin with thin scales.

Range. Native of southwestern Georgia and northwestern Florida to central Mississippi. Elevation: 100 to 500 ft. Stream banks, low woods, floodplains.

General Description. This is a small tree 20 to 40 ft tall and dbh to 2 ft. It is widely cultivated as an attractive ornamental. In comparison with *C. speciosa,* this southern catalpa has somewhat smaller leaves which are sometimes 3-lobed, panicle with more flowers, smaller flowers with more prominent purple spotting, blooming about two weeks later, smaller fruits with thinner walls, and bark with thinner scales. These are rather subtle differences, however, and the two are not easily identified unless both are available for direct comparison.

LILIOPSIDA—The Monocots

ARECIDAE

Arecaceae (Palmae): The Palm Family

This family has 210 genera and about 3000 species and is pantropical in distribution, with a few in the subtropics and warm-temperate latitudes. Only about 10 genera are native to the United States, one in the Southwest (*Washingtonia*) and the others in the Southeast. They are evergreen trees, shrubs, and woody vines. Palms are unusual in many ways. The usually unbranched *trunks* are formed only by primary growth with many scattered vascular bundles, and therefore they have no true wood or bark as in dicot trees. Although most are erect, some are prostrate. The *leaves,* although appearing compound when mature, are actually simple before they expand. Weak zones along the folds mechanically split as the leaf enlarges.

The palm family is one of three most important families (with legumes and grasses) for shelter, construction materials, furniture (rattan), food, fiber, wax, and oil. The numerous uses by humans are closely tied into the folklore of the countries where they occur and provide many of the necessities of the peoples and wildlife (Hora, 1981). Well-known members are the date palm (*Phoenix dactylifera* L.), coconut palm (*Cocos nucifera* L.), and oil palm (*Elaeis quineensis* Jacq.). Many serve as ornamentals for lawns and streets as well as inside of homes and other buildings. A fine, recent guide to the palms is by Meerow (1992).

Botanical Features of the Family

Leaves persistent, alternate, often very large, forming dense terminal rosettes, long-petiolate with broad to tubular sheath which often splits and is open at maturity; sim-

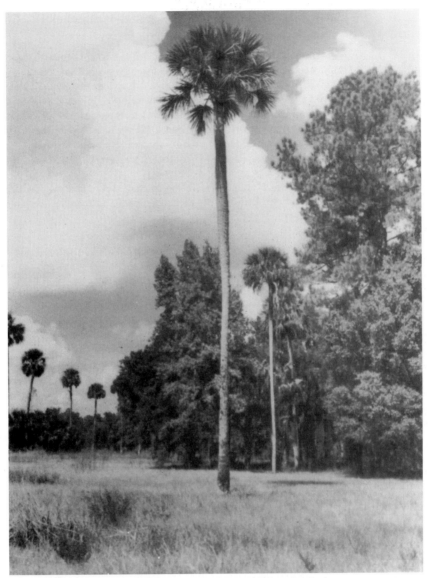

FIGURE 9-131   *Sabal palmetto.* Cabbage palmetto. (*Courtesy of U.S. Forest Service.*)

ple but mechanically splitting into narrow segments, into either pinnate (feather), palmate (fan), a somewhat intermediate costa-palmate, or bipinnate forms.

Flowers small, fragrant, perfect or imperfect, regular, perianth 3 to 6 parted, stamens 6, ovary 3-carpellate and superior; inflorescence a panicle enclosed at first by a large spathe; entomophilous, rarely anemophilous.

Fruit a fleshy or fibrous drupe.

Sàbal palmétto (Walt.) Lodd. ex J. A. & J. H. Schult.   Cabbage palmetto; palmetto palm

Distinguishing Characteristics (Fig. 9-131). *Leaves* fan-shaped (costa-palmate) from a short, stout midrib, the segments with threadlike fibers along the edges, blade 4 to 7 ft (1.2 to 2.1 m) in diameter, petiole 5 to 8 ft (1.5 to 2.4 m) long, without prickles. *Flowers* small, whitish yellow, in large, drooping panicles initially enclosed by a large, woody spathe; appearing mid to late summer. *Fruit* a globose, fleshy, black drupe, ca. ⅜ in. (10 mm) in diameter. *Trunk* unbranched, gray-brown, rough or ridged, often with persistent leaf bases.

Range. Outer Coastal Plain from southeastern North Carolina to southern Florida and the Keys and west along the Gulf Coast to northwestern Florida. Found along dunes, edges of salt marshes, hammocks, and inland flatwoods.

General Description. This is the common native tree palm to 50 ft tall and 1½ ft dbh in the southeast. See Brown (1976) for a description of reproductive biology, ecological life history, ecology, and distribution.

Washingtònia filífera (Linden ex André) H. Wendl.   California washingtonia

Distinguishing Characteristics (Fig. 9-132). *Leaves* fan-shaped (costa-palmate), 3 to 5 ft (0.9 to 1.5 m) in diameter, petiole 3 to 5 ft (0.9 to 1.5 m) long with hooked prickles along the side, the blade segments with threadlike filaments from the margins; old brown leaves hang down against the trunk in a thick mass. *Flowers* fragrant, white, appearing in late summer. *Fruit* an ellipsoidal, black drupe, ca. ⅜ in. (10 mm) in diameter. *Trunk* gray and smooth.

Range. Southwestern Arizona and southeastern California and south into Mexico. Elevation: 490 to 3300 ft. Moist, alkaline soils along streams and in mountain canyons.

General Description. This is the largest native palm of the United States and the only native palm of the southwestern United States. It reaches to 75 ft tall and 3 ft dbh. It is also cultivated across the southern United States.

The characteristic, persistent, dried leaves which hang down as a massive "skirt" provide cover and nesting sites for some birds and small mammals. But, when grown in yards and along streets, these skirts are usually cut because they are fire hazards and breeding sites for rats.

A similar but taller (to 100 ft or more) and thinner trunked (to 1½ ft dbh) palm commonly cultivated across the southern United States is the Mexican washingtonia, *W. robústa* H. Wendl., introduced from Mexico. The leaves are not as deeply split, the segments lack the threadlike filaments, and the tips are drooping.

COMMELINIDAE

Poaceae: The Grass Family

The Poaceae are a huge family with about 740 genera and nearly 8000 species worldwide in distribution. The grasses are primarily herbs, except for the bamboos.

Bamboos are perennial, of tree size (to 100 ft tall and 1 ft dbh), and "woody" but without secondary growth; *stems* hollow in the internodes; *leaves* alternate, sheathing at the base, the blades flat, long, straplike, mostly distichous, and often narrowed and jointed between the blade and sheath, and the blade deciduous from this joint; *flowers* individually lacking a perianth and inconspicuous, but enclosed in bracts and forming a conspicuous primary inflorescence

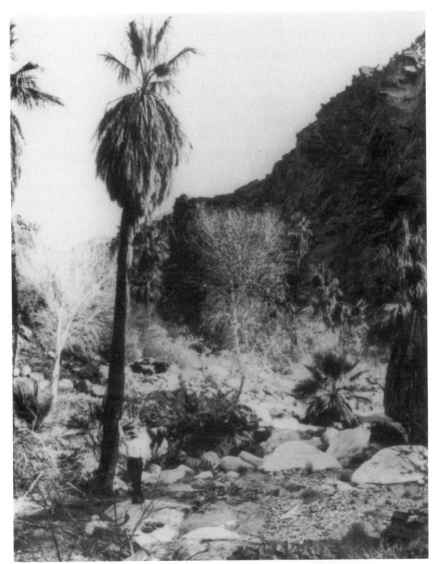

FIGURE 9-132   *Washingtonia filifera.* California washingtonia. (*Courtesy of U.S. Forest Service.*)

(spikelet) and these forming a larger secondary inflorescence, anemophilous; *fruit* a grain with a single seed.

There are many genera and species of bamboos, mainly from subtropical and tropical forests. These have numerous uses in papermaking, handicrafts, engineering, pipes, construction (called the "poor man's timber," Laarman and Sedjo, 1992), walking sticks, furniture, fishing poles, tools, split for mats, baskets, as edible young shoots, and food and shelter for wildlife.

Nine genera are cultivated in the United States as ornamentals. These are of two types, "clump-forming" and "running" bamboos. Although these seldom flower in North America, the running type can spread rapidly by rhizomes and are difficult to contain. Both types often persist from cultivation and can escape by means of discarded pieces of rhizome.

LILIIDAE

Agavaceae: The Century-plant Family

This is a small family, closely related to the lilies, with 18 genera and 580 species widespread in warm, arid regions of the Americas but now planted worldwide. They are short-stemmed herbs with a basal rosette or sparsely and irregularly-branched trees with terminal rosettes; the leaves are often stiff and succulent. Several genera are important as ornamentals, such as *Yucca, Agave, Sansevieria* (mother-in-law's tongue), as a source of fibers (*Agave,* sisal hemp; *Sansevieria,* bowstring hemp), and for a strong drink (pulque, fermented sap from *Agave* stems which is distilled into mescal or tequila).

Botanical Features of the Family

Leaves alternate, simple, basal or apical in rosettes, sheathing, usually fibrous, often succulent, stiff and sharp pointed, tapered and dagger- or swordlike, entire or prickly margined.

Flowers perfect or imperfect (and plants dioecious), mostly regular, 3-parted, ovary superior or inferior; inflorescence usually a panicle; pollinated by insects, birds, or bats.

Fruit a capsule or berry.

AGAVE L.   Century plant

This genus, with 200 to 300 species from the southwestern United States to tropical South America, has succulent, spine-tipped leaves in a basal rosette and an inferior ovary. They form conspicuous plants of the landscape. Agaves flower only once at the end of their lifetime. During vegetative growth this plant has a dense, basal rosette of large leaves and no obvious stem. Then in 8 to 25 years (not a century as the common name implies), it rapidly sends up a tall stem with a large panicle of yellow to greenish flowers. The plant dies as the seeds mature.

Although not considered as "trees" in the usual sense, and generally not included in tree books, there are several species of tree-size agaves in the Southwest, some reaching 25 to 35 ft tall. The one described here serves to show the general habit and size.

Agáve párryi Engelm.   Parry agave

Distinguishing Characteristics (Fig. 9-133).   *Rosette* 1 to 2 ft (3 to 6 dm) tall and 2 to 4 ft (6 to 12 dm) in diameter. *Leaves* 1 to 2 ft (3 to 6 dm) long, 3 to 4 in. (7.5 to 10 cm) wide, ashy gray, with a terminal spine tip. *Inflorescence* to over 16 ft (4.8 m) tall, the lateral branches horizontal and bearing many terminal flowers. *Flowers* with reddish buds, yellow when open. *Fruit* a dehiscing capsule.

FIGURE 9-133   Agave parryi. Parry agave. (*Courtesy of U.S. Forest Service.*)

Range.   This is found at 4500 to 8000 ft in the arid Southwest from central Arizona to western Texas and northern Mexico.

YUCCA L.   Yucca

This genus with 40 species in usually dry, subtropical America differs primarily from *Agave* by its superior ovary. Many species have the same habit as that of *Agave* with the basal rosette. However, several reach tree size. The most striking treelike yucca, because of its unusual branching pattern, is the Joshua-tree of the Southwest.

Yúcca brevifòlia Engelm.   Joshua-tree

Distinguishing Characteristics (Fig. 9-134).   *Leaves* evergreen, long, stiff, swordlike, spine-tipped, 8 to 14 in. (20 to 35 cm) long, ⅜ to ⅝ in. (8 to 15 mm) wide, clustered at the ends of branches, margin sharply serrate. *Flowers* 1¼ to 1½ in. (3 to 4 cm) long, bell-shaped with 6 greenish pale yellow tepals, waxy and night-blooming, in erect, terminal panicles 30 to 50 cm long; appearing in early spring. *Fruit* 2½ to 4¾ in. (6 to 12 cm) long, 2 in. (5 cm) in diameter, elliptical, becoming a dry but indehiscent capsule. *Trunk* irregularly branched, reddish-brown or gray, rough and deeply furrowed into plates; the branches often covered with dead leaves hanging downward.

Range.   Southwestern Utah, southern Nevada, western Arizona, and southern California. Elevation: 2000 to 6500 ft. Dry soils of the Mohave and Sonoran deserts and close to pinyon pines in the lower conifer forests of the San Bernardino Mountains. It occurs in groves on plains, slopes, and mesas.

FIGURE 9-134   *Yucca brevifolia*. Joshua-tree. (*Courtesy of the U.S. Forest Service.*)

General Description.   This is an irregularly branched, picturesque tree from a single trunk and the largest of the yuccas with a height to 32 ft tall and dbh of 1 to 3 ft. It is important as food, for nesting, and as shelter for wildlife in the area.

Yuccas also have an interesting interdependence with the Yucca moth—the moth is necessary for pollination, and the developing seeds provide food for the larvae. After gathering pollen from a flower and rolling the pollen into a little ball, the moth lays its eggs in the ovary of another flower and packs the ball of pollen onto the stigma, thus both pollinating the flower and providing a safe, food-filled place for the developing larvae which later burrow out of the fruit.

10

WHAT AFTER DENDROLOGY?

After a course in dendrology, one may think that there is little more to learn except just more trees. After all, the trees have been named and classified (Little, 1979), their characteristics described, drawn, or photographed (Elias, 1989; Little, 1980a and b; Young and Young, 1992), their habitats identified (Burns and Honkala, 1990), and their ranges mapped (Little, 1971, 1976, 1977, 1978; Viereck and Little, 1975).

Literature prior to the 1950s did deal mainly with these basic facts. Since the late 1960s, though, there has been an explosion of research on woody plants. Some studies were purely floristic (Clark, 1971; Godfrey, 1988); some revisionary (Burckhalter, 1992; Furlow, 1979); yet others dealt with genetics and improvement of commercial tree species (Nienstaedt and Teich, 1971; Zobel and Talbert, 1984); others dealt with physiological ecology (Kozlowski et al., 1990); ecological life history including pollination ecology and reproductive strategies (Brown, 1976); within-species variation and provenance studies (Adams and Turner, 1970; Baranski, 1975; Giannasi, 1978; Howe et al., 1993; Kreibel, 1993); between-species variation in micromorphology (Hardin, 1979a, 1992; Hardin and Stone, 1984); adaptive radiation (Stone, 1973); physiology and autecology (Kramer and Kozlowski, 1979; Kozlowski et al., 1990; D. B. Zobel, 1969); hybridization and introgression (Barnes et al., 1974; dePamphilis and Wyatt, 1990; Flake et al., 1978; Hardin, 1975; Ledig et al., 1969; Rushton, 1993; Tucker, 1993); genetic diversity and structure (Berg and Hamrick, 1993; Gibson and Hamrick, 1991; Hamrick et al., 1992; Loveless and Hamrick, 1984; Manos and Fairbrothers, 1987; Mosseler et al., 1993; Wagner et al., 1987); population genetics and relative gene flow correlated with life history (Hamrick et al., 1979; Mosseler et al., 1993); genetic effects of forest fragmentation (Young et al., 1993); and relationships of species, genera, or families (Eckenwalder, 1976; Hart, 1987; Malusa, 1992; Murrell, 1993; Price and Lowenstein, 1989; Price et al., 1987; Robson et al., 1993; Strauss and

Doerksen, 1990). More and more of these studies since the 1970s have used newer techniques of SEM, chromatography of flavonoids, electrophoresis of allozymes, radioimmunoassay of seed proteins, and RNA or DNA analysis.

We are now at a stage where the emphasis will be on inter- and intraspecific genetic variation (using modern techniques such as DNA sequencing); the adaptive significance of anatomical, morphological, cytological, and chemical differences; ecological life histories and reproductive strategies; phenetic, phyletic, and cladistic relationships among families, genera, and species; population biology and the dynamics of woody plant populations; and the mechanisms of speciation and evolution. Call it *modern dendrology.*

Numerous questions need to be asked of the modern dendrologist. For instance, what do we know about the function and importance of the individual or species population in an ecosystem? What do we know of the genetic basis of characters and character states that are used in our classifications? What do we know about the genetic structure, ecological life history, or autecology of most of our forest trees? What do we know about the extent or dimension of gene exchange in and between populations or the effective size of the breeding populations of trees? And how are these parameters affected by the increasing fragmentation of our forests? Why are certain tree species rare and endangered or threatened? How can we manage and maintain the critical habitats of rare and endangered tree species or the endangered herbaceous species of a forest floor? What do we know of the details of interspecific competition, plant–plant interactions, speciation, ecophenic versus ecotypic versus clinal variation? Has a wide-ranging species undergone ecotypic differentiation, or does it have a highly plastic "general-purpose genotype"? How is the degree of genetic variability correlated with life history and reproductive strategies? What do we really know of the nature of the effective reproductive barriers that maintain the morphological/ecological units that we call species? Does introgression in forest trees actually occur as much as some think, or is the apparent pattern of introgression due to some other cause? Is the introgression that does exist merely "evolutionary noise," or could it be a consistent feature of the adaptiveness of many plant species (a syngameon or compilospecies) and necessary for continued ecological exploitation and future progressive evolution or even survival?

The modern dendrologist faces exciting questions, and the answers to many of these are of utmost significance for forest management and maintenance of genetic diversity in our forest ecosystems throughout the world. At the very least, for both the professional and the environmentally aware, there is the prospect for a rewarding lifetime hobby, after dendrology, centered around the recognition of tree species, their silvical characteristics, and topographic and geographic locations.

There *is indeed* a great deal more—after dendrology.

GLOSSARY

abortive Lacking or defective.

abscission layer Layer of cells at base of leaf which, when developed, causes leaf to die and eventually drop.

accessory An additional part.

achene A small, dry, 1-seeded, unwinged fruit.

acicular Needlelike.

actinomorphic Radially symmetrical; regular flower.

aculeate "Spiny" or "prickly" leaf margin.

acuminate Long, tapering; attenuated.

acute The shape of an acute angle; sharp pointed but not attenuated.

adnate Fusion of unlike parts of a flower, such as the perianth and stamens which form the hypanthium.

agamospermy The asexual formation of a seed.

aggregate A cluster of fruits developed from separate pistils of a single flower and remaining together at maturity.

allelopathy The process in which a plant releases into the environment a chemical compound which inhibits or stimulates the growth of another plant in the same or neighboring habitat. In native plant communities, allelopathy may determine distribution patterns of plants in relation to their associates; in forestry, allelopathy may also affect yields or forest regeneration. Some important allelopathic trees are black walnut, eucalyptus, sugar maple, hackberry, balsam poplar, and sassafras.

allergenic Causing an allergic reaction such as dermatitis or nasal/bronchial irritation.

allogamy Cross-fertilization between flowers; including geitonogamy and xenogamy.

allopatric Two taxa with nonoverlapping geographical ranges.

ament A flexible, often pendent spike bearing apetalous, unisexual flowers.

anastomosing Interlacing.

androecium The collective term for all the stamens of a flower.

androgynous Having both staminate and pistillate flowers in the same inflorescence.

anemochory Wind dispersal of diaspores.

anemophilous Wind-pollinated.

aneuploid A chromosome number that is not an exact multiple of the base haploid number within a group.

angiosperm The flowering plants; literally "enclosed seeds" in a carpel.

anther The pollen-bearing portion of the stamen.

anthesis The time of opening of a flower when pollination can occur.

apetalous Without petals.

apiculate Abruptly pointed.

apomixis (n.), **apomictic** (adj.) Asexual reproduction as a substitute for the normal sexual process.

apophysis The part of a cone scale which is exposed when the cone is closed.

a posteriori Derived after observation of the facts.

appressed Flattened against.

a priori Derived by reasoning before the facts.

arborescent Treelike.

arcuate Pinnate venation in which the entire secondary veins narrowly arch upward toward the apex.

aril A fleshy appendage growing from the point of attachment of a seed and often covering the seed.

aristate Bearing a stiff bristle at the apex.

articulate Joined or jointed.

artificial classification Based upon a few convenient characters and a priori reasoning.

asepalous Without sepals.

association A group of species occurring in the same habitat with one or more dominant species as well as associated species; often designated by the names of the dominants, for example, spruce–fir or pine–oak.

attenuate Long, tapering; acuminate.

auriculate With earlike lobes at the base.

autecology Ecology of an individual plant or species.

autogamy Self-fertilization; pollination within one bisexual flower.

awl (awn) Subulate leaf type of conifers that are short, stiff, and tapered to a point.

axil Upper angle between the stem and the attached organ.

axile Situated on the axis.

axillary In an axil.

axis The central line of an organ; the "stem" to which structures are attached.

ballochory (autochory) Seed dispersal by ballistic means—being shot out of the fruit.

bark The outer layer of a woody stem; all tissues from the vascular cambium outward.

barochory Diaspore dispersal by weight (gravity).

basionym The name-bringing synonym in any change in position or rank of a taxon.

bast Fibrous constituents of the bark.

berry A simple fleshy fruit with the entire pericarp fleshy; with one to many seeds.

bi- or **bis-** Prefix denoting two, double, or twice.

bifid Two-cleft; split into two parts.

bilabiate Two-lipped.

bipinnate Twice pinnate.

bisexual Having both sex organs in the same flower; perfect, monoclinous.

blade   Lamina; the flattened, expanded part of a leaf.

b.m.   Board measure.

boss (n.) **bossed** (adj.)   A raised projection, usually pointed but not prickly.

bract   A modified leaf subtending a flower, branch of an inflorescence, or conifer cone scale.

bracteole   A tertiary bract.

bractlet   A secondary bract.

bud   An embryonic axis with its appendages.

bundle scar   A small scar in a leaf scar left by a vascular bundle.

buttress   Swollen base of tree trunk.

ca. (circa)   About; approximate.

cache   A secure place of storage, as a hoard of nuts.

calcicole (calciphile)   A plant restricted to, or growing best on, alkaline soils.

calyx   Collective term for all the sepals of a flower.

cambium   Lateral meristem responsible for secondary growth.

campanulate   Bell-shaped.

capitate   Shaped like a head.

capsule   A simple, dry, dehiscent fruit, the product of a compound pistil.

carpel   The basic unit of the gynoecium; a simple pistil; the megasporophyll of a flower.

catkin   See "ament."

character   A feature such as leaf shape or bark color.

character state   A particular character expression, such as ovate leaf shape or gray bark color.

ciliate   Descriptive of a margin fringed with hairs.

cladistics   A taxonomic approach to phylogeny emphasizing the branching of evolutionary lines and origin of character divergence.

cladogram   Diagram of cladistic relationships.

cleft   Divided into lobes separated by sinuses which extend more than halfway to the midrib.

climax   The terminal community in ecological succession capable of self-replacement under the prevailing climatic, edaphic, physiographic, biotic, and pyric (fire) conditions.

cline   A gradient of character states correlated with a geographical or ecological gradient.

clone   A population of individuals propagated vegetatively or by apomixis from a single original.

collateral   Accessory buds arranged on either side of the lateral bud.

comose   Seeds with long hairs on the surface, as in cotton or cottonwood.

community   All the organisms inhabiting a common environment and interacting with one another.

compilospecies   A species which incorporates genes and characters from other species through hybridization.

complete   A flower having sepals, petals, stamens, and carpels.

compound   Composed of several parts; compound leaf of leaflets, compound pistil of fused carpels.

compressed   Flattened.

cone   An aggregation of sporangia-bearing structures at the tip of a stem; best restricted to the conifers among seed plants.

conifer   A gymnosperm bearing cones.

coning   Development and maturation of a cone; "flowering" in conifers.

connate   Fusion of similar parts of a flower, for example, sympetalous corolla.

continuum   A gradual change in species composition along an environmental gradient.

convergent evolution   The independent origin of similar features in different evolutionary lines due to similar adaptive pressures.

cordate   Heart-shaped, with the notch at the base.

coriaceous   Thick and leathery.

cork   Outer bark of the cork oak; generally the outer layer of bark.

corolla   Collective term for all the petals of a flower.

corticolous   Growing on the bark of tree trunks or branches.

corymb   Short, broad, more or less flat-topped inflorescence, with branches arising spirally along the stem.

costa-palmate   Leaf of some palms which appears fan-shaped but has a short midrib (costa).

cove   A sheltered valley between opposing slopes.

crenate   Margin with rounded or blunt teeth.

crenulate   Finely crenate.

cultivar   A horticultural variant, either selected from the wild or produced in cultivation, but maintained under cultivation; reproduced by either sexual or asexual means.

cuneate   Wedge-shaped, tapering to a narrow base.

cuspidate   Abruptly tipped with a sharp, rigid point.

cyme   Inflorescence consisting of a central rachis terminated early by a flower, then lower lateral branches developing and either ending with a flower or another cyme.

cymose   Cymelike.

dbh (DBH)   Diameter breast-high ($4\frac{1}{2}$ ft or 1.3 m from the ground or 18 in. above butt swell).

deciduous   Not persistent; parts (leaves) dropping in the fall.

decompound   More than once divided or compounded.

decurrent   Said of a leaf base which extends down and is fused to the twig below the point of divergence; tree habit of diffusely branched, spreading form (deliquescent).

decussate   Opposite, 4-ranked leaf arrangement; each pair at right angles to the pairs above and below.

dehiscent   Opening.

deliquescent   Descriptive of a tree form lacking one central axis but rather with diffuse branches.

deltate   Triangular or delta-shaped. "Deltoid" is the three-dimensional form.

dentate   Margin with sharp teeth pointing outward.

denticulate   Minutely dentate.

determinate short shoot   Spur branch without a functional terminal bud.

diadelphous   Stamens formed into two groups by fusion of the filaments.

diaspore   The dispersed part of a plant; either seed, fruit, or cone.

dichotomous   *Y*-branching; equal forking into pairs.

diclinous   Flower which is unisexual; literally meaning "two couches."

dicotyledonous (dicot)   Having two cotyledons; members of the Magnoliopsida.

dimorphous   Having two morphological forms.

dioecious   Plant having unisexual flowers or cones; with only one sex per plant; literally meaning "two houses."

disjunct   A species population separated by a considerable distance from the main distributional range.

distichous   Leaves all in one plane, that is, in two ranks; either opposite or a ½ phyllotaxy if alternate.

double serrate   Margin with large teeth, each tooth having smaller teeth.

drupaceous   Drupelike.

drupe   A simple, usually 1-seeded, fleshy fruit with the outer pericarp fleshy and the endocarp bony; a stone fruit.

drupelet   A small drupe.

echinate   Armed with prickles.

ecology   Branch of biology dealing with relationships between organisms and their environment.

ecophene   A direct, nongenetic modification of a plant form by some environmental factor.

ecotone   A transitional zone between two habitats and communities.

ecotype   A heritable, morphological, or physiological form resulting from selection by an ecological condition.

eglandular   Without glands.

ellipsoid   A three-dimensional form having the outline of an ellipse.

elliptical   Plane figure resembling an ellipse, being widest at the center.

emarginate   Apex with a shallow, broad notch.

embryo   A young stage of the sporophyte plant in a seed.

endemic   A species restricted to a very limited, native, geographical area.

endocarp   Inner layer of the pericarp (fruit wall).

endosperm   The food reserve outside the embryo within a seed; a postzygotic structure of angiosperms.

endozoochory   Diaspore dispersal by being eaten by animals and passing through the digestive tract.

entire   Smooth margin.

entomophilous   Insect-pollinated.

epicormic   A shoot arising from an adventitious or dormant bud on a stem or branch of a woody plant; coppice or "water" sprout.

epigeal   Seed germination in which the cotyledons of the seedling are above the ground surface, as in maple or pine.

epigynous   Perianth appearing to arise from above the ovary; often used to describe a flower with an inferior ovary.

epipetalous   The fusion of filaments to the corolla; appearing as if the stamens were borne on the petals.

erose   Irregularly toothed, eroded, or "chewed."

estipulate   Without stipules.

evergreen   Remaining green throughout the year; not losing all the leaves at one time.

excurrent   Tree form with a main axis or trunk extending to the top of the crown and with secondary branches from the trunk.

exocarp   Outer layer of the pericarp (fruit wall).

exozoochory   Diaspore dispersal by being carried on the outside of an animal in fur or feathers, and so on.

exserted   Extending out, beyond the surrounding structures.

extant   Living at the present time.

extinct   Eliminated entirely.

extirpated   Eliminated from only a portion of the natural range.

extrorse   Facing or opening outward.

falcate Sickle- or scythe-shaped.

false whorl An apparent whorl of secondary branches in pines; considered "false" because the actual arrangement is a tight spiral.

family A level in the classification hierarchy between genus (below) and order (above); indicated by the suffix -aceae, pronounced -ay-see-ee.

fascicle A cluster or bundle.

fastigiate A very narrow tree form having upright branches close to the trunk.

fertilization Union of male and female gametes.

filament The stalk of the stamen which supports the anther.

fimbriate-margined Appearing fringed.

flabellate Fan-shaped.

flora The kinds of plants, taken collectively, which occupy a specified region.

flower A determinate short shoot usually bearing a perianth, stamens, and carpels.

fluted Regularly marked by alternating ridges and groovelike depressions.

foliaceous Leaflike in appearance and texture.

follicle A single carpellate, dry fruit dehiscing along one line (suture).

forest cover types A forest association, designated by the dominant species of trees.

formation One or more plant communities exhibiting a definite structure or life form and occurring in similar habitats, such as grassland, marsh, conifer forest, or deciduous forest.

fossil Remains of life of the geological past.

fruit The seed-bearing organ of a flowering plant; the ripened ovary.

fugacious Soon falling or fading; not permanent.

fusiform Spindle-shaped.

gallery forest A narrow forest along a waterway through a landscape otherwise devoid of trees.

gametophyte Haploid phase of life cycle which produces the gametes.

geitonogamy Cross-fertilization between flowers on a single plant; genetically the same as autogamy.

genotype Genetic constitution of an individual.

genus (sing.), **genera** (pl.) The level in the classification hierarchy between family (above) and species (below).

glabrate Becoming glabrous or nearly so.

glabrous Smooth; lacking hairs.

glandular Having glandular hairs; or the nature of a gland.

glaucescent Slightly glaucous.

glaucous Covered with a white wax in the form of minute flakes, rods, or granules; with a "bloom."

globose Spherical, globular.

glochids Minute, barbed prickles in some cacti.

gregarious Growing in clusters; colonial.

gymnosperm Seed plants bearing "naked seeds" or actually ovules exposed at pollination.

gynoecium Collective term for all the carpels of a flower.

habit The shape or form of a plant.

habitat The locality in which an organism lives.

halophyte A plant restricted to, or growing best in, high salt concentrations (salt flats, dunes, salt marshes).

hammock An isolated area of southern hardwood forests on an elevated, well-drained site, surrounded by extensive pines or marsh; a hardwood forest on deep loamy soils rich in humus.

head   A spherical or flat-topped inflorescence of sessile or nearly sessile flowers clustered on a common receptacle.

herbarium   A collection of plant specimens, pressed, dried, mounted on sheets, identified, and classified.

hesperidium   Type of berry with a thick, leathery rind and many radial sections.

heteroblastic change   Transition from juvenile to adult with a more or less abrupt change in morphology.

heteromorphism   Having different forms of a structure, such as leaves.

heterophylly   Having two or more different forms of leaves on the same plant.

hilum   Scar or point of attachment of a seed.

hirsute   With stiff or coarse hairs.

hoary   With dense, grayish white hairs.

homoplastic similarity   Similar character(s) in unrelated groups derived by convergent evolution.

hybrid   A cross between two different plants (usually species).

hybridization   Process of crossing two unlike plants (usually species).

hybrid swarm   Population consisting of hybrids, backcrosses, and successive generations.

hydrochory   Diaspore dispersal by water.

hypanthium   Structure of a flower usually derived by adnation of perianth and stamens, forming a cup or tube; may be free of ovary (resulting in perigny) or fused with ovary (epigny).

hypogeal   Seed germination in which the cotyledons of the seedling remain at or below the ground surface, as in oak and hickory.

hypogynous   Perianth arising below the ovary; often used to describe a flower with a superior ovary.

imbricate   Overlapping.

imperfect   Flower with only one sex; unisexual, diclinous.

inbreeding   Crossing within a single plant; autogamy or geitonogamy.

incised   Cut sharply and irregularly, to near the midrib.

incomplete   Flower lacking one of the four whorls (calyx, corolla, androecium, gynoecium).

indehiscent   Not splitting.

indeterminate short shoot   Spur branch having a functional terminal bud.

indigenous   Native and original to an area.

inequilateral   Asymmetrical leaf base.

inferior ovary   Ovary appearing below the perianth and stamens; the hypanthium fused with the ovary.

inflated   Bladderlike.

inflorescence   The arrangement of flowers on a branch system.

infraspecific   Classification categories below the species (subspecies, variety, form).

infructescence   The arrangement of fruits on a branch system.

inserted   Attached to or growing out of.

internode   That portion of a stem between two nodes.

introgression (introgressive hybridization)   A flow of genes from one species to another across a fairly strong barrier to interbreeding by means of hybridization and backcrossing.

introrse   Facing or opening inward.

involucral   Belonging to an involucre.

involucrate   Possessing an involucre.

involucre   A cluster of bracts subtending a flower or inflorescence.

irregular   Zygomorphic; bilateral symmetry in a flower.

keel   A central ridge; the united lower two petals of a papilionaceous flower (Fabaceae).

laciniate   Cut into lobes separated by deep, narrow, irregular incisions.

lactiferous   Production of milky sap.

lamina   Leaf blade.

lanceolate   Lance-shaped; much longer than wide, widest near the base and tapering to the apex.

lateral bud   Bud in the axil of a leaf.

latex   Milky sap.

layering   Rooting from the lower side of branches.

leaf   Primary lateral appendage of a stem; usually flattened and photosynthetic.

leaflet   A division of a compound leaf.

leaf scar   A scar left on a twig when the leaf drops.

legume   A dry fruit from a single carpel, either dehiscing along two lines (sutures) or indehiscent.

lenticel   A small corky spot or line on the surface of a twig, branch, or trunk, and allowing for gas exchange in and out.

lenticellate   Having lenticels on the twig.

lenticular   Shaped like a double-convex lens.

lepidote   Covered with minute, flattened, peltate trichomes or glands.

liana   Woody vine.

ligulate   Strap-shaped.

linear   Very long and narrow with nearly parallel sides.

lobe   Any protruding segment of an organ.

lobed   Leaf cut from ¼ to ½ the distance from the margin to the midrib; more generally, any degree of lobing.

long shoot   Stem with normally elongated internodes.

lunate   Crescent-shaped.

lustrous   Glossy, shiny.

marcescent (adj.), **marcescence** (n.)   Leaves withering and turning brown but persisting on the tree.

membranous   Thin, more or less flexible.

meristem   A localized plant tissue capable of cell division and giving rise to new cells and tissues.

merous   Having a specified number of parts.

mesic   Intermediate moisture regime, between xeric (dry) and hydric (wet).

mesocarp   Middle layer of the pericarp (fruit wall).

midrib   The primary vein of a leaf.

monadelphous   Stamens united into a tube by the union of the filaments.

monoclinous   Flower which is bisexual; literally meaning "one couch."

monocotyledonous (monocot)   Having but one cotyledon; members of the Liliopsida.

monoecious   Plant with both male and female flowers or cones; literally meaning "one house."

monotypic   Having only one representative (e.g., a monotypic genus has only one species).

morphology   Branch of biology dealing with form and structure.

mucro   A short, abrupt tip of a leaf or cone scale.

mucronate   Terminated by a mucro; bristle-tipped.

multiple   Coalesced fruits of an infructescence.

mutation   A change in the amount or structure of the genetic material; an inheritable change of a gene from one form to another.

naked bud   Bud without scales; usually covered with dense hairs.

natural classification   Grouping based on many characters of the plant and on an a posteriori reasoning.

naturalized   An introduced plant, escaped from cultivation, and reproducing naturally for enough years to have become part of the flora.

naval stores   Resin products used originally for ships, later for medicine and industry; tar and pitch are from burning resinous wood in the absence of air; turpentine and rosin are distillation products from resin collected from living trees.

nitrogen fixation   The assimilation of atmospheric nitrogen into ammonia and nitrates by true bacteria or Actinomycetes associated with the roots of certain plants.

node   The place on a twig that bears one or more leaves.

nomenclature   The naming of an organism.

nut   An indehiscent, dry fruit, usually 1-seeded (though from a compound ovary), with a hard pericarp and sometimes partially or entirely encased in an involucre or husk formed of bracts.

nutlet   Small nut.

oblique   Asymmetrical base of leaf.

oblong   Longer than wide, with margins nearly parallel.

obtuse   Blunt.

orbicular   Circular or nearly so.

ornithophilous   Bird-pollinated.

outcrossing   Crossing between individuals; xenogamy.

oval   Broadly elliptical with the width greater than ½ the length.

ovary   The basal portion of a pistil which encloses the ovules.

ovate   Longer than wide, with the widest part below the middle; the outline of an egg.

ovoid   Three-dimensional structure with the shape of an egg.

ovulate   Pertaining to the ovule, or possessing ovules.

ovule   The structure which develops into a seed after fertilization of the enclosed egg.

ovuliferous scale   A structure of a conifer cone in the axil of (and sometimes fused with) a bract and bearing one or more ovules.

palmate   Radiating from a common point; as fingers from the palm of a hand.

palmlike   Tree form with an unbranched trunk and top rosette of leaves.

palynology   A study of pollen and spores; either extinct or extant.

panduriform   Fiddle-shaped; obovate with concave sides below the middle and with two small basal lobes.

panicle   A compound, multibranched inflorescence, usually pyramidal in shape, in which the branches from the primary axis are again branched.

paniculate   In the form of a panicle.

papilionaceous (papilionate)   Butterflylike; descriptive of the flowers of the Fabaceae.

parallel veins   Many individual, free veins from base to apex of leaf.

parted   Divided by sinuses which extend nearly to the midrib.

patristic similarity   Similarity of characters derived from a common ancestor.

pectinate   Comblike; divided into long, narrow segments.

pedicel   The stalk of an individual flower in an inflorescence.

pedicelled   With a pedicel.

peduncle   Stalk of a single flower as in Magnolia; or, the stalk of an inflorescence (from base to first branch).

peg   Short projection on a conifer twig bearing a sessile or petiolate leaf and left on a twig following leaf drop.

peltate   Shield-shaped and attached from the center by a supporting stalk; the shape of an umbrella.

pendant, pendulous   Drooping, hanging down.

penniveined   Veined in a pinnate manner.

perennial   Lasting for three or more years.

perfect   Flowers with both sexes; bisexual, monoclinous.

perianth   The collective term for both calyx and corolla.

pericarp   Fruit wall, developed from the ovary wall.

periderm   Outer bark; a protecting layer of cork cells; forming first just beneath the epidermis, later deeper in cortex or secondary phloem.

perigynous   Perianth appearing to arise from a hypanthium surrounding but not fused to the superior ovary; often used to describe the flower with this structure.

persistent   "Evergreen" leaves lasting until the next season's leaves appear or persisting for several years.

petal   One unit of the corolla; inner perianth part.

petaloid   Petal-like.

petiolate   Having a petiole.

petiole   The stalk of a leaf.

petiolule   The stalk of a leaflet.

phenetic classification   Grouping based on overall similarity without regard to evolutionary relationships.

phenology   The study of time and sequence of recurring stages in the life history of an organism.

phenotype   The evident characteristics of an organism due to the interaction of genotype and environment.

phenotypic plasticity   Nonheritable variation in characteristics; ecophenic variation.

phloem   Conducting tissue, mainly of sieve-tube elements; inner bark.

phyllotaxy   Leaf arrangement on a stem.

phylogeny, phylogenetic   Evolutionary history of a group.

physiognomy   The general appearance of a plant community, based on external features; for example, tall, evergreen trees; low, deciduous trees; pine savanna; or bog.

pinnate   Featherlike, with a central axis and lateral branches.

pinnipalmate   Leaf venation somewhat intermediate between pinnate and palmate in which the lowermost pair of secondary veins are slightly larger and with larger tertiary veins than the other secondaries.

pistil   The evident ovary/style/stigma of a flower; a single separate carpel or the fusion product of several carpels forming one compound pistil.

pistillate   Flower with pistil(s) and without fertile stamens; female.

pollen   An immature stage of the male gametophyte with a hard, resistant cell wall; carried by some agent in the process of pollination.

pollination   Transfer of pollen from pollen sac (or anther) to ovule (or stigma).

polygamous   Mixture of perfect and unisexual flowers and either mainly monoecious or dioecious; i.e., polygamo-monoecious or polygamo-dioecious.

pome   A fleshy fruit from an inferior ovary with the hypanthium forming most of the fleshy structure.

prickle   Sharp-pointed, slender outgrowth of the epidermis of a twig or leaf.

provenance   Origin; locality where found or collected.

pseudoterminal bud   The distal lateral bud on a twig which assumes the function of the terminal bud; the twig apex is aborted; recognized by its leaf scar and aborted tip of the twig.

puberulent   Minutely hairy, scarcely visible to the unaided eye.

pubescent   A general term meaning hairy; or, fine, soft, short hairs.

pulvinus (sing.) **pulvini** (pl.)   The swollen base of a petiole functioning in turgor movements of the leaf.

pyriform   Pear-shaped.

raceme   Inflorescence with a central axis bearing pedicelled flowers.

rachilla   Branch of a rachis.

rachis   Axis of a compound leaf or of an inflorescence.

receptacle   The portion of the axis which bears the floral organs.

recombination   The bringing together of chromosomes (and genes) as a result of fertilization, and the formation of gene combinations in the offspring that differ from those of the parents.

recurved   Curved downward or backward.

reflexed   Bent downward.

regular   Actinomorphic; radial symmetry in a flower.

reniform   Kidney-shaped; wider than long and with a broad cordate base.

repand   Slightly and irregularly wavy.

resin cyst   Cell or cavity (blister) with resin.

reticulate   Forming an interlacing network.

retuse   Apex with a shallow and narrow notch.

revolute   Rolled backward, with the margin rolled toward lower side.

rhombic   Oval, but angular at the sides; diamond-shaped.

rosette   A tight cluster of leaves, either basal or apical on a stem.

rufous   Reddish brown.

rugose   Wrinkled (leaf surface) with sunken veins.

samara   An indehiscent, dry, winged fruit.

samaroid   Samaralike.

savanna   Grassland with widely spaced trees.

scabrous   With short, bristly hairs; rough to the touch.

scale   Small, often appressed leaf; part of the conifer cone which bears ovules.

schizocarp   Dehiscent fruit that splits into individual locules (carpels) each appearing as a simple fruit, as the schizocarpic samaras of maple.

scurfy   Covered with minute scales.

seed   A ripened ovule, following fertilization, and normally with an embryo.

segregation   The separation of chromosomes (and genes) at the time of meiosis.

self-incompatibility Genetically determined inability for self-fertilization.

sensu According to; following.

sensu lato (s. l., s. lat.) In the inclusive sense; broadly defined.

sensu stricto (s. str.) In the restricted sense; narrowly defined.

sepal A unit of the calyx; outer perianth part.

serotinous Cones that remain closed long after the seeds inside are mature.

serrate With sharp teeth pointing forward.

serrulate Minutely serrate.

sessile Lacking a stalk.

sheath A leaf base partly or completely surrounding the stem.

short shoot Short, lateral branch without internode elongation; either determinate or indeterminate.

simple Of one piece; not compound.

sinuate Shallowly indented, wavy in a horizontal plane. (See "undulate" for comparison.)

sinus A recess, cleft, or gap between two lobes.

s. l., s. lat., s. str. See "sensu lato" and "sensu stricto."

spatulate Spatula-shaped; elongated with widest point near the rounded apex and tapering to the base.

speciation Formation of a species.

species (sing. and pl.) The unit of the classification hierarchy below the genus; defined generally as a population of potentially interbreeding individuals set apart from another species by more or less consistent and persistent differences in morphology, ecology, and breeding behavior.

spike Inflorescence consisting of a central axis bearing sessile flowers.

spine A sharp, modified leaf or stipule.

spinose Spinelike or with spines.

spiral Leaf arrangement on a stem which winds around from base to apex; alternate.

sporophyte Diploid phase of the life cycle which includes the vascular plant.

spray Flattened, frondlike branchlets in some conifers (Cupressaceae).

spur A short, compact branch with no internode elongation; short shoot.

stamen The basic unit of the androecium; the microsporophyll of a flower.

staminate Flower with stamens and without fertile pistils; male.

stellate Star-shaped.

stem Main aerial axis of a plant.

sterigma (sing.), **sterigmata** (pl.) See "peg."

sterile Lacking reproductive structures.

stigma Top part of the pistil that is receptive of pollen.

stipular scar Scar left on twig after stipules drop.

stipulate With stipules.

stipule A leafy appendage attached to the petiole or twig at the base of the petiole; in pairs, one on each side or sometimes fused together.

striate With fine grooves, ridges, or lines of color.

strigose Having stiff, straight, appressed hairs, usually pointing the same direction.

strobilus (pl. **strobili**) See "cone."

style Slender part of a pistil between the ovary and stigma; if lacking then the stigma is sessile.

subulate Short, narrow, tapered, sharp-pointed leaf; awn or awl.

succession The orderly process of community change; the sequence of communities that replace one another in a given area culminating in a climax community.

succulent   Juicy, pulpy, fleshy.

superior ovary   Ovary above the origin of the perianth and stamens.

superposed   Bud(s) inserted just above the lateral bud.

suture   Line of dehiscence.

sympatric   Two or more taxa with overlapping geographical ranges.

sympetalous   With petals fused.

syndrome   A number of characteristics occurring together and characterizing a specific function or adaptation.

syngameon   The most inclusive group of introgressing species.

synoecious   Plant with perfect flowers.

synonym   A rejected plant name which is replaced by another for some nomenclatural or taxonomic reason.

synzoochory   Diaspore dispersal by animals collecting seeds or fruits for a cache or for burying.

systematics   Study of the diversity of organisms including description, classification, nomenclature, and evolutionary relationships.

taxon (pl. **taxa**)   General term for any taxonomic group, at any unspecified level of the classification hierarchy.

taxonomy   See "systematics."

tepal   Undifferentiated perianth part, separate or fused.

terete   Round in cross section.

terminal bud   Bud which terminates the twig; lacking an associated leaf scar.

ternate   In threes.

thorn   A sharp, modified branch in the axil of a leaf or terminating the twig.

tomentose   Densely woolly with soft, curled, matted hairs.

tomentum   The dense, matted hairs of a tomentose condition.

trichome   Any type of hair on the surface.

trichotomous   Three-forked.

trident   Three-toothed.

trifoliolate   With three leaflets.

trigonous   Three-angled.

tripinnate   Three-times pinnate.

truncate   As though cut off at right angle to the midrib.

turbinate   Top-shaped.

twig   The last year's growth of a woody stem.

type specimen   A specimen designated to serve as a reference point for a scientific name (species or infraspecific taxon); it is not necessarily the most typical. The *type* of a genus is a species; the *type* of a family is a genus and the one which forms the root of the family name.

umbel   Inflorescence consisting of several pedicelled flowers all attached at the same point at the top of the peduncle.

umbellate   Umbel-like.

umbo   A protuberance, as on the apophysis of a cone scale.

undulate   Wavy in a vertical plane; crisped. (See "sinuate" for comparison.)

unifoliolate   A leaf having only a single leaflet; usually described as "simple."

unisexual   Having only one sex; either diclinous flowers or dioecious plants.

valvate   Meeting at the edges and not overlapping, as in bud scales.

valve   One of the sections into which dehiscent fruits are split.

vascular   With xylem and phloem tissues.
vein   Strand of vascular tissue in a leaf or other laminar structure.
vernal   Appearing in spring.
verticillate   Whorled.
vestiture   Any covering of hairs.
villous   With long, silky, straight hairs.

whorl   Cyclic arrangement, three or more per node.
wood   Secondary xylem.
woolly   With long, matted hairs.

xenogamy   Cross-fertilization between flowers on different plants; outcrossing.
xeric   Dry.
xerophyte   A plant adapted to dry conditions.
xylem   Conducting tissue formed mainly of tracheids or vessels and tracheids.

zygomorphic   Bilaterally symmetrical; irregular flower.

REFERENCES

Abrams, M. D., 1992. Fire and the development of oak forests, *BioScience* **42**:346–353.

Adams, R. P., 1986. Geographic variation in *Juniperus silicicola* and *J. virginiana* of the southeastern United States: Multivariate analyses of morphology and terpenoids, *Taxon* **35**:61–75.

_____, and B. L. Turner, 1970. Chemosystematic and numerical studies of natural populations of *Juniperus ashei* Buch., *Taxon* **19**:728–751.

Anderson, E., 1949. *Introgressive Hybridization,* Wiley, New York.

Avery, T. E., and H. E. Burkhart, 1983. *Forest Measurements,* 3d ed., McGraw-Hill, New York.

Bailey, L. H., Hortorium Staff, 1976. *Hortus Third: A Concise Dictionary of Plants Cultivated in the United States and Canada,* Macmillan, New York.

Bailey, V. L., 1962. Revision of the genus *Ptelea* (Rutaceae), *Brittonia* **14**:1–45.

Bakuzis, E. V., and H. L. Hansen, 1965. *Balsam Fir,* University of Minnesota Press, Minneapolis.

Baranski, M. J., 1975. An analysis of variation within white oak (*Quercus alba* L.), *N. C. Agric. Exp. Sta. Tech. Bull.* **236**, Raleigh.

Barnes, B. V., 1975. Phenotypic variation of trembling aspen in western North America, *For. Sci.* **22**:319–328.

_____, and B. P. Dancik, 1985. Characteristics and origin of a new birch species, *Betula murrayana,* from southeastern Michigan, *Canad. J. Bot.* **63**:223–226.

_____, _____, and T. L. Sharik, 1974. Natural hybridization of yellow birch and paper birch, *For. Sci.* **20**:215–221.

_____, and W. H. Wagner, Jr., 1981. *Michigan Trees: A Guide to the Trees of Michigan and the Great Lakes Region.* University of Michigan Press, Ann Arbor.

Berg, E. E., and J. H. Hamrick, 1993. Regional genetic variation in turkey oak, *Quercus laevis, Canad. J. Forest Res.* **23**:1270–1274.

Berlin, B., 1992. *Ethnobiological Classification,* Princeton University Press, N.J.

Black–Schaefer, C. L., and R. L. Beckmann, 1989. Foliar flavonoids and the determination of ploidy and gender in *Fraxinus americana* and *F. pennsylvanica* (Oleaceae), *Castanea* **54**:115–118.

Borror, D. J., 1960. *Dictionary of Word Roots and Combining Forms,* Mayfield, Palo Alto, Calif.

Braun, E. L., 1950. *Deciduous Forests of Eastern North America,* Blakiston, Philadelphia.

Brickell, C. D. (ed.), 1980. International code of nomenclature for cultivated plants—1980, *Regnum Veget.* **104**.

Briggs, D., and S. M. Walters, 1984. *Plant Variation and Evolution,* 2d ed., Cambridge University Press, New York.

Brown, K., 1976. Ecological studies of the cabbage palmetto, *Sabal palmetto, Principes* **20**:3–10, 49–56, 98–115, 148–156.

Brunsfeld, S. J., P. S. and D. S. Soltis, P. A. Gadek, C. J. Quinn, D. D. Strenge, and T. A. Ranker, 1994. Phylogenetic relationships among the genera of Taxodiaceae and Cupressaceae: Evidence from rbcL sequences, *Syst. Bot.* **19**:253–262.

Buchholz, J. T., 1938. Cone formation in *Sequoia gigantea*. I. "The relation of stem size and tissue development to cone formation." II. "The history of the seed cone," *Amer. J. Bot.* **25**:296–305.

―――, 1939. The generic segregation of the sequoias, *Amer. J. Bot.* **26**:535–538.

Burckhalter, R. E., 1992. The genus *Nyssa* (Cornaceae) in North America: A revision, *Sida* **15**:323–342.

Burleigh, T. D., 1938. The relation of birds to the establishment of Longleaf pine seedlings in southern Mississippi, *U.S. For. Serv. Southeast. For. Exp. Sta. Occas. Pap.* **75**.

Burns, R. M., and B. H. Honkala. 1990. *Silvics of North America. Vol. 1, Conifers; Vol. 2, Hardwoods,* USDA Handb. 654, Washington, D.C.

Camp, W. H., 1950. A biogeographic and paragenetic analysis of the American beech, *Yearb. Amer. Phil. Soc.* **1950**:166–169.

Campbell, C. S., and T. A. Dickinson, 1990. Apomixis, patterns of morphological variation, and species concepts in subfam. Maloideae (Rosaceae), *Syst. Bot.* **15**:124–135.

Camus, A., 1938. *Les Chênes. Monographie du Genre* Quercus, 2 vols., Lechevalier and Fils, Paris.

Clark, R. C., 1971. The woody plants of Alabama, *Ann. Missouri Bot. Gard.* **58**:99–242.

Clarkson, R. B., and D. E. Fairbrothers, 1970. A serological and electrophoretic investigation of eastern North American *Abies* (Pinaceae), *Taxon* **19**:720–727.

Clausen, J., 1951. *Stages in the Evolution of Plant Species,* Cornell University Press, Ithaca, N.Y.

Clewell, A. F., and D. B. Ward, 1987. "White Cedar in Florida and along the Northern Gulf Coast," in A. D. Laderman (ed.), *Atlantic White Cedar Wetlands,* Westview Press, Boulder and London, pp. 69–82.

Coker, W. C., and H. R. Totten, 1945. *Trees of the Southeastern States,* 3d ed., University of North Carolina Press, Chapel Hill.

Collier, H. O. J., 1963. Aspirin. *Sci. Amer.* **209**:97–108.

Cooke, G. B., 1946. *The Planting and Growing of Cork Oak Trees in the United States,* Crown Cork and Seal Co., Baltimore, Md.

Coombes, A. J., 1985. *Dictionary of Plant Names,* Timber Press, Portland, Oreg.

Cooper, A. W., and E. P. Mercer, 1977. Morphological variation in *Fagus grandifolia* Ehrh. in North Carolina, *J. Elisha Mitchell Sci. Soc.* **93**:136–149.

Cottam, W. P., J. M. Tucker, and F. S. Santamour, Jr., 1982. *Oak Hybridization at the University of Utah,* State Arboretum of Utah Publication 1, Salt Lake City.

Critchfield, W. B., 1957. *Geographic Variation in* Pinus contorta, Maria Moors Cabot Found. Publ. 3, Cambridge, Mass.

_____, 1984. Impact of the Pleistocene on the genetic structure of North American conifers, *Proc. North Amer. Forest Biol. Work. (Logan, Utah)* **8**:70–118.

_____, and E. L. Little, Jr., 1966. *Geographic Distribution of the Pines of the World,* USDA Miscl. Publ. 991, Washington, D.C.

Cronquist, A. 1988. *The Evolution and Classification of Flowering Plants,* 2d ed., The New York Botanical Garden, Bronx, N.Y.

Cunningham, F. E., 1957. A seed key for five Northeastern birches, *J. For.* **55**:844.

Currey, D. R., 1965. An ancient Bristlecone pine stand in eastern Nevada, *Ecology* **46**:564.

Dallimore, W., and A. B. Jackson, 1967. *A Handbook of Coniferae and Ginkgoaceae,* 4th ed. by S. G. Harrison, St. Martin's Press, New York.

Daubenmire, R. F, and J. Daubenmire, 1968. Forest vegetation of eastern Washington and northern Idaho. *Wash. Agri. Exp. Sta. Tech. Bull. 60,* Pullman.

Davis, M. B., 1976. Pleistocene biogeography of temperate deciduous forests, *Geosci. Man.* **13**:13–26.

_____, 1983. Holocene vegetational history of the eastern United States. *In* Wright, H. E., Jr. (ed.), *Late-Quaternary Environments of the United States, Vol. 2, The Holocene,* University of Minnesota Press, Minneapolis.

Dayton, W. A., 1945. What is dendrology? *J. For.* **43**:719–722.

Decker, J. P., 1952. Tolerance is a good technical term. *J. For.* **50**:40–41.

_____, 1959. Shade–tolerance: A revised semantic analysis, *For. Sci.* **5**:93.

DeHond, P. E., and C. S. Campbell, 1989. Multivariate analyses of hybridization between *Betula cordifolia* and *B. populifolia* (Betulaceae), *Canad. J. Bot.* **67**:2252–2260.

Delcourt, H. R., P. A. Delcourt, and T. Webb, III, 1983. Dynamic plant ecology: The spectrum of vegetational change in space and time, *Quaternary Sci. Rev.* **1**:153–175.

Delcourt, P. A., and H. R. Delcourt, 1981. "Vegetation Maps for Eastern North America: 40,000 yr B.P. to the Present," in R. C. Romans (ed.), *Geobotany II,* Plenum, New York.

Del Tredici, P., 1991. Ginkgos and people—A thousand years of interaction, *Arnoldia* **51**(2):2–15.

Dengler, H. W., 1966. Say it with Holly, *Amer. For.* **72**:1–3.

_____, 1967. Bayberries and bayberry candles, *Amer. For.* **73**:5–7.

Den Ouden, P., and B. K. Boom, 1965. *Manual of Cultivated Conifers Hardy in the Cold- and Warm-Temperate Zone,* Martinus Nijhoff, The Hague.

dePamphilis, C. W., and R. Wyatt, 1989. Hybridization and introgression in buckeyes (*Aesculus:* Hippocastanaceae): A review of the evidence and a hypothesis to explain long-distance gene flow, *Syst. Bot.* **14**:593–611.

_____, and _____, 1990. Electrophoretic confirmation of interspecific hybridization in *Aesculus* (Hippocastanaceae) and the genetic structure of a broad hybrid zone, *Evolution* **44**:1295–1317.

Desmarais, Y., 1952. Dynamics of leaf variation in the sugar maples, *Brittonia* **7**:347–387.

Dickinson, T. A., 1985. Biology of Canadian weeds, *Crataegus crus-galli* L. *sensu lato, Canad. J. Pl. Sci.* **65**:641–654.

Dickson, A., 1965. Growing Christmas trees in the northeast, *J. For.* **63**:855–857.

Dorr, L. J., and K. C. Nixon, 1985. Typification of the oak (*Quercus*) taxa described by S. B. Buckley (1809–1884), *Taxon* **34**:211–228.

Duncan, W. H., and M. B. Duncan, 1988. *Trees of the Southeastern United States,* University of Georgia Press, Athens.

Eckenwalder, J. E., 1976. Re–evaluation of Cupressaceae and Taxodiaceae: A proposed merger, *Madroño* **23**:237–256.

———, 1980. Foliar heteromorphism in *Populus* (Salicaceae), a source of confusion in the taxonomy of Tertiary leaf remains, *Syst. Bot.* **5**:366–383.

Egler, F. E., 1977. *The Nature of Vegetation: Its Management and Mismanagement.* Author, Norfolk, Conn.

Elias, T. S., 1989. *Field Guide to North American Trees,* Grolier Book Clubs, Danbury, Conn.

Elliott, D., 1994. Bee Gums, Rabbit Gums & Mountain Toothbrushes, *Wildlife in North Carolina* **58**(10):25–27.

Elmore, F. H., 1976. *Shrubs and Trees of the Southwest Uplands,* Southwest Parks and Monuments Assoc., Tucson, Ariz.

Eyde, R. H., 1963. Morphological and paleobotanical studies of the Nyssaceae. I. A Survey of the modern species and their fruits, *J. Arnold Arbor.* **44**:1–52.

———, 1988. Comprehending *Cornus:* Puzzles and progress in the systematics of the dog-woods, *Bot. Rev.* **54**:233–351.

Eyre, F. H. (ed.), 1980. *Forest Cover Types of the United States and Canada,* Society of American Foresters, Washington, D.C.

Faegri, K., and L. van der Pijl, 1979. *The Principles of Pollination Ecology,* 3d ed., Perga-mon Press, New York.

Fernald, M. L., 1950. *Gray's Manual of Botany,* 8th ed., American Book, New York.

Flake, R. H., E. von Rudloff, and B. L. Turner, 1969. Quantitative study of clinal variation in *Juniperus virginiana* using terpenoid data, *Proc. Nat. Acad. Sci.* **64**:487–494.

———, L. Urbatsch, and B. L. Turner, 1978. Chemical documentation of allopatric intro-gression in *Juniperus, Syst. Bot.* **3**:129–144.

(FNA) Flora of North America Editorial Committee, eds., 1993. *Flora of North America North of Mexico. Vol. 1 Introduction; Vol. 2 Pteridophytes and Gymnosperms,* Oxford University Press, New York.

Fowells, H. A., 1949. Cork oak planting tests in California, *J. For.* **47**:357–365.

Franklin, E. C., 1970. Survey of mutant forms and inbreeding depression in species of the family Pinaceae, *USDA Forest Serv. Res. Pap. SE-61,* Washington, D.C.

Fraver, S., 1992. The insulating value of serotinous cones in protecting pitch pine (*Pinus rigida*) seeds from high temperatures, *J. Penn. Acad. Sci.* **65**:112–116.

Frodin, D. G., 1984. *Guide to Standard Floras of the World,* Cambridge University Press, New York.

Furlow, J. J., 1979. The systematics of the American species of *Alnus* (Betulaceae), *Rhodora* **81**:1–121, 151–248.

Fry, W., and J. R. White, 1930. *Bigtrees.* Stanford University Press, Stanford, Calif.

Garin, G. I., 1958. Longleaf pines can form vigorous sprouts, *J. For.* **56**:430.

Giannasi, D. E., 1978. Generic relationships in the Ulmaceae based on flavonoid chemistry, *Taxon* **27**:331–344.

Gibson, J. P., and J. L. Hamrick, 1991. Heterogeniety in pollen allele frequencies among cones, whorls, and trees of table mountain pine (*Pinus pungens*), *Amer. J. Bot.* **78**:1244–1251.

Gillis, W. T., 1971. Systematics and ecology of poison-ivy and the poison-oaks (*Toxicoden-dron,* Anacardiaceae), *Rhodora* **73**:72–159, 161–237, 370–443, 465– 540.

Gleason, H. A., and A. Cronquist, 1991. *Manual of Vascular Plants of Northeastern United States and Adjacent Canada,* 2d ed,, New York Botanical Garden, Bronx, N.Y.

Gledhill, D., 1989. *The Names of Plants,* Cambridge University Press, New York.

Godfrey, R. K., 1988. *Trees, Shrubs, and Woody Vines of Northern Florida and Adjacent Georgia and Alabama,* University of Georgia Press, Athens.

Graham, S. A., R. P. Harrison, Jr., and C. E. Westell, Jr., 1963. *Aspens: Phoenix Trees of the Great Lakes Region,* University of Michigan Press, Ann Arbor.

Grant, V., 1963. *The Origin of Adaptations,* Columbia University Press, New York.

————, 1981. *Plant Speciation,* 2d ed., Columbia University Press, New York.

Grant, W. F., and B. K. Thompson, 1975. Observations on Canadian birches, *Betula cordifolia, B. neoalaskana, B. populifolia, B. papyrifera,* and *B.* ×*caerulea, Canad. J. Bot.* **53**:1478–1490.

Greuter, W., et al., 1994. International Code of Botanical Nomenclature (Tokyo Code), *Regn. Veget.* **131**.

Hamrick, J. L., M. J. W. Godt, and S. L. Sherman-Broyles. 1992. Factors influencing levels of genetic diversity in woody plant species, *New Forests* **5**:95–124.

————, Y. B. Linhart, and J. B. Mitton, 1979. Relationships between life history characteristics and electrophoretically detectable genetic variation in plants, *Ann. Rev. Ecol. Syst.* **10**:173–200.

Hardin, J. W., 1957a. A revision of the American Hippocastanaceae, *Brittonia* **9**:145–171, 173–195.

————, 1957b. Studies in the Hippocastanaceae. IV. Hybridization in *Aesculus, Rhodora* **59**:185–203.

————, 1974. Studies of the southeastern United States flora IV. Oleaceae, *Sida* **5**:274–285.

————, 1975. Hybridization and introgression in *Quercus alba, J. Arnold Arbor.* **56**:336–363.

————, 1979a. Patterns of variation in foliar trichomes of eastern North American *Quercus, Amer. J. Bot.* **66**:576–585.

————, 1979b. *Quercus prinus* L.—nomen ambiguum, *Taxon* **28**:355–357.

————, 1990. Variation patterns and recognition of varieties of *Tilia americana* s.l., *Syst. Bot.* **15**:33–48.

————, 1992. Foliar morphology of the common trees of North Carolina and adjacent states, *North Carolina Agric. Res. Serv. Tech. Bull. 298,* Raleigh.

————, and R. L. Beckmann, 1982. Atlas of foliar surface features in woody plants, V. *Fraxinus* (Oleaceae) of eastern North America, *Brittonia* **34**:129–140.

————, and G. P. Johnson, 1985. Atlas of foliar surface features in woody plants, VIII. *Fagus* and *Castanea* (Fagaceae) of eastern North America, *Bull. Torrey Bot. Club* **112**:11–20.

————, and D. E. Stone, 1984. Atlas of foliar surface features in woody plants, VI. *Carya* (Juglandaceae) of North America, *Brittonia* **36**:140–153.

Harlow, W. M., W. A. Cote, Jr., and A. C. Day, 1962. The opening mechanism of pine cone scales, *J. For.* **62**:538–540.

Hart, J. A., 1987. A cladistic analysis of conifers: Preliminary results, *J. Arnold Arbor.* **68**:269–307.

Heiser, C. B., 1973. Introgression re-examined, *Bot. Rev.* **39**:347–366.

Holmgren, P. K., N. H. Holmgren, and L. C. Barnett (eds.), 1990. *Index Herbariorum. Part 1: The Herbaria of the World.* New York Botanical Garden, Bronx, N.Y.

Hora, B. (ed.), 1981. *The Oxford Encyclopedia of Trees of the World,* Oxford University Press, Oxford.

Hosner, J. F., 1960. Relative tolerance to complete inundation of fourteen bottomland tree species, *For. Sci.* **6**:246–251.

Howe, G., W. Hackett, R. Klevorn, and G. Furnier, 1993. Photoperiodic effects on growth and development of black cottonwood, *Amer. J. Bot.* **80**(6):74 (abstract).

Hu, H. H., 1948. How Metasequoia, the "Living fossil," was discovered in China, *J. New York Bot. Gard.* **49**:201–207.

Jacobson, G. L., Jr., T. Webb III, and E. C. Grimm, 1987. "Patterns and rates of vegetation change during the deglaciation of eastern North America," in W. F. Ruddiman and H. E. Wright, Jr. (eds.), *The Geology of North America,* Vol. K–3, *North America and Adjacent Oceans during the Last Deglaciation,* Geol. Soc. Amer., Boulder, Colo.

Jeffrey, C., 1973. *Biological Nomenclature,* Edward Arnold, London.

Jepson, W. L., 1910. *The Silva of California,* University of California Press, Berkeley.

Johnson, G. P., 1988. Revision of *Castanea* sect. *Balanocastanon* (Fagaceae), *J. Arnold Arbor.* **69**:25–49.

Jones, G. N., 1946. *American Species of Amelanchier,* The University of Illinois Press, Urbana.

———, 1968. Taxonomy of American species of Linden (*Tilia*), *Illinois Biol. Monogr. 39,* Urbana, Ill.

Jones, S. B., Jr., and A. E. Luchsinger, 1986. *Plant Systematics,* 2d ed., McGraw-Hill, New York.

Judd, W. S., R. W. Sanders, and M. J. Donoghue, 1994. Angiosperm family pairs: Preliminary phylogenetic analyses, *Harvard Papers in Botany* **5**:1–51.

Kapp, R. O. 1969. *How to Know Pollen and Spores,* Wm. C. Brown, Dubuque, Iowa.

Kologiski, R. L., 1977. The phytosociology of the Green Swamp, North Carolina, *N. C. Agric. Exp. Sta. Tech. Bull. 250,* Raleigh.

Kozlowski, T. T., P. J. Kramer, and S. G. Pallardy, 1990. *The Physiological Ecology of Woody Plants,* Academic Press, San Diego, Calif.

Kramer, P. J., and T. T. Kozlowski, 1979. *Physiology of Woody Plants,* Academic Press, New York.

Kreibel, H. B., 1957. Patterns of genetic variation in sugar maple, *Ohio Agric. Exp. Sta. Bull. 791,* Columbus, Ohio.

———, 1993. Intraspecific variation of growth and adaptive traits in North American oak species, *Ann. Sci. For.* **50**(Suppl. 1):153s–165s.

Kuchler, A. W., 1964. Potential natural vegetation of the conterminous United States, *Amer. Geogr. Soc. Spec. Publ. 36,* New York.

Laarman, J. G., and R. A. Sedjo, 1992. *Global Forests: Issues for Six Billion People,* McGraw-Hill, New York.

Langdon, O. G., 1963. Range of South Florida Slash pine, *J. For.* **61**:384–385.

Lanner, R. M., 1975. *Pinyon Pines and Junipers in the Southwestern Woodlands: The Pinyon–Juniper Ecosystem: A Symposium,* Utah State University, Logan.

Leaf, A. L., and K. G. Watterston, 1964. Chemical analysis of Sugar maple sap and foliage as related to sap and sugar yields, *For. Sci.* **10**:288–292.

Ledig, F. T., R. W. Wilson, J. W. Duffield, and G. Maxwell, 1969. A descriminant analysis of introgression between *Quercus prinus* L. and *Quercus alba* L., *Bull. Torrey Bot. Club* **96**:156–163.

Li, Hui–Lin, 1964. *Metasequoia:* A living fossil, *Amer. Sci.* **54**:93–109.

Linnaeus, C., 1753. *Species Plantarum,* Stockholm, Sweden.

Little, E. L., Jr., 1971. Atlas of United States trees, vol. 1, Conifers and important hardwoods, *USDA Miscl. Publ. 1146,* Washington, D.C.

———, 1976. Atlas of United States trees, vol. 3, Minor western hardwoods, *USDA Miscl. Publ. 1314,* Washington, D.C.

———, 1977. Atlas of United States trees, vol. 4, Minor eastern hardwoods, *USDA Miscl. Publ. 1342,* Washington, D.C.

———, 1978. Atlas of United States trees, vol. 5, Florida, *USDA Miscl. Publ. 1361,* Washington, D.C.

_____, 1979. Checklist of United States trees (Native and Naturalized), *USDA Handb. 541,* Washington, D.C.

_____, 1980a. *The Audubon Society Field Guide to North American Trees, Eastern Region,* Alfred A. Knopf, New York.

_____, 1980b. *The Audubon Society Field Guide to North American Trees, Western Region,* Alfred A. Knopf, New York.

_____, and W. B. Critchfield, 1969. Sub-divisions of the genus *Pinus* (Pines), *USDA Miscl. Publ. 1144,* Washington, D.C.

_____, and K. W. Dorman, 1954. Slash pine (*Pinus elliottii*), including South Florida Slash pine, *USDA Southeast. For. Exp. Sta. Pap. 36,* Washington, D.C.

_____, and B. H. Honkala, 1976. Trees and shrubs of the United States: A bibliography for identification, *USDA Miscl. Publ. 1336,* Washington, D.C.

Loveless, M. D., and J. L. Hamrick, 1984. Ecological determinants of genetic structure in plant populations, *Ann. Rev. Ecol. Syst.* **15**:65–95.

Mabberley, D. J., 1987. *The Plant Book,* Cambridge University Press, New York.

Malusa, J., 1992. Phylogeny and biogeography of the pinyon pines (*Pinus* subsect. *Cembroides*). *Syst. Bot.* **17**:42–66.

Manos, P. S., 1993. Foliar trichome variation in *Quercus* section *Protobalanus* (Fagaceae), *Sida* **15**:391–403.

_____, and D. E. Fairbrothers, 1987. Allozyme variation in populations of six northeastern American red oaks (Fagaceae: *Quercus* subg. *Erythrobalanus*), *Syst. Bot.* **12**:365–373.

Meerow, A. W., 1992. *Betrock's Guide to Landscape Palms,* Betrock Information Systems, Cooper City, Fla.

Mergen, F., 1963. Ecotypic variation in *Pinus strobus, Ecology* **44**:716–727.

Meyer, F. G., and J. W. Hardin, 1987. Status of the name *Aesculus flava* Solander (Hippocastanaceae), *J. Arnold Arbor.* **68**:335–341.

Millar, C. I., S. H. Strauss, M. T. Conkle, and R. D. Westfall, 1988. Allozyme differentiation and biosystematics of the California closed–cone pines, *Syst. Bot.* **13**:351–370.

Miller, G. N., 1955. The genus *Fraxinus,* the ashes, in North America, north of Mexico, *Cornell University Agric. Exp. Sta. Mem.* **335**:1–64.

Miller, R. F., and P. E. Wigand, 1994. Holocene changes in semiarid pinyon–juniper woodlands, *BioScience* **44**:465–474.

Mirov, N. T., 1967. *The Genus Pinus,* Ronald Press, New York.

Mosseler, A. J., K. N. Egger, and D. J. Innes, 1993. Life history and the loss of genetic diversity in red pines, *Amer. J. Bot.* **80**(6):81 (abstract).

Murrell, Z. E. 1993. Phylogenetic relationships in *Cornus* (Cornaceae), *Syst. Bot.* **18**:469–495.

Nienstaedt, H., and A. Teich, 1971. The genetics of white spruce, *USDA For. Serv. Res. Pap. WO–15,* Washington, D.C.

Nixon, K. C., 1993. Infrageneric classification of *Quercus* (Fagaceae) and typification of sectional names, *Ann. Sci. For.* **50**(Suppl. 1):25s–34s.

O'Connell, M. M., M. D. Bentley, C. S. Campbell, and B. J. W. Cole, 1988. Betulin and lupeol in bark from four white–barked birches, *Phytochemistry* **27**:2175–2176.

Palmer, E. J., 1948. Hybrid oaks of North America, *J. Arnold Arbor.* **29**:1–48.

Parks, C. R., J. F. Wendel, M. M. Sewell, and Y.–L. Qiu, 1994. The significance of allozyme variation and introgression in the *Liriodendron tulipifera* complex (Magnoliaceae), *Amer J. Bot.* **81**:878–889.

Price, R. A., and J. M. Lowenstein, 1989. An immunological comparison of the Sciadopityaceae, Taxodiaceae, and Cupressaceae, *Syst. Bot.* **14**:141–149.

———, J. Olsen–Stojkovich, and J. M. Lowenstein, 1987. Relationships among the genera of Pinaceae: An immunological comparison, *Syst. Bot.* **12**:91–97.

Proctor, M., and P. Yeo, 1972. *The Pollination of Flowers,* Taplinger, New York.

Radford, A. E., 1986. *Fundamentals of Plant Systematics,* Harper & Row, New York.

———, W. C. Dickison, J. R. Massey, and C. R. Bell, 1974. *Vascular Plant Systematics,* Harper & Row, New York.

Reed, A. H., 1954. *The New Story of the Kauri,* Reed Publications, Wellington, N.Z.

Reed, P. B., Jr., 1988. National list of plant species that occur in wetlands: National summary, *U.S. Fish Wildl. Serv. Biol. Rept.* **88**(24).

Reveal, J. L., and M. L. Seldin, 1976. On the identity of *Halesia carolina* L. (Styracaceae), *Taxon* **25**:123–140.

Robson, K. A., J. Maze, R. K. Scagel, and S. Banerjee, 1993. Ontogeny, phylogeny, and intraspecific variation in North American *Abies* Mill. (Pinaceae): An empirical approach to organization and evolution, *Taxon* **42**:17–34.

Rushton, B. S., 1993. Natural hybridization within the genus *Quercus* L., *Ann. Sci. For.* **50**(Suppl. 1):73s–90s.

Santamour, F. S., Jr., 1962. The relation between polyploidy and morphology in white and biltmore ashes, *Bull. Torrey Bot. Club* **89**:228–232.

Schreiner, E. J., 1949. Poplars can be bred to order, *USDA Yearbook Separate 2119,* Washington, D.C.

———, 1950. Genetics in relation to forestry, *J. For.* **48**:33–38.

Schulman, E. 1958. Bristlecone pine, oldest known living thing, *Natl. Geogr.* **113**:355–372.

Scott, C. W., 1960. *Pinus radiata,* Food and Agric. Organization of the United Nations, Rome.

Sharik, T. L., and B. V. Barnes, 1976. Phenology of shoot growth among diverse populations of yellow birch (*Betula alleghaniensis*) and sweet birch (*B. lenta*), *Canad. J. Bot.* **54**:2122–2129.

Show, S. B., and E. I. Kotok, 1929. Cover type and fire control in the national forests of northern California, *USDA Bull. 1495,* Washington, D.C.

Smith, J. P., Jr., 1977. *Vascular Plant Families,* Mad River Press, Eureka, Calif.

Smouse, P. E., and L. C. Saylor, 1973a. Studies of the *Pinus rigida–serotina* complex: I. A Study of geographic variation, *Ann. Missouri Bot. Gard.* **60**:174–191.

———, and ———, 1973b. Studies of the *Pinus rigida–serotina* complex: II. Natural hybridization among *Pinus rigida–serotina* complex, *P. taeda* and *P. echinata. Ann. Missouri Bot. Gard.* **60**:192–203.

Spurr, S. H., and B. V. Barnes, 1980. *Forest Ecology,* 3d ed., Wiley, New York.

Squillace, A. E., 1966. Geographic variation in Slash pine, *For. Sci. Monogr. 10.*

Stace, C. A., 1989. *Plant Taxonomy and Biosystematics,* 2d ed., Edward Arnold, London.

Stearn, W. T., 1992. *Botanical Latin,* David and Charles, London.

Stebbins, G. L., Jr., 1950. *Variation and Evolution in Plants,* Columbia University Press, New York.

Steiner, K. C., 1979. Patterns of variation in bud-burst timing among populations in several *Pinus* species, *Silvae Genet.* **28**:85–194.

———, 1980. "Past and present trends in dendrology instruction," in P. P. Feret and T. L. Sharik (eds.), *Proceedings, Dendrology in the Eastern Deciduous Forest Biome,* pp. 142–156, Virginia Polytechnic Institute and State University, *Publ. FWS–2–80,* Blacksburg.

Steinhoff, R. J., and J. W. Andresen, 1971. Geographic variation in *Pinus flexilis* and *P. strobiformis* and its bearing on the taxonomic status, *Silvae Genet.* **20**:159–167.

Stone, D. E., 1973. Patterns in the evolution of amentiferous fruits, *Brittonia* **25**:371–384.

Stone, E. L., Jr., and M. H. Stone, 1943. "Dormant" versus adventitious buds, *Science* **98**:62.

Strauss, S. H., 1967. *Forest Trees of the Pacific Slope,* Dover, New York.

_____, and A. H. Doerksen, 1990. Restriction fragment analysis of pine phylogeny, *Evolution* **44**:1081–1096.

Stuessy, T. F., 1990. *Plant Taxonomy,* Columbia University Press, New York.

Sudworth, G. B., 1927. Check list of forest trees of the United States, *USDA Circ. 92,* Washington, D.C.

_____, 1967. *Forest Trees of the Pacific Slope,* Dover, New York.

Terrell, E. E., S. R. Hill, J. H. Wiersema, and W. E. Rice, 1986. A Checklist of names for 3000 vascular plants of economic importance, *USDA Handb. 505,* Washington, D.C.

Thor, E., and P. E. Barnett, 1974. Taxonomy of *Abies* in the southern Appalachians: Variation in balsam monoterpenes and wood properties, *For. Sci.* **20**:32–40.

Tillson, A. H., and C. H. Muller, 1942. Anatomical and taxonomic approaches to subgeneric segregation in American *Quercus, Amer. J. Bot.* **29**:523–529.

Tiner, R. W., 1991. The concept of a hydrophyte for wetland identification. *BioScience* **41**:236–247.

Trelease, W., 1924. The American oaks, *Mem. Nat. Acad. Sci. USA* **20**:1–255.

Tucker, J. M., 1993. Hybridization in California oaks. *J. Internatl. Oak Soc.* **3**:4–13.

_____, and H. S. Haskell, 1960. *Quercus dunnii* and *Q. chrysolepis* in Arizona, *Brittonia* **12**:196–219.

van der Pijl, L., 1982. *Principles of Dispersal in Higher Plants,* 3d ed., Springer-Verlag, Berlin.

Viereck, L. A., and E. L. Little, Jr., 1975. Atlas of United States trees: vol. 2, Alaska trees and common shrubs, *USDA Miscl. Publ. 1293,* Washington, D.C.

Wagner, D. B., G. R. Furnier, M. A. Saghai-Maroof, S. M. Williams, B. Dancik, and R. W. Allard, 1987. Chloroplast DNA polymorphisms in lodgepole and jack pines and their hybrids, *Proc. Natl. Acad. USA* **84**:2097–2100.

Waller, G. R. (ed.); 1987. *Allelochemicals: Role in Agriculture and Forestry.* ACS Symposium Series 30. Amer. Chem. Society, Washington, D.C.

Walters, D. R., and D. J. Keil, 1988. *Vascular Plant Taxonomy,* 3d ed., Kendall/Hunt, Dubuque, Iowa.

Ward, D. B., 1963. Contributions to the flora of Florida—2, Pines (Pinaceae), *Castanea* **28**:1–10.

_____, and A. F. Clewell, 1989. Atlantic white cedar (*Chamaecyparis thyoides*) in the southern states, *Florida Scientist* **52**:8–47.

Watson, F. D., 1983. A Taxonomic Study of Pondcypress and Baldcypress (*Taxodium* Richard), Ph.D. dissertation, Dept. of Botany, North Carolina State University, Raleigh.

_____, 1985. The nomenclature of pondcypress and baldcypress (Taxodiaceae), *Taxon* **34**:506–509.

Whittaker, R. H., 1956. Vegetation of the Great Smoky Mountains, *Ecol. Monogr.* **26**:1–80.

Williams, S., 1939. Secondary vascular tissues of the oaks indigenous to the United States: I. The importance of secondary xylem in delimiting Erythrobalanus and Leucobalanus. *Bull. Torrey Bot. Club* **66**:353–365.

Wilson, K. A., and C. E. Wood, Jr., 1959. The genera of Oleaceae in the Southeastern United States, *J. Arnold Arbor.* **40**:369–384.

Woodland, D. W., 1991. *Contemporary Plant Systematics,* Prentice Hall, Englewood Cliffs, N.J.

Wright, H. E., 1983. *Late Quaternary Environments of the United States: Vol. 2, The Holocene,* University of Minnesota Press, Minneapolis.

Wright, J. W., 1955. Species crossability in spruce in relation to distribution and taxonomy, *For. Sci.* **1**:319–349.

Young, A. G., H. G. Merriam, and S. I. Warwick, 1993. The effects of forest fragmentation on genetic variation in *Acer saccharum* Marsh. (sugar maple) populations, *Heredity* **71**:277–289.

Young, J. A., and C. G. Young, 1992. *Seeds of Woody Plants,* Timber Press, Portland, Oreg.

Zimmerman, M. H., and C. L. Brown, 1971. *Trees: Structure and Function,* Springer-Verlag, New York.

Zobel, B. J., 1951. The natural hybrid between Coulter and Jeffrey pines, *Evolution* **5**:405–413.

_____, and J. Talbert, 1984. *Applied Forest Tree Improvement,* Wiley, New York.

_____, G. Van Wyk, and P. Stahl, 1987. *Growing Exotic Forests,* Wiley, New York.

Zobel, D. B., 1969. Factors affecting the distribution of *Pinus pungens,* an Appalachian endemic, *Ecol. Monogr.* **39**:303–333.

Zomlefer, W. B., 1994. *Guide to Flowering Plant Families,* University of North Carolina Press, Chapel Hill.

Zon, R., 1907. A new explanation of the tolerance and intolerance of trees, *Proc. Soc. Amer. For.* **2**:79–94.

INDEX

Page numbers in **boldface** indicate illustrations; names in *italics* indicate synonyms.

METRIC SCALE–20 cm

10 mm = 1 cm

10 cm = 1 dm

100 cm = 1 m

1000 m = 1 km